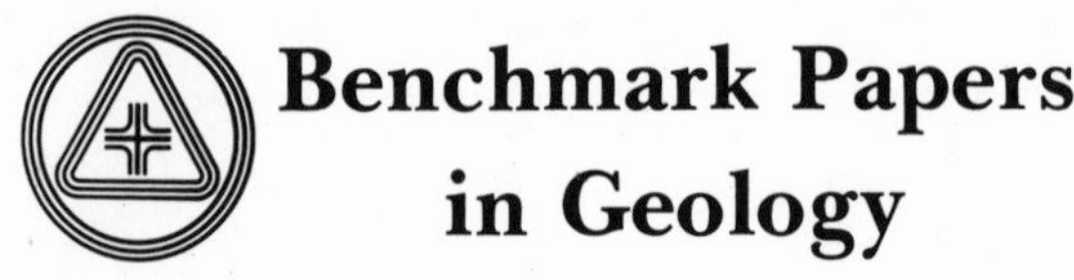

Series Editor: Rhodes W. Fairbridge
Columbia University

Published Volumes

ENVIRONMENTAL GEOMORPHOLOGY AND LANDSCAPE CONSERVATION, VOLUME I: Prior to 1900 / Donald R. Coates
RIVER MORPHOLOGY / Stanley A. Schumm
SPITS AND BARS / Maurice L. Schwartz
TEKTITES / Virgil E. Barnes and Mildred A. Barnes
GEOCHRONOLOGY: Radiometric Dating of Rocks and Minerals / C. T. Harper
SLOPE MORPHOLOGY / Stanley A. Schumm and M. Paul Mosley
MARINE EVAPORITES: Origin, Diagenesis, and Geochemistry / Douglas W. Kirkland and Robert Evans
ENVIRONMENTAL GEOMORPHOLOGY AND LANDSCAPE CONSERVATION, VOLUME III: Non-Urban Areas / Donald R. Coates
BARRIER ISLANDS / Maurice L. Schwartz
GLACIAL ISOSTASY / John T. Andrews
GEOCHEMISTRY OF GERMANIUM / Jon N. Weber
ENVIRONMENTAL GEOMORPHOLOGY AND LANDSCAPE CONSERVATION, VOLUME II: Urban Areas / Donald R. Coates
PHILOSOPHY OF GEOHISTORY: 1785–1970 / Claude C. Albritton, Jr.

Additional volumes in preparation

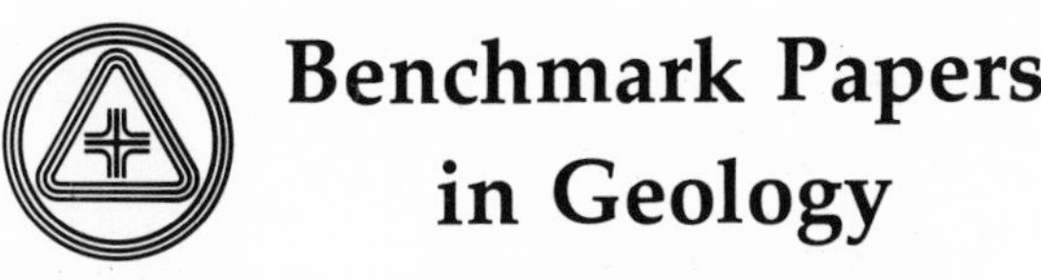

A *BENCHMARK®* Books Series

ENVIRONMENTAL GEOMORPHOLOGY AND LANDSCAPE CONSERVATION

Volume II: Urban Areas

Edited by
DONALD R. COATES
State University of New York at Binghamton

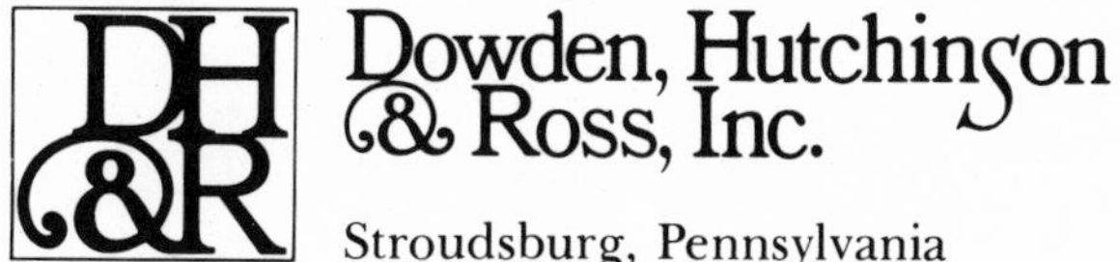

To Jeanne, Jada, and Heather, my beautiful and innocent second-generation environmentalists.

Benchmark Papers in Geology, Volume 12
Library of Congress Catalog Card Number: 72 – 778822
ISBN: 0 – 87933 – 047 – 3

Manufactured in the United States of America.

Exclusive distributor outside the United States and Canada: John Wiley & Sons, Inc.

74 75 76 5 4 3 2 1

Library of Congress Cataloging in Publication Data (Revised)

Coates, Donald Robert, 1922- comp.
Environmental geomorphology and landscape conservation.

(Benchmark papers in geology)
Includes bibliographies.
CONTENTS: v. 1. Prior to 1900.--v. 2. Urban areas. --v. 3. Non-urban.
1. Geomorphology--Addresses, essays, lectures. 2. Human ecology--Addresses, essays, lectures. 3. Conservation of natural resources--Addresses, essays, lectures. I. Title.
GB406.C62 333.7'2'08 72-77882
ISBN 0-87933-005-8 (v. 1)

Acknowledgments and Permissions

ACKNOWLEDGMENTS

AMERICAN GEOGRAPHICAL SOCIETY—*Soviet Geography*
Changes in the Geography of Population Centers in Connection with Creation of the Tsimlyansk Reservoir
Satellite Cities and Towns of Moscow

ASSOCIATION OF ENGINEERING GEOLOGISTS—*Engineering Geology in Southern California*
Landslides and Hillside Development

INDIANA ACADEMY OF SCIENCES—*Proceedings of the Indiana Academy of Sciences for 1968*
Urban Geology—A Need and a Challenge

INSTITUTE OF GOVERNMENTAL STUDIES, UNIVERSITY OF CALIFORNIA, BERKELEY—*Open Space for the San Francisco Bay Area: Organizing to Guide Metropolitan Growth*

UNION RESEARCH INSTITUTE, HONG KONG—*River Control in Communist China* (Communist China Problem Research Series EC 31)

UNIVERSITY OF CALIFORNIA—*Flood Control in Metropolitan Los Angeles*
The Flood Problem

U.S. GEOLOGICAL SURVEY—*Hydrology for Urban Land Planning–A Guidebook on the Hydrologic Effects of Urban Land Use* (U.S. Geological Survey Circular 554)

PERMISSIONS

The following papers have been reprinted with the permission of the authors and the copyright holders.

AMERICAN ACADEMY OF POLITICAL AND SOCIAL SCIENCES—*Annals of the American Academy of Political and Social Sciences*
The Place of Nature in the City of Man

AMERICAN GEOGRAPHICAL SOCIETY—*Geographical Review*
The Geography of New York City's Water Supply: A Study of Interactions

AMERICAN GEOPHYSICAL UNION
Transactions of the American Geophysical Union
Water-Spreading as Practiced by the Santa Clara Water-Conservation District, Ventura County, California
Water Resources Research
Effects of Construction on Fluvial Sediment, Urban and Suburban Areas of Maryland
Stream Channel Enlargment Due to Urbanization

AMERICAN SOCIETY OF LANDSCAPE ARCHITECTS—*Landscape Architecture*
Landscape: A Vanishing Resource: Open Space, Now or Never
Man Versus Gravity: Making Up for 200-Year Loss in Pittsburgh

CIVIC TRUST—*Derelict Land*

DEPARTMENT OF GEOGRAPHY, UNIVERSITY OF CHICAGO—*Choice of Adjustment to Floods*
Six Partially Protected Towns

DONALD R. COATES—*Coastal Geomorphology*
Barrier Islands: Natural and Controlled

ECONOMIC GEOLOGY PUBLISHING COMPANY—*Economic Geology*
Artificial Recharge of Ground Water on Long Island, New York

GEOLOGICAL SOCIETY OF AMERICA—*Engineering Geology Case Histories*
Ground-Water Management in the Raymond Basin, California

GEOLOGICAL SURVEY OF CANADA—*Report of the Commission Appointed to Investigate Turtle Mountain, Frank, Alberta* (Canada Department of Mines Memoir 27)

INSTITUTE OF BRITISH GEOGRAPHERS—*Transactions of the Institute of British Geographers*
Mass Movements Associated with the Rainstorm of June 1966 in Hong Kong

LONGMANS, GREEN AND CO. LTD., LONDON—*The Lower Swansea Valley Project*
A Case History of Derelict Land in Swansea 1900 to 1966

MINISTRY OF THE INTERIOR, JERUSALEM, ISRAEL—*The Israel Physical Master Plan*

NATIONAL AUDUBON SOCIETY—*Audubon*
Subdividing and Conquering the Desert

NATIONAL PARKS AND CONSERVATION ASSOCIATION—*National Parks and Conservation Magazine*
Countryside

NATIONAL RESEARCH COUNCIL OF CANADA—*Canadian Building Digest*
Trees and Buildings

SCIENTIFIC AMERICAN, INC.—*Scientific American*
The Metabolism of Cities

TIME, INC.—*Fortune*
Urban Sprawl

Series Editor's Preface

The philosophy behind the "Benchmark Papers in Geology" is one of collection, sifting, and rediffusion. Scientific literature today is so vast, so dispersed, and, in the case of old papers, so inaccessible for readers not in the immediate neighborhood of major libraries that much valuable information has been ignored by default. It has become just so difficult, or so time consuming, to search out the key papers in any basic area of research that one can hardly blame a busy man for skimping on some of his "homework."

This series of volumes has been devised, therefore, to make a practical contribution to this critical problem. The geologist, perhaps even more than any other scientist, often suffers from twin difficulties—isolation from central library resources and immensely diffused sources of material. New colleges and industrial libraries simply cannot afford to purchase complete runs of all the world's earth science literature. Specialists simply cannot locate reprints or copies of all their principal reference materials. So it is that we are now making a concerted effort to gather into single volumes the critical material needed to reconstruct the background of any and every major topic of our discipline.

We are interpreting "Geology" in its broadest sense: the fundamental science of the Planet Earth, its materials, its history, and its dynamics. Because of training and experience in "earthy" materials, we also take in astrogeology, the corresponding aspect of the planetary sciences. Besides the classical core disciplines such as mineralogy, petrology, structure, geomorphology, paleontology, and stratigraphy, we embrace the newer fields of geophysics and geochemistry, applied also to oceanography, geochronology, and paleoecology. We recognize the work of the mining geologists, the petroleum geologists, the hydrologists, the engineering and environmental geologists. Each specialist needs his working library. We are endeavoring to make his task a little easier.

Each volume in the series contains an Introduction prepared by a specialist (the volume editor)—a "state of the art" opening or a summary of the objects and content of the volume. The articles, usually some thirty to fifty reproduced either in their entirety or in significant extracts, are selected in an attempt to cover the field, from the key papers of the last century to fairly recent work. Where the original works are in foreign languages, we have endeavored to locate or commission translations. Geologists, because of their global subject, are often acutely aware of the oneness of our world. The selections cannot, therefore, be restricted to any one country, and whenever possible an attempt is made to scan the world literature.

To each article, or group of kindred articles, some sort of "Highlight Commentary" is usually supplied by the volume editor. This should serve to bring that article into historical perspective and to emphasize its particular role in the growth of the field. References, or citations, wherever possible, will be reproduced in their entirety—for by this means the observant reader can assess the background material available to that particular author, or, if he wishes, he too can double check the earlier sources.

A "benchmark" in surveyor's terminology, is an established point on the ground, recorded on our maps. It is usually anything that is a vantage point, from a modest hill to a mountain peak. From the historical viewpoint, these benchmarks are the bricks of our scientific edifice.

Rhodes W. Fairbridge

Contents

III. GEOMORPHIC HAZARDS

IV. LANDSCAPE ABUSE

V. LANDSCAPE MANAGEMENT

Contents by Author

Introduction

This is the second volume of a trilogy dealing with man's utilization and transformation of the earth's surface. Man's very lifestyle—his living, working, and playing on the land — causes him automatically to become a geomorphic agent and a force of change to the environment he inhabits. Indeed, in the course of this activity man produces his own special brand of landscape metamorphism. In Volume I some of the changes that occurred prior to 1900 were explored. In Volumes II and II we concentrate on events of the twentieth century. It is necessary to divide the material because of the vast amount of literature available, the complexity of the problems, and the interrelationships of many different disciplines. This division is made most conveniently on the basis of man's utilization of the land—whether he uses it primarily as a place to assemble for purposes of commerce, industry, and the distribution of goods and services, or whether the land is used as its own resource. This rationale was explained in Volume I: "Because urbanization is the most important sector in the change in man's habitation pattern, it has become necessary to separate his arena of activity in this setting from his actions in the nonurban region" (p. 2). All three volumes in this collection have a common thread: to describe that aberration of man whereby short-sighted objectives yield environmental disruption, but also to discuss remedial policies that attempt to preserve and rehabilitate the damaged terrain. Just as the rapid expansion of cities in the twentieth century has led to an almost unique set of problems, so too man's interference with nature in nonurban regions is no less serious and has reached staggering proportions. Thus, it is important in this volume to attempt to obtain a balance between the treatment of urban and nonurban areas, as well as to indicate appropriate management procedures that can lead to greater environmental and ecologic harmony.

In this volume we deal with the physical aspects of what is happening to the lands and waters on, near, and under cities, specifically during the twentieth century; but, of course, not all the problems are unique to this period. However, many features of the twentieth century have contributed to an accelerated pace of urbanization — for example, the population explosion, the increasing flexibility in available types of energy, the rapidly accelerating technological advances (most obviously, the automobile) with related industrialization, and, not least, the effects of two world wars. Concomitant with urbanization has been a massive interruption of natural processes and the development of new anthropogenic landscapes. Prior to our present century, the greatest events in the course of human civilization were the agricultural revolution and the industrial revolution; the twentieth century is depicted as starting the "urban revolution." In the following quotations, Nelson describes the dimensions of the terrain changes that are occurring and Schmid discusses some of the attendant problems. These problems are the subject of their informative articles:

> The twentieth century may go down in history as an urban age. Urbanism is becoming increasingly significant throughout the world, and the United States, too, is strongly affected by this modern trend. Southern California, perhaps better than other areas, epitomizes the recent dominance of the city. The area had few attractions during its early period of European settlement —its qualities have been recognized as assets for urban–industrial development only in recent decades. Once the proper stage was reached, however, the mature nature of the American economy and the advanced state of industrial technology have made possible extremely rapid growth. Today an artificial landscape of urban – industrial patterns and forms dominates Southern California (Nelson, 1959, p. 80).

> Urbanization is perhaps the dominant social, economic, and political movement in the contemporary American scene. Large numbers of people are moving to cities and in cities to new locations; considerable acreages of land are converted from rural to urban uses; large capital investments have been made; substantial fortunes have been made through land speculation and development, and some have been lost. Fraud and bribery in public zoning and other actions have occurred or are widely believed to have occurred, especially in growing suburban areas. All in all, suburbanization is lively, exciting, and even engrossing—but not necessarily wholly desirable in all its ramifications. To one familiar with American land history, all of this is strangely reminiscent of what took place during the nineteenth century. Not the least of these similarities is a general lack of understanding of the true nature of the processes involved and a state of poorly devised public measures to deal with the undesirable aspects of each (Schmid, 1968, preface).

Gulick (1958) analyzes the problems of urbanization in a slightly different context and contends:

> It is my thesis that urbanization in and of itself, as a pattern of life, increases the dependence of our culture on the natural resources, and that urbanization furthermore makes for a revised scale of conservation priorities (p. 117).

He discusses this viewpoint under the major headings of water, air and water pollution, energy consumption, general living standards, recreational opportunities, land, and flood control.

> Looking at these various impacts together, I think it can be demonstrated that the pattern of human settlement known as "urbanization" brings on a higher and different drain on national resources than is involved in a nonurban pattern of life. Those who make resource projections and draw conservation programs need to have this in mind (p. 129).

Thus, conservation projects should keep these factors in mind, and Dasmann (1968) has pointed out:

> There is little doubt that in the 1960's, unlike the 1930's many of the major conservation battles are being fought, not on the farmlands and the wildlands, but in the cities. It is in the cities and their environs that the greatest deterioration of the human environment is taking place. It is the influence of urban populations and urban growth that results in many of our major land-use conflicts. It is in the cities that the decisions about land use throughout America will be made (p. 299).

Therefore, when considering the compounded urban–suburban network and its influence on geomorphology, environment, and conservational needs, a multitude of facets come into play in a complex matrix of interactions and feedback mechanisms. Detwyler and Marcus (1972) talk about the "urban ecosystem" and how it is subject to the principle of "environmental unity" in which all elements and processes of the environment are related and interdependent. This is an open system that is not self-contained, because matter and energy are continuously being exchanged throughout a much larger environment. The system has three fundamental interactions: (1) modification of the environment, (2) influence of the physical environment on urban form, functions, and growth, and (3) continuous feedback in the city from man, culture, and physical environment.

Although the main purpose of this volume is to provide the reader with articles that are leaders in the field and indicate the scope and status of the subject areas, it has been necessary for me to contribute an extended commentary that links these materials into a fluent and unifying fabric. As in the other volumes of this trilogy, selection of the appropriate articles has been extremely difficult because of the wealth of excellent materials, especially in certain areas such as water resources, land-use planning, and open spaces. The following factors were considered important determinants for inclusion of articles:

1. *Date of article.* Such articles, as those by the Geological Survey of Canada (1912), Freeman (1936), and Brashears (1946) represent early and first works on the subjects.

2. *Author.* There are always leaders and recognition must be given to their stature as scientists. Typical of this group (but not exclusive) are Leopold, Legget, McHarg, White, Whyte, and the Wolmans.

3. *Agency or organization.* Certain government or private groups have played significant roles on the environmental scene and through their publications reflect their work and attitudes; examples are the Audubon Society, U.S. Water Resources Council, and U.S. Geological Survey.

4. *Foreign literature.* Although much of this book uses United States examples, a sufficient selection of other articles are presented to document the international flavor of the subject. Material from Canada, China, England, Hong Kong, Israel, and the Soviet Union is included.

Each criterion, therefore, had to be blended into the various topical areas to assure a reasonable coverage of the subject matter. The relatively recent origin of many of the articles is indicative of the fact that numerous papers are only just now being generated that cover the ground in sufficient depth and breadth to merit reproduction. To represent this wide range of material, 32 publications have been selected. Because of the limited size of this volume, several have had to be severely abridged; it is hoped that they retain their major essence and thrust. In addition, quotations and ideas from other experts are presented with the commentaries in order to broaden the perspectives.

The complex problems of urban growth and planning involve nearly all disciplines — the natural sciences, the social sciences, the humanities, and the managerial and engineering technologies. All these disciplines are so intertwined that certain limits and guidelines must be established or all will be lost in the confusion of a smorgasbord. Furthermore, although the space setting of a city has a distinct and limited positional status, its true boundaries extend to a much larger domain where it plays a wider role, affecting such matters as the water resource base. The gargantuan task of trying to define and confine discussion so that it is meaningful leads to decisions that will not be agreed upon by all. However, this book is intended to stress the geomorphic habitat of man in the city environment, and so emphasis is placed on his use of land and water and the changes he creates. The matter of open space and greenbelts is a key subject in this context. Hazards such as floods and landslides are considered, irrespective of whether natural or man-induced. Coastal areas are also included, because it is usually only in or near the urbanized areas that man attempts to make any major modification of shore features. Laws and legal affairs are also referenced because they provide an important avenue for conservation and preservation practices. In contrast, a variety of extremely important topics and fields in urban studies are less relevant geomorphically and thus cannot be included in this volume. Such topics include works related to cultural, social, and political problems. It is recognized that questions dealing with taxes, crime, ghettos, budget allocations, and community services and facilities are extremely significant, so much so that they often receive planning priority over the physical systems of the area. Nor does this volume cover some of the geologic concerns of city planning, such as the nature of bedrock, the structural character of foundations for engineering works, and problems regarding earthquake or volcanic hazards (see Betz, in press, *Environmental Geology,* Benckmark Series). Pollution is a topic that has become so vast that justice cannot be done in these volumes and it will also be treated elsewhere in the Benchmark Series. Pollution is acknowledged as being a vital concern, but space permits only a few brief comments in these pages.

The words "city" and "urban area" are often used synonymously. In addition, a series of other terms are used in discussions of built-up locations. Although there are no worldwide standards (see Part II), there is a general notion that in order of size communities would range from hamlet, to village, town, city, metropolis, and megalopolis. Lewis Mumford calls the city ". . . the structure especially equipped to store and transmit the goods of civilization, sufficiently condensed to afford the maximum amount of facilities in a minimum space." The terms "city" and "country" are generally viewed as opposites in the same fashion as "urban" and "rural." Recently, the "urban – rural fringe" nomenclature has elicited a number of articles and books, although it has more similarities to, than differences from, the established term of "surburban." Additional terms have been used in the literature to cover various conceptual ideas, such as "conurbation," "townscape," and "cityscape." For our purpose, urban areas include places with a free concentration of people who share many facilities and services and are mutually affected by single, local geomorphic events, such as a flood or landslide. Urbanization is the process of change in land occupancy, and often involves the conversion of rural lands to such nonagrarian purposes as housing, commerce, and industry. In the context of the city, landscape conservation is associated with such ideas as open areas, greenbelts, and those natural features of the land that are in jeopardy owing to neglect, lack of management, or by deliberate acts that violate them.

Literature of Urban Geomorphology and Conservation

Until recently, there were no books largely devoted to a discussion of topics relevant to the subject of the geomorphology and conservation of landscapes in the urban areas. An outstanding book, *Cities and Geology,* by Legget (1973) and the collection of articles presented by Detwyler and Marcus (1972) in *Urbanization and Environment* have happily aided in remedying this situation. There is a variety of books that deal with single topics within the general field of the urban land–water ecosystem. These include *Floods* (Hoyt and Langbein, 1955), *Dredge Drain Relcaim* (Van Veen, 1962), *Taming Megalopolis* (Eldridge, ed., 1967, two volumes), *The Last Landscape* (Whyte, 1968), *Engineering Geology in Southern California* (Lung and Proctor, eds., 1969), *Metropolitan Open Space and Natural Process* (Wallace, ed., 1970), and *Planned Urban Environments* (Strong, 1971). Legget shows how geology is neglected in Lewis Mumford's books, and the word is used only three times in *Urban Planning Guide* (Claire, ed., 1969). Geology is entirely omitted from the classic *Megalopolis: The Urbanized Northeastern Seaboard of the United States* (Gottman, 1961). Texts on urban geography rarely contain material oriented to geomorphic processes. Instead they are almost completely devoted to such subjects as the demographic character of populations, occupational–industrial–municipal descriptions, location and spacing of settlement patterns, and theories of urban structure (Johnson, 1970).

Nearly all academic disciplines have researchers who specialize in some facet of urban affairs or problems, and university-sponsored urban-center institutes are today producing publications at a monumental rate. With careful reading, some of these writings can be translated into ideas related to the subject matter of this volume. At this time, however, governmental organizations have proved to be a more rewarding source of information. For example, the U.S. Army Corps of Engineers has provided a wealth of data and ideas from their Waterways Experiment Station and the Coastal Engineering and Research Center. The U.S. Geological Survey has accelerated programs of research and publication in urban areas. Their series of circulars, "Water in the Urban Environment" (see the articles in this volume by Leopold and Guy), could easily serve as a text on the subject. Within the past 5 years, many state governments have started to produce geologic publications that are especially directed to those who make decisions concerning land and resource use in urban areas. In most of these reports, the greatest emphasis concerns the geomorphic part of the environment. A partial listing of these includes: Illinois (McComas, 1968; Hackett and McComas, 1969), Kansas (Hilpman, ed., 1968), Michigan (Mozola, 1969, 1970), California (California Division of Mines and Geology, 1971), Vermont (Stewart, 1971), Alabama (Alabama Geological Survey, 1971), Pennsylvania (Geyer and McGlade, 1972), and Washington (Artim, 1973).

Foreign publications also provide a wealth of important data and information for urban land and resource managers. For example, in Christiansen (1970), along with an analysis of the geology, pedology, and climate of the area of Saskatoon, Canada, the subject of "geotechnology" is taken to include the topics of groundwater resources, slope stability, engineering properties of tills, sand and gravel resources, land use, and land capability for outdoor recreation. In the Foreword to this book, prepared by Y. O. Fortier and R. F. Legget, it is stated:

> This publication is a pioneer example of what can be done in bringing together essential information about the region surrounding one of the important Prairie cities of Canada. It is the result of a co-operative study, . . . which developed fruitfully from an initial investigation of local geology only. It shows what can be done by a group of local experts in the several fields that are treated. It can serve to show what is desirable, if not indeed essential for all the urban areas of Canada (and of other countries too) as they face the complex problems associated with the doubling of their population before the end of the century.

In addition to the specialized sources just mentioned, a host of journals, government serials, university papers, proceedings volumes, and magazines are wholly or in part devoted to publication of environmental matters that are of importance to a complete consideration of the land – water ecosystems of urban areas. Numerous journals use the terms "environment," "geology," "urban," and "conservation" (or their derivatives) as part of the journal name. Many are referenced throughout this book. Certain universities and academic departments have become well known for their publications and emphasis on a special subject, such as the University of Chicago's Department of Geography, with a series of reports on flooding. Many magazines in the area of more popular literature also contain useful important information that is necessary to provide the full spectrum of ideas for making a complete assessment of the problems of urban environments and their solutions. An interesting appraisal of the diversity of these materials is made by De Bell (1970). In writing about "a future that makes environmental sense," he observes:

> For the past few years, I've noticed two trends in literature about the future. Journals, like *Audubon Magazine, Sierra Club Bulletin,* and *Cry California,* are generally concerned about imminent ecological disaster — the death of canyons and valleys, the end of whales, big cats, eagles, falcons, pelicans, and even man. The magazines popularizing science, Popular Science and Popular Mechanics, speak of the technological utopia of the future—a television screen attached to every telephone, a helicopter on every rooftop, and sleek supersonic transports for the fortunate few within them who cannot hear the sonic boom. The two kinds of journal seem oblivious of each other and mutually exclusive. Yet there is a connection: The more we strive to reach the popular science future, the more likely we are to achieve the ecological disaster. (p. 153).

Thus there is a large literature in the general field of this volume, and it must be read and analyzed carefully to obtain a full understanding and comprehension of the multidisciplined and interdisciplined character of the urbanized landscape.

Organization of This Volume

The interlocking structure of the many different components in the complex array of urban environmental considerations makes it difficult to compartmentalize the subject material. A division of these materials into five large parts, however, provides a logical and convenient forum for analysis.

Part I: Overview of Urban Areas. This section provides a synopsis for the book and sets the stage for the types of problems and for the considerations that are necessary for their solution. Three articles delineate the following frames of reference: (1) analysis of the physical ecosystem that constitutes the city, (2) the importance of retaining natural habitats, and (3) the contribution that geomorphology can make in urban studies.

Part II: Water Resources. Water is of overriding importance in the health and welfare of cities, and it is discussed under two separate headings. The three articles that deal with surface-water hydrology treat the many upsets that occur because of the paving over of natural areas and the resultant changes in streamflow regimes. Cities are generally water debtors and must draw supplies from other regions. One article discusses the New York City experience and another shows how the creation of water reservoirs in the Soviet Union displaces former inhabitants of the area. The three articles that treat groundwater hydrology deal with laws, problems in overpumped areas, and land changes. Conservation of water can be accomplished through legal processes and court actions, as well as by such physical means as artificially replenishing groundwater reservoirs by inducing recharge through wells and by water spreading of surface runoff.

Part III. Geomorphic Hazards. This part is also divided into two separate sections. Four articles depict a range of features and events associated with floods. Flooding statistics throughout the United States are provided, and special treatment of floods in California, China, and other areas is given. Various means for flood-proofing that include both structural and institutional controls are analyzed. The articles on landslides show this phenomenon to be an ever-present danger to those cities built on or near hilly and mountainous slopes. The classic slide at Frank, Alberta, is analyzed, as is recent landsliding in Hong Kong. Land development on the hillsides of southern California is discussed, along with stabilization procedures and the effects of grading ordinances on planning.

Part IV. Landscape Abuse. There are two interwoven themes in this unit that illustrate land-use degradation. One aspect is largely physical; four articles show how accelerated erosion at construction sites produces abnormally large erosion and sedimention and also how changes occur in the morphology of stream channels because of the alteration of normal surface runoff. The other form of land deterioration is more insidious and has become known as "urban sprawl," which involves the disregard of natural features during haphazard development.

Part V. Landscape Management. Although various conservation techniques and planning procedures are mentioned in many chapters, a series of short articles in this part portrays a wide range of approaches for land-use conservation. Examples are drawn from the United States and other countries, including England, Israel, and the Soviet Union. Such materials should be helpful in providing ideas for the decision makers and those planning land-utilization policies. Cities present many problems and challenges today but also provide what may well be the incubators for civilization's future. The geomorphologist can add measurably to a greater understanding of the urban ecosystem, because he is in the preferred position of knowing the physical systems of the substrate; thus he will know which land-utilization practices cause the minimum distortion to natural processes, thereby enhancing the amenities of life.

I
Overview of Urban Areas

Editor's Comments on Papers 1, 2, and 3

1 **Wolman:** *The Metabolism of Cities*

2 **McHarg:** *The Place of Nature in the City of Man*

3 **Wayne:** *Urban Geology—A Need and a Challenge*

The purpose of Part I is to set the stage and provide a generalized perspective for the remainder of the book. Such a synthesis will be a guideline for the special and detailed treatment of the components that constitute the geomorphic environmental framework of urban areas. This expository and descriptive approach may provide a basis for understanding the types and dimensions of problems created by urbanization. Hopefully, it will also point the way for the creation of an attitude and planning context that will prove helpful in reaching new levels for "design with nature."

Cities did not just suddenly emerge on the human scene in the twentieth century. However, there is overwhelming evidence that a new era was ushered in during this time, marked by the accelerated transformation of cities due to such factors as (1) modern technology (e.g., mass production of the automobile), (2) improved energy sources (e.g., petroleum products and hydroelectric power), and (3) engineering construction methods (e.g., extensive highway networks, skyscrapers, and water importation systems). Sjoberg (1965) shows that although the first cities were established some 5,500 years ago, large-scale urbanization began less than 100 years ago. "World's earliest cities first evolved from villages in lower Mesopotamia and in the Nile valley. Soon thereafter cities also arose in similar alluvial regions to the east, first in the Indus valley and then along the Yellow River . . ." (p. 56). An article by Wittfogel in Volume II of this trilogy deals with the importance of hydrography in early civilizations.

Both the location and the growth of cities are related to topographic–hydrographic features or to socioeconomic pressures. Cities therefore develop where (1) they are easily defended, (2) trade routes or marketplaces facilitate the distribution of goods and services, (3) living and work areas are exceptionally well protected from the forces of nature, (4) there is ready access to natural resources such as water, ore, and fossil fuels, (5) climate is amenable and healthy, and (6) advantages accrue to the developer on both private *and* public levels. Many cities in Europe developed from the fortified villages of the Middle Ages. Cities in the Near East were often located on caravan routes; numerous coastal cities have flourished because of protected harbors in bays and estuaries. The fresh water of rivers and lakes has been especially decisive in many cities; however, others have blossomed in desert locations, having been made possible by air conditioning and importation of water (e.g., Los Angeles, Phoenix, Tucson, and Albuquerque). New cities are being built as adjuncts to existing metropolitan areas as well as being created in remote sites, such as Brasilia in Brazil and the Siberian cities in the Soviet Union. Of course, many times these factors converge. In the United States, where fortified cities were generally unnecessary, water and safe harbors seemed to be dominant considerations. For example, 12 of the 13 largest cities are located on the shoreline of an ocean or Great Lake, and all cities with over 1 million population, except one, are located on a major river, ocean, or lake.

Urban Concept

The concept of urbanism is used in different senses in various parts of the world and is defined differently by various disciplines. Wheatley (1972) classifies the different approaches as being (1) reliance on ideal-type constructs, (2) formulation of ecological theories, (3) delineation of trait complexes, (4) conceptualization of the city as a center of dominance, and (5) an expediential approach, usually based on the size of the urban population. Eldridge (1967a), in his opening remarks to *Taming Megalopolis,* states:

> It is becoming increasingly more difficult to talk and write about "the city." Max Weber and Louis Wirth could catalog the city's qualities as opposed to rurality and describe the people and life to be found there. But in the latter half of the twentieth century it is nearly impossible to analyze the city as place; the indeterminacy of this urban area befuddles all careful qualification and quantification, of its form, style, and inhabitants. People and their institutions overflow the central city bowl, course through suburbia and the hinterland to coalesce once again into a next urban place. The high density of rural Ceylon and Indonesia do not *a city make* nor the low densities of Westchester non-urbanism. In fact, what is *urban* (as differentiated from the physical fact of the city) can be defined as a socio-cultural structure rather than mere space.

Davis (1959) makes a distinction between urbanization and city growth per se:

> Around the world today city growth is disproportionate to urbanization. The discrepancy is paradoxical in the industrial nations and worse than paradoxical in the nonindustrial (p. 52).

He uses the term urbanization in terms of the proportion of the total population concentrated in urban settlements.

> . . . urbanization is a finite process, a cycle through which nations go in their transition from agrarian to industrial society (p. 43).

He also shows "The close association between economic development and urbanization. . . ." Eldridge (1967a) points out that "Modernization and urbanization may be roughly equivalent terms. . . ."

The United Nations defines an urban agglomeration as the city proper and the "thickly settled territory . . . adjacent" to the city.

> In a United Nations survey of the census procedures of 52 countries, it was found that the usual practice was to give a specific and detailed definition of urban areas, while rural areas were treated as merely residual to urban areas and consisting of "the remainder of the country." It is, therefore, the definition of the urban area upon which the urban–rural classification is often based (UNESCO, 1964, p. 52).

In the U.N. study five main concepts were used to define urban areas: (1) administrative area, (2) population size, (3) local government area, (4) urban characteristics, and (5) predominant economic activity. For example, when population is taken into consideration, urban areas may have 274 inhabitants (Burma), 300 (Iceland), 5,000 (India), 30,000 (Japan), 1,000 (Malaya), 5,000 (Pakistan), or 1,000 (Singapore). In countries such as Ceylon, the Philippines, and Thailand, population is not considered in the classification of urban areas.

In Canada an urban place is restricted to localities of more than 1,000; in the United States it must be 2,500. "Urbanized areas" were first defined by the U.S. Bureau of the Census in 1950, and additional criteria were established in 1960. The Bureau of the Budget has defined the Standard Metropolitan Statistical Area (SMSA). Some other countries use "conurbation." In 1960 this "urbanized area" contained at least one city of 50,000 inhabitants, but comparable data were not available before 1960. Thus 1960 was the first year new criteria were established which carefully delineated the categories of American population. Because of such cultural and semantic conflicts in nomenclature, it is important to provide a working-type frame of reference for a geomorphic appraisal of what constitutes the appropriate subject material for a treatise dealing with processes of urbanization and the urban areas. The primary focus is in the pattern of land and water utilization. Thus, whenever man congregates and builds his dwellings and places of business together, he superimposes on the land–water ecosystem a different set of values, constraints, and usage than man does in a country setting with one house surrounded by many acres of land. Therefore, in this volume we emphasize the concentration of people, whether it is a "town," "suburb," or "city," whereas Volume III is devoted to land that is used as its own resource for such purposes as agriculture, grazing, timbering, mining, and recreation (when removed and not continguous to the urban area).

Growth of Cities and Land-Use Patterns

Clawson (1959) contends that in the twentieth century there are three major elements of change in the American landscape: (1) cities are growing and spreading over the land surrounding urban centers, (2) increasingly larger areas of land and water are being used for recreation purposes, and (3) extensive networks of superhighways transform rural areas and affect land use over large regions. A variety of pressures has been interacting that have triggered this growth and change in living styles. Linton (1970) states:

> By mid-twentieth century, rural agricultural America had learned its lessons well and had surpassed England, its teacher, to become the urban–industrial society of the world. During the years between 1860 and 1960 little effort was made to understand the changes that were occurring and their effects. Attempts to cope with environmental destruction from population growth, urbanization and industrial expansion were practically nil, and those that

> were made nearly always came too late. What was done generally was in reaction to a crisis. The nation's environmental ills, when diagnosed at all, were diagnosed superficially, and corrective action, when prescribed, treated the symptoms and not the disease (p. 313).

Davis (1959) points out other aspects of urbanization.

> The rapid growth of cities in the advanced countries, painful though it was, had the effect of solving a problem—the problem of the rural population. The growth of cities enabled agricultural holdings to be consolidated, allowed increased capitalization and in general resulted in greater efficiency (p. 51).

> Thus persistent human multiplication promises to frustrate the ceaseless search for space — for ample residential lots, wide-open suburban school grounds, sprawling shopping centers, one-floor factories, broad freeways. It seems plain that the only way to stop urban crowding and to solve most of the urban problems besetting both the developed and the underdeveloped nations is to reduce the overall rate of population growth (p. 53).

In discussing the change of a moderate sized city into a metropolis, Blumenfeld (1965) says:

> The transformation was set in motion toward the end of the 19th century and early in the 20th with the invention of the telephone, the electric streetcar, the subway and the powered elevator. Even more far-reaching was the impact on the city of the automobile and the truck. With the acquisition of these aids to communication and mobility the city burst its eggshell and emerged as a metropolis (p. 67).

> [The growth of Leningrad (now 4 million and only 1 million in 1921)] . . . is especially remarkable in view of the Soviet government's policy of restricting the growth of major cities, a policy based on Karl Marx's condemnation of big cities because of their pollution of air, water and soil (p. 68).

> Attempts to halt the growth of the big city have been made ever since the phenomenon first appeared on the human scene. They have been singularly unsuccessful. Elizabeth I of England and after her Oliver Cromwell tried to limit the growth of London by circling it with an enforced greenbelt, but this method failed (p. 68).

The twentieth-century growth of cities is happening on an international scale. In 1800 only slightly more than 1 percent of the world's population lived in cities of 100,000 or more (Clawson, 1971), but by 1930 the figure was 11 percent, and 20 percent in 1960. The proportion varied in 1960, being 42 percent in United States, 33 percent in Western Europe, 24 percent in the Soviet Union, 12 percent in Asia, and 8 percent in Africa. When smaller cities and urbanized areas are considered, England was the first country with more than half the population in cities, which occurred by 1900. At that time the United States had only 37 urbanized areas (Pickard, 1967) whereas by 1960 there were 212 areas with over 50,000 population. By this time the growth rate of central cities had slowed to 9 percent, whereas in the suburban fringes the rate was 48 percent. In 1960, 70 percent of the population was considered urban, of which 64 percent were in cities of more than 50,000. By 1967 this had increased to 66 percent. Of the total population growth in the United States, two thirds is found in suburban areas. The population in urbanized areas throughout the world is now 30 percent, and United Nations projections estimate this number will double by the year 2000.

The three articles selected for reproduction in Part I provide insight into the various parameters that must be considered in an analysis of environmental factors associated with urban areas. The growth of large cities and adjoining areas has become such a significant factor that Gottman (1961) talks about the "revolution in land use," and shows how populations are "exploding far beyond the city limits" with an "interpenetration of urban and rural" areas that necessitated his resurrection of the term "megalopolis."

> Some two thousand years before the first European settlers landed on the shores of the James River, Massachusetts Bay, and Manhattan Island, a group of ancient people, planning a new city-state in the Peloponnesus in Greece, called it Megalopolis, for they dreamed of a great future for it and hoped it would become the largest of the Greek cities. . . . Through the centuries the world Megalopolis has been used in many senses by various people, and it has even found its way into Webster's dictionary which defines it as "a very large city." Its use, however, has not become so common that it could not be applied in a new sense, as a geographical place name for the unique cluster of metropolitan areas of the Northeastern seaboard of the United States (p. 4).

In the United States the rate of conversion of rural lands to other purposes amounts to well over 1 million acres per year. [A monograph by Bogue (1956) traces this development when it was emerging as a dominant land-use pattern.] Total land used for urban development is nearly equaled by total land for highways, railroads, and airports outside of urban areas, 27 million to 25 million acres in 1959. This represents about 2.75 percent of the total land area (the comparable figure in England was about 15 percent). "Cropland acreage decreased from 478 million acres in 1950 to 437 million in 1967 and is still decreasing. The average annual decrease in cropland has been almost 2.5 million acres per year since 1950" (U.S. Department of Agriculture, 1970a, p. 190). Such changes created 900,000 fewer operating farms in 1970 than in 1960. At least 1 million acres are being lost to the urbanized areas, and other losses occur in construction activities associated with highways, dams, and reservoirs, and in mining, especially strip mining. Much of the loss occurs because new cities are not as compact; the city of 1960 covers three times as much area as the city of 1920. The Washington, D.C., metropolitan area typifies this type of growth and is expanding at a rate of 25 square miles per year ". . . or about one percent of the metropolitan area annually will be converted from farm, swamp, and hillside to subdivision, street, and park between now and the year 2000" (Metropolitan Washington Council of Governments, 1968). Clawson (1971, p. 49) provides a table (Table 1) which illustrates representative land-use figures in percentages for many cities in the United States.

Urban Physical System

Having considered urban areas and their consumption of land, we next evaluate the physical system that operates within the city. This topic is beautifully analyzed in the classic paper by Dr. Abel Wolman, Professor Emeritus of Sanitary Engineering, Johns Hopkins University. Wolman is recognized in numerous awards as being the premier scientist in his field. He is a member of the National Academy of Sciences and numerous engineering societies. He was instrumental in the development of water chlorination methods that are now used throughout the world. In addition he has served on boards of and been advisor to numerous government agencies, including the Atomic Energy Commission, Tennessee Valley Authority, Office of Science and Technology, U.S. Public Health Service, Maryland Water Resources Commission, and Maryland State Planning Commission. He has received honorary degrees, medals, and citations for "recognition of distinguished contributions to public health as an administrator, educator, and world citizen."

Detwyler and Marcus (1972) also show the importance of considering the city as

> . . . the totality of natural social, and artificial components aggregated in populous places. . . . The city may also be thought of functionally—as an open ecosystem for perpetuating urban culture by exchanging and converting great quantities of material and energy (pp. 5–7).

The urban environment is constituted by the total of all external conditions that influence the life of the inhabitants—the cultural system and the physical system (see

Table 1. Land-use figures for U.S. cities

Type of land use	102 Cities over 100,000	40 Cities over 250,000
Streets	17.5	18.3
Residential	31.6	32.3
Commercial	4.1	4.4
Industrial	4.7	5.4
Railroads	1.7	2.4
Undeveloped	22.3	12.5
Recreation area	4.9	5.3
Schools/colleges	2.3	1.8
Airport	2.0	2.5
Cemeteries	1.0	1.1
Public housing	0.5	0.4
Other	3.0	5.1

White House Conference on Natural Beauty, 1965). The physical urban ecosystem transforms the land, water, and air resources into living by-products, which create waste that feeds back into the system, thus contaminating both the city and surrounding countryside. In Volume I we discussed this overall process as the *law of reciprocity* — nature affects man and man affects nature. Liquid wastes may be pumped back into the ground and rivers, and solid wastes transported out of the area by rivers or dumped into adjacent countryside as landfill, which changes the topographic and ecologic character of the site. Water moves into the city by natural means, such as rivers, springs, lakes, oceans, and precipitation, or by man's engineering works in canals, wells, and pipes. Within the city, water flows in various conduits, gutters, and altered riverways, thus completely transforming the natural landscape and hydrologic system.

Details of these hydrologic changes are considered in other sections, but at this stage it will be useful to enlarge on the subject of the atmospheric variations caused by man [see also Ducktown, Tennessee, in Coates (1973)]. The geomorphologist is interested in man's contamination of the city atmosphere, because a special microclimate is created whereby winds are changed, temperature and precipitation increase, and air chemistry is modified. These transformations produce changes in the water budget and lead to accelerated weathering of lands and buildings in the cityscape.

> Applying the principles of the radiation and heat balances at the interface of the atmosphere and the solid ground surface, we can anticipate the impact of Man as his cities spread, replacing a richly vegetated countryside with blacktop and concrete. Not only do the thermal properties of the surface change, but the hydrologic factors of evaporation and transpiration are changed as well, altering the water balance itself. The vertical walls of buildings not only add to surfaces or reflection and radiation, but they also change the aerodynamic character of the surface, altering the flow patterns of air and the speed of winds.
>
> In the urban environment the absorption of solar radiation causes higher ground temperatures for two reasons: First, foliage of plants is absent, so that the full quantity of solar energy falls upon the bare ground. Absence of foliage also means absence of transpiration, which elsewhere produces a cooling of the lower air layer through the latent heat flux. A second factor is that roofs and pavements of concrete and asphalt hold no moisture and evaporative cooling does not occur as it would from a moist soil. The thermal effect is that of converting the city into a hot desert (Strahler and Strahler, 1973, p. 150).

In a review of literature on the microclimate of cities, Peterson (1973) points out the "heat island" effect, whereby night temperatures are 10 to 20°F higher in cities than in surrounding areas. An average of 67 case studies showed temperatures 1.2°C hotter throughout the year in cities than in the environs. Relative humidity was several percent lower, and studies in European cities indicate about 10 percent more precipitation in cities. In a discussion of climate in cities, it was stated in *World and News Reports* (September 17, 1973) that cities have 10 percent more cloud cover than adjacent areas

now and the year 2000" (Metropolitan Washington Council of Governments, 1968). Clawson (1971, p. 49) provides a table (Table 1) which illustrates representative land-use figures in percentages for many cities in the United States.

Urban Physical System

Having considered urban areas and their consumption of land, we next evaluate the physical system that operates within the city. This topic is beautifully analyzed in the classic paper by Dr. Abel Wolman, Professor Emeritus of Sanitary Engineering, Johns Hopkins University. Wolman is recognized in numerous awards as being the premier scientist in his field. He is a member of the National Academy of Sciences and numerous engineering societies. He was instrumental in the development of water chlorination methods that are now used throughout the world. In addition he has served on boards of and been advisor to numerous government agencies, including the Atomic Energy Commission, Tennessee Valley Authority, Office of Science and Technology, U.S. Public Health Service, Maryland Water Resources Commission, and Maryland State Planning Commission. He has received honorary degrees, medals, and citations for "recognition of distinguished contributions to public health as an administrator, educator, and world citizen."

Detwyler and Marcus (1972) also show the importance of considering the city as

> . . . the totality of natural social, and artificial components aggregated in populous places. . . . The city may also be thought of functionally—as an open ecosystem for perpetuating urban culture by exchanging and converting great quantities of material and energy (pp. 5–7).

The urban environment is constituted by the total of all external conditions that influence the life of the inhabitants—the cultural system and the physical system (see

Table 1. Land-use figures for U.S. cities

Type of land use	102 Cities over 100,000	40 Cities over 250,000
Streets	17.5	18.3
Residential	31.6	32.3
Commercial	4.1	4.4
Industrial	4.7	5.4
Railroads	1.7	2.4
Undeveloped	22.3	12.5
Recreation area	4.9	5.3
Schools/colleges	2.3	1.8
Airport	2.0	2.5
Cemeteries	1.0	1.1
Public housing	0.5	0.4
Other	3.0	5.1

as little damage as possible to the natural environment, especially the hydrologic systems. He places high priority on open space, including all surface water and riparian lands as far back from water bodies as possible. This includes all marshes and wetlands, all floodplains to the 50-year level (2 percent flooding probability), and all aquifer recharge areas where water percolates into the ground. Lands steeper than 12 degrees should not be developed because of high erosion risks, and agricultural land should have only limited development because of its importance to regional ecology. Thus he identifies the following eight components that must be integrated into the land-management system: surface water, floodplains, marshes, aquifers, aquifer recharge areas, steep slopes, forests and woodlands, and prime agricultural land. His approach to land management has greatly influenced other workers and planners in the field.

From the standpoint of raw materials, urban areas seem to have an unending appetite to consume earth resources. For example, the Los Angeles metropolitan region each year requires 15,000,000 tons of aggregate for highways alone. Whenever possible, multiple land use should be considered, instead of single use, such as happened in Austin, Texas, when real-estate developers built over the last remaining sand and gravel deposits, thus requiring the importation of these resources (with consequent higher prices) from localities many miles away. For further information on the geologic aspects of cities, the reader is referred to the outstanding book by Legget (1973), who points out:

> A new city can never be planned and designed in total disregard of its environment, upon which it cannot be just imposed. It must fit at least with the topographic limitations of the chosen site. It will be influenced inevitably by the geological conditions beneath the surface of the site. . . . Fundamentally, a new urban center must incorporate the landscape of its site as an integral part of its plan. Requirements of the regional plan must be reconciled with the main environmental features. The plan must take account of geological and foundation conditions, respecting the agricultural importance of some soils and protecting the original character of the landscape to the extent that is possible. Drainage of the site and the supply of water and of building materials are all geological factors that must be given consideration. Assurance must be had that the plan will not interfere with the winning of building materials (especially sand and gravel) that may lie under part of the site but rather allow for their extraction prior to use of this part of the area for building. The necessity for "looking below the surface" as a part of the planning process must therefore be appreciated from the very earliest stages of site consideration (p. 65).
>
> Geology, and all other relevant disciplines, simply must be given due consideration in the future planning of cities if disasters are to be avoided and man-made environments ensured that are at least conducive to decent living and reasonable civic pride. The fact that due consideration for geology in planning work can, in many cases, be shown to save money will usually win over the most recalcitrant of critics (p. 72).

and 24 percent more rain during the week than on weekends; and in the 1951–1965 period LaPorte, Indiana (30 miles downwind from the air pollution of the steel mills at Gary and South Chicago) experienced 246 percent more hail, 31 percent more precipitation, and 38 percent more thunderstorms than before 1951. H. Landsberg has shown that the smoke pall of cities affects a region 50 times the built-up area.

Air pollution created within cities hastens the breakdown of earth materials and buildings. Conservation News (v. 38, n. 6, p. 12, 1973) points out that modern traffic and factory fumes in Athens, Greece, are severely pitting the 2,400-year-old Parthenon and rusting the iron bars used in attempted restoration. The director of the Acropolis has termed the problem a "catastrophe" because priceless masterpieces have already been destroyed. Venice also suffers from disastrous loss of statues because of fumes from the adjacent industrial city of Mestre, and is now removing all open-air statues to protection inside buildings. The original statues are being replaced with replicas. A favorite illustration used in many textbooks concerning man-induced weathering in cities is the case of Cleopatra's Needle in New York City. This obelisk of granite originally had deep-cut hieroglyphics, which reportedly had been nearly unchanged in Egypt for 3,500 years. It was brought to Central Park in 1880, and in less than 50 years many of the writings had become largely obliterated. Several articles have been written about this phenomenon; the geology text by Gilluly, Waters, and Woodford (1959, p. 55) summarizes the opinion that the accelerated destruction was caused by "frost, frequent wetting, and air rich in carbon dioxide and other acid-forming substances." Rhodes Fairbridge (personal communication, January 15, 1974) stated that Cleopatra's Needle has peeled off on one side, whereas the opposite side is quite well preserved. This difference has nothing to do with prevailing winds or insolation, as commonly quoted. Instead it is attributed to the obelisk having laid sideways in the Nile muds, where sulfate salts rotted the feldspars and crystallized, causing fretting and flaking. Further information on this monument and other aspects of rock changes in man-made environments can be found in Winkler (1973).

The last two articles reproduced here (by McHarg and by Wayne) are closely linked and are written on the theme of the importance of preserving nature in the urban environment and the type of analysis that will produce the least amount of disorder to the natural ecosystem. Ian McHarg is an international authority in landscape architecture and has been instrumental in the development of the idea of "design with nature." William Wayne is a well-known geomorphologist with extensive experience in the public domain as geologist with the Indiana Geological Survey; he has also served on the Indiana University faculty and is now Professor of Geology at the University of Nebraska.

In 1963 McHarg began a new type of approach to urban planning that challenged the normal practice of treating open space as a residual after other economic and social needs of land-use development had been satisfied. Instead he proposed that landscape management should start with an awareness and understanding of nature, and the need for early indentification of areas necessary for continuance of natural processes. Such knowledge should then be used by decision makers to influence patterns of development. His writings show a primary concern that modern technology should do

Additional reading along this line is contained in such planning reports as that prepared by the Metropolitan Washington Council of Governments (1968):

> Rocks, rivers, soils, and other natural features are often so familiar that they are overlooked when development decisions are made. Crumbling roads, cracked foundations, polluted waters, unwarranted flood damage, standing cesspools, lost vistas, denuded forests, and even higher produce prices are often the results. This is unnecessarily expensive, hazardous, and sacrificial. A better understanding of the physical environment and recognition of its implications for urban developments can help prevent these results from recurring.
>
> This study is an effort to assemble such material for urban analysis in an "ecological framework". . . . In combination with other information, it will be useful in making decisions concerning land use location, densities, and open space and resource preservation.

This publication contains specialized guides for planners, such as a composite map that indicates areas where public policy should reflect the limitations and constraints for development that are imposed by the physical environment. Areas of shallow bedrock were considered to be most restrictive to urbanization because they require installation of water and sewer lines prior to housing or commercial use. The paper by W. J. Wayne presents an excellent summation of the role the geomorphologist can play in urban planning, since most of the article deals with the land–water interface of the ecosystem [see also McGill (1964), Kaye (1968), and Cloud (1969)].

1

Reprinted with permission from *Sci. Amer.*, **213**(3), 179–188, 190 (1965)

The Metabolism of Cities

In the U.S. today attention is focused on shortages of water and the pollution of water and air. There is plenty of water, but supplying it requires foresight. Pollution calls for public economic decisions

by Abel Wolman

The metabolic requirements of a city can be defined as all the materials and commodities needed to sustain the city's inhabitants at home, at work and at play. Over a period of time these requirements include even the construction materials needed to build and rebuild the city itself. The metabolic cycle is not completed until the wastes and residues of daily life have been removed and disposed of with a minimum of nuisance and hazard. As man has come to appreciate that the earth is a closed ecological system, casual methods that once appeared satisfactory for the disposal of wastes no longer seem acceptable. He has the daily evidence of his eyes and nose to tell him that his planet cannot assimilate without limit the untreated wastes of his civilization.

No one article could describe the complete metabolism of the modern city. Moreover, many of the metabolic inputs such as food, fuel, clothing, durable goods, construction materials and electric energy present no special problem. Their supply is handled routinely, in part through local initiative and in part through large organizations (public or private) that operate about as effectively in one city as another. I shall be concerned therefore with three metabolic problems that have become more acute as cities have grown larger and whose solution rests almost entirely in the hands of the local administrator. Although he can call on many outside sources for advice, he must ultimately provide solutions fashioned to the unique needs of his own community. These three problems are the provision of an adequate water supply, the effective disposal of sewage and the control of air pollution.

That these three problems vary widely from city to city and that they are being managed with widely varying degrees of success is obvious to anyone who reads a daily newspaper. It is ironic, for example, that New York City, which houses the nation's (if not the world's) greatest concentration of managerial talent, should be running short of water while billions of gallons of fresh water flow past it to the sea. It is not easy for people living in arid countries, or even for those living in the southwestern part of the U.S., to have much sympathy with New York's plight.

This summer, while New Yorkers were watching their emptying reservoirs and hoping for rain, Californians were busy building an aqueduct that would carry water some 440 miles from the Sacramento River, near Sacramento, to Los Angeles and other cities in the southern part of the state. And thanks to earlier examples of foresight, people in southern California were watering their lawns and filling their swimming pools without restriction, while in New York and New Jersey lawns were dying and pools stood empty. In the water-rich Middle Atlantic states water shortages are largely the result of delayed action and failures of management—sometimes exacerbated by political jockeying.

If American cities have had such unequal success in supplying their citizens with water, it is hardly surprising that some should have an even less satisfactory record in controlling water and air pollution, areas in which the incentives for providing remedies are much weaker than those that motivate the supplying of water. To make matters worse, pollutants of water and air often do not respect state boundaries. For example, the wastes of five states—Michigan, Indiana, Ohio, Pennsylvania and New York—have contributed to the accelerated pollution of Lake Erie. "The lake," according to the U.S. Public Health Service, "has deteriorated in quality at a rate many times greater than its normal aging process." The fourth-largest and shallowest of the five Great Lakes, Lake Erie is the main water supply for 10 million U.S. citizens as well as for the huge industrial complex that extends for 300 miles along the lake's southern shore from Detroit to Buffalo. The combination of treated and partially treated municipal sewage and industrial wastes that enters Lake Erie directly, and also reaches it indirectly through a network of rivers, has disrupted the normal cycle of aquatic life, has led to the closing of a number of beaches and has materially changed the commercial fishing industry. Last month the five states, in consultation with the Public Health Service, reached agreement on a major program of pollution abatement.

Although engineers concerned with water supply, sewage disposal and air pollution are accustomed to thinking in terms of large volumes, few laymen quite appreciate the quantities of water, sewage and air pollutants involved in

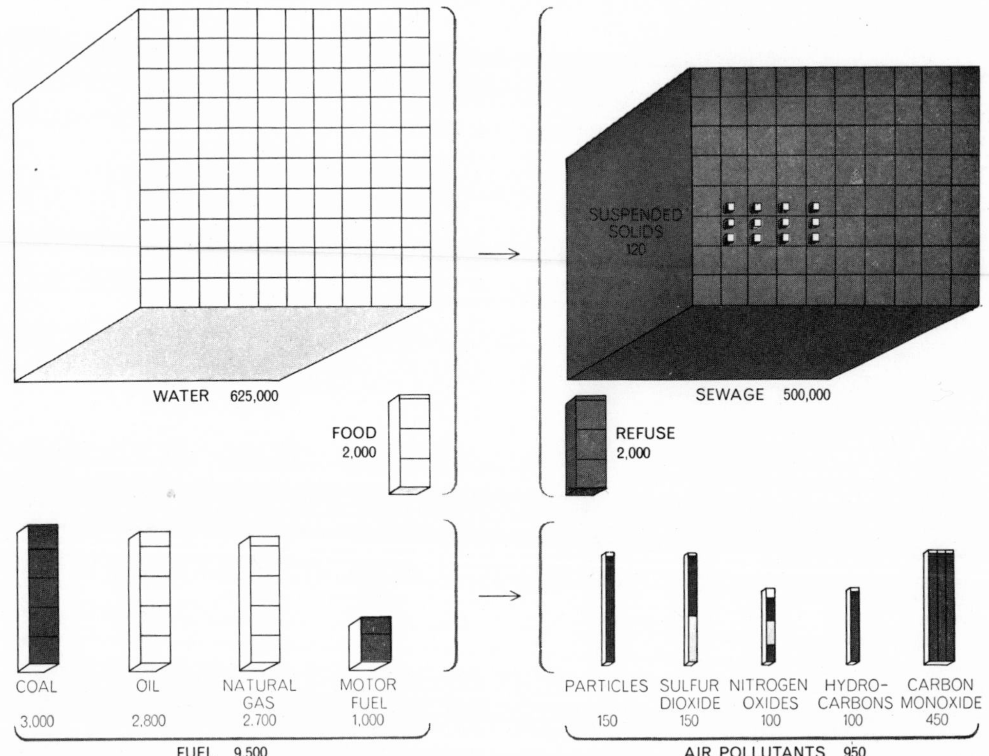

METABOLISM OF A CITY involves countless input-output transactions. This chart concentrates on three inputs common to all cities, namely water, food and fuel, and three outputs, sewage, solid refuse and air pollutants. Each item is shown in tons per day for a hypothetical U.S. city with a population of one million. Water, which enters the city silently and unseen, overshadows all other inputs in volume. More than .6 ton (150 gallons) must be supplied to each inhabitant every day. After about 20 percent of the water has been diverted to lawns and other unrecoverable uses, it returns, contaminated, to the city's sewers. The city's most pervasive nuisance, air pollution, is accounted for chiefly by the combustion of fuels. (If refuse is burned in incinerators, it can also contribute heavily, but that contribution is not included here.) The various air pollutants are keyed by shading and color to the fuel responsible. Most of the particle emission (soot and fly ash) is produced by coal burned in electric power plants, and in well-designed plants more than 90 percent of the particles can be removed from the stack gases. For this hypothetical city one may assume that 135 of the 150 tons of particles produced by all fuel consumers are removed before they reach the atmosphere. All other emissions, however, pollute the atmosphere in the volumes shown. Sulfur dioxide is based on use of domestic fuels of average sulfur content.

the metabolism of a modern city. The illustration above expresses these quantities in the form of an input-output chart for a hypothetical American city of one million population. The input side of the chart shows the requirements in tons per day of water, food and fuels of various kinds. The output side shows the metabolic products of that input in terms of sewage, solid refuse and air pollutants. The quantities shown are a millionfold multiplication of the daily requirements of the average city dweller. Directly or indirectly he uses about 150 gallons (1,250 pounds) of water, four pounds of food and 19 pounds of fossil fuels. This is converted into roughly 120 gallons of sewage (which assumes 80 percent recovery of the water input), four pounds of refuse (which includes food containers and miscellaneous rubbish) and 1.9 pounds of air pollutants, of which automobiles, buses and trucks account for more than half.

As of 1963 about 150 million out of 189 million Americans, or 80 percent, lived in some 22,000 communities served by 19,200 waterworks. These 150 million people used about 23 billion gallons per day (b.g.d.), a volume that can be placed in perspective in several ways. In 1960 the amount of water required for all purposes in the U.S. was about 320 b.g.d., or roughly 15 times the municipal demand. The biggest user of water is irrigation, which in 1960 took about 140 b.g.d. Steam electric utilities used about 98 b.g.d. and industry about 60 b.g.d. Since 1960 the total U.S. water demand has risen from about 320 b.g.d. to an estimated 370 b.g.d., of which municipalities take about 25 b.g.d. [*see illustration on opposite page*].

Thus municipalities rank as the smallest of the four principal users of water. Although it is true that water provided for human consumption must sometimes meet standards of quality that need not be met by water used in agriculture or industry, nevertheless throughout most of the U.S. farms, factories and cities frequently draw water from a common supply.

For the country as a whole the supply

of available water is enormous: about 1,200 b.g.d. This is the surface runoff that remains from an average daily rainfall of some 4,200 b.g.d. About 40 percent of the total precipitation is utilized where it falls, providing water to support vegetation of economic value: forests, farm crops and pasturelands. Another 30 percent evaporates directly from the soil or returns to the atmosphere after passing through vegetation that has no particular economic value except insofar as it may prevent erosion of the land.

It is obvious that one cannot expect to capture and put to use every drop of the 1,200 b.g.d. flowing to the sea. The amount that can be captured depends on what people are willing to pay for water. One recent estimate places the economically available supply at somewhat less than half the total, or 560 b.g.d. In my opinion this estimate is too conservative; I would suggest a figure of at least 700 b.g.d.

Even this volume would be inadequate by the year 2000—if all the water withdrawn for use were actually consumed. This, however, is not the case now and will not be then; only a small fraction of the water withdrawn is consumed. In 1960 "consumptive use," as it is called, amounted to about 90 b.g.d. of the 320 b.g.d. withdrawn. Most of the remaining 230 b.g.d. was returned after use to the source from which it was taken, or to some other body of water (in some instances the ocean). A small fraction of the used water was piped into the ground to help maintain local water tables.

Estimates by a Senate Select Committee a few years ago projected a consumptive use of about 120 b.g.d. in 1980 and of nearly 160 b.g.d. in the year 2000, when total demand may reach 900 b.g.d. It will be apparent in the illustration on the next page, where these projections are plotted, that agriculture accounts for the biggest consumptive use of water. It is conservatively estimated that 60 percent of the water employed for irrigation is lost to the atmosphere as the result of evaporation directly from the soil or indirectly by transpiration through the leaves of growing plants. (The amount of water incorporated into plant tissue is insignificant; roughly 1,000 gallons of water is needed to produce about 10 cents' worth of crop.) In contrast, from 80 to 98 percent of the water withdrawn by municipalities, industry and electric utilities is available for reuse. It is for this reason that the projected withdrawal rate of 900 b.g.d. in the year 2000 should not prove difficult to meet, whether the economically available supply is 560 b.g.d. or 700 b.g.d. Of the 900 b.g.d. that may be required in A.D. 2000 to meet human, industrial and agricultural needs, approximately 740 b.g.d. should be available for reuse.

These estimates, moreover, are pessimistic in that they make only minor allowances for reductions in industrial or agricultural demands as a result of technological changes and in that they provide for no significant increase in the cost of water to hasten such changes. Thus we must reasonably conclude that for many years beyond A.D. 2000 total water shortages for the U.S. as a whole are highly improbable.

If water is going to remain so plentiful into the 21st century, why should New York and other cities find themselves running short in 1965? The immediate answer, of course, is that there has been a five-year drought in the northeastern U.S. With the completion in 1955 of two new reservoirs in the upper reaches of the Delaware River, and with the extension of the Delaware aqueduct to a total distance of more than 120 miles, New York City believed it could satisfy its water needs until the year 2000. This confident forecast reckoned without the unprecedented drought.

There is no point in criticizing New York's decision to depend so heavily on the Delaware watershed for its future needs. The question is what New York should do now. As long ago as 1950, in an earlier water shortage, New York was advised to build a pumping station on the Hudson River 65 miles north of the city to provide an emergency supply of 100 million gallons per day, or more

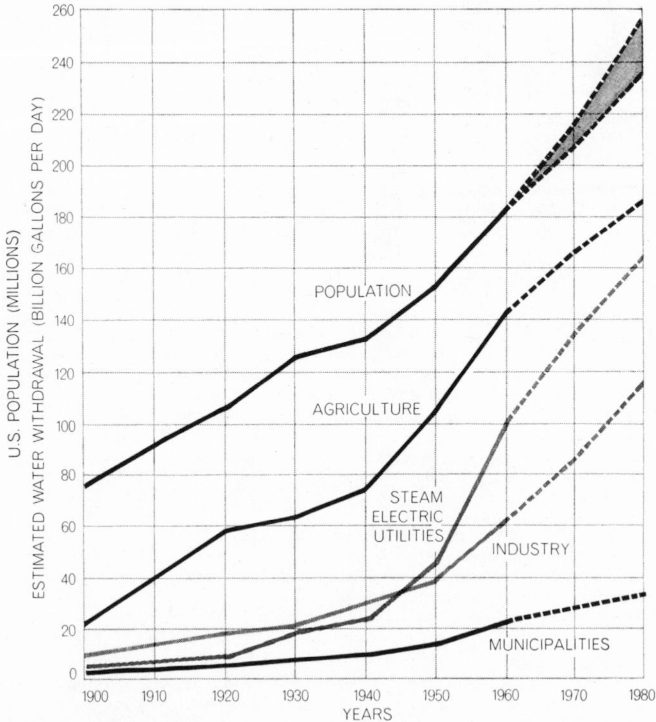

U.S. WATER REQUIREMENTS will be 53 percent greater in 1980 than in 1960, according to the most recent estimates of the Department of Commerce. Virtually all water used by agriculture is for irrigation; nearly 60 percent of all irrigated land in the U.S. is in five Western states (California, Texas, Colorado, Idaho and Arizona) where water tends to be scarcest. Steam power plants need water in huge amounts simply to condense steam. In 1960 municipalities used about 22 billion gallons per day (b.g.d.), which represented only about 7 percent of the total water withdrawal of about 320 b.g.d. The important distinction between water "withdrawal" and "consumptive use" is shown in the illustration on next page.

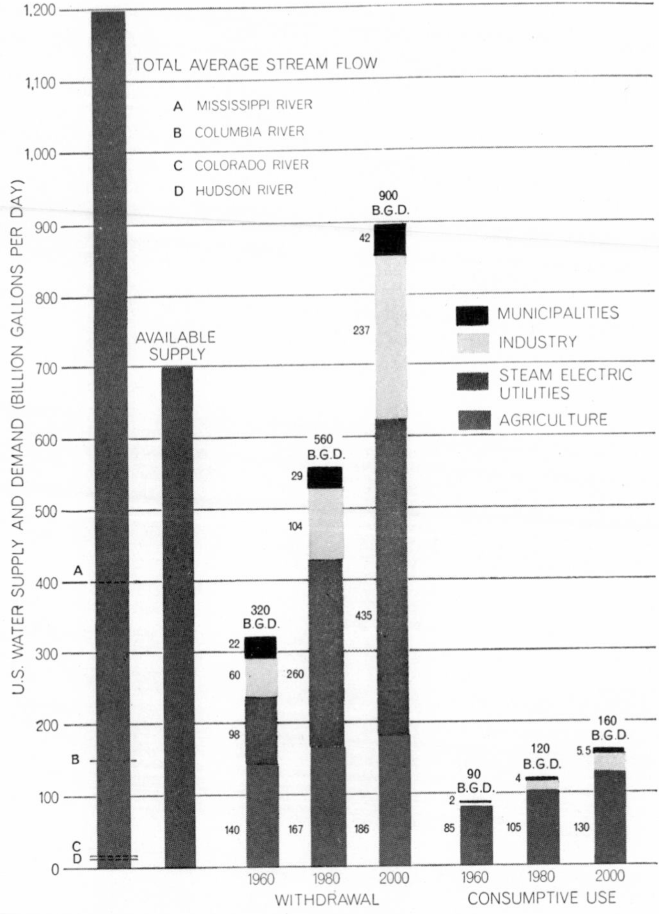

U.S. WATER SUPPLY consists of the approximately 1,200 b.g.d. that flows to the sea through the nation's waterways. This is the streamflow that results from an average precipitation volume of some 4,200 b.g.d. About 70 percent of all precipitation returns to the atmosphere without ever reaching the sea. The average flow of four important rivers is marked on the streamflow column. The author estimates that about 700 b.g.d. of the total streamflow can be made available for use at a cost acceptable to consumers. The estimates of water withdrawal and consumptive use for 1980 and 2000 are (with slight rounding) those published a few years ago by a Senate Select Committee. The 1980 estimate is 13 percent higher than that of the Department of Commerce shown in the illustration on the preceding page. "Consumptive use" represents the amount of water withdrawn that subsequently becomes unavailable for reuse. Except for irrigation, consumptive use of water is and will remain negligible. Thus a 700-b.g.d. supply should easily meet a 900-b.g.d. demand.

as needed. (New York City's normal water demand is about 1.2 b.g.d. The average flow of the Hudson is around 11 b.g.d.) The State of New York gave the city permission to build the pumping station but stipulated that the station be dismantled when the emergency was over. By the time the station was built (at a point somewhat farther south than the one recommended) the drought had ended; the station was torn down without ever having been used. This July the city asked the state for permission to rebuild the station, a job that will take several months, but as of mid-August permission had not been granted.

Meanwhile there has been much talk of building atomic-energy desalination plants as the long-term solution to New York's water needs. The economic justification for such proposals has never been explained. New York now obtains its water, delivered by gravity flow to the city, for only about 15 cents per 1,000 gallons (and many consumers are charged only 12 cents). The lowest predicted cost for desalination, assuming a plant with a capacity of 250 million or more gallons per day, is a highly optimistic 30 to 50 cents per 1,000 gallons. Since a desalination plant would be at sea level, its entire output would have to be pumped; storage and conveyance together would add about 20 cents per 1,000 gallons to the basic production cost. Recent studies in our department at Johns Hopkins University have shown that if desalinated water could be produced and delivered for as little as 50 cents per 1,000 gallons, it would still be cheaper to obtain fresh water from a supply 600 miles away. (The calculations assume a water demand of 100 million gallons per day.) In other words, it would be much cheaper for New York City to pipe water 270 miles from the St. Lawrence River, assuming that Canada gave its consent, than to build a desalination plant at the edge of town. New York City does not have to go even as far as the St. Lawrence. It has large untapped reserves in the Hudson River and in the upper watershed of the Susquehanna, no more than 150 miles away, that could meet the city's needs well beyond the year 2000.

Few cities in the U.S. have the range of alternatives open to New York. The great majority of inland cities draw their water supplies from the nearest lake or river. Of the more than 150 million Americans now served by public water supplies, nearly 100 million, or 60 percent, are reusing water from sources that have already been used at least once for domestic sewage and industrial waste disposal. This "used" water has of course been purified, either naturally or artificially, before it reaches the consumer. Only about 25 percent of the 25 b.g.d. now used by municipalities is obtained from aquifers, or underground sources. Such aquifers supply about 65 b.g.d. of the nation's estimated 1965 requirement of 370 b.g.d. Most of the 65 b.g.d. is merely a subterranean portion of the 1,200 b.g.d. of the precipitation flowing steadily to the sea. It is estimated, however, that from five to 10 b.g.d. is water "mined" from aquifers that have been filled over the centuries. Most of this mining is done in West Texas, New Mexico, Arizona and California.

The fact that more than 150 million Americans can be provided with safe drinking water by municipal waterworks, regardless of their source of supply, attests the effectiveness of modern water-treatment methods. Basically the treatment consists of filtration and chlorination. The use of chlorine to kill bacteria in municipal water supplies was introduced in 1908. It is fortunate that such a cheap and readily available substance is so effective. A typical requirement is about one part of chlorine to a million parts of water (one p.p.m.). The amount of chlorine needed to kill bacteria and also to "kill" the taste of dissolved organic substances—many of which are introduced naturally when rainwater comes in contact with decaying vegetation—is adjusted by monitoring the amount of free chlorine present in the water five to 10 minutes after treatment. This residual chlorine is usually held to about .2 p.p.m. In cases where unusually large amounts of organic compounds are present in the water, causing the public to complain of a bad taste, experience has shown that the palatability of the water can often be improved simply by adding more chlorine. Contrary to a widely held impression, free chlorine itself has little taste; the "bad" taste usually attributed to chlorine is due chiefly to organic compounds that have been too lightly chlorinated. When they are more heavily chlorinated, the bad taste usually disappears.

Throughout history impure water has been a leading cause of fatal disease in man; such waterborne diseases as typhoid fever and dysentery were still common in the U.S. less than a century ago. In 1900 the U.S. death rate from typhoid fever was 35.8 per 100,000 people. If such a rate persisted today, the deaths from typhoid would far exceed those from automobile accidents. By 1936 the rate had been reduced to 2.5 per 100,000, and today the disease is almost unknown in the U.S.

In underdeveloped nations, where many cities are still without adequate water supplies, waterborne diseases are among the leading causes of death and debility. In Central and South America more than a third of 75 million people living in towns or cities with a population of more than 2,000 are without water service. Similarly, in India about a third of the urban population of 80 million are without an adequate water

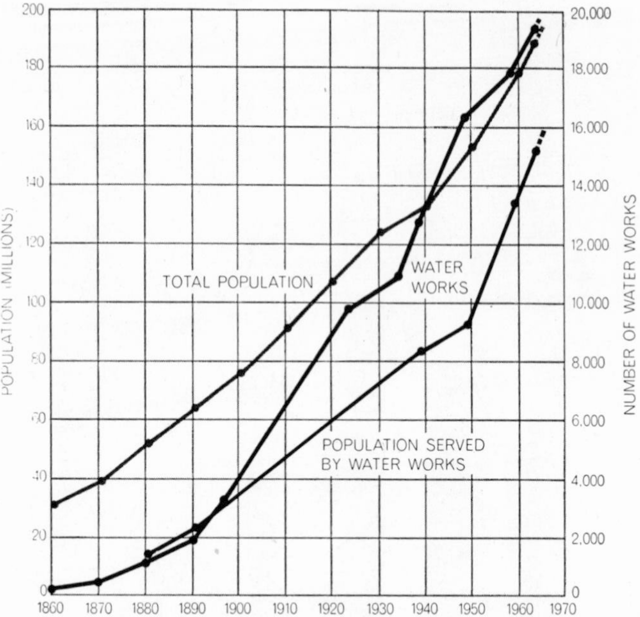

GROWTH OF MUNICIPAL WATER SUPPLIES accelerated after 1880, when less than a fourth of the U.S. population was served by waterworks. By 1939 the number served by waterworks exceeded 60 percent and by 1963 the figure had reached nearly 80 percent.

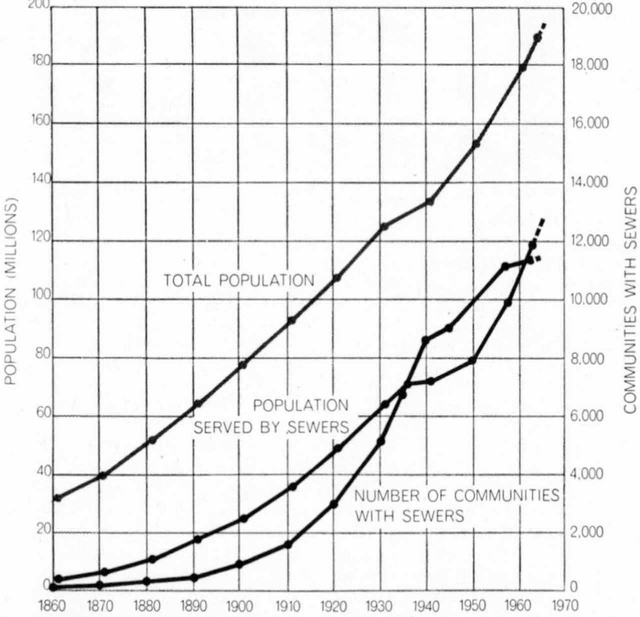

GROWTH OF SEWERAGE FACILITIES has lagged behind the growth of community water supplies, chiefly because people are reluctant to pay taxes for what long seemed a nonessential service. Nevertheless, 63 percent of the population was served by sewers in 1962.

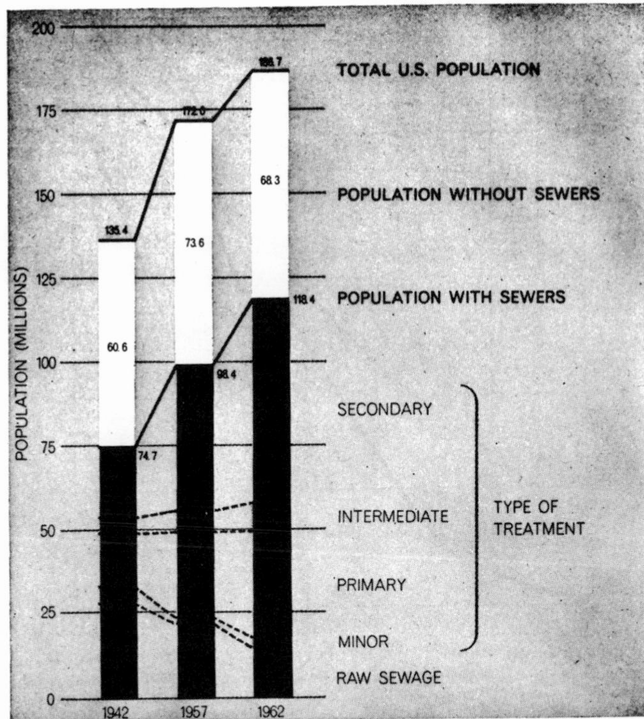

RACE BETWEEN SEWERS AND POPULATION GROWTH is depicted in this chart. Between 1942 and 1957 population outstripped the increase in sewerage service. Between 1957 and 1962 sewerage service grew slightly faster than population. People without sewers do not necessarily contribute to the water pollution problem if they use effective septic tanks and cesspools. The principal pollution is caused by communities—and by industries—that discharge wastes into waterways with little treatment or no treatment at all. Data for this chart and the two preceding ones were supplied by the U.S. Public Health Service.

supply. As the article on Calcutta in this issue [*page 90*] points out, that city is regarded as the endemic center of cholera for all of southeast Asia.

No general prescription can be offered for bringing clean water to the vast urban populations that still lack it. I have found in my own experience, however, that the inhabitants of communities both large and small can do much more to help themselves than is customarily recognized. If the small towns and villages of India and elsewhere wait for their central governments to install public water supplies, most of them will wait indefinitely. It is surprising how much can be accomplished with local labor and local materials, and the benefits in health are incalculable.

In the larger cities, where self-help is not feasible, municipal water systems can be built and made to pay their way if an appropriate charge is made for water and if the systems can be financed with long-term loans, as they have been financed traditionally in the U.S. Such loans, however, have only recently been made available to underdeveloped countries. A few years ago, when loans for waterworks had to be paid off in six to 12 years, the total value of external bank loans made to South American countries for water supply and sewerage projects was less than $100,000 in a six-year period. Under the leadership of the Pan-American Health Organization and the U.S. Agency for International Development bankers were encouraged to extend the repayment period to 28 or 30 years. Today the total value of bank loans made to South American countries for waterworks and sewerage systems has surpassed $660 million.

Outside the U.S., as within it, adequate water resources are generally available. The problem is to treat water as a commodity whose cost to the user must bear a fair relation to the cost of its production and delivery. The total U.S. investment in municipal waterworks is about $17.5 billion (replacement cost would approach $50 billion), or about half the nation's investment in telephone service. More significant than investment is the cost of service to the consumer. The average American family pays about $3 a month for water, which it cannot live without, compared with about $7.30 for telephone service. One might also note that the average household expenditure for alcoholic beverages is more than $15 a month. It should be clear that Americans can afford to pay for all the water they need.

The question of fair payment and allocation of costs is even more central to the problem of controlling water pollution than to the problem of providing water. Whereas 150 million Americans were served by waterworks in 1963, only about 120 million were served by sewers [*see bottom illustration on preceding page*]. Thus the wastes of nearly 70 million Americans, who live chiefly in the smaller towns and suburbs, were still being piped into backyard cesspools and septic tanks. When these devices are properly designed and the receiving soils are not overloaded, they create no particular sanitation hazard. Unfortunately in too many suburban areas neither of these criteria is met.

The principal pollution hazard arises where sewage collected by a sewerage system is discharged into a lake or river without adequate treatment or without any treatment at all [*see illustration on this page*]. As of 1962 the wastes of nearly 15 million Americans were discharged untreated and the wastes of 2.4 million received only minor treatment. The wastes of 32.7 million were given primary treatment: passage through a settling basin, which removes a considerable portion of the suspended solid matter. Intermediate treatment, which consists of a more nearly complete removal of solids, was applied to the wastes of 7.4 million people. Secondary treatment, the most adequate form of sewage treatment, was applied to the wastes of 61.2 million people. The term "secondary treatment" covers a variety of techniques, often used in combination: extended aeration, activated sludge (an accelerated form of bacterial degradation), filtration through beds of various materials, stabilization ponds.

It can be seen from the chart on the opposite page that although there was a significant improvement in sewage treatment in the U.S. between 1942 and 1962, a big job remains to be done. Only in the past five years of this period did the rate of sewer installation begin to overtake population growth. The present U.S. investment in sewers and sewage-treatment works is about $12 billion (again the replacement value would be much higher). The Public Health Service estimates that replacing obsolete facilities, improving the standard of treatment and providing for population growth will require an annual investment of more than $800 million a year in treatment works for the rest of the decade. This does not include the cost of extending the sewage-collection systems into new urban and suburban developments. This may add another $800 million to the annual requirements, making an approximate total of more than $1.6 billion a year.

Unfortunately some municipalities have not found a satisfactory or painless method for charging their residents for this vital service. Many simply float bonds to meet capital costs and add the cost to the individual's bill for property taxes. In Baltimore (where the tax bill is completely itemized) it was decided some years ago that sewerage costs should not be included in the citizen's *ad valorem* taxes but should be made part of his water bill. In the Baltimore system the charge for sewerage service is half the water service charge. A good many other cities charge for sewerage service on a similar basis.

Cities, of course, account for only a part, and probably not the major part, of the pollution that affects the nation's waterways. Industrial pollution is a ubiquitous problem. Industrial pollutants are far more varied than those in ordinary sewage, and their removal often calls for specialized measures. Even in states where adequate pollution-control laws are on the books, there are technological, economic and practical obstacles to seeing that the laws are observed. The Federal Water Pollution Control acts of 1954 and 1962, which enlarged the role of the Public Health Service in determining the pollution of interstate waterways, have sometimes been helpful in strengthening the hand of local law-enforcement agencies.

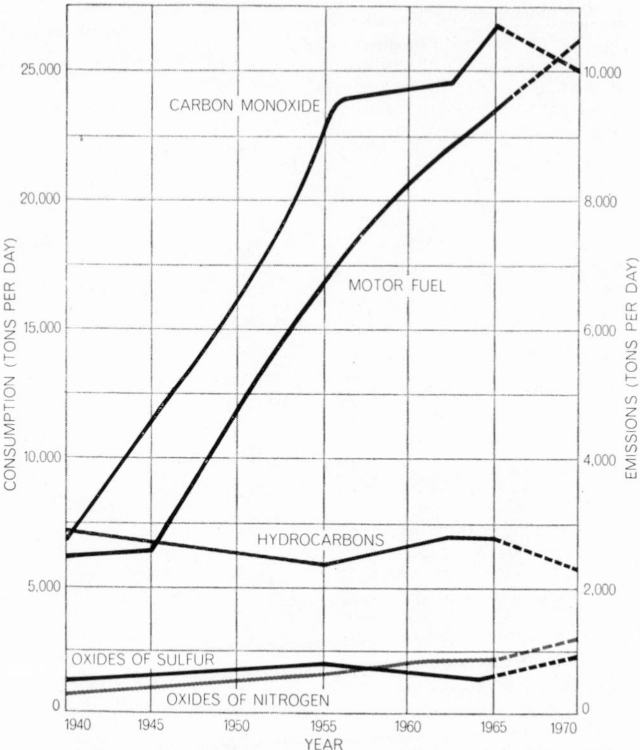

LOS ANGELES AIR POLLUTION is tied closely to the steep rise in automobile use in Los Angeles County. This chart compares gasoline consumption with the computed output from all sources of carbon monoxide, hydrocarbons, oxides of nitrogen and oxides of sulfur. Motor vehicles produce only small amounts of the last two substances and their output has been controlled chiefly by curbs on the emission of pollutants by industry. Carbon monoxide and hydrocarbon emissions should decline when cars start carrying exhaust-control systems.

My final topic—air pollution—is much harder to discuss in quantitative terms than water pollution, which it otherwise resembles in many ways. It is never going to be possible to provide a collection system for air pollution emissions, almost all of which result from combustion processes. Every house, every apartment, every automobile, truck, bus, factory and power plant is vented directly into the open air and presumably will have to remain so.

There are perhaps only three general approaches to controlling the amount of pollutants entering the atmosphere. One is to switch from a fuel that produces undesirable combustion products to one that produces fewer such products. Thus fuel oil produces less soot and fly ash than bituminous coal, and natural gas produces less than either. The second expedient is to employ a new technology. For example, atomic power plants produce none of the particulate and gaseous emissions that result from the burning of fossil fuels. One must then decide, however, whether the radioactive by-products that are released into the environment—either in the short run or the long—by an atomic power station are more or less hazardous than the fossil-fuel by-products they replaced. The third recourse is to remove the undesired components from the vented gases. Fly ash, for example, can be largely removed by suitable devices where coal or oil is used in large volume, as in a power plant, but cannot readily be removed from the flue gases of thousands of residences. The problem of dealing with many small offending units also arises in trying to reduce the unburned hydrocarbons and carbon monoxide emitted by millions of automobiles.

At this point it is worth asking: Why should air pollution be considered objectionable? Many people enjoy the smell of the pollutants released by a steak sizzling on a charcoal grill or by dry leaves burning in the fall. The cigarette smoker obviously enjoys the smoke he draws into his lungs. In other words, a pollutant per se need not necessarily be regarded as a nuisance. If by accident or design the exhaust gases emitted by a diesel bus had a fragrant aroma (or worse yet, led to physiological addiction), not many people would complain about traffic fumes.

The criteria of what constitutes an objectionable air pollutant must therefore be subjectively defined, unless, of course, one can demonstrate that a particular pollutant is a hazard to health. In the absence of a demonstrated health hazard the city dweller would probably list his complaints somewhat as follows: he objects to soot and dirt, he does not want his eyes to burn and water, he dislikes traffic fumes and he wishes he could see the clear blue sky more often.

Many conferences have been held and many papers written on the possible association of air pollution with disease. As might be expected, firm evidence of harmfulness is difficult to obtain. The extensive epidemiological data collected in the U.S. on smoking and human health suggest that in general place of residence has a minor influence on the incidence of lung cancer compared with the smoking habit itself. British statistics, however, can be interpreted to show that at times there is something harmful in the British air. In any event, it will be difficult to demonstrate conclusively—no matter how much one may believe it to be so—that air pollution is associated with long-term deterioration of the human organism. Eric J. Cassell of the Cornell University Medical College recently summarized the situation as follows: "I do not think that it is wrong to say that we do not even know what disease or diseases are caused by everyday pollution of our urban air.... We have a cause, but no disease to go with it."

Two diseases frequently mentioned as possibly associated with air pollution are chronic bronchitis and pulmonary emphysema. In Britain some investigators have found strong associations between chronic bronchitis and the level of air pollution, as measured by such indexes as fuel use, sulfur dioxide in the air and sootfall. In California the death rate from emphysema increased fourfold in the seven-year period from 1950 to 1957. This increase may indicate nothing more than the fact that older people go to California to retire, but there is objective evidence that emphysematous patients in Los Angeles showed improved lung function when allowed to breathe carefully filtered air for 48 hours.

In response to mounting public concern, and the urging of President Johnson, Congress two years ago passed the Clean Air Act, which states in its preamble that "Federal financial assistance and leadership is essential for the development of cooperative Federal, state, regional and local programs designed to prevent and control air pollution." The regulatory abatement procedures authorized in the act are similar to those found in the most recent Water Pollution Control Act. When an interstate pollution problem is identified, the Public Health Service is empowered, as a first step, to call a conference of state and local agencies. The second step is to call a public hearing, and the third step, if needed, is to bring a court action against the offenders.

The Clean Air Act takes special cognizance of air pollution caused by motor vehicles; it requires the Secretary of Health, Education, and Welfare to report periodically to Congress on progress made on control devices. He is also invited to recommend any new legislation he feels is warranted. Eventually the secretary may help to decide if all new U.S. motor vehicles should be equipped with exhaust-control sys-

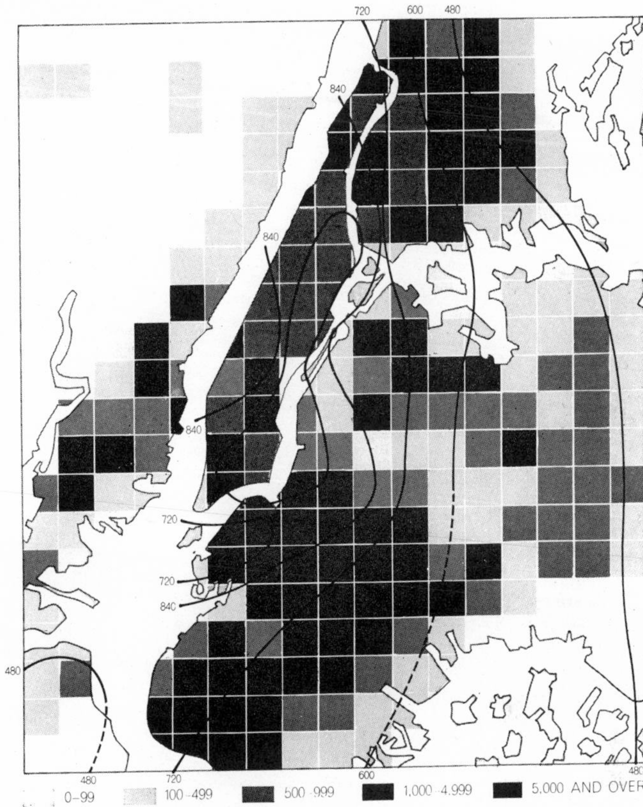

NEW YORK AIR POLLUTION contains large components of sulfur dioxide and particulate matter (soot and fly ash). The grid shows for the central part of New York City the computed output of sulfur dioxide per square mile in tons per year based on fuel used for space heating and producing hot water. About 55 percent more sulfur dioxide is released into the atmosphere by such "point sources" as power stations and industrial plants. The total figure for the entire city is estimated at more than 600,000 tons a year. The grid is taken from a larger map prepared under the direction of Ben Davidson of the Geophysical Sciences Department of New York University. The contour lines show the average dustfall levels in tons per year as measured by New York City's Department of Air Pollution Control.

tems, such as "afterburners," to reduce the large amounts of unburned hydrocarbons and carbon monoxide that are now released.

California studies in the 1950's showed that exhaust gases accounted for 65 percent of all the unburned hydrocarbons then produced by motor vehicles. Another 15 percent represented evaporation from the fuel tank and carburetor, and 20 percent escaped from the vent of the crankcase. As a first step in reducing these emissions California began in 1961 to require the use of crankcase blowby devices, which became standard on all U.S. cars beginning with the 1963 models.

A new California law will require exhaust-control systems on all 1966 automobiles and light trucks sold in the state. The law is intended to reduce by 70 or 80 percent the amount of hydrocarbons now present in exhaust gases and to reduce the carbon monoxide by 60 percent. All the carbon monoxide is generated by combustion and is now released in the exhaust. The steady rise in carbon monoxide vented into the atmosphere of Los Angeles County is plotted in the illustration on the opposite page.

No one questions that an affluent society can afford to spend its money without a strict accounting of benefits received. Any reasonable expenditure that promises to improve the quality of life in the modern city should be welcomed. It is not obvious, however, that any American city except Los Angeles will be significantly benefited by the installation of exhaust-control systems in motor vehicles. The cost of these systems will not be trivial. At an estimated \$40 to \$50 per car, such systems would add more than \$300 million to the sales price of new cars in an eight-million-car year—and this does not include the annual cost of their inspection and maintenance. If one objective of reducing the air pollution caused by automobiles is to increase the life expectancy of the city dweller, or simply to make his life more pleasant, it can be argued that \$300 million a year could be spent more usefully in other directions.

In most large cities, for example, the electric utilities consume up to half of all fuel burned. Most utilities have made reasonable efforts to reduce the emission of soot and fly ash; virtually all new power plants, and many old ones, are now equipped with devices capable of removing a large fraction of such emissions. Utilities, however, are still under pressure, both from the public and from supervising agencies, to use the cheapest fuels available. This means that in New York and other eastern-seaboard cities the utilities burn large volumes of residual fuel oil imported from abroad, which happens to contain between 2.5 and 3 percent of sulfur, compared with only about 1.7 percent for domestic fuel oil. When the oil is burned, sulfur dioxide is released. Recent studies show that the level of sulfur dioxide in New York City air is almost twice that found in other large cities.

Sulfur dioxide is difficult to remove from stack gases, but it is estimated that for about \$1 a barrel most of the sulfur could be removed from the oil before it is burned. For the volume of oil

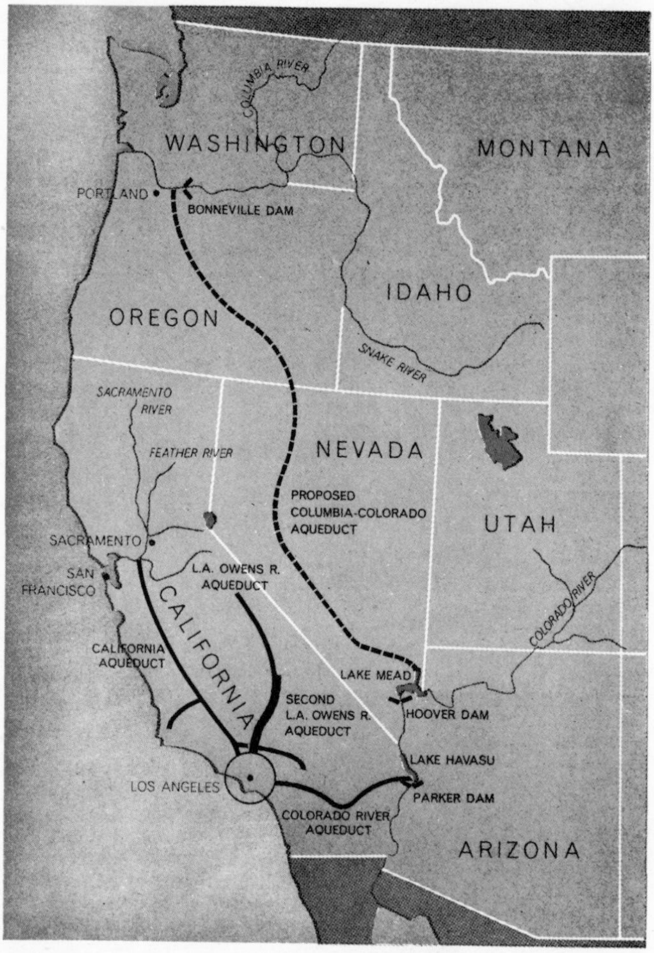

DISTANT TRANSPORTATION OF WATER has been practiced in the West for many years. Los Angeles now has three major sources of supply to meet its daily demand of 470 million gallons. About 15 percent comes through the 300-mile Colorado aqueduct, completed in 1941, about 21 percent is pumped from local wells and the remainder, 64 percent, comes from Owens Valley, 340 miles to the north. An enlargement of the Owens Valley supply system (*color*) is nearly completed. Meanwhile the state is building a new 444-mile aqueduct (*color*) that will deliver water from the Sacramento River to southern California. Proposals are now being made to move water from the Columbia River, which accounts for more than 12 percent of total U.S. streamflow, to the arid Southwest. The water might be taken from below Bonneville Dam and diverted some 800 miles to Lake Mead on the Colorado River, following the general route shown (*broken colored line*).

burned by the Consolidated Edison Company in New York City the added cost would come to about $15 million annually. If the cost were divided among Consolidated Edison's three million customers, the average electric bill would be increased about $5 per year. One would like to know how this expenditure would compare in improving the quality of New York City's air with New York's pro rata share of the more than $300-million-a-year investment that would be required by the installation of exhaust-control systems in motor vehicles. That share would be on the order of $8 million a year. Perhaps New Yorkers should insist on both investments. But these are only two of many options, all of them expensive. It is the responsibility of the city administrator and the public health officer to make choices and assign priorities, even while admitting that air pollution is never beneficial.

One must also recall that when large-scale changes are contemplated, the whole spectrum of society is involved. Rarely do all forces march forward in step, particularly where public policy and scientific verity are not crystal clear. Competitive forces delay correctives until public opinion rises in wrath and pushes for action on an *ad hoc* and intuitive basis.

Let me sum up by observing that in the case of water supply the accomplishments of the U.S. have been extraordinarily good, not only in the prevention of waterborne and water-associated diseases but also in providing water generously for comfortable living in most places at most times. The prospect for the future is likewise good. The realities are that we are not running out of water and that we are capable of managing our water resources intelligently.

In the area of water and air pollution our successes are only partial. Rapid urbanization and industrialization have intensified the problems of controlling both. At the same time one must concede that there is much stronger scientific justification for mounting vigorous programs to abate water pollution than to abate air pollution. Nevertheless, public pressure on behalf of the latter is increasing, and as has happened so often in the past, we may find action running ahead of knowledge. This is not necessarily to be deplored.

My own view coincides with that recently expressed by P. B. Medawar of University College London at a symposium on the interaction of man and his environment. "We are not yet qualified," he said, "to prescribe for the medical welfare of our grandchildren.... I should say that present skills are sufficient for present ills."

WORLD'S LARGEST FILTRATION PLANT was completed last year by the city of Chicago. Located on Lake Michigan, its normal rating is 960 million gallons per day, but it can safely provide 1.7 b.g.d. Another filtration plant helps to meet Chicago's average daily demand of .9 b.g.d. and to supply 61 nearby suburban communities. Chicago's per capita water use of 256 gallons per day, almost half of it metered, is about 100 gallons higher than that of New York, where residential use is not metered. Because of growing industrial pollution of Lake Michigan, Chicago's drinking water had an unpleasant odor on 89 days in 1964, up from 72 days in 1963.

2

Reprinted from *Ann. Amer. Acad. Political Social Sci.*, **352**, 1–12 (Mar. 1964)

The Place of Nature in the City of Man

By IAN L. MCHARG

ABSTRACT: Unparalleled urban growth is pre-empting a million acres of rural lands each year and transforming these into the sad emblems of contemporary urbanism. In that anarchy which constitutes urban growth, wherein the major prevailing values are short-term economic determinism, the image of nature is attributed little or no value. In existing cities, the instincts of eighteenth- and nineteenth-century city builders, reflected in the pattern of existing urban open space, have been superseded by a modern process which disdains nature and seems motivated by a belief in salvation through stone alone. Yet there is a need and place for nature in the city of man. An understanding of natural processes should be reflected in the attribution of value to the constituents of these natural processes. Such an understanding, reflected in city building, will provide a major structure for urban and metropolitan form, an environment capable of supporting physiological man, and the basis for an art of city building which will enhance life and reflect meaning, order, and purpose.

Ian L. McHarg, M.L.A., M.C.P., Philadelphia, Pennsylvania, is Chairman of the Department of Landscape Architecture and Professor of City Planning at the University of Pennsylvania. He has a private practice in City Planning and Landscape Architecture in partnership with Dr. David A. Wallace. His interest in the subject of values toward nature and the physical environments which are their products has been reflected in many articles, among them "Man and Environment," a chapter in The Urban Condition, edited by Leonard Duhl, "The Ecology of the City," published in the American Institute of Architects Journal, 1963. On this same subject, he conceived and moderated a series of twenty-four television programs entitled "The House We Live In," initiated by WCAU-CBS and subsequently shown by National Educational Television.

BEFORE we convert our rocks and rills and templed hills into one spreading mass of low grade urban tissue under the delusion that because we accomplish this degradation with the aid of bulldozers, atomic piles and electronic computers we are advancing civilization, we might ask what all this implies in terms of the historic nature of man. . . ."—Lewis Mumford.[1]

The subject of this essay is an inquiry into the place of nature in the city of man. The inquiry is neither ironic nor facetious but of the utmost urgency and seriousness. Today it is necessary to justify the presence of nature in the city of man; the burden of proof lies with nature, or so it seems. Look at the modern city, that most human of all environments, observe what image of nature exists there—precious little indeed and that beleaguered, succumbing to slow attrition.

William Penn effectively said, Let us build a fair city between two noble rivers; let there be five noble squares, let each house have a fine garden, and let us reserve territories for farming. But that was before rivers were discovered to be convenient repositories for sewage, parks the best locus for expressways, squares the appropriate sites for public monuments, farm land best suited for buildings, and small parks best transformed into asphalted, fenced playgrounds.

Charles Eliot once said, in essence, This is our city, these are our hills, these are our rivers, these our beaches, these our farms and forests. I will make a plan to cherish this beauty and wealth for all those who do or will live here. And the plan was good but largely disdained. So here, as elsewhere, man assaulted nature disinterestedly, man assaulted man with the city; nature in the city remains precariously as residues of accident, rare acts of personal conscience, or rarer testimony to municipal wisdom, the subject of continuous assault and attrition while the countryside recedes before the annular rings of suburbanization, unresponsive to any perception beyond simple economic determinism.

Once upon a time, nature lay outside the city gates a fair prospect from the city walls, but no longer. Climb the highest office tower in the city, when atmospheric pollution is only normal, and nature may be seen as a green rim on the horizon. But this is hardly a common condition and so nature lies outside of workaday experience for most urban people.

Long ago, homes were built in the country and remained rural during the lives of persons and generations. Not so today, when a country house of yesterday is within the rural-urban fringe today, in a suburb tomorrow, and in a renewal area of the not-too-distant future.

When the basis for wealth lay in the heart of the land and the farms upon it, then the valleys were verdant and beautiful, the farmer steward of the landscape, but that was before the American dream of a single house on a quarter acre, the automobile, crop surpluses, and the discovery that a farmer could profit more by selling land than crops.

Once men in simple cabins saw only wild nature, silent, implacable, lonely. They cut down the forests to banish Indians, animals, and shadows. Today, Indians, animals, and forests have gone and wild nature, silence, and loneliness are hard to find.

When a man's experience was limited by his home, village, and environs, he lived with his handiworks. Today, the automobile permits temporary escapes

[1] Lewis Mumford, *Man's Role in Changing the Face of the Earth* (Chicago: The University of Chicago, 1956), p. 1142.

from urban squalor, and suburbanization gives the illusion of permanent escape.

Once upon a time, when primeval forests covered Pennsylvania, its original inhabitants experienced a North Temperate climate, but, when the forests were felled, the climate became, in summer, intemperately hot and humid.

Long ago, floods were described as Acts of God. Today, these are known quite often to be consequences of the acts of man.

As long ago, droughts were thought to be Acts of God, too, but these, it is now known, are exacerbated by the acts of man.

In times past, pure air and clean abundant water were commonplaces. Today, "pollution" is the word most often associated with the word "atmosphere," drinking water is often a dilute soup of dead bacteria in a chlorine solution, and the only peoples who enjoy pure air and clean water are rural societies who do not recognize these for the luxuries they are.

Not more than two hundred years ago, the city existed in a surround of farm land, the sustenance of the city. The farmers tended the lands which were the garden of the city. Now, the finest crops are abject fruits compared to the land values created by the most scabrous housing, and the farms are defenseless.

In days gone by, marshes were lonely and wild, habitat of duck and goose, heron and egret, muskrat and beaver, but that was before marshes became the prime sites for incinerator wastes, rubbish, and garbage—marshes are made to be filled, it is said.

When growth was slow and people spent a lifetime on a single place, the flood plains were known and left unbuilt. But, now, who knows the flood plain? *Caveat emptor.*

Forests and woodlands once had their own justification as sources of timber and game, but second-growth timber has little value today, and the game has long fled. Who will defend forests and woods?

Once upon a time, the shad in hundreds of thousands ran strong up the river to the city. But, today, when they do so, there is no oxygen, and their bodies are cast upon the shores.

THE MODERN METROPOLIS

Today, the modern metropolis covers thousands of square miles, much of the land is sterilized and waterproofed, the original animals have long gone, as have primeval plants, rivers are foul, the atmosphere is polluted, climate and microclimate have retrogressed to increased violence, a million acres of land are transformed annually from farm land to hot-dog stand, diner, gas station, rancher and split level, asphalt and concrete, billboards and sagging wire, parking lots and car cemeteries, yet slums accrue faster than new buildings, which seek to replace them. The epidemiologist can speak of urban epidemics—heart and arterial disease, renal disease, cancer, and, not least, neuroses and psychoses. A serious proposition has been advanced to the effect that the modern city would be in serious jeopardy without the safeguards of modern medicine and social legislation. Lewis Mumford can describe cities as dysgenic. There has arisen the recent specter, described as "pathological togetherness," under which density and social pressure are being linked to the distribution of disease and limitations upon reproduction. We record stress from sensory overload and the response of negative hallucination to urban anarchy. When one considers that New York may well add 1,500 square miles of new "low-grade tissue" to its perimeter in the next twenty years, then one recalls Loren Eiseley's image and sees the cities of man as gray, black, and brown blemishes upon the green earth with dynamic tentacles extending from them and asks: "Are these the evidence of man, the planetary disease?"

WESTERN VIEWS: MAN AND NATURE

Yet how can nature be justified in the city? Does one invoke dappled sunlight filtered through trees of ecosystems, the shad run or water treatment, the garden in the city or negative entropy? Although at first glance an unthinkable necessity, the task of justifying nature in the city of man is, with prevailing values and process, both necessary and difficult. The realities of cities now and the plans for their renewal and extension offer incontrovertible evidence of the absence of nature present and future. Should Philadelphia realize the Comprehensive Plan, then $20 billion and twenty years later there will be less open space than there is today. Cities are artifacts becoming ever more artificial—as though medieval views prevailed that nature was defiled, that living systems shared original sin with man, that only the artifice was free of sin. The motto for the city of man seems to be: salvation by stone alone.

Of course, the medieval view of nature as rotten and rotting is only an aspect of the historic Western anthropocentric-anthropomorphic tradition in which nature is relegated to inconsequence. Judaism and Christianity have been long concerned with justice and compassion for the acts of man to man but have traditionally assumed nature to be a mere backdrop for the human play. Apparently, the literal interpretation of the creation in Genesis is the tacit text for Jews and Christians alike—man exclusively divine, man given dominion over all life and nonlife, enjoined to subdue the earth. The cosmos is thought to be a pyramid erected to support man upon its pinnacle; reality exists only because man can perceive it; indeed, God is made in the image of man. From origins in Judaism, extension into classicism, reinforcement in Christianity, inflation in the Renaissance, and absorption into ninteenth- and twentieth-century thought, the anthropocentric - anthropomorphic view has become the tacit Western posture of man versus nature. The nineteenth- and twentieth-century city is the most complete expression of this view. Within the Western tradition exists a contrary view of man and nature which has a close correspondence to the Oriental attitude of an aspiration to harmony of man in nature, a sense of a unitary and encompassing natural order within which man exists. Among others, the naturalist tradition in the West includes Duns Scotus, Joannes Scotus Erigena, Francis of Assisi, Wordsworth, Goethe, Thoreau, Gerald Manley Hopkins, and the nineteenth- and twentieth-century naturalists. Their insistence upon nature being at least the sensible order within which man exists or a Manifestation of God demanding deference and reverence is persuasive to many but not to the city builders.

Are the statements of scientists likely to be more persuasive?

David R. Goddard:[2]

> No organism lives without an environment. As all organisms are depletive, no organism can survive in an environment of its exclusive creation.

F. R. Fosberg:[3]

> An ecosystem is a functioning, interacting system composed of one or more organisms and their effective environment,

[2] Transcript, WCAU-TV, "The House We Live In."

[3] F. R. Fosberg, "The Preservation of Man's Environment," *Proceedings of the Ninth Pacific Science Congress, 1957,* Vol. 20, 1958, p. 160.

both physical and biological. All ecosystems are open systems. Ecosystems may be stable or unstable. The stable system is in a steady state. The entropy in an unstable system is more likely to increase than decrease. There is a tendency towards diversity in natural ecosystems. There is a tendency towards uniformity in artificial ecosystems or those strongly influenced by man.

Paul Sears:[4]

> Any species survives by virtue of its niche, the opportunity afforded it by environment. But in occupying this niche, it also assumes a role in relation to its surroundings. For further survival it is necessary that its role at least be not a disruptive one. Thus, one generally finds in nature that each component of a highly organized community serves a constructive or at any rate, a stabilizing role. The habitat furnishes the niche, and if any species breaks up the habitat, the niche goes with it. . . . To persist organic systems must be able to utilize radiant energy not merely to perform work, but to maintain the working system in reasonably good order. This requires the presence of organisms adjusted to the habitat and to each other so organized to make the fullest use of the influent radiation and to conserve for use and reuse the materials which the system requires.

Complex creatures consist of billions of cells, each of which, like any single-celled creature, is unique, experiences life, metabolism, reproduction, and death. The complex animal exists through the operation of symbiotic relationships between cells as tissues and organs integrated as a single organism. Hans Selyé describes this symbiosis as intercellular altruism, the situation under which the cell concedes some part of its autonomy towards the operation of the organism and the organism responds to cellular processes.

Aldo Leopold has been concerned with the ethical content of symbiosis:[5]

> Ethics so far studied by philosophers are actually a process in ecological as well as philosophical terms. They are also a process in ecological evolution. An ethic, ecologically, is a limitation on freedom of action in the struggle for existence. An ethic, philosophically, is a differentiation of social from anti-social conduct. These are two definitions of one thing which has its origin in the tendency of interdependent individuals and groups to evolve modes of cooperation. The ecologist calls these symbioses. There is as yet no ethic dealing with man's relation to the environment and the animals and plants which grow upon it. The extension of ethics to include man's relation to environment is, if I read the evidence correctly, an evolutionary possibility and an ecological necessity. All ethics so far evolved rest upon a single premise that the individual is a member of a community of interdependent parts. His instincts prompt him to compete for his place in the community, but his ethics prompt him to cooperate, perhaps in order that there may be a place to compete for.

The most important inference from this body of information is that interdependence, not independence, characterizes natural systems. Thus, man-nature interdependence presumably holds true for urban man as for his rural contemporaries. We await the discovery of an appropriate physical and symbolic form for the urban man-nature relationship.

NATURAL AND ARTIFICIAL ENVIRONMENTS

From the foregoing statements by natural scientists, we can examine certain extreme positions. First, there

[4] Paul B. Sears, "The Process of Environmental Change by Man," in *Man's Role in Changing the Face of the Earth,* ed. W. L. Thomas, Jr. (Chicago: University of Chicago Press, 1956).

[5] Aldo Leopold, *A Sand County Almanac* (Oxford: Oxford University Press, 1949), pp. 202, 203.

can be no conception of a completely "natural" environment. Wild nature, save a few exceptions, is not a satisfactory physical environment. Yet the certainty that man must adapt nature and himself does not diminish his dependence upon natural, nonhuman processes. These two observations set limits upon conceptions of man and nature. Man must adapt through both biological and cultural innovation, but these adaptations occur within a context of natural, nonhuman processes. It is not inevitable that adapting nature to support human congregations must of necessity diminish the quality of the physical environment. Indeed, all of preindustrial urbanism was based upon the opposite premise, that only in the city could the best conjunction of social and physical environment be achieved. This major exercise of power to adapt nature for human ends, the city, need not be a diminution of physiological, psychological, and aesthetic experience.

While there can be no completely natural environments inhabited by man, completely artificial environments are equally unlikely. Man in common with all organisms is a persistent configuration of matter through which the environment ebbs and flows continuously. Mechanically, he exchanges his substance at a very rapid rate while, additionally, his conceptions of reality are dependent upon the attribution of meaning to myriads of environmental stimuli which impinge upon him continuously. The materials of his being are natural, as are many of the stimuli which he perceives; his utilization of the materials and of many stimuli is involuntary. Man makes artifices, but galactic and solar energy, gases of hydrosphere and atmosphere, the substance of the lithosphere, and all organic systems remain elusive of human artificers.

Yet the necessity to adapt natural environments to sustain life is common to many organisms other than man. Creation of a physical environment by organisms as individuals and as communities is not exclusively a human skill. The chambered nautilus, the beehive, the coral formation, to select but a few examples, are all efforts by organism to take inert materials and dispose them to create a physical environment. In these examples, the environments created are complementary to the organisms. They are constructed with great economy of means; they are expressive, they have, in human eyes, great beauty, and they have survived periods of evolutionary time vastly longer than the human span.

Simple organisms utilize inert materials to create physical environments which sustain life. Man also confronts this necessity. Man, too, is natural in that he responds to the same laws as do all physical and biological systems. He is a plant parasite, dependent upon the plant kingdom and its associated microorganisms, insects, birds, and animals for all atmospheric oxygen, all food, all fossil fuel, natural fibers and cellulose, for the stability of the water cycle and amelioration of climate and microclimate. His dependence upon the plant and photosynthesis establishes his dependence upon the microorganisms of the soil, particularly the decomposers which are essential to the recycling of essential nutrients, the insects, birds, and animals which are in turn linked to survival of plant systems. He is equally dependent upon the natural process of water purification by microorganisms. The operation of these nonhuman physical and biological processes is essential for human survival.

Having concluded that there can be neither a completely artificial nor a completely natural environment, our attention is directed to some determinants of optimal proportions. Some indication may be inferred from man's evolutionary history. His physiology and some significant part of his psychology derive from the billions of years of his biological history. During the most recent human phase of a million or so years, he has been preponderantly food gatherer, hunter, and, only recently, farmer. His urban experience is very recent indeed. Thus, the overwhelming proportion of his biological history has involved experience in vastly more natural environments than he now experiences. It is to these that he is physiologically adapted.

According to F. R. Fosberg:[6]

> It is entirely possible that man will not survive the changed environment that he is creating, either because of failure of resources, war over their dwindling supply, or failure of his nervous system to evolve as rapidly as the change in environment will require. Or he may only survive in small numbers, suffering the drastic reduction that is periodically the lot of pioneer species, or he may change beyond our recognition. . . . Management and utilization of the environment on a true sustaining yield basis must be achieved. And all this must be accomplished without altering the environment beyond the capacity of the human organism, as we know it, to live in it.

HUMAN ECOSYSTEMS

There are several examples where ecosystems, dominated by man, have endured for long periods of time; the example of traditional Japanese agriculture is perhaps the most spectacular. Here an agriculture of unequaled intensity and productivity has been sustained for over a thousand years, the land is not impoverished but enriched by human intervention, the ecosystem, wild lands, and farm lands are complex, stable, highly productive, and beautiful. The pervasive effect of this harmony of man-nature is reflected in a language remarkable in its descriptive power of nature, a poetry succinct yet capable of the finest shades of meaning, a superb painting tradition in which nature is the icon, an architecture and town building of astonishing skill and beauty, and, not least, an unparalleled garden art in which nature and the garden are the final metaphysical symbol.

In the Western tradition, farming in Denmark and England has sustained high productivity for two or more centuries, appears stable, and is very beautiful; in the United States, comparable examples exist in Amish, Mennonite, and Pennsylvania Dutch farming.

Understanding of the relationship of man to nature is more pervasive and operative among farmers than any other laymen. The farmer perceives the source of his food in his crops of cereal, vegetables, roots, beef, fish, or game. He understands that, given a soil fertility, his crop is directly related to inputs of organic material, fertilizer, water, and sunlight. If he grows cotton or flax or tends sheep, he is likely to know the source of the fibers of his clothes. He recognizes timber, peat, and hydroelectric power as sources of fuel; he may well know of the organic source of coal and petroleum. Experience has taught him to ensure a functional separation between septic tank and well, to recognize the process of erosion, runoff, flood and drought, the differences of altitude and orientation. As a consequence of this acuity, the farmer has developed a formal expression which reflects an understanding of the major natural processes. Characteristically, high ground and steep slopes are given over to forest and woodland as a source of timber, habitat for game, element in erosion control,

[6] F. R. Fosberg, "The Preservation of Man's Environment," *Proceedings of the Ninth Pacific Science Congress, 1957,* Vol. 20, 1958, p. 160.

and water supply. The more gently sloping meadows below are planted to orchards, above the spring frost line, or in pasture. Here a seep, spring, or well is often the source of water supply. In the valley bottom, where floods have deposited rich alluvium over time, is the area of intensive cultivation. The farm buildings are related to conditions of climate and microclimate, above the flood plain, sheltered and shaded by the farm woodland. The septic tank is located in soils suitable for this purpose and below the elevation of the water source.

Here, at the level of the farm, can be observed the operation of certain simple, empirical rules and a formal expression which derives from them. The land is rich, and we find it beautiful.

Clearly, a comparable set of simple rules is urgently required for the city and the metropolis. The city dweller is commonly unaware of these natural processes, ignorant of his dependence upon them. Yet the problem of the place of nature in the city is more difficult than that of the farmer. Nature, as modified in farming, is intrinsic to the place. The plant community is relatively immobile, sunlight falls upon the site as does water, nutrients are cycled through the system in place. Animals in ecosystems have circumscribed territories, and the conjunction of plants and animals involves a utilization and cycling of energy and materials in quite limited areas. The modern city is, in this respect, profoundly different in that major natural processes which sustain the city, provide food, raw materials for industry, commerce, and construction, resources of water, and pure air are drawn not from the city or even its metropolitan area but from a national and even international hinterland. The major natural processes are not intrinsic to the locus of the city and cannot be.

NATURE IN THE METROPOLIS

In the process of examining the place of nature in the city of man, it might be fruitful to consider the role of nature in the metropolitan area initially, as here, in the more rural fringes, can still be found analogies to the empiricism of the farmer. Here the operative principle might be that natural processes which perform work or offer protection in their natural form without human effort should have a presumption in their favor. Planning should recognize the values of these processes in decision-making for prospective land uses.

A more complete understanding of natural processes and their interactions must await the development of an ecological model of the metropolis. Such a model would identify the regional inventory of material in atmosphere, hydrosphere, lithosphere, and biosphere, identify inputs and outputs, and both describe and quantify the cycling and recycling of materials in the system. Such a model would facilitate recognition of the vital natural processes and their interdependence which is denied today. Lacking such a model, it is necessary to proceed with available knowledge. On a simpler basis, we can say that the major inputs in biological systems are sunlight, oxygen-carbon dioxide, food (including nutrients), and water. The first three are not limiting in the metropolis; water may well be limiting both as to quantity and quality. In addition, there are many other reasons for isolating and examining water in process. Water is the single most specific determinant of a large number of physical processes and is indispensible to all biological processes. Water, as the agent of erosion and sedimentation, is causal to geological evolution, the realities of physiography. Mountains, hills, valleys, and plains experience variety of climate and microclimate consequent upon their physiography; the twin combination of physiography and climate determines the incidence and distribution of plants and animals, their niches, and habitats. Thus, using water as the point of departure, we can recognize its impact on the making of mountains and lakes, ridges and plains, forests and deserts, rivers, streams and marshes, the distribution of plants and animals. Lacking an ecological model, we may well select water as the best indicator of natural process. In any watershed, the uplands represent the majority of the watershed area. Assuming equal distribution of precipitation and ground conditions over the watershed, the maximum area will produce the maximum runoff. The profile of watersheds tends to produce the steeper slopes in the uplands with the slope diminishing toward the outlet. The steeper the slope, the greater is the water velocity. This combination of maximum runoff links maximum volume to maximum velocity —the two primary conditions of flood and drought. These two factors in turn exacerbate erosion, with the consequence of depositing silt in stream beds, raising flood plains, and increasing intensity and incidence of floods in piedmont and estuary.

The natural restraints to flooding and drought are mainly the presence and distribution of vegetation, particularly on the uplands and their steep slopes. Vegetation absorbs and utilizes considerable quantites of water; the surface roots, trunks of trees, stems of shrubs and plants, the litter of forest floor mechanically retard the movement of water, facilitating percolation, increasing evaporation opportunity. A certain amount of water is removed temporarily from the system by absorption into plants, and mechanical retardation facilitates percolation, reduces velocity, and thus diminishes erosion. In fact, vegetation and their soils act as a sponge restraining extreme runoff, releasing water slowly over longer periods, diminishing erosion and sedimentation, in short, diminishing the frequency and intensity of oscillation between flood and drought.

Below the uplands of the watershed are characteristically the more shallow slopes and broad plains of the piedmont. Here is the land most often developed for agriculture. These lands, too, tend to be favored locations for villages, towns, and cities. Here, forests are residues or the products of regeneration on abandoned farms. Steep slopes in the piedmont are associated with streams and rivers. The agricultural piedmont does not control its own defenses. It is defended from flood and drought by the vegetation of the uplands. The vegetation cover and conservation practices in the agricultural piedmont can either exacerbate or diminish flood and drought potential; the piedmont is particularly vulnerable to both.

The incidence of flood and drought is not alone consequent upon the upland sponge but also upon estuarine marshes, particularly where these are tidal. Here at the mouth of the watershed at the confluence of important rivers or of river and sea, the flood component of confluent streams or the tidal component of floods assumes great importance. In the Philadelphia metropolitan area, the ocean and the estuary are of prime importance as factors in flood. A condition of intense precipitation over the region combined with high tides, full estuary, and strong onshore winds combines the elements of potential flood. The relation of environmental factors of the upland component and the agricultural piedmont to flood and drought has been discussed. The estuarine marshes and their vegetation constitute the major defense against the tidal components of floods. These areas act as enormous storage reservoirs absorbing mile-feet of potentially destructive waters, reducing flood potential.

This gross description of water-related processes offers determinism for the place of nature in the metropolis. From this description can be isolated several discrete and critical phases in the process. Surface water as rivers, streams, creeks, lakes, reservoirs, and ponds would be primary; the particular form of surface water in marshes would be another phase; the flood plain as the area temporarily occupied by water would be yet another. Two critical aspects of ground water, the aquifer and its recharge areas, could be identified. Agricultural land has been seen to be a product of alluvial deposition, while steep slopes and forests play important roles in the process of runoff. If we could identify the proscriptions and permissiveness of these parameters to other land use, we would have an effective device for discriminating the relative importance of different roles of metropolitan lands. Moreover, if the major divisions of upland, piedmont, and estuary and the processes enumerated could be afforded planning recognition and legislative protection, the metropolitan area would derive its form from a recognition of natural process. The place of nature in the metropolis would be reflected in the distribution of water and flood plain, marshes, ridges, forests, and farm land, a matrix of natural lands performing work or offering protection and recreational opportunity distributed throughout the metropolis.

This conception is still too bald; it should be elaborated to include areas of important scenic value, recreational potential, areas of ecological, botanical, geological, or historic interest. Yet, clearly, the conception, analogous to the empiricism of the farmer, offers opportunity for determining the place of nature in the metropolis.

NATURE IN THE CITY

The conception advocated for the metropolitan area has considerable relevance to the problem of the place of nature in the city of man. Indeed, in several cities, the fairest image of nature exists in these rare occasions where river, flood plain, steep slopes and woodlands have been retained in their natural condition—the Hudson and Palisades in New York, the Schuylkill and Wissahickon in Philadelphia, the Charles River in Boston and Cambridge. If rivers, flood plains, marshes, steep slopes, and woodlands in the city were accorded protection to remain in their natural condition or were retrieved and returned to such a condition where possible, this single device, as an aspect of water quality, quantity, flood and drought control, would ensure for many cities an immeasurable improvement in the aspect of nature in the city, in addition to the specific benefits of a planned watershed. No other device has such an ameliorative power. Quite obviously, in addition to benefits of flood control and water supply, the benefits of amenity and recreational opportunity would be considerable. As evidence of this, the city of Philadelphia has a twenty-two mile water front on the Delaware. The most grandiose requirements for port facilities and water-related industries require only eight miles of water front. This entire water front lies in a flood plain. Levees and other flood protection devices have been dismissed as exorbitant. Should this land be transformed into park, it would represent an amelioration in Philadelphia of incomparable scale.

Should this conception of planning for water and water-related parameters be effectuated, it would provide the major framework for the role of nature in the city of man. The smaller elements of the face of nature are more difficult to justify. The garden and park, unlike house, shop, or factory, have little "functional" content. They are, indeed, more metaphysical symbol than utilitarian function. As such, they are not amenable to quantification or the attribution of value. Yet it is frequently the aggregation of these gardens and spaces which determines the humanity of a city. Values they do have. This is apparent in the flight to the suburbs for more natural environments—a self-defeating process of which the motives are clear. Equally, the selection of salubrious housing location in cities is closely linked to major open spaces which reflects the same impulse. The image of nature at this level is most important, the cell of the home, the street, and neighborhood. In the city slum, nature exists in the backyard ailanthus, sumac, in lice, cockroach, rat, cat, and mouse; in luxury highrise, there are potted trees over parking garages, poodles, and tropical fish. In the first case, nature reflects "disturbance" to the ecologist; it is somewhat analogous to the scab on a wound, the first step of regeneration towards equilibrium, a sere arrested at the most primitive level. In the case of the luxury highrise, nature is a canary in a cage, surrogate, an artifice, forbidden even the prospect of an arrested sere.

Three considerations seem operative at this level of concern. The first is that the response which nature induces, tranquility, calm, introspection, openness to order, meaning and purpose, the place of values in the world of facts, is similar to the evocation from works of art. Yet nature is, or was, abundant; art and genius are rare.

The second consideration of some importance is that nature in the city is very tender. Woodlands, plants, and animals are very vulnerable to human erosion. Only expansive dimensions will support self-perpetuating and self-cleansing nature. There is a profound change between such a natural scene and a created and maintained landscape.

The final point is related to the preceding. If the dimensions are appropriate, a landscape will perpetuate itself. Yet, where a site has been sterilized, built upon, buildings demolished, the problem of creating a landscape, quite apart from creating a self-perpetuating one, is very considerable and the costs are high. The problems of sustaining a landscape, once made, are also considerable; the pressure of human erosion on open space in urban housing and the inevitable vandalism ensure that only a small vocabulary of primitive and hardy plants can survive. These factors, with abnormal conditions of ground water, soil air, atmospheric pollution, stripping, and girdling, limit nature to a very constricted image.

THE FUTURE

Perhaps, in the future, analysis of those factors which contribute to stress disease will induce inquiry into the values of privacy, shade, silence, the positive stimulus of natural materials, and the presence of comprehensible order, indeed natural beauty. When young babies lack fondling and mother love, they sometimes succumb to moronity and death. The dramatic reversal of this pattern has followed simple maternal solicitude. Is the absence of nature—its trees, water, rocks and herbs, sun, moon, stars and changing seasons—a similar type of deprivation? The solicitude of nature, its essence if not its image, may be seen to be vital.

Some day, in the future, we may be able to quantify plant photosynthesis in the city and the oxygen in the atmosphere, the insulation by plants of lead from automobile exhausts, the role of diatoms in water purification, the amelioration of climate and microclimate by city trees and parks, the insurance of negative ionization by fountains, the reservoirs of air which, free of combustion, are necessary to relieve inversion pollution, the nature-space which a biological inheritance still requires, the stages in land regeneration and the plant and animal indicators of such regeneration, indeed, perhaps, even the plant and animal indicators of a healthy environment. We will then be able to quantify the necessities of a minimum environment to support physiological man. Perhaps we may also learn what forms of nature are necessary to satisfy the psychological memory of a biological ancestry.

Today, that place where man and nature are in closest harmony in the city is the cemetery. Can we hope for a city of man, an ecosystem in dynamic equilibrium, stable and complex? Can we hope for a city of man, an ecosystem with man dominant, reflecting natural processes, human and nonhuman, in which artifice and nature conjoin as art and nature, in a natural urban environment speaking to man as a natural being and nature as the environment of man? When we find the place of nature in the city of man, we may return to that enduring and ancient inquiry—the place of man in nature.

3

Reprinted from *Proc. Indiana Acad. Sci. 1968,* **78**, 49–63 (1969)

Urban Geology—A Need and A Challenge[1]

WILLIAM J. WAYNE[2]

The Scope of Urban Geology

Every use man makes of land is affected by the shape of the land and by the physical properties of the materials that lie beneath the surface. He depends on either the surface or the materials beneath it for food, water, and fuel; for building sites, building materials, and foundation support; for waste disposal; and for recreation.

Geology is the study of the earth. It encompasses investigation of the surface, the materials beneath the surface, and all the natural processes that have produced those materials and landforms. Environmental geology is one of the names currently in vogue for the specific phase of geology that deals with the interrelationships of geologic processes, earth materials, and the ways in which man has met and used this part of his environment.

Where man has congregated in large numbers and most extensively disturbed natural conditions is where most of the conflicts between man and his environment are likely to take place. Thus the geology of man's environment becomes most important in and near urban centers; the term *urban geology* is virtually synonomous with *environmental geology*. Urban geology involves the recognition and understanding of those geologic processes that continuously work to bring conditions on the earth's surface toward a state of equilibrium—the natural forces that operate more or less slowly but are powerfully effective in the creation of landscapes and the disruption of some of man's works on those landscapes.

Our population has increased greatly in recent decades, and with that population increase our intensive uses of land have also expanded greatly. Because of this expansion and the resulting elimination of open space surrounding urban centers, we find ourselves having increasingly less freedom to make mistakes in the development of land for uses more intensive than farming.

When an error is made in developing a homesite in a rural environment, rarely is more than a single structure and one family affected; an error of similar magnitude in developing homesites in an urban environment, however, can involve many dwellings and cause incon-

[1] Approved for publication by the State Geologist, Indiana Geological Survey, Department of Natural Resources.

[2] Indiana Geological Survey; joined Department of Geology, University of Nebraska, Lincoln, in September 1968.

venience and unnecessary expense to many families. It is therefore in and near cities—the areas of large population concentrations—where it is of greatest importance that the men who guide our changes in land use recognize the ways in which natural forces act upon natural materials and upon the works of man. The failure to recognize potentially destructive geologic processes can lead to unnecessary expenses in the urban and urbanizing areas for engineering works, costly damage to structures, and perhaps even the loss of human lives.

Less spectacularly, damage may be to health, or may be limited to the inconvenience of wet basements or backed up drains. Nevertheless, as man's use of land expands, the need to have a complete and thorough knowledge of the geology of his environment becomes continuously more important. The costs of correcting mistakes increase many fold after available open land has been used up.

In comprehensive planning for the future development of a community, all the needs and interests of the area must be inventoried and evaluated. Ideally, potential problems should be forseen early in the planning process so that they can be adequately handled in the ordinances—zoning and others—that make planning effective. One basic phase of a comprehensive planning study—and one that is often neglected—is an evaluation of the geologic resources of the planning area.

The Role of a Geologist

Geologists are well equipped to contribute to several aspects of comprehensive studies in which conflicts of land use frequently arise. Unfortunately, geologists are sometimes asked to help explain the cause of a problem that might have been prevented if they had been consulted before the land was developed. They often find themselves cast in the role of trouble shooters and pessimists rather than advisors who can advance constructive suggestions that will help determine the optimum use of available land.

Application of geologic study to urbanizing environments requires the ability of a generalist who is particularly well versed in geomorphology, engineering geology, economic geology, and hydrogeology, and who also has an understanding and appreciation of the principles and administration of land-use planning. And he must be able to make the results of his geologic studies readily understandable to and usable by the nongeologically trained professional planners and citizens of the community to whom the decisions regarding urban development are entrusted.

Reports on urban geology should include a brief but adequate review of the general geologic features of the area for which the report is prepared (31). The report must be directed, though, toward specific geologic phenomena that are likely to be of concern in planning the community. Features of the land about which geologists are especially well qualified to supply knowledge and evaluation are: (*1*) economic mineral resources and potential; (*2*) geologic conditions that, if unrecognized, could become hazards to property or health; (*3*) water-supply potential; (*4*) waste-disposal sites; and (*5*) geologic significance of outstanding scenic and educationally stimulating natural areas.

Mineral Resources that Serve Urban Development

Mineral resources that are used extensively in construction, such as sand, gravel, and crushed stone, must be exploited close to their markets (Fig. 1). These resources have a large bulk and low value per ton and are generally surface mined. Maintenance of a high quality supply at a low delivered price is important to the growth of every expanding urban area. To keep construction costs low haulage distances for aggregates must be short, because much of the final delivered price is the cost of hauling (9, 24, 25).

Figure 1. Gravel pit in suburban area of Indianapolis (13, pl 5A) where operation is almost completely surrounded by urban land uses. A worked-out part of the pit not visible in this photograph has been reclaimed for recreational uses.

One of the most important pieces of information that a community should include in a comprehensive planning study is a map showing the distribution of potentially workable reserves of mineral resources. It is of no value to permit mineral extraction from land that has no mineral-resource potential, yet to restrict the industry from land that does. Only after the availability of the resource is known can a planner evaluate a particular area of a surface mineral resource and recommend a zoning ordinance that reflects that evaluation. Such a study was prepared for Marion County, Indiana, in 1958 (12) as a by-product of a county mapping project (13) and was used in designing zoning regulations for the county.

Among the major objections voiced by residents of many communities to the opening or continued operation of gravel pits, clay pits or crushed limestone quarries are the traffic, the dust of processing, the noise and rocks of blasting, and the resulting wasteland they must live with after the resource has been worked out (26). Some mineral-resource operators have become increasingly aware of this criticism in recent years, and many of them are becoming sensitive to the desires of their communities that they leave the worked-out land in a readily usable condition.

Mineral producers should be invited to participate in the development of operating standards to control traffic, noise, and dust that both they and their neighbors can accept and of subsequent land-use plans for the area when they leave it (1). The concept of sequential land use applies particularly well to the surface-mined bulk mineral commodities used in construction. While the deposit is being worked the land can be shaped according to a predetermined design, so that it will fit well into a second planned use after the resource has been worked out and the equipment removed (21). Reclamation according to such a plan is much less expensive than reclamation after abandonment. In many places the graded and shaped abandoned pit or quarry will have great value to the community as a recreation site, or as building lots, or an industrial site; thus it can be made into a desirable and productive area rather than a wasteland that remains an eyesore or health hazard (3).

Natural Hazards

Many millenia are needed for natural processes to create landscapes. Landscape-producing forces work in small increments, however, and only small amounts of time are required for some of these to take place. The force of earth or rock moving across an unstable slope or of flood water passing down a valley is great, and where the works of man happen to stand in the way, they may be damaged or destroyed.

Some natural hazards to life or property cannot be predicted well enough to let us avoid them entirely—the path of a particular tornado, for example. Many "accidents of nature" that result from failure to understand some fundamental geologic processes, however, can be recognized by an alert geologist and their potential for damage forecast so that land uses and construction standards can be designed to reduce or eliminate the danger.

From the earliest of civilization, man has used rivers for transportation, water supply, and waste removal. Consequently he has found the land along the rivers desirable places to build communities in spite of the knowledge that high water would come regularly; he accepted this inconvenience for the advantages of being able to use the river the rest of the time.

The flood plain, though, is the domain of the stream that built it. It is the relief valve of the river—the place where the excess water can spread out and slow down when upstream areas and tributaries deliver more water than the channel can carry. When man forgets this or fails to recognize it, he and his works can be damaged.

We no longer use any but the largest rivers for transportation. We have, however, inherted the floodplain locations and have developed them even further. One of the results of urban expansion on floodplains has been an increasingly great property loss and inconvenience each time a heavy runoff causes the land to be inundated. Increased urbanization upstream in the drainage basin also increases the runoff rate (11, 19). Thus we have had to design and build expensive flood control works to protect our investments from the inevitable high water.

Flood plains are underlain by sediments dropped by a river in flood. They are a normal unit on most geologic maps; therefore their delineation is one of the contributions of a geologic study to the planning process. Land-use regulation that restricts construction of damageable structures from areas of flooding is a far less expensive way of reducing future flood damage than is building more and bigger retaining structures and levees. Identification of flood plain land by geologic or soils mapping permits it to be zoned as future open land.

Gravity and water combine to produce downslope movement of masses of loose rock or soil on many hillsides. The degree of stability or instability of a particular slope is largely a factor of both steepness and moisture content and the kind of material that underlies it. For example, slopes of 1:1 are generally stable in the mudstones of Morgan County and western Brown County, Indiana; slopes of 2:1 are normally stable in unweathered young glacial till of central Indiana; but slopes of 3:1 are required for stability in the thick weathered part of the

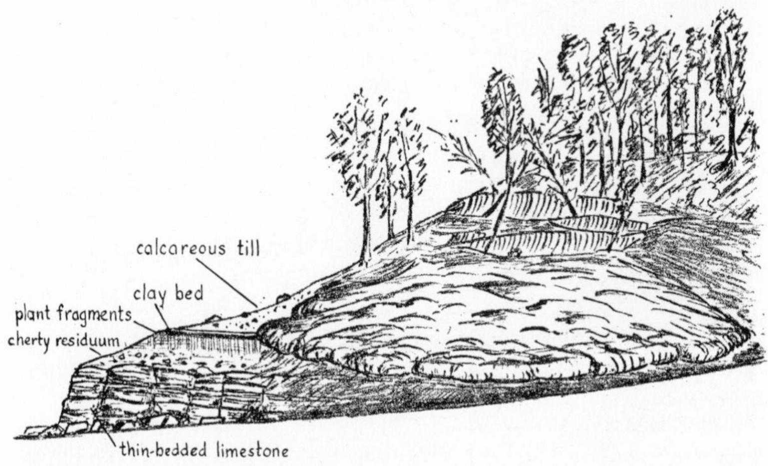

Figure 2. Terain sketch and diagram of the geology along State Road 46 in Owen County where mudflows and slump have resulted from an oversteepened slope and a perched water table held by a thin Pleistocene clay bed.

older glacial tills of southern Indiana. Where unusual conditions exist, such as a clay bed that serves to inhibit downward movement of moisture within a sequence of silty glacial sediments (Fig. 2), even more gentle slopes may develop.

Slopes that seem to be stable under natural conditions may become unstable if moisture content, loading, or steepness should be increased through urban development. Such an alteration is likely to result in slumps, slides, mudflows (Fig. 3), and, in areas of bedrock, rock falls, and rock slides. At the least, such mass wasting induced by changes in slope equilibrium is likely to bring on expensive maintenance problems, such as removal of debris from the base of road cuts (Fig. 3) or rebuilding retaining walls. Where structures are built on such slopes, damage or destruction can be extensive. In addition to the natural phenomena that can take place, recent studies in Illinois (34) have shown that the addition of detergents, such as those found in laundry wastes and septic tank effluent, to unconsolidated clayey sediments will decrease the strength of the material and increase its tendency to move downslope.

Most slopes that are likely to become unstable can be recognized in the field by a geologist who is trained in their evaluation; the local significance of this natural process should be reviewed in every geologic study for land-use planning (18, 28).

Not all land underlain by sensitive materials is on slopes, however. Areas underlain by muck, peat, marl, and other soft sediments that ac-

Figure 3. Mudflow on road cut in weathered Illinoian till along State Road 37 near Morgan-Monroe county line. The high clay content of the weathered till prevented it from remaining stable at the original cut dimensions, although a similar cut in unweathered till probably would have remained stable at that slope.

cumulated under conditions of ponding but are now above water level are outlined on those geologic maps that show surface materials in detail. Such sediments are unusually common in Indiana in resort areas around the natural freshwater lakes, as well as in some other parts of the state where bodies of water have been completely filled by sediments. These materials are not stable for foundations, and normal construction procedures cannot be used if they are developed intensively for urban uses. The high water table normally present would also create drainage and waste-disposal problems. Recognition and delineation of this material in the planning process is important if the land is to be used without danger or damage to its occupants.

Underground mining produces underground void space. Abandoned mine openings collapse and cause minor subsidence at the surface. Maps of underground mines on file in the offices of the Indiana Geologic Survey provide for Indiana the kind of information needed by planners who would avoid such land for construction until it has again become stable.

Water Supply

An automobile in every garage and electric power for every home made possible the development of large residential housing additions far from the edges of cities that would normally supply the utility needs of large numbers of families. Subdivisions have been created where each home has a private water supply and an electric pump to deliver the water to the home. Not all attractive home sites in Indiana have enough available ground water to supply a private home, though. And construction of several rural schools has been well along before anyone realized that some water supply other than a well drilled on the school grounds would have to be found before the school could open for classes.

An evaluation of the ground-water resources of the planning area should be included as a part of a comprehensive plan and should be available for the use of planning commissions in every urbanizing area. Hydrogeologic maps, which provide such an evaluation, can be prepared by a geologist, using the basic data derived from a geologic map and data on existing water wells. In Indiana generalized maps of this kind suitable for county and city planning purposes are being prepared by geologists in the Division of Water of the Department of Natural Resources (27).

Not all impoundments hold enough water to become ponds or lakes. Artificial lakes, both large and small, have been built over materials that allow the water to leak out as fast as it runs in as well as in places that are watertight. A geologic report for planning purposes would outline those places where high leakage rates could be expected and areas where lakes and ponds can be built successfully. Had such information been available and in use by the plan commissions of Indiana cities and counties, many investments and tax dollars of Indiana citizens could have been saved during the past quarter century.

Waste and Refuse Disposal

Different geologic materials and the soil profiles developed on them have different capabilities for absorption and transmittal of moisture. Although detailed planning for septic tank disposal fields probably is better done from a modern soils map and field studies, broad aspects of planning for on-site disposal of liquid household wastes can be done readily from the data available in a geologic study.

Movement of liquid wastes from the soil downward to the water table is an aspect of sewage disposal, though, that requires the attention of a geologist. Surface water that seeps downward through soil and highly permeable materials such as sand or gravel and fractured, weathered, or cavernous rock is likely to carry with it surface contaminants. Where sewage and other liquid wastes are disposed of in the soil, some of them are likely to be flushed downward, particularly during periods of heavy rainfall. Runoff from livestock feed lots is another source of concentrated contaminants that has entered and damaged some ground-water aquifers in Indiana.

In some parts of Indiana, where closely-spaced houses depend on both water wells and septic tanks, water supplies high in coliform bacteria are not unusual. Even though the bacteria may be filtered or have time to die before reaching a well intake, some wells have been seriously affected by a high nitrate content, which may cause illness, or by other chemicals or detergents that manage to reach an aquifer. A geologic report to a plan commission should outline areas where migration of liquid wastes is likely to damage nearby water supplies.

Septic tank disposal fields do not all function effectively—many are open to the surface. Nutrients from this effluent can cause very rapid eutrophication of lakes downstream, as can barn lot and pasture runoff.

When solid wastes are made part of the earth as in a dump or a sanitary landfill, they begin to undergo the same processes as do natural earth materials. Some of the rainwater that lands on the surface permeates the earth and passes through the soil and rocks on its way to a discharge area or to the water table. While it percolates through earth materials it dissolves any substances that may be soluble and carries the leachate away as part of the ground water. After it migrates beyond the limits of the landfill the leachate from a sanitary landfill can be expected to behave as would any vadose or phreatic water in the same geologic environment.

Our present knowledge about leachate migration is too meagre to permit us to speak in authoritative terms, although landfills that are located in impermeable or slowly permeable materials such as shale, clay, or clayey till or are separated geologically from an aquifer by such materials probably are unlikely to cause any contamination of ground water. Landfills in permeable materials, though, particularly limestone or dolomite, are likely to yield a leachate that will migrate rather rapidly and may cause considerable damage to underground water sources

(5, 20, 33). Areas geologically favorable and unfavorable for solid waste disposal sites should be outlined in every geologic report prepared as part of a comprehensive planning study (16).

Natural Areas

Where people are, they are expected to go to school, and they want to recreate. Many outstanding scenic areas or unusual outcrops that have geologic significance have been lost to recreation or education because they were not recognized by those who plan future land use, although they may have been well known to geologists, ecologists, and naturalists for a long time. Some of these areas, if the land is to be most advantageously used, probably should be considered for preservation as natural areas or for development into park sites. The geologist is remiss in his responsibility if he neglects to call attention to such areas so that the planner can understand their significance before they have been overwhelmed by urbanization. Once destroyed, they cannot be reclaimed (15).

Programs of Research in Urban Geology

Less than a decade ago, few geologists and fewer planners seemed to be aware of ways in which geologic data could be applied to land use problems (29). More recently, though, the United States Geological Survey has recognized the need to provide geologic data for use in land use planning (17). Several state geological surveys, most notably those of California and Illinois, have also undertaken studies intended to supply geologic information to planners (2, 6, 7, 10). The Indiana Geological Survey has provided reports to a few plan commissions or their consultants on request during the past decade; some of the reports have been published (8, 12, 30), and others are available only as file reports.

Some of the data needed to prepare geologic reports for use in comprehensive land-use planning studies of rapidly urbanizing parts of Indiana have been acquired by Indiana Geological Survey geologists as part of other studies during the past 15 to 20 years. Several specific new research programs will be needed, though, if our geologists are going to be able to answer the kinds of questions that we can now anticipate. At this time I would like to suggest the following program of research in urban geologic studies for Indiana:

1. *The preparation of county or urban community geologic reports.* —Geologic reports must be written specifically for use by a city, county, area, or metropolitan plan commission that is developing a comprehensive study of its area of jurisdiction and must be directed to that audience. A standard geologic report does not provide the needed information without interpretation. Table 1 is an outline that has served well in the preparation of such reports and can be adapted to most areas in Indiana and other midwest states.

Indiana Geological Survey geologists have prepared several county or community reports at the request of plan commissions or their consultants during past years, but many requests for information were received too close to the planning organization's deadline to permit the geologist to do more than quickly draw together a report based on information on hand but acquired for some other purpose. Unfortunately such reports will be as variable in quality and in value to the user as the amount and quality of data on hand for the geologist to use in their preparation. A special research program could anticipate areas for study far enough in advance that most rush jobs could be avoided when specific requests are received.

Geologic mapping for urban studies must be done on as large a scale as is practicable. At one time, maps prepared at 1 inch to 1 mile (1/63,360) were considered adequate and maps at 1/250,000 and 1/125,000 were thought satisfactory for many purposes. Urban studies will require greater detail, however. California geologists are mapping some urban areas on a scale of 600 feet to the inch (2), and the floodway mapping program of the U. S. Army Corps of Engineers is being done on an even larger scale.

County mapping for land-use studies probably will be satisfactorily presented on a map with a scale of an inch to the mile. Maps for a pilot study of Madison County, Indiana are being prepared at an inch to the mile although they were compiled at a scale of 1/24,000 (32). Highly urban areas as well as complicated or problem areas probably should be presented on a larger scale, however. The study should include a basic map showing the distribution of surficial geologic units described in a non-technical style and must be supplemented by a series of geologic planning maps on which attention is called to specific aspects of geology as related to land use (Table 1). These maps would include waste disposal, ground-water potential, slope stability, economic materials, and other subjects that may be appropriate (10, 16, 22).

2. *Geologic studies of ground-water contamination.*—Small scale studies of some wells in the limestone terrane of south-central Indiana a few years ago led to a recommendation presented in Bulletin S. E. 15 of the State Board of Health that much of the bacterial contamination of wells in such regions can be reduced or eliminated entirely by a more positive seal to prevent the entrance of surface water and storm water into the open annular space around the casing of a well (Fig. 4). Research in urban geologic problems should include additional studies of this kind in other geologic environments, undertaken on the university level or cooperatively by the State Board of Health, Division of Water, and the State Geological Survey.

3. *Migration of landfill leachates.*—Although contaminants are known to have reached the water table and to have migrated away from a landfill site under some conditions (4), few studies have been undertaken to determine the significance of different geologic conditions on the movement of leachate from sanitary landfills. Such a study has

been proposed on a state level in Indiana, to be done by three state agencies jointly. Detailed geologic and geophysical investigation of a study area in each of six different geological environments will be the responsibility of the Indiana Geological Survey. A water sampling program and water-quality analysis in and around each pilot site and the hydrology and evaluation of leachate migration and dilution will be undertaken by the State Board of Health and the Division of Water.

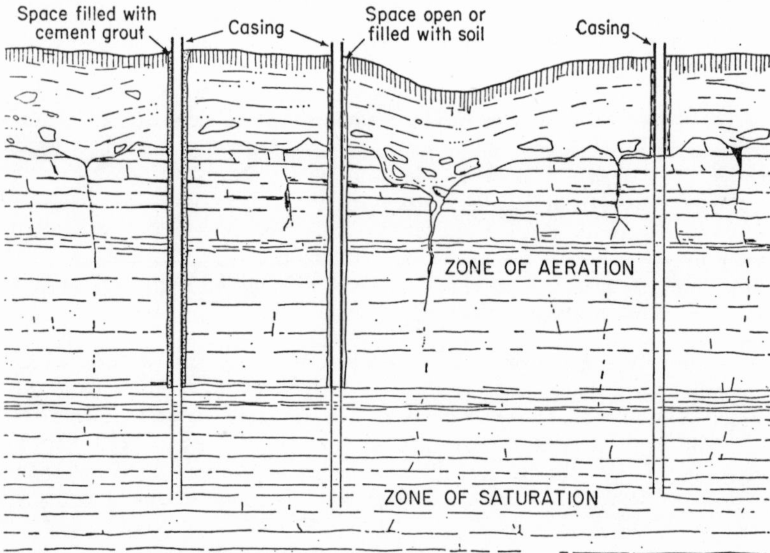

Figure 4. Many water wells in the areas of shallow bedrock in Indiana have been completed without sealing the annular space around the casing of the well to a great enough depth to keep seepage of contaminated vadose water from entering the hole. If the annular space has been left open or has been backfilled loosely with soil or with cuttings, it remains a conduit through which surface water can drain downward rapidly and enter water-producing zones. Wells in which this space has been filled with cement grout or, under certain conditions, with thick drilling mud, and in which the sealed casing extends downward far enough to keep out surface waters in permeable or cavernous rock, are not likely to be damaged by polluted surface water.

4. *Reclamation of quarried wasteland.*—Worked-out and abandoned land from which bulk mineral-industry commodities have been removed is a wasteland near many urban areas. Unconsolidated materials, such as gravel and sand, can be reshaped by a subsequent land owner if necessary, but the sand and gravel industry has started a continuing program of research to find better and more economical ways of preparing the land for re-use (14). Land underlain by consolidated rocks such as limestone are much more difficult to reclaim for subsequent productive use. A study of the rock properties that affect reshaping land as well as other possible techniques of converting worked-out land

at a reasonable cost might reduce the time involved for sequential beneficial use.

5. *Damages from natural hazards of geologic origin.*—Though much less spectacular in Indiana than in California (18) or Alaska (23), natural hazards exist in the state, and damages have taken place. Both field and laboratory studies of the geology and geometry of stable and unstable slopes would help in recognizing the conditions that produce instability of earth materials and in predicting more accurately where and under what conditions problems will occur in each geologic environment.

Such a research program as this will have to be undertaken as soon as possible if we are to be able to apply our geologic sophistication to aid in the solution of these urban problems where geologic data can help. The longer we wait to start, the longer we will find ourselves forced to answer questions without sufficient information. If planners are to call on geologists for help, the geologists must be in a position to supply it.

The Training of Geologists for Urban Studies

As a newly-developing use of geologic information, urban geology requires that the geologist limit his presentation and evaluation to those aspects of geology that apply directly to land use problems. It is an applied field of geology in which the practitioner needs to understand not only the geologic aspects of the problems but must also be aware of the principles and techniques of the land-use planning profession. Until 1967 few, if any, colleges and universities presented course material to train geologists to consider this field for employment. Some of the geologists who applied their knowledge to the solution of urban problems had picked up their background in the needs of communities through service on local planning commissions, and others did so through encountering the problems in the course of routine geologic studies and becoming interested in solving them. Most frequently the man was an engineering geologist, a ground water geologist, or an economic geologist.

Within the past year, a few universities have offered courses in urban and/or environmental geology. At Indiana University I presented a series of non-credit evening lectures on the subject in the spring semester of 1967 and offered a 3-hour credit course in it in the spring semester of 1968. At the same time Dr. James Hackett left the Illinois State Geological Survey to set up a graduate program in environmental geology at Virginia Polytechnic Institute. Paul Hilpman of the Kansas Geological Survey began teaching a two-semester course in urban geology at the University of Missouri in Kansas City in 1967, and an evening course was offered at Oregon in the spring of 1968. The University of Nebraska also has just added to its curriculum a one-semester course in the subject to be taught for the first time in 1969-70.

The Indiana course, as well as the one to be offered at Nebraska, was intended to introduce students to the ways in which geologic data can be used to help solve problems in land-use planning. It was designed to follow a course in physical geology and to present the subject to undergraduate majors and minors as well as provide a course in land use applications of geology to non-majors. At Indiana it was especially popular with graduate students in earth-science education. Those who had completed and done well in only one course in geology were able to complete the course successfully, but the amount of classroom participation was directly related to the geologic background of the individual students. No textbook exists that is suitable for this course, but the use of selected readings, many of which are cited here, provided material that was current as well as appropriate.

For a geology undergraduate who would like to direct his professional efforts into this field, the normal B. S. requirements in geology should be met if possible, but electives would have to include such courses as urban geography, land-use planning, and other courses in urban studies. It would be possible at Indiana University to qualify for a certificate in urban studies along with a strong A.B. degree in geology. On the graduate level a seminar in urban geologic problems coupled with regular advanced courses in hydrogeology, economic geology, limnology, and engineering techniques in geology would provide the required background to become a successful urban geologist.

A non-geologist who enters any phase of land-use planning should anticipate the inclusion of a course in urban geology about his fourth year, after he has acquired an adequate background in beginning geology and related courses in geography and allied subjects to enable him to master the material presented. He would not, of course, be trained to make geologic studies, but should at the conclusion of a course in urban geology be able to read a geologic report with understanding and to recognize the need for a geologic study in the planning process.

Summary

Urban land uses are rapidly converting open land into intensively used land. Generally, in planning those uses, a comprehensive study has included everything except an evaluation of the land in three dimensions. Geologists are eminently well equipped to supply the missing data, but they must also be aware of the needs of the urban community and the kinds of information needed by planners if they are to write reports usable by planners. Urban and environmental geology is a newly expanding field in the use of geologic data to help solve some urban problems in the planning stage. It is likely to become a part of the curriculum in many college geology departments within the next few years.

Literature Cited

1. AHERN, V. P. 1964. Land-use planning and the sand and gravel producer. National Sand and Gravel Association, Silver Spring, Maryland 30 p.
2. CAMPBELL, IAN, and B. W. TROXEL. 1965. Geologic hazards. California Div. Mines and Geology, Mineral Info. Service **18**:161-163.
3. CARNES, W. G., and others. 1966. Landscape reclamation. Landscape Architecture, January 1966 (9 papers on reclamation of worked-out land).
4. CARTWRIGHT, KEROS, and M. R. MCCOMAS. 1968. Geophysical surveys in the vicinity of sanitary landfills in northeastern Illinois. Groundwater **6**:22-30, 8 figs.
5. DEUTSCH, MORRIS. 1963. Groundwater contamination and legal controls in Michigan. U.S. Geol. Survey Water-Supply Paper 1961. 79 p., 23 figs.
6. FLAWN, P. T. 1965. Geology and urban development. Baylor Univ. Geol. Studies, Bull. **8**:5-7.
7. FRYE, JOHN. 1967. Geological information for managing the environment. Illinois State Geol. Survey, Environmental Geology Notes 18. 12 p.
8. GATES, G. R. 1960. Geologic considerations in urban planning for Bloomington, Indiana. Indiana Geol. Survey, Rept. Prog. 25. 21 p., 1 pl., 1 table.
9. GOLDMAN, H. B. 1959. Urbanization and the mineral industry. California Div. Mines, Mineral Info. Service. **12**(12):1-5, 9 figs.
10. HACKETT, J. E. 1968. Geologic factors in community development at Illinois. Illinois State Geol. Survey, Environmental Geology Notes, No. 22. 16 p., 4 figs.
11. HARRIS, E. E. and S. E. RANTZ. 1964. Effects of urban growth on streamflow regime of Permanente Creek, Santa Clara County, California. U.S. Geol. Survey, Water Supply Paper 1591-B. 18 p.
12. HARRISON, WYMAN. 1960. A special report on the geology of Marion County, Indiana. Metropolitan Planning Commission of Marion County, Mineral Res. Rept. 1. 53 p., 1 pl., 13 figs., 4 tables.
13. HARRISON, WYMAN. 1963. Geology of Marion County, Indiana. Indiana Geol. Survey, Bull. 28. 78 p., 5 pls., 11 figs., 4 tables.
14. JOHNSON, CRAIG. 1966. Practical operating procedures for progressive rehabilitation of sand and gravel sites. National Sand and Gravel Assn. Project No. 2. 75 p., 71 figs.
15. LINDSEY, A. A. 1968. Indiana's new system of scientific areas and nature preserves. Proc. Indiana Acad. Science, **77**:75-83.
16. MCCOMAS, MURRAY. 1968. Geology related to land use in the Hennepin region. Illinois State Geol. Survey, Circ. 422, 24 p., 10 figs., 2 tables.
17. MCGILL, J. T. 1964. Growing importance of urban geology. U.S. Geol. Survey, Circ. 487. 4 p.
18. MORTON, D. M., and ROBERT STREITZ. 1967. Landslides. California Div. of Mines and Geology, Mineral Info. Service. **20**:123-129, 135-140.
19. SAVINI, JOHN, and J. C. KAMMERER. 1961. Urban growth and the water regimen. U.S. Geol. Survey, Water-Supply Paper 1591-A. 42 p.
20. SHEAFFER, J. R., BERNDT VON BOEHM, and J. E. HACKETT. 1963. Refuse disposal practices in northeastern Illinois. Northeastern Illinois Metropolitan Area Planning Commission, Tech. Rept. 3, 72 p., 13 figs.
21. SCHELLIE, K. L., and D. A. ROGIER. 1963. Site utilization and rehabilitation practices for sand and gravel operations. National Sand and Gravel Assn. Spec. Rept. 80 p., 47 figs., 4 tables.
22. SCHLICKER, H. G., and R. J. DEACON. 1967. Engineering geology of the Tualatin Valley region, Oregon. Oregon Dept. Geology and Mineral Industries, Bull. 60. 103 p., 4 pls. 45 figs., 5 tables.

23. SCHMIDT, R. A. M. 1964. Geology in a hurry. Geotimes 9(3):13-15. 2 figs.

24. SHERIDAN, M. J. 1967. Urbanization and its impact on the mineral aggregate industry in the Denver, Colorado, area. U.S. Bur. Mines, Info. Circ. 8320. 53 p., 28 figs.

25. STEPHENSON, R. C., and others. 1966. The interaction of urbanization and the mineral industries. Ohio State Univ. Nat. Res. Inst. Ann. Symposium 1965 (collection of 10 papers).

26. STOLLMAN, ISRAEL. 1962. Land-use control in the surface extraction of minerals, Part 1. Am. Soc. of Planning Officials, Planning Advisory Service, Info. Rept. 153. 17 p.

27. UHL, JOHN. 1966. Water resources of Johnson County. Indiana Dept. Natur. Res., Div. Water.

28. VARNES, D. J. 1950. Relation of landslides to sedimentary features, p. 229-246. *In* Trask, P. D., ed., Applied Sedimentation. New York, J. Wiley & Sons, Inc.

29. WAYNE, W. J. 1960. Geologic contributions to community planning. Unpublished manuscript of paper read at Am. Assn. Advancement Sci. meeting, Dec. 1960, 20 p.

30. WAYNE, W. J. 1968a. Geology of Morgan County (unpublished). Morgan Co. (Indiana) Plan Commission. 25 p., 2 pls., 3 figs.

31. WAYNE, W. J. 1968b. Urban geology as a necessity. Indiana Governor's Conf. on Nat. Resources, Feb. 27, 1968. p. 19-21.

32. WAYNE, W. J. in preparation. Urban geology of Madison County. Indiana Geol. Survey, Special Report.

33. WEAVER, LEO. 1961. Refuse disposal—its significance, p. 104-110. *In* Ground Water Contamination Symposium volume. Taft Sanitary Eng. Center, Tech. Rept. W 61-5.

34. WHITE, W. A. and S. M. BREMSER. 1966. Effects of soap, a detergent, and a water softener on the plasticity of earth materials. Illinois State Geol. Survey, Environ. Geology Notes 12. 15 p.

II
Water Resources

Editor's Comments on Papers 4 Through 9

4 Leopold: *Hydrology for Urban Land Planning—A Guidebook on the Hydrologic Effects of Urban Land Use*

5 Van Burkalow: *The Geography of New York City's Water Supply: A Study of Interactions*

6 Khromov: *Changes in the Geography of Population Centers in Connection with Creation of the Tsimlyansk Reservoir*

7 Freeman: *Water-Spreading as Practiced by the Santa Clara Water-Conservation District, Ventura County, California*

8 Brashears: *Artificial Recharge of Ground Water on Long Island, New York*

9 Mann: *Ground-Water Management in the Raymond Basin, California*

Urbanization and man's development of water as a resource distort many aspects of the land – water ecosystem, a subject that falls within the realm of the geomorphologist. Feth (1973, p. 4) has summed this up in a table, reproduced here (Table 2). A new approach to help planners assess the relative importance of urban water problems has been developed by Schneider, Rickert, and Spieker (1973). It is based on a numerical matrix that lists 51 categories of potentially helpful information, which can be cross indexed with nine potential major problem categories that include such items as water supply and erosion. The report points out that the final decision on the management of the water resources data rests with the planner, since he has the responsibility to consider the relation of water resources to all other resources, including the social, economic, cultural, and physical.

There is a staggering number of publications of all varieties dealing with water resources because this is one of the most vital areas for the sustenance and welfare of mankind (see also Volumes I and III of this trilogy). Special mention must be made of numerous reports by the U.S. Geological Survey, such as their Water-Supply Papers, and of many other important publications that have been prepared, often in cooperation with various state agencies. An excellent review of U.S. water resources was prepared by the Water Resources Council (1968) (see Paper 10), and Piper (1965) summarized the question "Has the United States enough water?". Entire issues of some journals are devoted to water planning, such as vol. 40 no. 9 of *Town & Country Planning* (1972) concerning the problem in Great Britain. In discussing the need for regional planning, as set in the context of the 1963 British Water Resources Act, it was stated

> The thrust of this has already been unmistakably demonstrated in the central valley of Scotland. The designation of Livingston New Town and its subsequent rate of expansion have been made possible by implementing a scheme which turns Loch Lomand into a reservoir from which most of Central Scotland is served. This extensive supply network, which has been described as a water grid fully analogous to the electricity grid, is thus a crucial feature of regional planning . . . (Diamond, 1972, p. 404).

This British Water Resources Act of 1963 empowers the River Authorities to

> (1) construct and operate a comprehensive network for the collection of hydrologic data, (2) conduct surveys and formulate proposals for action in the River Authority's area, (3) establish "minimum acceptable flows," (4) license all water withdrawals, (5) levy abstraction charges, and (6) construct, operate and co-ordinate reservoirs and other facilities that control, or make accessible, water resources (Craine, 1969, p. 45).

In the United States numerous federal laws deal with water resources; the Water Resources Planning Act of 1965 is typical of more recent legislation. Its purpose is to encourage the conservation, development, and utilization of water and related land resources of the country on a comprehensive and coordinated basis by the various levels of government and in the private sector.

The Water Resources Council (1968) in the United States points out the need for extensive urban water planning in a variety of areas, including the need to attempt to reduce the annual $1 billion loss by flooding.

> In an era of accentuating urban problems, the management of water resources is both an aspect of overall urban problems and a functional subsystem. It is for this reason that traditional water resources planning approaches are being restructured in more flexible forms. Water is one of the more important determinants of urban life, but it is only one such determinant. This is why emphasis must be placed on the interrelationships among the several urban resources, their uses, and other environmental and ecological factors that together account for living patterns and set their limits (p. 26).

Five crucial areas are listed then that need evaluation because the urban system is not a closed system, and few urban areas can be sustained by water found within their own boundaries.

1. Drainage: the encroachment of urban development on stream banks and beds and intensive development of floodplains have diminished the storage area.

2. Water supply: importation is necessary because local sources do not meet the demands.

3. Water quality: often storm and sanitary sewers are combined in a single conduit.

4. Environmental quality and recreation: city people travel to the country for renewal, whereas use of water to make the city environment more tranquil and appealing would also be helpful.

5. Basin and urban planning: most river basins have mixed urban and rural elements, so planning must consider the entire basin as an integral unit for coordination into a master plan.

Regional studies of this sort have been carried out by groups such as the New England River Basins Commission (1973) and the Temporary State Commission on the

Water Supply Needs of Southeastern New York (1972a, 1972b). These latter reports show the need for regional planning in the largely metropolitan area of 12 million. By the year 2020, the projected population of the New York region will be 20 million and will require 1,660 million gallons of water per day, of which only one third can be obtained from local sources.

Many specialized reports concerning hydrology and urban areas have been published in the last few years. Typical of these are the studies of Schneider (1968), who presents data on water sources from 222 cities, and Ferguson (1972), who studied the Houston metropolitan area for the following purposes:

> 1. To determine, on the basis of historical data and hydrologic analysis, the magnitude and frequency of flood peaks and flood volume.
> 2. To determine the effect of urban development on flood peaks and volume.
> 3. To ascertain the variation in water quality under varying flow conditions and at different seasons (p. 1).

Investment in water resources costs considerable money, as pointed out in a 1971 report by the Office of Water Resources Research that states ". . . it is evident that average expenditures by local governments on urban water resources will be $12 billion or more annually through 1980."

Surface-Water Hydrology

Three articles have been selected for this selection to show the many different dimensions of urbanism and its relation to surface water. Another aspect, flooding, because of its special and dramatic importance, will be discussed separately in Part III. The Leopold article is the clearest, most cogent, and one of the earliest written on the many different ways in which the hydrologic regime is upset by urbanization. Van Burkalow presents the best single analysis of the many considerations that are involved when a metropolitan community, New York City, imports water from a great distance. The paper by Khromov shows examples from the Soviet Union of the displacement of people and towns when new reservoirs are constructed. He notes some interesting side effects whereby a number of economic advantages may occur, such as new communities that are better planned than the originals.

Luna B. Leopold, the illustrious son of one of the original conservation leaders in America, Aldo Leopold, is Senior Research Hydrologist of the U.S. Geological Survey. As Chief Hydrologist, he headed the Water Resources Division from 1957–1966. He is the author and co-author of numerous scientific papers and several books, an international authority on water resources, and a research innovator in the fields of hydrology, river mechanics, and environmental affairs. His leadership has been recognized by the receipt of numerous awards and membership in many organizations, including the National Academy of Sciences. He has served as President of the Geologic Society of America. Thus any treatment of hydrology would be incomplete without the inclusion of a sample of his work. His article on the hydrology of urban land use shows the many ramifications that need analysis, as well as the possibility of remedial action when needed. In an earlier study of some of these aspects, Savini and Kammerer (1961) show how

> Urbanization raises a double problem, namely an increased demand for municipal, industrial, and recreational purposes, and a decrease in locally generated ground-water supply because of the "roofing over" with housing, pavements, and industrial buildings areas that formerly consisted of moisture-holding soil and small streams (p. 3).

Schneider (1968) also speaks of the importance of problems that are created during the urbanization process, which includes the loss of natural recharge surfaces:

> Expansion of metropolitan areas poses persistent problems in management of the hydrologic environment. Adequate hydrologic data are prerequisite to proper planning and engineering design of urban environments.
>
> The obliteration of natural drainage courses, the building of houses, and the paving of large areas have created changes in natural patterns of storm runoff and ground-water recharge. The accelerated accumulations of the wastes of urban living have resulted in chemical, biological, and sediment pollution. The flooding of urban areas is a common problem, especially where storm drainage facilities are overtaxed by the increased runoff (p. 1).

It must be pointed out this is not a new problem, but one that has become more aggravated and accelerated in the twentieth century. The will of Benjamin Franklin indicates his concern about such phenomena, and how he predicted the problem's occurrence in Philadelphia as it applied in 1790 at the time of his death:

> And having considered that the covering of a groundplot of the city with buildings and pavements, which carry off most of the rain and prevent its soaking into the Earth and renewing and purifying the Springs, whence the water of wells must gradually grow worse, and in time be unfit for use, as I find has happened in all old cities, I recommend that at the end of the first hundred years, if not done before, the corporation of the city . . . [bring] by pipes, the water of Wissahickon Creek into the town, so as to supply its inhabitants (Smyth, 1907, p. 506).

A significant study on urbanization and flooding (Johnson and Sayre, 1973) was made of the Houston metropolitan area and concluded that

> The relationships indicate that as urbanization increases the impervious surface from 1 to 35 percent, the magnitude of a 2-year peak is increased by a factor of 9 and the magnitude of a 50-year peak is increased by a factor of 5. Other analyses indicate that urbanization also significantly increases the magnitude of annual runoff (p. 1).

Table 2. Hydrologic effects during a selected sequence of changes in land and water use associated with urbanization

Change in land or water use	Possible hydrologic effect
Transition from preurban to early urban stage	
Removal of trees or vegetation, construction of scattered city-type houses and limited water and sewage facilities.	Decrease in transpiration and increase in storm flow. Increased sedimentation of streams.
Drilling of wells.	Some lowering of water table.
Construction of septic tanks and sanitary drains.	Some increase in soil moisture and perhaps a rise in water table. Perhaps some waterlogging of land and contamination of nearby wells or streams from overloaded sanitary drain system.
Transition from early urban to middle-urban stage	
Bulldozing of land for mass housing; some topsoil removal; farm ponds filled in.	Accelerated land erosion and stream sedimentation and aggradation. Increased flood flows. Elimination of smallest streams.
Mass construction of houses; paving of streets; building of culverts.	Decreased infiltration, resulting in increased flood flows and lowered ground-water levels. Occasional flooding at channel constrictions (culverts) on remaining small streams. Occasional over-topping or undermining of banks of artificial channels on small streams.
Discontinued use and abandonment of some shallow wells.	Rise in water table.
Diversion of nearby streams for public water supply.	Decrease in runoff between points of diversion and disposal.
Untreated or inadequately treated sewage discharged into streams or disposal wells.	Pollution of streams or wells. Death of fish and other aquatic life. Inferior quality of water available for supply and recreation at downstream populated areas.
Transition from middle- to late-urban stage	
Urbanization of area completed by addition of more houses and streets, and of public, commercial, and industrial buildings.	Reduced infiltration and lowered water table. Streets and gutters act as storm drains creating higher flood peaks and lower base flow of local streams.
Larger, quantities of untreated waste discharged into local streams.	Increased pollution of streams and concurrent increased loss of aquatic life. Additional degradation of water available to downstream users.
Abandonment of remaining shallow wells because of pollution.	Rise in water table.
Increase in population requires establishment of new water-supply and distribution systems, construction of distant reservoirs viverting water from upstream sources within or outside basin.	Increase in local streamflow if supply is from outside basin.

Table 2. continued

Change in land or water use	Possible hydrologic effect
Channels of streams restricted at least in part to artificial channels and tunnels.	Increased flood damage (higher stage for a given flow). Changes in channel geometry and sediment load. Aggradation.
Construction of sanitary drainage system and treatment plant for sewage.	Removal of additional water from area, further reducing infiltration recharge of aquifer.
Improvement of storm drainage system.	
Drilling of deeper, large-capacity industrial wells.	Lowered water-pressure surface of artesian aquifer; perhaps some local overdrafts and land subsidence. Overdraft of aquifer may result in salt-water encroachment in coastal areas and in pollution or contamination by inferior or brackish waters.
Increased use of water for air conditioning.	Overloading of sewers and other drainage facilities. Possibly some recharge to water table, owing to leakage of disposal lines.
Drilling of recharge wells.	Raising of water-pressure surface.
Wastewater reclamation and utilization.	Recharge to ground-water aquifers. More efficient use of water resources.

Source: From Feth (1973, p. 4), after Savini and Kammerer, 1961.

The prodigious use of water in urban areas often requires its importation from distant regions. Of the 35 largest cities in the United States, 5 have supplies from the Great Lakes, 10 from major rivers, 3 from groundwater, and the remainder import much of their water from distant reservoirs. For example, one out of eight Americans uses water that is transported more than 75 miles. Industry, mostly located in cities, is one of the biggest consumers, with water use of about 200 billion gallons per day. The article by Anastasia Van Burkalow provides many important aspects that are involved when cities must seek water supplies from distant regions (see also Martin, 1960). Van Burkalow has been on the faculty at Hunter College of the City University of New York since 1938 and served as Chairman, Department of Geology and Geography, from 1961–1973. Her research has been in the areas of geomorphology, geography, and enrivonmental geology. The article on New York's water supply system, as well as the Khromov paper on the Tsimlyansk Reservoir in the Soviet Union, shows some of the problems associated with the displacement of people and towns. In the United States, the principle of *eminent domain* is used as the legal power for taking private property at the reservoir site. (For additional reading on geomorphology and eminent domain regarding sand and gravel deposits, see Coates, 1971.)

Other massive water importation schemes have been and are being further developed in California and Australia. In California, 70 per cent of the water is in the north, whereas 77 per cent of the population lives in the south. The need for water by the metropolitan areas and in irrigation prompted the California Water Plan, called by some "the most expensive faucet in history." In 1960, California voters passed the largest state bond issue at that time for $1.75 billion to start construction of projects that would take water from the north and pipe it to the south. This has necessitated building 21 dams and reservoirs, 22 pumping stations, 685 miles of tunnels, pipelines, and canals, and a 15,800-acre man-made lake behind the highest dam in North America with a 700-foot-deep reservoir. To date, the project has cost well over $2 billion, and by the year 2000 total expenditures will amount to $11 billion.

The first really long-distance importation of water was to Kalgoorlie, the West Australian mining center, 400 miles from a dam site, Mundaring, in the coastal hills. It was completed in the 1890s. The Australian Snowy Mountain Hydroelectric Project is another massive engineering enterprise that diverts water from rivers that drain east from the eastern mountain ranges to the west, where the water will be used for the generation of power, for towns, and for the irrigation of 1,000 square miles of land.

Perhaps the most daring water scheme thus far suggested is the North American Water and Power Alliance (NAWAPA) proposed in an April 1964 publication by the Ralph M. Parsons Company. This grandiose concept is continental in scope—to take water flowing unused into the Arctic and redistribute it throughout the continent to such places as the Prairie Provinces in Canada, the Great Lakes Basin, semiarid lands of the High Plains, southwestern parts of the United States, and northern Mexico. The centerpiece for the plan would be the creation of a 500-mile-long reservoir in the Rocky Mountain Trench. The lake would be 3,000 feet above sea level, and from it water would flow south through a series of gigantic aqueducts. Costs were estimated at $100 billion with a construction time of 25 years.

In the Soviet Union, there has been a long-ranging debate about the Ob–Yenisei–Irtysh diversion scheme. The purpose of this design would be to bring water from the northward-flowing rivers of western Siberia to supply the Caspian Desert area and to create an artificial sea in Asia with a surface area larger than England. An even grander scheme is the proposed damming of the Congo (Zaine) to flow into Lake Chad and thence to irrigate the southern Sahara. Recently, serious research is being conducted, partly under the sponsorship of the National Science Foundation and partly under the U.S. Army Cold Regions Research and Engineering Laboratory (Weeks and Campbell, 1973), concerning the feasibility of transporting icebergs from Antarctica for use in coastal cities. Preliminary studies estimate water could be produced at a price only 1/100 the cost of desalinization of seawater.

Groundwater Hydrology

The three articles on groundwater deal with its use, methods for recharging aquifers, and the effects produced by excessive withdrawal of this important resource. V. M. Freeman's paper is one of the earliest to report results from induced recharge by water-spreading techniques in California. He presents data that indicate the effectiveness of scarifying stream channels to produce higher percolation rates. The article by M. L. Brashears is important because it is the best written and one of the earliest publications on artificial recharge on Long Island, New York. During the 1942–1952 period, he was District Geologist in charge of the U.S. Geological Survey investigations in New York and New England, and instrumental in the appraisal of groundwater resources. Since 1952, Brashears has been a partner in the firm Leggette, Brashears & Graham, Consulting Ground-Water Geologists. Brashears also discusses how laws have influenced and made necessary the practice of groundwater recharge, and in the article by John F. Mann another aspect of legal affairs in the use of groundwater is discussed. Mann is a consulting geologist and hydrologist who has written articles on groundwater, and has had wide experience in groundwater litigation proceedings and in a variety of commissioned hydrologic investigations. His paper about the Raymond Basin Adjudication (Pasadena *v.* Alhambra) reports a precedent-making law case, because it established the *doctrine of mutual prescription.* This case is also significant because it rested upon hydrologic data, and hydrologists are involved in determining the resulting water allocations (see also Reis, 1965, 1967).

Groundwater use has greatly expanded in the twentieth century because of better well-drilling techniques and expansion of new energy sources to fuel the pumps, with special advantages to agricultural irrigation. However, excessive pumping in many areas has led to "groundwater mining" and the need to exercise various conservation methods. Such methods can be categorized as either "constructional" or "legal." The constructional techniques consist of such practices as water spreading, removal of silt-clogging particles on the land, channeling watercourses, and development of artificial pits and depressions. As early as 1889, Denver had begun a modest-sized recharge project to maintain domestic water supplies. By 1955, there were 120 public-supply recharge projects in 15 states, with 87 in California and 13 in Massachusetts. The Los Angeles metropolitan area provides a representative example of spreading techniques:

> During the 1958–59 year, approximately 170,000 acre-feet were delivered to the Orange County Water District and the Los Angeles County Flood Control District for spreading in the Santa Ana and San Gabriel river basins. (The Flood Control District derives its funds from a general property tax; the Orange County Water District, however, has imposed a unique use tax of $3.90 an acre-foot on all groundwater pumping in Orange County in an attempt to assess the costs of replenishment upon the pumpers directly.) Since 1949, the Orange County Water District has spread almost 500,000 acre-feet of water, and a recent report indicated that average well levels had risen over 10-½ feet in the previous two years.
>
> The spreading of water for percolation in underground aquifers may be desirable for several reasons. First, raising the water table in areas near the coast may prevent further encroachment of sea water in addition to reducing the salinity of wells already contaminated. Second, the underground basins may function as valuable storage reservoirs, particularly when the cost of surface storage in an urbanized area may be almost prohibitive. And,

> third, the network of underground basins may function as a distribution system transporting water to all parts of the area—in fact, carrying water directly to the pumps of existing well-owners (Hirshleifer, DeHaven, and Milliman, 1960, pp. 292–293).

Groundwater use on Long Island, New York, and the methods employed for its conservation have been described in many publications, including scientific reports and articles for popular consumption. A good example of governmental interest in reaching the general public and making them aware of problems and possible solutions is the Cohen, Franke, and Foxworthy (1970) booklet. They describe the objectives, needs, problems, and alternatives in groundwater resources under (1) continuing the present methods of development, (2) use of barrier injection wells, (3) artificial recharge through man-constructed basins, (4) allowing controlled saltwater intrusion, and (5) alternative sources such as the desalinization of seawater and the use of atomic energy to convert Long Island Sound into a freshwater reservoir.

Long Island presents an especially interesting case study in groundwater use and associated problems, including groundwater mining, declining water tables, saltwater intrusion, and man-made pollution of shallow aquifers. In 1903 Kings and Queens counties were supplied with water from about a dozen private water companies, numerous wells and ponds owned by the city of New York, and from domestic and industrial wells. Most of the waste water was exported from the area through public sewers, but in less urbanized areas much of the water was returned to the shallow aquifer through cesspools and septic tanks. By 1933 nearly all the groundwater used for public supply and a considerable amount of self-supplied industrial pumpage was wasted to sewers, and an extensive deep cone of depression had developed on the water table. Some public supply wells in Brooklyn became contaminated by seawater. These conditions and the use of groundwater for air conditioning resulted in the passage of legislation ruling that pumped water in excess of 70 gallons per minute (45 gpm since 1954) for air conditioning and cooling must be returned to the source aquifer. By 1936, despite conservation measures, the water table had declined to a record low and was below sea level in Kings County and the southwest part of Queens County; the deepest point was 35 feet below sea level. It is calculated that 49 billion gallons of fresh water were removed from storage from 1903 to 1936, and that two to three times that amount had been mined, inasmuch as nearly all the fresh water in the shallow aquifer had been replaced or contaminated by seawater.

> The decline of the water table was due to excessive pumping from both the shallow and deep aquifers, to wasting to sewers of all water from public-supply and some industrial wells, and to a substantial decrease in natural recharge owing to extensive paving of streets and building construction (Perlmutter and Soren, 1962, p. 138).

An interesting series of events occurred after wells that had been producing 27 million gallons per day were shut down in 1947 because of litigation during condemnation proceedings. After this date, a sharp rise of the water table began and by 1961 the recovery had been as much as 40 feet.

> The recovery of the water table created seepage problems in parts of the subway system and in inadequately waterproofed basements of buildings constructed during the period of low water table. Seepage at several subway stations in Flatbush increased from less than 20 gpm in 1947 to as much as 1,000 gpm in 1961 . . . (p. 138).

Thus conservation of groundwater is a blend of physical methods and legislation. Another physical technique first initiated in Nassau County in 1928 was the construction of artificial recharge pits. By 1960, there were 400 pits on Long Island and today there are more than 2,100 (Seaburn and Aronson, 1973).

> One of the major methods of disposing of storm runoff from urban and suburban areas on Long Island, New York, is to divert the water into recharge basins. This method of disposal . . . helps to augment and conserve water in Long Island's ground-water reservoir — the sole source of fresh water for nearly 3 million people in Nassau and Suffolk Counties.
>
> More than 2,100 recharge basins were in operation on Long Island in 1969. These basins are undoubtedly a major influence on the hydrologic system of the island.
>
> Most of the recharge basins on Long Island are unlined open pits that dispose of storm runoff from residential, commercial and industrial areas, and from highways. . . . The area of basins that dispose of storm runoff generally ranges from 0.1 to 30 acres and average 1.5 acres. The average depth below land surface is 10 feet, but the depth of a few is as much as 40 feet (p. 80).

The conservation of groundwater is made more difficult when contaminated by urban-area waste products, a topic that is briefly discussed in Part IV. It must also be mentioned that the Long Island area has no monopoly on the problems of saltwater intrusion of coastal aquifers since many coastal cities in Florida, Texas, and California are also affected. For example, seawater encroachment into freshwater aquifers was first noted at Redondo Beach, California, in 1912. In parts of southern California the saltwater intrusion has now reached nearly 2 miles inland.

The last geomorphic effect to be mentioned where man's use of a resource has altered the land–water ecosystem concerns the topic of subsidence (see also Volume III, pp. 203 – 204, 237 – 258, of this trilogy). Subsidence can be a major environmental response to man's altering of the fluid regimes that underlie cities. Poland and Davis (1969) describe the example of Long Beach, California, where from 1937 to 1962, 913 million barrels of oil, 484 million barrels of water, and 832 billion cubic feet of gas were removed from underlying sediments to depths of 6,000 feet. Subsidence began in 1937, and by 1962 much of the heavily urbanized area had subsided a minimum of 2 feet and as much as 27 feet which resulted in extensive flooding by the ocean. The cost of repairing the damaged structures and equipment exceeded $100 million during this period. Salt water is now being injected into the ground to counteract the subsidence, and appreciable areas are now above sea level again.

In Italy surveys show that Venice has sunk 4 inches in the past 50 years, and engineers give rates of 1/10 inch per year. Erosion is also occurring, not only through the natural forces of tidal flow, storms, and the like, but by man-induced processes:

> The fleets of large motorboats (vaporettas) and small speedboats (motoscafi) which are rapidly replacing the traditional gondolas of romantic memory are also contributing to the decline. The wash of their powerful engines surges from one side of the canals to the other, gnawing away at the city's underpinnings (Christie, 1967, p. 40).

Mexico City grew rapidly from 500,000 in 1895 to 1 million in 1922 to 5 million inhabitants by 1960. Since the city was built on old lake beds with marshy areas, the earth materials consisted of highly compressible silts and clays. Owing to draining of the wetlands and groundwater withdrawals from underground reservoirs, the center of the city subsided 1.5 meters between 1900 and 1940, and by 1960 had subsided as much as 7 meters.

> As Mexico City builds higher and higher—soaring skyscrapers for business and government offices, luxurious hotels for tourists—it also sinks lower. The subsidence of the soil, as much as 25 feet in some areas since the beginning of this century, creates a particularly complex set of problems . . . (de la Haba, 1973, p. 655).

Japan is another area where overdraft of groundwater in urban areas has caused extensive subsidence. In one part of Tokyo, where 2 million people live, the ground has subsided below high-tide level, and in Osaka 600,000 people live in an area that has similar conditions.

4

Reprinted from *Hydrology for Urban Land Planning—A Guidebook on the Hydrologic Effects of Urban Land Use* (U.S. Geol. Surv. Circ. 554), Government Printing Office, Washington, D.C., 1968, pp. 1–18

HYDROLOGY FOR URBAN LAND PLANNING—A GUIDEBOOK ON THE HYDROLOGIC EFFECTS OF URBAN LAND USE

By Luna B. Leopold

This circular attempts to summarize existing knowledge of the effects of urbanization on hydrologic factors. It also attempts to express this knowledge in terms that the planner can use to test alternatives during the planning process. Because the available data used in this report are applied to a portion of the Brandywine Creek basin in Pennsylvania, this can be considered as a report on the basic hydrologic conditions of the Brandywine Creek basin prior to the beginning of major urbanization. Because the available data are not yet adequate, this report can be considered as a compilation of tentative suggestions in the form of an explanatory, not a definitive, handbook.

The application of current knowledge of the hydrologic effects of urbanization to the Brandywine should be viewed as a forecast of conditions which may be expected as urbanization proceeds. By making such forecasts in advance of actual urban development, the methods can be tested, data can be extended, and procedures improved as verification becomes possible.

PLANNING PROCEDURES AND HYDROLOGIC VARIABLES

A planning document presented to a community for adoption must always be more suggestive than coercive. This is true not only because the planner is unable to foresee the innumerable complications of actual development, but also because there are many detailed alternatives which would accomplish generally similar results. The planner is particularly concerned with both the constraints and the opportunities offered by the principal physiographic characteristics of the area, especially the location of hillslopes, soils, and streams. The existing pattern of land use and the accompanying distribution of woods and agriculture are parameters which over a period of years may actually change, albeit slowly. Roads, villages, industries, and other manmade features are more or less permanent and exert their greatest influence in their effect on further development, especially through land values.

Of particular concern to the planner are those alternatives that affect the hydrologic functioning of the basins. To be interpreted hydrologically, the details of the land-use pattern must be expressed in terms of hydrologic parameters which are affected by land use. These parameters in turn become hydrologic variables by which the effects of alternative planning patterns can be evaluated in hydrologic terms.

There are four interrelated but separable effects of land-use changes on the hydrology of an area: changes in peak flow characteristics, changes in total runoff, changes in quality of water, and changes in the hydrologic amenities. The hydrologic amenities are what might be called the appearance or the impression which the river, its channel and its valleys, leaves with the observer. Of all land-use changes affecting the hydrology of an area, urbanization is by far the most forceful.

Runoff, which spans the entire regimen of flow, can be measured by number and by characteristics of rise in streamflow. The many rises in flow, along with concomitant sediment loads, control the stability of the stream channel. The two principal factors governing flow regimen are the percentage of area made impervious and the rate at which water is transmitted across the land to stream channels. The former is governed by the type of land use; the latter is governed by the density, size, and characteristics of tributary channels and thus by the provision of storm sewerage. Stream channels form in response to the regimen of flow of the stream. Changes in the regimen of flow, whether through land use or other changes, cause adjustments in the stream channels to accommodate the flows.

The volume of runoff is governed primarily by infiltration characteristics and is related to land slope and soil type as well as to the type of vegetative cover. It is thus directly related to the percentage of the area covered by roofs, streets, and other impervious surfaces at times of hydrograph rise during storms.

A summary of some data on the percentage of land rendered impervious by different degrees of urbanization is presented by Lull and Sopper (1966). Antoine (1964) presents the following data on the percentage of impervious surface area in residential properties:

Lot size of residential area (sq ft)	*Impervious surface area (percent)*
6,000	80
6,000–15,000	40
15,000	25

The percentage decreases markedly as size of lot increases. Felton and Lull (1963) estimate in the Philadelphia area that 32 percent of the surface area is impervious on lots averaging 0.2 acre in size, whereas only 8 percent of the surface area is impervious on lots averaging 1.8 acres.

As volume of runoff from a storm increases, the size of flood peak also increases. Runoff volume also affects low flows because in any series of storms the larger the percentage of direct runoff, the smaller the amount of water available for soil moisture replenishment and for ground-water storage. An increase in total runoff from a given series of storms as a result of imperviousness results in decreased ground-water recharge and decreased low flows. Thus, increased imperviousness has the effect of increasing flood peaks during storm periods and decreasing low flows between storms.

The principal effect of land use on sediment comes from the exposure of the soil to storm runoff. This occurs mainly when bare ground is exposed during construction. It is well known that sediment production is sensitive to land slope. Sediment yield from urban areas tends to be larger than in unurbanized areas even if there are only small and widely scattered units of unprotected soil in the urban area. In aggregate, these scattered bare areas are sufficient to yield considerable sediment.

A major effect of urbanization is the introduction of effluent from sewage disposal plants, and often the introduction of raw sewage, into channels. Raw sewage obviously degrades water quality, but even treated effluent contains dissolved minerals not extracted by sewage treatment. These minerals act as nutrients and promote algae and plankton growth in a stream. This growth in turn alters the balance in the stream biota.

Land use in all forms affects water quality. Agricultural use results in an increase of nutrients in stream water both from the excretion products of farm animals and from commercial fertilizers. A change from agricultural use to residential use, as in urbanization, tends to reduce these types of nutrients, but this tendency is counteracted by the widely scattered pollutants of the city, such as oil and gasoline products, which are carried through the storm sewers to the streams. The net result is generally an adverse effect on water quality. This effect can be measured by the balance and variety of organic life in the stream, by the quantities of dissolved material, and by the bacterial level. Unfortunately data describing quality factors in streams from urban versus unurbanized areas are particularly lacking.

Finally, the amenity value of the hydrologic environment is especially affected by three factors. The first factor is the stability of the stream channel itself. A channel, which is gradually enlarged owing to increased floods caused by urbanization, tends to have unstable and unvegetated banks, scoured or muddy channel beds, and unusual debris accumulations. These all tend to decrease the amenity value of a stream.

The second factor is the accumulation of artifacts of civilization in the channel and on the flood plain: beer cans, oil drums, bits of lumber, concrete, wire—the whole gamut of rubbish of an urban area. Though this may not importantly affect the hydrologic function of the channel, it becomes a detriment of what is here called the hydrologic amenity.

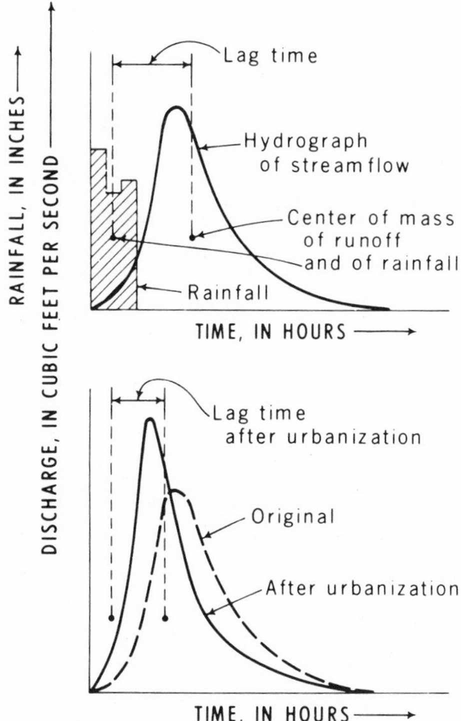

Figure 1.—Hypothetical unit hydrographs relating runoff to rainfall, with definitions of significant parameters.

The third factor is the change brought on by the disruption of balance in the stream biota. The addition of nutrients promotes the growth of plankton and algae. A clear stream, then, may change to one in which rocks are covered with slime; turbidity usually increases, and odors may develop. As a result of increased turbidity and reduced oxygen content desirable game fish give way to less desirable species. Although lack of quantitative objective data on the balance of stream biota is often a handicap to any meaningful and complete evaluation of the effects of urbanization, qualitative observations tend to confirm these conclusions.

AVAILABILITY OF DATA AND THE TECHNIQUE OF ANALYSIS

Basic hydrologic data on both peak flow and volume of runoff may be expressed in terms of the characteristics of the unit hydrograph, that is, the average time distribution graph of flow from a unit or standard storm. The unit hydrograph shows the percentage of the total storm runoff occurring in each successive unit of time. The standard storm may be, for example, a typical storm which produced 1 inch of runoff (fig. 1). Such data are derived from the study of individual storms and the associated runoff graphs measured at gaging stations.

One factor stating the relation between the storm and the runoff is lag time. This is defined as the time interval between the center of mass of the storm precipitation and the center of mass of the resultant hydrograph. Lag time is a function of two basin parameters—the mean basin slope and the basin length. These factors empirically correlate with lag time if expressed in the form of the basin ratio (basin length L divided by the square root of the mean basin gradient, s). This basin ratio is also related to drainage area. As drainage area increases, the basin length increases and the average value of slope generally decreases. Thus, natural basin characteristics can be translated into flood-flow characteristics.

Lag time may be materially altered by the effects of urbanization on the basin surface. Water runs off faster from streets and roofs than from natural vegetated areas. This tends to decrease the lag time. The construction of artificial channels, especially storm sewers, also decreases lag time. As the time required for a given amount of water to run off shortens, the peak rate of runoff (flood peak) increases.

In addition to the basin ratio and lag time, the regimen of a stream, however, can be described in many other ways, including flood

3

frequency, flow duration, mean annual flood, discharge at bankfull stage, and frequency of bankfull stage. This is evidenced in past studies of the effects of urbanization on the hydrology of an area. Many different techniques of relating rainfall to runoff have been used, along with various parameters to measure the degree of urbanization. In order to evaluate our present knowledge, it is necessary to express the results of these studies in some common denominator.

Most reports on hydrologic effects of urbanization present the conclusions in a form which is more useful to the hydrologist than to the urban planner. This circular will attempt to interpret the hydrologic conclusions of these studies in terms that are meaningful to the planner. Two forms of presentation will be used.

The first is a slight modification of a method previously used by several investigators, especially D. G. Anderson (1968) and L. D. James (1965). The percentage of an area sewered is plotted against the percentage of the area rendered impervious by urbanization; isopleth lines (lines of equal value of the ratio) on the graph show the ratio of peak discharge under urbanized conditions to the peak discharge under rural or unurbanized conditions. Such a graph will be different for different drainage area sizes and for different flow frequencies.

The second method utilizes a relationship between the degree of urbanization and the frequency at which the original channel capacity would be exceeded.

Table 1 is an interpretation and summary of the effects of urbanization on peak discharges based on previous studies. Results of the studies were interpreted and extrapolated to a common denominator of 1 sq mi (square mile), a practical unit of size for planning.

Carter (1961) developed a technique that followed the reasoning previously used by Snyder (1938) and that showed lag time as a function of basin characteristics. For 20 streams in the vicinity of Washington, D.C., Carter developed this relation for natural basins, for partly sewered, and for completely sewered basins. As in most studies the difficulty comes in translating these descriptive terms to quantitative measures of urbanization. From data presented by Carter, values were read for a basin ratio of 0.12 representing a 1-sq-mi area having an estimated length of 1.2 miles and an average slope of 100 feet per mile. It was further assumed that in Carter's study, "partly sewered" is equivalent to 50 percent sewered and 20 percent impervious. These conditions provide some of the data shown in table 1.

Table 1.—*Increase in discharge as a result of urbanization in a 1-square-mile area*

[Discharge is mean annual flood; recurrence interval is 2.3 years. Data are expressed as ratio of discharge after urbanization to discharge under previous conditions. Data from James (1965) have no superscript]

Percentage of area served by storm sewerage	Percentage of area made impervious			
	0	20	50	80
0	1.0	[1]1.2	[1]1.8	[1]2.2
		[2]1.3	[2]1.7	[2]2.2
		1.3	1.6	2.0
20	1.1	[3]1.9	1.8	2.2
		1.4	—	—
50	1.3	[4]2.1	[1]3.2	[1]4.7
		[1]2.8	2.0	2.5
		[5]3.7	—	—
		[6]2.0	2.5	[3]4.2
		1.6	—	—
80	1.6	1.9	—	3.2
100	1.7	[1]3.6	[1]4.7	[4]5.6
		2.0	2.8	[1]6.0
		—	—	3.6

[1] Anderson (1968).
[2] Martens (1966).
[3] Wilson (1966).
[4] Carter (1961).
[5] Wiitala (1961).
[6] Espey, Morgan, and Masch (1966).

As an indication of the change in impervious area resulting from urbanization, Harris and Rantz (1964) showed that an area near Palo Alto, Calif., changed from 5.7 percent to 19.1 percent impervious in a 10-year period.

One of the most complete analyses of urbanization effects was made by D. G. Anderson (1968) in his study of the urbanization in Fairfax County, Va., near the metropolitan complex of the Nation's Capital. Anderson's analysis follows the procedure suggested earlier by Carter, but Anderson included a larger array of data from 64 gaging stations. Anderson closely confirmed the conclusions of Carter, but he carried the analysis further in a plot of the ratio of peak discharge to the mean annual flood for different percentages of basin imperviousness and for flood flows exceeding the mean annual flood. For table 1, data from Anderson's study were read directly from his graph at the 2.33-year recurrence interval and expressed two separate conditions of sewerage. The first condition was expressed as "main channels natural, upstream drainage sewered"; this was assumed to be 50 percent sewered. The second condition was expressed as "completely sewered drainage basin"; this was assumed to be 100 percent sewered.

Wiitala (1961) presented data on urbanized versus rural conditions for a medium-sized watershed in Michigan. His data were translated into a ratio of peak discharges and it was assumed from his report that the urbanized condition represented 20 percent impervious area and 50 percent sewered area.

Martens (1966) reported on three small drainage basins in and near Charlotte, N.C. Using flood-frequency curves from long-term records at gaging stations in the State, he constructed a graph similar to that of Anderson; that is, ratio to mean annual flood for various degrees of basin imperviousness. As before, the difficulty lies in ascertaining the relation of Martens' urbanized condition to the degree sewered. In reading from Martens' graph for recurrence interval 2.33 years, it is assumed that the conditions he discussed include no sewerage and represent changes in impervious area only.

Wilson (1966) presented data on flood frequency for four drainage basins of 1.1 to 11.2 sq mi near Jackson, Miss. He presented his analysis in the form of discharge of mean annual flood plotted against drainage area size, and he interpolated lines to represent the percentage of the basin having storm sewers and improved channels. It is assumed that his description "20 percent of basin with storm sewers and improved channels" would be equivalent to 20 percent impervious and 20 percent sewered. Similarly, his value of 80 percent was assumed to be 80 percent sewered and 80 percent impervious.

Espey, Morgan, and Masch (1966) analyzed runoff data from urban and rural areas in Texas. To utilize this study, data were used corresponding to a basin length of 5,500 feet and a slope of 0.02. It was also assumed from his description of the area that "urban" could be expressed as 50 percent sewered and 20 percent impervious.

James (1965) analyzed runoff data from a 44-sq-mi basin south of Sacramento, Calif., within which 12 sq mi had been urbanized. From the basic data on flow, he obtained empirical coefficients used to route a series of synthetic flows by using a mathematical model expressed as a digital computer program. The results were plotted in a series of curves which separated the effects of flood frequency, drainage area, and degree of urbanization. Though the derived curves do not present field data, they also were incorporated into table 1.

Thus in table 1 are compiled, with certain necessary assumptions, the data for seven published and unpublished references which report measurements of the effect of urbanization on peak flow. Although interpretations were necessary to express the degree of urbanization in quantitative terms, there is considerable agreement among the data.

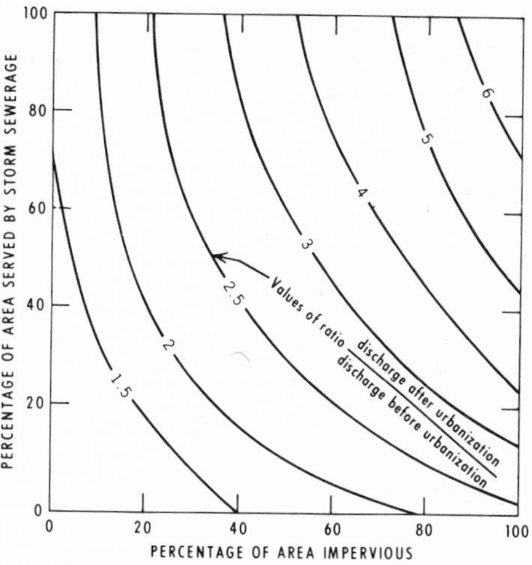

Figure 2.—Effect of urbanization on mean annual flood for a 1-square-mile drainage area. (Based on data from table 1.)

Data from table 1 have been transposed into the graph shown in figure 2. The ratios of peak discharge of urbanized to rural areas are presented for different percentages of sewerage and impervious area; lines of equal values of the ratio are drawn through the data. Briefly, these data show that for unsewered areas the differences between 0 and 100 percent impervious will increase peak discharge on the average 2.5 times. For areas that are 100 percent sewered, peak discharge for 0 percent impervious will be about 1.7 times the mean annual flood and the ratio increases to about eight for 100 percent impervious areas. Figure 2, then, reduces the basic data to the same units applicable to a 1-sq-mi drainage basin and to the mean annual flood.

A basin produces big flows from large and intense storms and smaller flows from less intense but more frequent storms. The great or catastrophic event is rare, and the storm of ordinary magnitude is frequent. These events can be arranged in order of magnitude and counted. For example, all discharge events exceeding 400 cfs (cubic feet per second) can be tabulated from the record at a stream-gaging station and arranged in order of magnitude; the values in the array can be plotted as a discharge-frequency curve. This has been done for the gaging station on West Branch Brandywine Creek at Coatesville, Pa., for 9 years of record (fig. 3). The theory and practice of constructing such flow-frequency curves is well known. The plotting position or frequency often used is defined as

$$R = \frac{n+1}{m}$$

where R is the recurrence interval in years, n is number of years of record, and m is the rank of the individual event in the array.

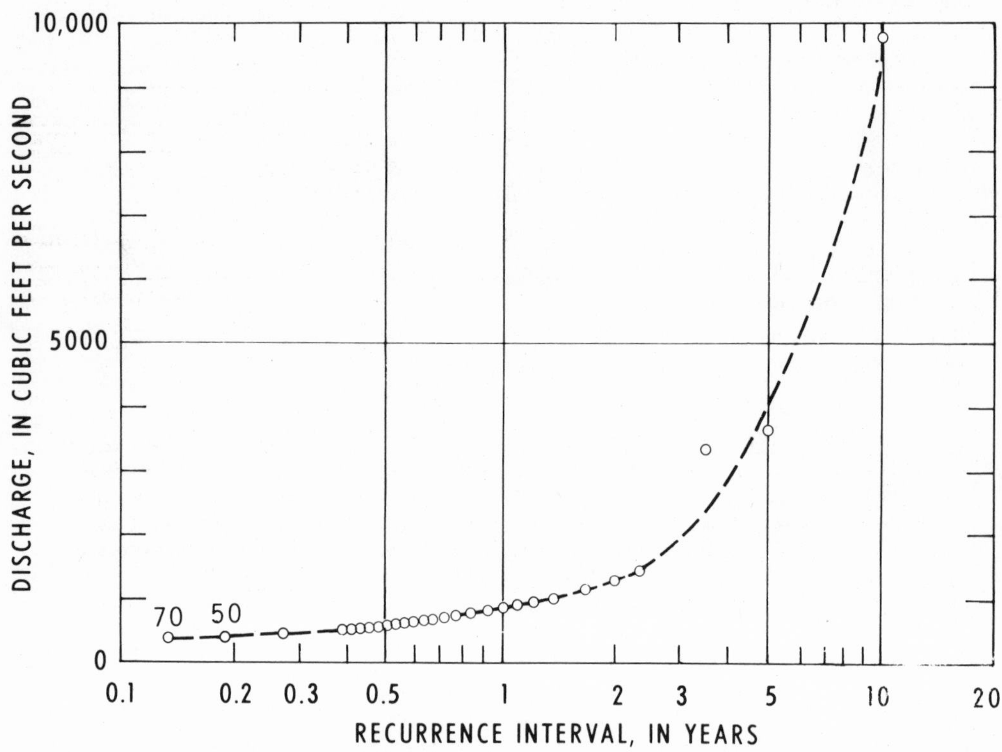

Figure 3.—Flood-frequency curve for partial-duration series, West Branch Brandywine Creek at Coatesville, Pa., based on data for 1942, 1944–51.

6

Note in figure 3 that the largest flow in the 9-year record was nearly 10,000 cfs. The number 50 printed on the graph means that there were 50 flows equal to or exceeding 500 cfs. Once a year, on the average, a discharge value of about 900 cfs will be equalled or exceeded.

A slightly different result would be obtained if, instead of using the peak flow for each storm, only the largest flow in each year were included in the array. The principle involved is similar. The arithmetic mean of the peak flows for the nine annual events is the "average annual flood." The statistics of this array are such that the recurrence interval of this average annual flood is the same regardless of the length of record, which specifically is 2.3 years. That is to say, a flood of that magnitude can be expected to be equaled or exceeded on an average of once in 2.3 years, or 10 times in 23 years.

Studies of river channels have shown that rivers construct and maintain channels which will carry without overflow a discharge somewhat smaller than the average annual flood. In fact the recurrence interval of the bankfull stage in most rivers is a flow having a recurrence interval of about 1.5 to 2 years.

Urbanization tends to increase the flood potential from a given basin. The channel then will receive flows which exceed its capacity not just once in 1.5 to 2 years on the average but more often. It is now proposed to estimate how much more often and to indicate the effect of this increased frequency on the channel itself.

EFFECT OF URBANIZATION ON INCREASING FREQUENCY OF OVERBANK FLOW

Taking the East Branch of Brandywine Creek as an example, the flow-frequency curve can be constructed for a typical subbasin having a 1-sq-mi drainage area. Figure 4*A* shows the relation of average annual flood to drainage area, and figure 4*B* shows the flood-frequency curve for annual peaks for basins in the Brandywine area. The diagrams shown in figure 4 are similar to those published in the nationwide series of flood reports, U.S. Geological Survey Water-Supply Papers 1671–1689.

From these curves a discharge-frequency relationship is developed for a drainage area of 1 sq mi. The average annual flood is read from the upper graph of figure 4 as 75 cfs, and the lower graph is used to construct the frequency curve in figure 5 pertaining to a 1-sq-mi basin marked "unurbanized."

The arithmetic for the construction of the curve is as follows:

Recurrence interval of annual flood [1] (years)	Ratio to mean annual flood [2]	Discharge [3] (cfs)	Recurrence interval duration series [4] (years)
1.1	0.55	41	0.4
1.5	.75	56	.92
2.0	.90	68	1.45
2.3	1.0	75	1.78
5	1.45	110	4.5
10	1.9	145	9.5

[1] Only the highest flood each year.
[2] From figure 4*B*.
[3] Obtained by multiplying ratios by 75 cfs from figure 4*A* for a drainage area of 1 sq mi.
[4] All peaks during the year. The values in this column are mathematically related to those in the first.

The graph marked "unurbanized" in figure 5 is constructed on semilogarithmic paper from the data listed in the third and fourth columns of the preceding table. The ordinate is the discharge, and the lower abscissa is the recurrence interval in the duration series. An auxiliary scale gives the average number of floods in a 10-year period (calculated as 10 years divided by the recurrence interval). Thus, the flow expected to occur once in 10 years would be about 145 cfs and the fifth largest would be 75 cfs. The latter would also be the average value of the largest flows each year during the 10-year record and thus would be the "average annual flood." It would plot, therefore, at an abscissa position approximately at 2.3-year recurrence interval.

The effect of urbanization on the average annual flood is shown in figure 2, which shows the increase in average annual flood for different degrees of urbanization as measured by the increase in percentages of impervious area and area served by storm sewers. For convenience these are tabulated as follows:

Percentage of area sewered	*Percentage of area impervious*	*Ratio to average annual flood*
0	0	1
20	20	1.5
40	40	2.3
50	50	2.7
80	60	4.2
100	60	4.4

7

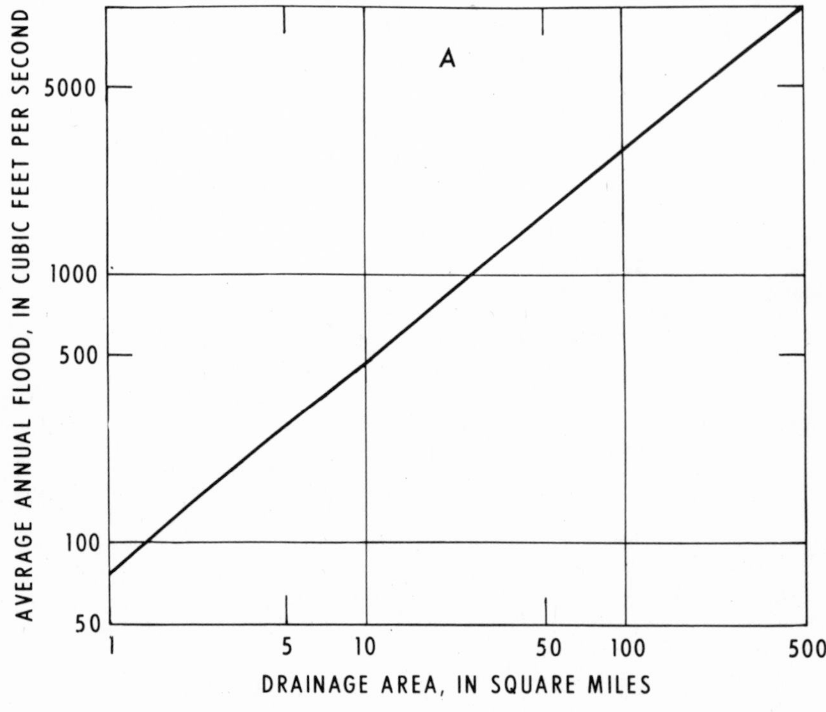

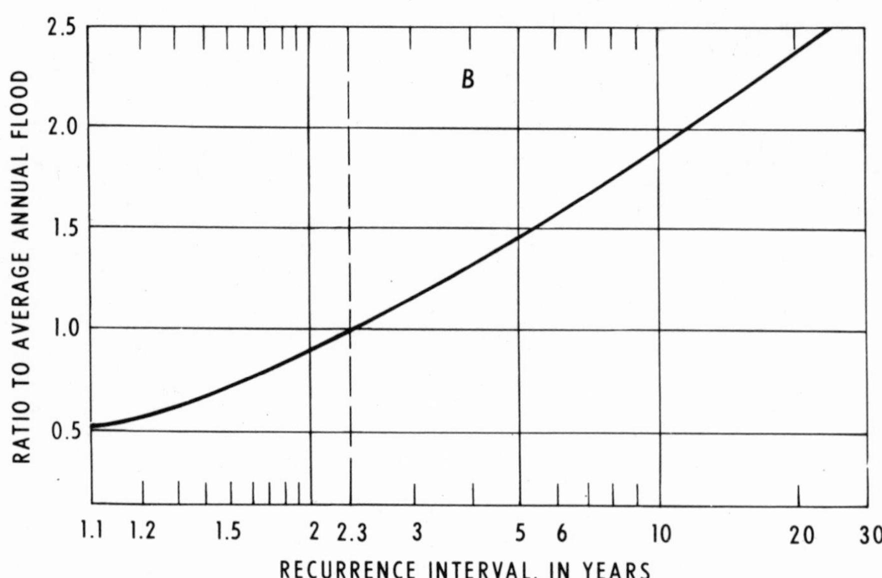

Figure 4.—Regional flood-frequency data for the Brandywine Creek basin, Pennsylvania. *A*, Relation of average annual flood to drainage area. *B*, Flood-frequency curve for annual peaks.

8

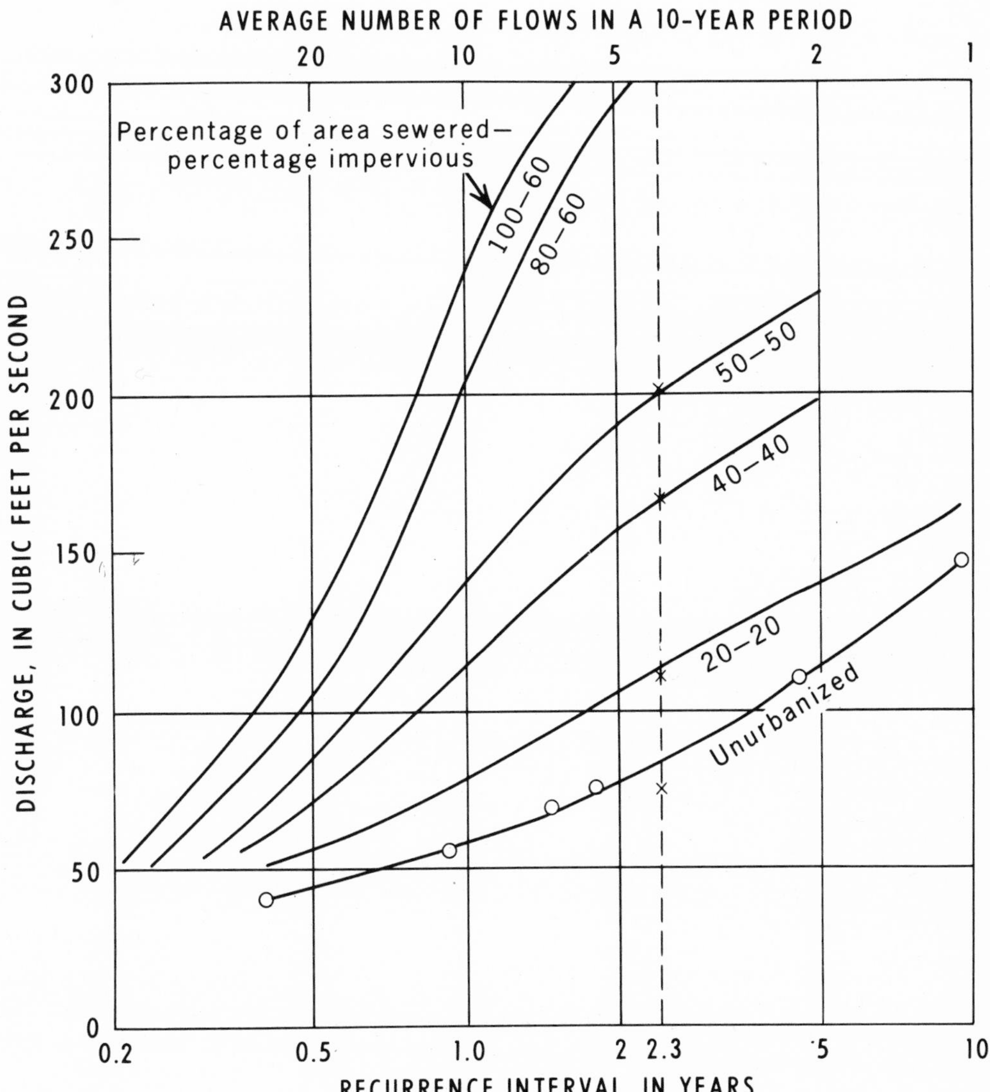

Figure 5.—Flood-frequency curves for a 1-square-mile basin in various states of urbanization. (Derived from figures 2 and 4.)

9

The average annual flood of 75 cfs was then multiplied by these ratios and plotted as shown in figure 5 at the 2.3-year interval. These values form the basis of a series of frequency curves for combinations of sewered area and impervious area. The shapes of the curves are guided by the principle that the most infrequent floods occur under conditions that are not appreciably affected by imperviousness of the basin.

The most frequent flows are therefore increased by smaller ratios than would be the average annual flood. Also, the most frequent flows are decreased in number because low flows from an urbanized area are not sustained by ground water as in a natural basin. The curves representing urbanized conditions therefore converge at low flow values.

Obviously the frequency curves in figure 5 are extrapolations based on minimal data and require corroboration or revision as additional field data become available.

The flood-frequency curve under original (unurbanized) condition passes through a value of 67 cfs at a recurrence interval of 1.5 years. At bankfull condition natural channels generally can carry the flow having that recurrence interval. If one assumes that this flow approximates the capacity of the natural channels, the intersection of the estimated curves for different degrees of urbanization with the discharge value of 67 cfs can be used to estimate the in-

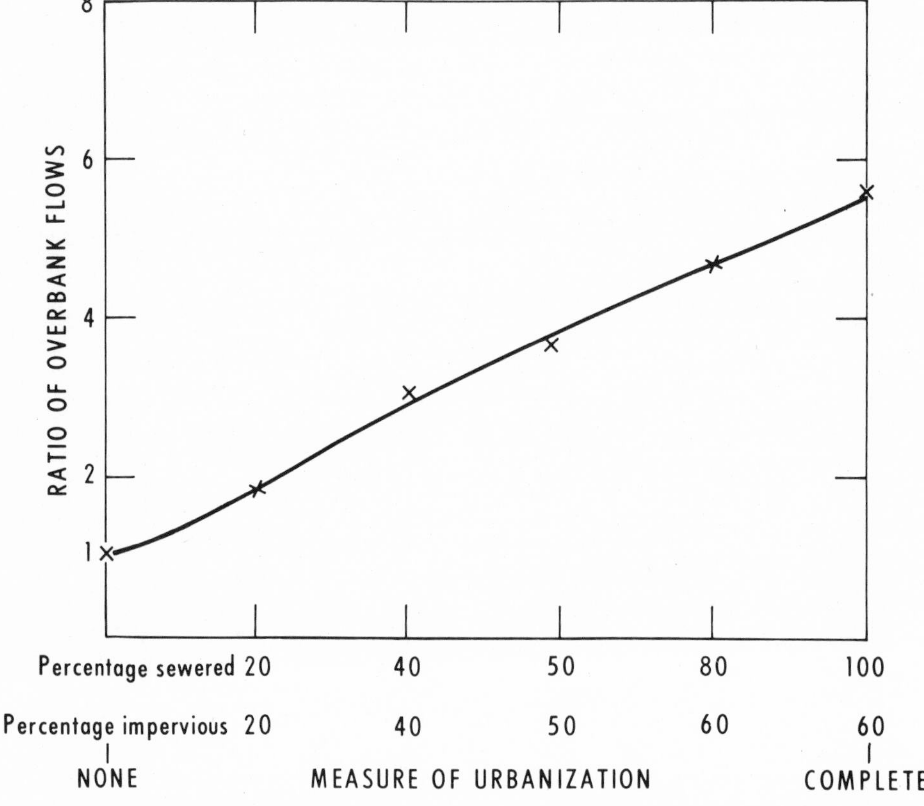

Figure 6.—Increase in number of flows per year equal to or exceeding original channel capacity (1-square-mile drainage area), as ratio to number of overbank flows before urbanization, for different degrees of urbanization. (Derived from figure 5.)

10

crease in number of flows equal to or exceeding natural channel capacity. An auxiliary scale is shown at the top of figure 5 to facilitate this.

For example, under natural conditions it is expected that a 10-year record would show about seven flows equal to or exceeding 67 cfs, or channel capacity. But if the average annual flood were increased 1.5 times (from 75 to 112 cfs) corresponding to 20 percent sewered and 20 percent impervious, the new frequency curve indicates that 14 flows of 67 cfs or greater would occur in a 10-year period, or a twofold increase in number of flows. Similarly, the ratio of number of flows exceeding bankfull capacity was read from the intersection of the other curves in figure 5 with the ordinate value of 67 cfs to obtain the ratios plotted in figure 6.

Figure 6 shows that with an area 50 percent sewered and 50 percent impervious, for example, the number of flows equal to or exceeding bankfull channel capacity would, over a period of years, be increased nearly fourfold.

LOCAL STORAGE TO COMPENSATE FOR PEAK FLOW INCREASE

Urbanization tends to increase both the flood volume and the flood peak. But the increase can be compensated so that the discharge through channels downstream is maintained to any degree desired within the range which existed prior to urbanization. It is obvious that reservoir storage is installed on a river in order to reduce the magnitude of peak discharge by spreading the flow over a longer time period. Channels themselves provide temporary storage and act as if they were small reservoirs. Overbank flooding on to the flat flood plain is a way that natural rivers provide for temporary storage and thus decrease flood peaks downstream. This effect of storage has been fully investigated and described (for example see Leopold and Maddock, 1954, especially p. 36–49).

The provision of flood storage upstream, then, will decrease flood peaks and compensate for the increase caused by urbanization. This storage could take many forms including the following:

1. Drop inlet boxes at street gutter inlets.
2. Street-side swales instead of paved gutters and curbs.
3. Check dams, ungated, built in headwater swales.
4. Storage volumes in basements of large buildings receiving water from roofs or gutters and emptying into natural streams or swales.
5. Off channel storage volumes such as artificial ponds, fountains, or tanks.
6. Small reservoirs in stream channels such as those built for farm ponds.

Various types of storage volumes could be used simultaneously in various mixes. The effectiveness depends on the volume of storage relative to the volume of inflow during a storm peak period. Design criteria to guide city engineers and developers are needed.

SEDIMENT PRODUCTION

The basic data available for analyzing the effect of urbanization on sediment yield, though sparse, have been summarized to some extent in the literature. Especially valuable is the report by Wolman (1964) who summarized not only the data obtained from sediment sampling stations in streams in Eastern United States but also studied the sediment yield from building construction activities. Sediment yields from urbanized or developing areas ranged from 1000 to more than 100,000 tons per square mile per year.

It should be recognized that sediment yield per square mile decreases with increasing drainage area, but nevertheless it is apparent that unurbanized drainage basins yield 200 to 500 tons per square mile per year, on the average. These figures are slightly higher for the farmed Piedmont lands, which may be expected to produce sediment yield of 500 tons per square mile per year, such as the Watts Branch basin near Rockville, Md.

The data on urbanized areas studied by Wolman are plotted in figure 7 together with data from suspended load sampling stations of the U.S. Geological Survey as summarized by Wark and Keller (1963).

In the graph (fig. 7) three bands or zones are labeled *A*, *C*, and *UC*. Wolman and Schick (1967) differentiated the following types of activity: *A*, agricultural or natural; *C*, under-

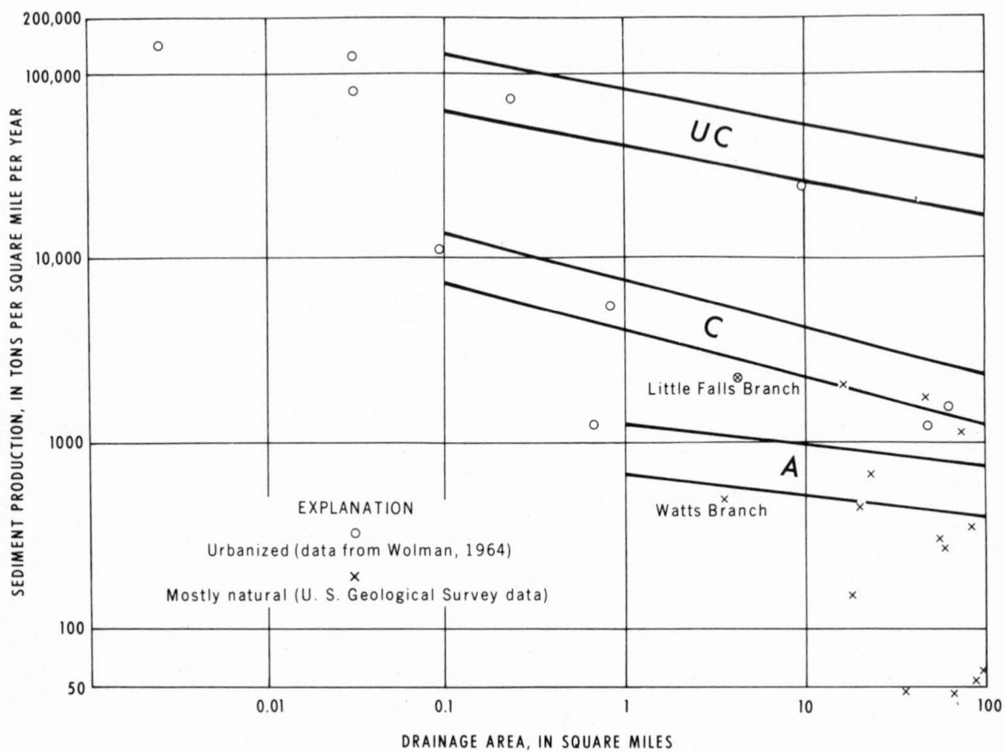

Figure 7.—Annual sediment production per square mile for urbanized and natural areas. Zones: *A*, agricultural; *C*, under construction; *UC*, under construction and undiluted.

going building construction, but highly diluted before reaching channels; and *UC*, undiluted sediment yields delivered to stream channels from construction sites.

They found that when building sites are denuded for construction, excavations are made, and dirt is piled without cover or protection near the site, the sediment movement in a rill or stream channel is very large in terms of tons per year immediately downhill from the construction site. If the channel contains little water except during storms (an ephemeral stream), there is no chance for dilution; during storm flow the sediment movement is great. If the construction debris gets into perennial channels, or for other reasons is distributed along a channel or dispersed over a wide area, the dilution lowers the yield per square mile per year. Thus, Wolman and Schick drew the distinction between agricultural, construction, and construction-undiluted.

For very small areas, Wolman (1964) said, "Because construction denudes the natural cover and exposes the soil beneath, the tonnage of sediment derived by erosion from an acre of ground under construction in developments and highways may exceed 20,000 to 40,000 times the amount eroded from farms and woodlands in an equivalent period of time."

Figure 7 shows the data as a relation between annual sediment yield per square mile and drainage basin size. The usual suspended load station is on a basin of more than 10 sq mi in area. Seldom is urbanization complete for basins of this size.

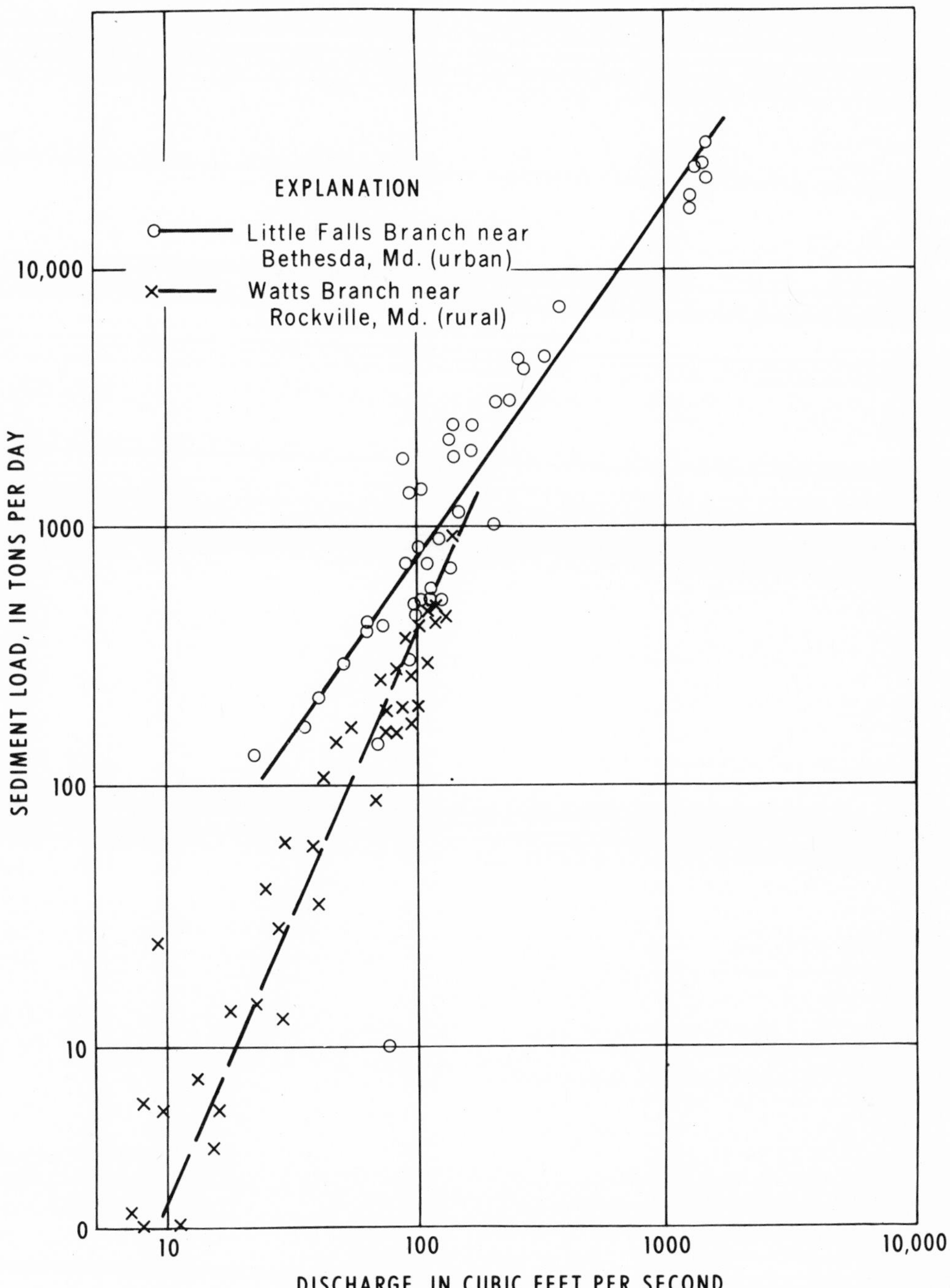

Figure 8.—Relation of sediment yield and discharge for an urban and a rural or unurbanized area.

13

The data measured or estimated by Wolman (1964) in small urbanizing, developed or industrial areas show clearly that the sediment yield is larger by 10 to 100 times that of rural areas. Guy and Ferguson (1962) observed an increase of 250 times in an area near Kensington, Md.

To illustrate the difference in sediment samples obtained during storm flow, actual data for two stations are shown in figure 8. The sediment rating curve, which is a plot of the discharge at any moment in time against the concurrent rate of sediment transport, gives an indication of the order of magnitude of the increase in sediment production from developed, as against rural, areas. The sediment rating curves in figure 8 are for stations near Washington, D.C. Watts Branch drains an area primarily used for farming though urban influences have recently extended into the basin. Little Falls Branch near Bethesda drains a nearly completely urbanized community, consisting of Bethesda and parts of Chevy Chase, Md.

Note that the sediment rating curves tend to converge at high discharges. One might suppose that at those discharges the urbanized areas are actually contributing no more sediment than the unurbanized ones. This is not the case, however, owing to the fact that as a result of urbanization, the number of high flows increases materially. Because most of the sediment during the year is carried during periods of high flow, the result is that urbanized areas yield on the average larger sediment loads than the unurbanized ones.

The difference in drainage basin size between Watts Branch (3.7 sq mi) and Little Falls Branch (4.1 sq mi) is not alone sufficient to explain the larger discharges in the latter basin. For about the same number of sample storms, note that Little Falls Branch data include discharges varying from 20 to 1500 cfs. In contrast, Watts Branch data (unurbanized) include flows ranging from 7 to 150 cfs. At least some of this difference is probably due to the effect of urbanization on increasing peak flow from a storm of given size, as discussed earlier. The two basins are only 10 miles apart and storms are comparable.

Keller (1962) compared the sediment rating curves for Northwest Branch of Anacostia River near Colesville, Md., a relatively unurbanized basin, and the Anacostia River basin near Hyattsville, Md., which is partly urbanized. He found the sediment production to be about four times greater in the urbanized area.

Most sediment carried by a stream is moved by high flows. In Brandywine Creek, for example, about 54 percent of the total sediment transported annually by the river (drainage area 312 sq mi) is carried by flows that occur, on the average, about 3 days each year.

In the tabulation below, a comparison is made between sediment yield from Watts Branch, a rural landscape, and Little Falls Branch, an urban one. These basins are of the size and type represented in East Branch Brandywine Creek.

	Drainage area (sq mi)	*Tons per year*	*Tons per year per sq mi*
Watts Branch in Rockville, Md. (rural)	3.7	1,910	516
Little Falls Branch near Bethesda, Md. (urban)	4.1	9,530	3,220

Sediment production is importantly related to land slope. Using multiple correlation techniques for a large variety of data from experimental watersheds, Musgrave (1947) developed a multiple correlation in which the rate of erosion is found to be proportional to the 1.35 power of land slope and to the 0.35 power of the slope length. The same conclusion had been derived theoretically by Horton (1945) and verified by comparison with the percentage of area eroded in the Boise River basin, Idaho. Sediment yield, therefore, is more highly sensitive to land slope than to length of slope but is postively correlated with both.

Some idea, however, can be obtained of the difficulty in keeping steep slopes stable after the original vegetation has been disturbed, particularly during construction. If, for example, land slopes of 5 and 10 percent are compared, the doubling of the slope would increase the erosion rate by 2.3 times.

Increased slope length does not have such a large effect on erosion rate. Doubling slope length would increase the erosion rate by only 22 percent.

Because a slope of 10 percent drops 10 feet in a 100-foot horizontal, temporary storage in the form of depressions which might hold silt would be nearly absent. For land slopes above 10 percent, stream channels also would tend to be nearly devoid of areas or depressions which could hold up sediment during its passage downhill. From a practical standpoint, therefore, a figure of about 10 percent probably would be a physical and economic limit beyond which construction would be especially harmful insofar as sediment production is concerned. Any such limiting slope, however, would have to be determined by detailed economic studies.

Wark and Keller (1963) related the average annual sediment discharge in the Potomac River basin to percentage of forest cover and, separately, to the percentage of land in crops. Average annual sediment yield increased from 50 to 400 tons per square mile per year, or eightfold, as forest cover in the basin declined from 80 percent to 20 percent. Sediment yield increased from 70 to 300 tons per square mile per year, or fourfold, as land in crops increased from 10 to 50 percent.

EFFECT OF INCREASED PEAK FLOWS ON SEDIMENT YIELD

It has been pointed out in the comparison of sediment rating curves for urban versus rural areas that the rating curves do not appear to be as much different as the values of sediment yield on an annual yield basis. It has been mentioned that a slight increase of sediment concentration can make a large difference in total annual sediment yield owing to the fact that urban areas produce a larger number of high flows. If the number of flows above bankfull stage is increased by urbanization, the banks and bed of a channel in erodible material will not remain stable, but the channel will enlarge through erosion. Computation indicates the seriousness of this factor.

For example, assume that a channel is capable of carrying 55 cfs at bankfull stage. In the Brandywine area this represents a channel draining a basin slightly less than 1 sq mi in area. The channel necessary to carry 55 cfs at bankfull stage would probably have a velocity of slightly less than 2.5 feet per second and would be about 2 feet deep and 11 feet wide. In figure 2, urbanization might cause a flow of this frequency to increase 2.7 times, or 150 cfs. If this channel had to adjust itself to carry a flood of 150 cfs at bankfull stage, it is estimated that the new velocity would be about 2.5 feet per second, and the necessary depth and width would have changed respectively to about 3 feet and 20 feet. In other words, this stream would deepen about 50 percent and increase in width a little less than twice its original size. If such erosion takes place through at least one-fourth mile of channel length in a drainage basin of 1 sq mi, the amount of sediment produced by this erosion would be 50,000 cubic feet. At 100 pounds per cubic foot, this amounts to 2,500 tons.

This amount can be compared with the mean annual sediment yield for Watts Branch, an unurbanized area near Rockville, Md. Annual sediment yield of Watts Branch is 516 tons per square mile. Thus, the channel erosion alone under the assumptions made would produce as much sediment as 5 years' usual production from an unurbanized area of the same size. Therefore, one can visualize that as urbanization proceeds, not only does construction activity have the potential of increasing sediment loads many thousands of times while construction is in progress, but also the result of the urbanization through its increase in peak flow would produce large amounts of sediment from channel enlargement as well. This emphasizes the need to provide temporary storage far upstream to counteract the tendency of urbanization to increase the number and size of high flows.

WATER QUALITY

There is little doubt that as urbanization increases, particularly from industrial use of land and water, the quality of water decreases. However, quantitative data to support this observation are sparse. There are two principal effects of urbanization on water quality. First, the influx of waste materials tends to increase the dissolved-solids content and decrease the dissolved-oxygen content. Second, as flood peaks increase as a result of the increased area of imperviousness and decreased lag time, less water is available for ground-water recharge. The stream becomes flashier in that flood peaks are higher and flows during nonstorm periods are lower.

A recent study on the Passaic River at Little Falls, N.J., by Anderson and Faust (1965) provides quantitative data on the effect of urbanization and industrialization on water quality. Seventeen years of data for the flow and chemical quality of the 760-sq-mi drainage basin were analyzed. During these 17 years, diversions of water for domestic and industrial supplies increased more than 30 percent between 1950 and 1963. Returns of waste waters into the basin became as much as 10 percent of the water withdrawn. Analysis of the data showed that at relatively low discharge the dissolved-solids content increased about 10 ppm (parts per million) between 1948 and 1955 but increased 75 ppm between 1955 and 1963. That is, during the period of greatest population growth the dissolved-solids content increased nearly 40 percent in a period of 8 years.

A long-term change in the average content of dissolved oxygen was also noted. Between 1950 and 1964 the dissolved-oxygen content dropped from an average of 78 percent of saturation to 62 percent of saturation. Further, the analysis demonstrated that these average changes in water quality occurred in all seasons of the year.

An aspect of population growth not generally appreciated is the large segment of population using septic tanks for disposal of sewage. In a given area this segment often becomes large before community water and sewerage systems are built. For the planner it should be important to know how septic-tank installations can affect water quality in streams and in the ground. In the upper East Branch of Brandywine Creek, a basin of 37 sq mi, the population in 1967 was 4,200. As of that date, there were no community water or sewerage systems; all the population was served by individual wells and septic tanks. Population projections indicate that the basin will have 14,000 persons by the year 1990. During the initial part of this projected growth at least, the number of wells and septic tanks can be expected to increase materially.

The soil, containing as it does a flourishing fauna of micro-organisms, tends to destroy or adsorb pathogenic bacteria. Effluent draining from the seepage field of a septic tank tends therefore to be cleansed of its pathogens. McGauhey and Krone (1954) showed that the coliform count was reduced by three orders of magnitude in moving from an injection well a distance of 50 feet through sand and gravel. In 100 feet the count was reduced to a small number. As for rate of movement, Mallmann and Mack (1961) showed that bacteria introduced into a permeable soil by a septic-tank seepage field moved 10 feet in 2 days and 20 feet in 3 days and appeared in a well 30 feet away after 10 days.

Both the rate and effectiveness of the process of pathogen reduction depend on the type of soil as has been summarized by Olson (1964), who emphasized that position of the ground-water table is a critical factor in the transmission of pollutants.

Studies by Wayman, Page, and Robertson (1965) of the changes in primary sewage effluent through natural materials in conditions of saturated flow showed that "most soils removed over 90 percent of the bacteria from sewage within a few feet of travel * * * [but there was] severe clogging in the finer-grained soils." They found, however, that "dissolved solids moved through the columns [of soil] virtually unaffected * * *."

The same authors report on infiltration of polluted river water through sandy loam. "ABS [synthetic detergent] and coliform bacteria are significantly reduced by infiltration through the unsaturated zone; dissolved solids do not seem to be removed * * *. Once a pollutant gets into the ground water (saturated flow) little additional change in removal of ABS or dissolved solids, even for movement over extensive horizontal distances, is to be expected. This result is in agreement with the data * * * for flow of sewage effluent through various soil columns (saturated flow)."

The data are not definitive regarding the minimum distance a septic-tank seepage field should be separated from a stream channel, but the application of data cited above with general principles does indicate some tentative rules of thumb which might be useful to the planner. A perennial stream represents the intersection of the saturated zone (water table) with the earth's surface. The observations indicate that, for soil cleansing to be effective, contaminated water must move through unsaturated soil at least 100 feet. Owing to the gentle gradient of the water table near the perennial stream and the fact that seepage water moves vertically as well as toward a nearby channel, it would seem prudent that no septic tank should be as close to a channel as about 300 feet, if protection of the stream water quality is to be achieved. The distance should probably be greater from a perennial than from an ephemeral channel. (An ephemeral stream is one which contains flowing water only in storm periods.) In general, it might be advisable to have no source of pollution such as a seepage field closer than 300 feet to a channel or watercourse.

Even this minimum setback does not prevent the dissolved materials (nitrates, phosphates, chlorides) from enriching the stream water and thus potentially encouraging the proliferation of algae and otherwise creating a biotic imbalance.

The only detailed study of the effect of urbanization on water temperature is that of E. J. Pluhowski (1968), some of whose results are summarized here. He chose five streams on Long Island for detailed analysis and found that streams most affected by man's activities exhibit temperatures in summer from 10° to 15°F above those in an unurbanized control. Connetquot River, the control stream, flows through one of the few remaining undeveloped areas of central Long Island. Temperatures in reaches most affected by ponding, realinement, or clear cutting of trees are significantly higher in summer, but winter temperatures are 5° to 10°F colder than those observed in reaches unaffected by man.

Solar radiation is the predominant factor in the energy balance determining a stream's thermal pattern. The more solar energy a stream absorbs, the greater its temperature variation diurnally as well as seasonally. By greatly increasing the surface area exposed to the sun's radiation, the construction of ponds and lakes has profoundly affected stream temperature regimen. On Long Island, Pluhowski found that ponds having mean depth of about 2 feet or less substantially increase downstream diurnal temperature fluctuations whereas ponds deeper than 2 feet exhibit a dampening effect on daily temperatures. For example, during the period October 31 to November 2, 1967, the mean daily range of temperatures at Swan River, in south-central Long Island, varied from 9°F in a reach immediately below a shallow pond (mean depth, 0.5 foot) to 3°F below Swan Lake (mean depth, 3 feet). In reaches unaffected by man's activities, the mean daily temperature fluctuation was about 4°F.

Under natural conditions, less than 5 percent of the streamflow on Long Island originates as direct surface runoff. With the conversion of large areas of western Long Island from farmland to suburban use during the last 20 years, the proportion of streamflow originating as surface runoff has increased sharply. As a direct consequence, streams most affected by street runoff may exhibit temperature patterns that are markedly different from those observed in streams flowing through natural settings. During the period August 25 to 27, 1967, a series of heavy rainstorms overspread Long Island. Throughout this period, temperatures at each of the five observation sites on Connetquot River showed little day-to-day change. In contrast, temperatures in the upper reaches of East Meadow Brook, which drains highly urbanized central Nassau County, increased steadily in response to the relatively warm street runoff. Pluhowski found that by August 27, water temperatures had risen 10° to 12°F above prestorm levels and were 15°F higher than concurrent temperatures in the control stream.

SELECTED REFERENCES

Anderson, D. G., 1968, Effects of urban development on floods in northern Virginia: U.S. Geol. Survey open-file rept., 39 p., 5 figs.

Anderson, Peter W., and Faust, Samuel D., 1965, Changes in quality of water in the Passaic River at Little Falls, New Jersey, as shown by long-term data, *in* Geological Survey research 1965: U.S. Geol. Survey Prof. Paper 525-D, p. D214–D218.

Antoine, L. H., 1964, Drainage and best use of urban land: Public Works [New York], v. 95, p. 88–90.

Carter, R. W., 1961, Magnitude and frequency of floods in suburban areas, *in* Short papers in the geologic and hydrologic sciences: U.S. Geol. Survey Prof. Paper 424-B, p. B9–B11.

Espey, W. H., Morgan, C. W., and Masch, F. D., 1966, Study of some effects of urbanization on storm runoff from a small watershed: Texas Water Devel. Board Rept. 23, 109 p.

Felton, P. N., and Lull, H. W., 1963, Suburban hydrology can improve watershed conditions: Public Works, v. 94, p. 93–94.

Guy, H. P., and Ferguson, G. E., 1962, Sediment in small reservoirs due to urbanization: Am. Soc. Civil Engineers Proc., HY 2, p. 27–37.

Harris, E. E., and Rantz, S. E., 1964, Effect of urban growth on streamflow regimen of Permanente Creek, Santa Clara County, California: U.S. Geol. Survey Water-Supply Paper 1591-B, 18 p.

Horton, R. E., 1945, Erosional development of streams and their drainage basins, hydrophysical approach to quantitative morphology: Geol. Soc. America Bull., v. 56, no. 3, p. 275–370.

James, L. D., 1965, Using a computer to estimate the effects of urban development on flood peaks: Water Resources Research, v. 1, no. 2, p. 223–234.

Keller, F. J., 1962, The effect of urban growth on sediment discharge, Northwest Branch Anacostia River basin, Maryland *in* Short papers in geology and hydrology: U.S. Geol. Survey Prof. Paper 450-C, p. C129–C131.

Leopold, L. B., and Maddock, T., Jr., 1954, The flood control controversy: New York, The Ronald Press Company, 275 p.

Leopold, L. B., Wolman, M. G., and Miller, J. P., 1964, Fluvial processes in geomorphology: San Francisco, Calif., W. H. Freeman and Co., 522 p.

Lull, H. W., and Sopper, W. E., 1966, Hydrologic effects from urbanization of forested watersheds in the northeast: Upper Darby, Pa., Northeastern Forest Expt. Sta., 24 p.

McGauhey, P. H., and Krone, R. B., 1954, Report on the investigation of travel of pollution: California State Water Pollution Control Board Pub. 11, 218 p.

Mallmann, W. L., and Mack, W. N., 1961, Biological contamination of ground water: Robert A. Taft Sanitary Eng. Center Tech. Rept. W61-5, p. 35–43.

Martens, L. A., 1966, Flood inundation and effects of urbanization in metropolitan Charlotte [North Carolina]: U.S. Geol. Survey open-file rept., 54 p.

Musgrave, G. W., 1947, Quantitative evaluation of factors in water erosion—First approximation: Jour. Soil and Water Conserv., v. 2, no. 3, p. 133–138.

Olson, G. W., 1964, Application of soil survey to problems of health, sanitation, and engineering: Cornell Univ. Agr. Expt. Sta. Mem. 387, 77 p.

Pluhowski, E. J., 1968, Urbanization and its effect on stream temperature: Baltimore, Md., Johns Hopkins Univ., Ph. D. dissert. (in preparation).

Snyder, F. F., 1938, Synthetic unit hydrographs: Am. Geophys. Union Trans., v. 19, p. 447–454.

Swenson, H. A., 1964, Sediment in streams: Jour. Soil and Water Conserv., v. 19, no. 6, p. 223–226.

Wark, J. W., and Keller, F. J., 1963, Preliminary study of sediment sources and transport in the Potomac River Basin: Interstate Comm. on Potomac River Basin, Washington, D.C., Tech. Bull. 1963-11, 28 p.

Wayman, C., Page, H. L., and Robertson, J. B., 1965, Behavior of surfactants and other detergent components in water and soil-water environments: Federal Housing Adm. Tech. Studies Pub. 532, 136 p.

Wiitala, S. W., 1961, Some aspects of the effect of urban and suburban development upon runoff: U.S. Geol. Survey open-file rept., 28 p.

Wilson, K. V., 1966, Flood frequency of streams in Jackson, Mississippi: U.S. Geol. Survey open-file rept., 6 p.

Wolman, M. G., 1964, Problems posed by sediment derived from construction activities in Maryland—Report to the Maryland Water Pollution Control Commission: Annapolis, Md., 125 p.

Wolman, M. G., and Schick, P. A., 1967, Effects of construction on fluvial sediment, urban and suburban areas of Maryland: Water Resources Research, v. 3, no. 2, p. 451–462.

U. S. GOVERNMENT PRINTING OFFICE : 1972 O - 468-019

5

Reprinted from *Geograph. Rev.*, **49**(3), 369–386 (1959)

THE GEOGRAPHY OF NEW YORK CITY'S WATER SUPPLY: A STUDY OF INTERACTIONS

ANASTASIA VAN BURKALOW

A CITY must often look outside its own boundaries for its water. Smaller communities can usually obtain an adequate water supply from local ground or surface waters, and even a large city can meet its water needs from local sources if it is near a large river (London, Philadelphia, Washington, Pittsburgh, and St. Louis) or lake (Chicago and Buffalo). New York City, however, has no nearby lake and no usable river; for the Hudson River, being an estuary, is brackish.[1] And early in the nineteenth century the city began to outgrow its local ground and surface water supplies. It has therefore had to go gradually farther and farther afield, eventually as much as 125 miles, to tap the surface waters of other watersheds.

New York first did this as early as 1842, when the Croton water system went into operation. This ended the use of local wells and ponds for public supply in Manhattan (New York City did not then include the other boroughs), though some Manhattan industries still use water from their own private wells. Other parts of the present city continued to depend on local sources for a longer time: the Bronx until it was annexed to the city in 1874 (west Bronx) and 1895 (east Bronx); Richmond until it received Catskill water in 1917; parts of Brooklyn until 1947, when pumping for public supply was stopped because of depletion of the ground water; and parts of Queens even today.[2] However, the inadequacy of the local sources

[1] Farther up the Hudson a layer of fresh water, brought in by tributary streams, floats on top of the brackish water, and from that fresh surface layer some Hudson Valley communities (Poughkeepsie, Rensselaer, and Waterford, for example) take their public water supplies. Treatment is necessary, of course, to counteract the fairly heavy pollution. In the early 1950's, when the most recent expansion of New York City's water supply was being planned, some citizens' groups favored a Hudson River source instead of the Cannonsville Reservoir. However, the nearest the city has come to using Hudson River water was to build a temporary pumping plant near Chelsea, 10 miles south of Poughkeepsie. This plant, capable of pumping 100 million gallons per day (mgd) of river water into the city system, was authorized by the state Water Power and Control Commission for emergency use only, in case of shortage before completion of the first two stages of the Delaware system, and was not to be used after 1957. It was never needed and has now been demolished.

[2] Wells of the Jamaica Water Supply Company and the New York Water Service Corporation provide the public supply for parts of Queens, furnishing an average of nearly 50 mgd in recent years, which is about 3½ per cent of the average daily consumption of the entire city. Little additional ground water is now used in the city for public supply. City-owned wells in Brooklyn have long been out of use, and those in Queens and Nassau Counties, with a dependable yield of 70 mgd, and in Rich-

➤ DR. VAN BURKALOW is associate professor in the Department of Geology and Geography at Hunter College, New York City.

was felt in Brooklyn and Queens as early as the 1890's, and it is said that need for additional sources of water helped influence Brooklyn, at least, to become part of Greater New York in 1898.[3] One of the first concerns of the Greater City was to add to its water supply, which by then consisted of an enlarged Croton system and the Bronx-Byram watershed.[4] Construction of the Catskill system, authorized in 1905, was begun in 1907, and in late 1915 Catskill water first reached the city. By the time this system was completed in 1927, plans were already being discussed for the Delaware system. Construction was finally begun in 1937 (court action and the depression had delayed it) but was interrupted by World War II. Finally, in 1951, the Rondout Reservoir was completed.[5] It was followed by the Neversink in 1952 and the Pepacton (East Delaware watershed) in 1955. The final stage, the Cannonsville Reservoir (West Delaware watershed), now under construction, is slated for completion in 1962.

Thus New York City now depends on seven distant watersheds, Croton, Bronx River, Esopus, Schoharie, Rondout, Neversink, and East Delaware, and is developing an eighth, the West Delaware. Their dependable yields are given in Table I, and their locations are shown on the map, Figure 1. Within their combined area of 1969 square miles, half again as large as Rhode Island, water is taken from more than a thousand streams, big and little. It is stored in 27 reservoirs and controlled natural lakes and is brought to the city through more than 350 miles of aqueducts and tunnels (Fig. 1).

---

mond County, with a dependable yield of 5 mgd, have been kept as stand-bys in recent years. They were used extensively only in the dry period of 1949–1950 (see N. M. Perlmutter and Theodore Arnow: Ground Water in Bronx, New York, and Richmond Counties, With Summary Data on Kings and Queens Counties, New York City, New York, *New York State Dept. of Conservation, Water Power and Control Commission, Bull. GW-32,* Albany, 1953) and in 1957–1958 while the Delaware Aqueduct was closed for cleaning. Now that Delaware water is available, the Long Island well water is not considered necessary, and the city plans to sell its Long Island wells (see the *New York Times,* Feb. 2, 1958).

[3] Russell Suter: Engineering Report on the Water Supplies of Long Island, *New York State Dept. of Conservation, Water Power and Control Commission, Bull. GW-2,* 1937, p. 35.

[4] This consisted of the Bronx River watershed above Kensico Dam, from which water still enters the city's water-supply system, and the adjacent Byram River watershed. From its Byram Lake and Wampus Pond a dependable yield of 5 mgd could be led into the Bronx River by a tunnel and open channel. However, since April 12, 1955, none of this water has been allowed to enter the New York City system. In 1958 Byram Lake was bought by a resident of Mt. Kisco and presented to that village, which had for many years met about half of its public water-supply needs by buying that very water from New York City.

The Bronx-Byram watershed, too small to be shown clearly on Figure 1, lies close to the southeastern edge of the Croton watershed, near the New York–Connecticut boundary.

[5] Water from the Rondout Reservoir, on Rondout Creek, reaches the city via the Delaware Aqueduct, but Rondout Creek is a tributary of the Hudson River, not of the Delaware. Strictly speaking, therefore, it is not part of the Delaware system, and it was not subject to the limitations set up in 1931 by the United States Supreme Court.

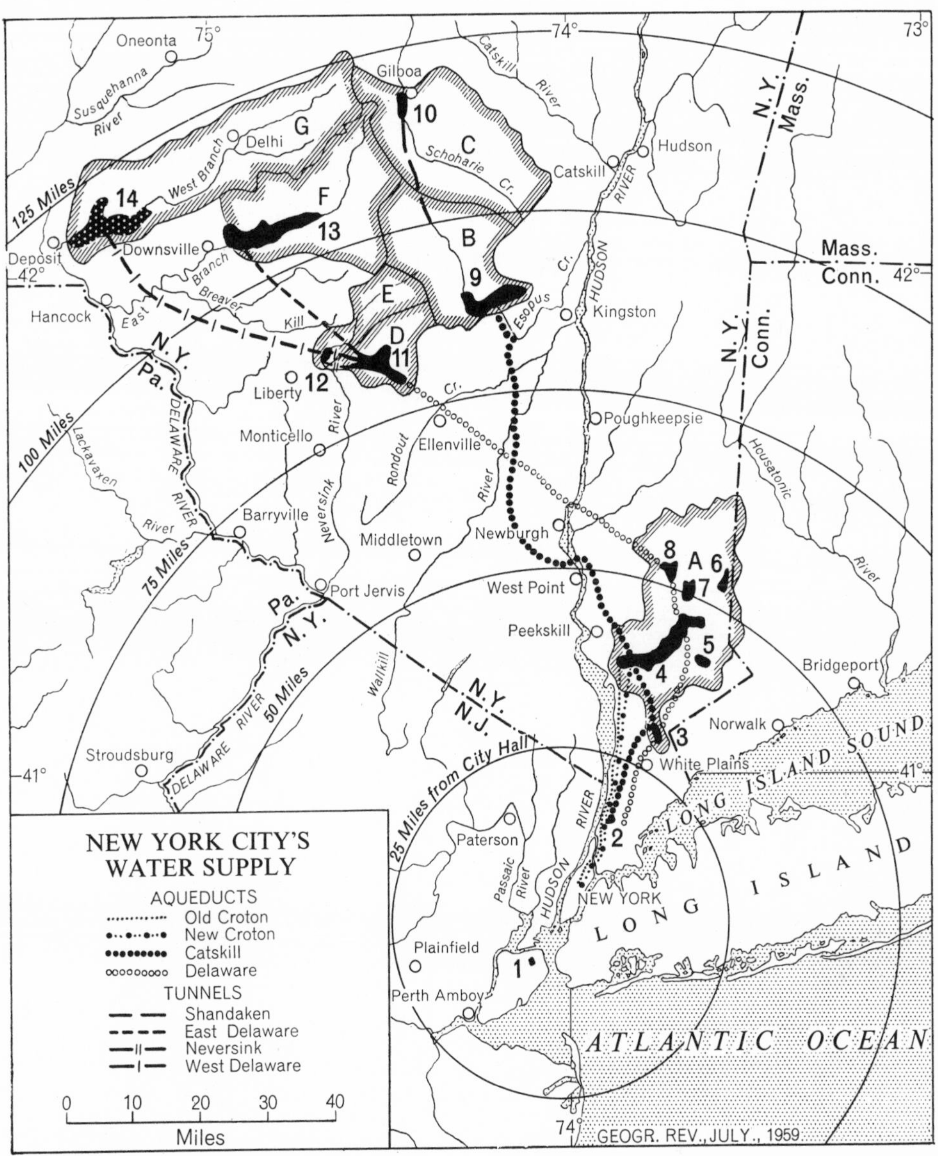

FIG. 1—The sources of New York City's water supply. Watersheds are shown by heavy boundary; key: A, Croton; B, Esopus; C, Schoharie; D, Rondout; E, Neversink; F, East Delaware; G, West Delaware. Reservoirs are shown in black; key: 1, Silver Lake; 2, Hill View; 3, Kensico; 4, Croton; 5, Cross River; 6, East Branch; 7, Middle Branch; 8, West Branch; 9, Ashokan; 10, Schoharie; 11, Rondout; 12, Neversink; 13. Pepacton; 14, Cannonsville (under construction). Adapted from map in "The Water Supply of the City of New York" (see text footnote 13 below), pp. 40–41.

TABLE I—NEW YORK CITY'S WATERSHEDS

WATERSHED	AREA (*sq. mi.*)	DEPENDABLE YIELD (*mill. gal. daily*)	WATERSHED	AREA (*sq. mi.*)	DEPENDABLE YIELD (*mill. gal. daily*)
Croton	375	325	Neversink	93	115[b]
Bronx River	13	5	East Delaware	372	375[b]
Esopus	257	345	West Delaware[a]	450	310[b]
Schoharie	314	220			
Rondout	95	120[b]	TOTAL	1,969	1,815[c]

[a] Under construction.

[b] Additional water must be held to replenish the stream in dry weather (see text, p. 385).

[c] To this must be added the 5 mgd dependable yield that can be drawn from wells in the Borough of Richmond if necessary, which will make a total dependable yield of 1820 mgd available in 1962.

Source: "Brief Descriptive Outline of New York City's Water Supply Works" (Board of Water Supply, City of New York, June, 1958).

TABLE II—WATERSHED PRECIPITATION
(*In inches*)

WATERSHED	AVERAGE	MINIMUM	YEAR	MAXIMUM	YEAR
Long Island	43.22[a]	29.90	1931	56.50	1889
Croton	47.68[b]	32.29	1935	63.76	1901
Esopus	49.32[c]	33.70	1957	73.08	1928
Schoharie	42.68[d]	30.68	1911	60.35	1928
Rondout	49.03[c]	33.65	1941	73.54	1928
Neversink	51.55[e]	37.36	1941	71.24	1938
East Delaware	43.79[e]	33.38	1957	54.43	1938
West Delaware	41.74[e]	33.22	1957	51.53	1938

Averages are for (*a*) 78 years; (*b*) 89 years; (*c*) 51 years; (*d*) 50 years; (*e*) 20 years. All periods end with 1957.

Sources: *52nd Ann. Rept. New York City Board of Water Supply, 1957; Ann. Rept. New York City Dept. of Water Supply, Gas and Electricity, 1951* (for Croton's maximum and minimum).

Several aspects of the physical and cultural geography of the source areas have affected the amount and quality of the water available to New York City and the construction problems encountered in building the dams and aqueducts. And the development of this extensive water-supply system has left its imprint on the physical and cultural geography of the source areas and also of still more distant areas in the lower Delaware Valley. It is with these interrelationships that the present paper is concerned.

HOW THE GEOGRAPHY OF THE WATERSHED AREAS AFFECTS THE CITY'S WATER SUPPLY

FACTORS THAT INFLUENCE THE AMOUNT OF WATER AVAILABLE

Precipitation. In the watersheds the average precipitation is well over 40 inches a year, but the amount received in individual years may vary a good deal from the average (Table II).

It is the amount of water available in the driest year on record that is the dependable yield of a watershed, the minimum with which a city might have to get along and below which consumption should be kept. Unfortunately, in many cities of the United States consumption equals or exceeds dependable yield, and no reserve is left for emergencies or for future growth of the city.[6] As a result there are water shortages from time to time, when the use of water must be curtailed. This is what happened in New York in 1949. Consumption was about 25 per cent greater than dependable yield of the then existing facilities,[7] and a severe drought in the summer and fall caused a serious water shortage. Disaster was prevented only by an intensive water-saving campaign, which in about three months reduced the consumption by nearly 25 per cent.[8] Completion of the Rondout, Neversink, and Pepacton Reservoirs has increased the dependable yield (now 1510 million gallons per day, counting ground-water resources on Staten Island but not on Long Island) comfortably beyond current consumption (1153 mgd in 1958),[9] and completion of the Cannonsville Reservoir will give a total dependable yield of 1820 mgd, which it is thought will be adequate until about the end of the century.[10]

In the rainiest periods the reservoirs cannot hold all the available water, and large amounts spill over the dams and are lost. Carrying capacity of the aqueducts also limits the amount of water that can reach the city. Thus nature determines the minimum amount of water available to the city, but man has determined the maximum, because the reservoirs and aqueducts he has built will not accommodate nature's maximum.

Interstate Character of the Delaware River Drainage Basin. In the Delaware system man has placed still another limit on the maximum supply available to the city, this time by court decree. The Delaware River serves as boundary first between Pennsylvania and New York and then, for many miles, between Pennsylvania and New Jersey, and its broad estuary lies between Delaware and New Jersey. Its headwaters, however, from which New York City takes water, are in New York State, and when the Delaware plan was first announced in 1928, the approval of the Water Power and Control Commission of New York State was granted. Residents of New Jersey, Pennsylvania, and Delaware were at once concerned lest they be deprived of water

[6] In 1955 this was true of 42 per cent of the country's major public water-supply systems, according to a survey made by the Water and Sewerage Industry and Utilities Division of the Business and Defense Services Administration of the United States Department of Commerce (see the *New York Times,* Apr. 7, 1955).

[7] *45th Ann. Rept. New York City Board of Water Supply, 1950.*

[8] *Ann. Rept. New York City Dept. of Water Supply, Gas and Electricity, 1950,* p. 108.

[9] Letter from Department of Water Supply, Gas and Electricity, City of New York, Jan. 22, 1959.

[10] K. R. Kennison: The Development of the Delaware Projects, *Municipal Engineers Journ.,* Vol. 40, 1954, 4th quarterly issue, pp. 131–168; reference on p. 152.

for their needs. Accordingly, in 1929 New Jersey went to the United States Supreme Court to enjoin New York City from taking any water from the Delaware River or its tributaries. Pennsylvania acted as intervener. The Court decision in May, 1931, permitted the city to take 440 mgd, enough only for the first two stages of the Delaware plan (Neversink and Pepacton Reservoirs), instead of the 600 mgd originally proposed. Efforts were made to provide for the third stage, the Cannonsville Reservoir, as part of an interstate development of the river, proposed by the Interstate Commission on the Delaware River Basin (Incodel) for power development and control of floods and pollution as well as for water supply. New York, New Jersey, and Delaware accepted the plan, but in 1952 Pennsylvania rejected it. Thereupon New York City reopened the original case before the Supreme Court and asked for an additional 50 mgd from the Neversink and Pepacton Reservoirs and 310 mgd from the proposed Cannonsville Reservoir. This request was granted by a decision in 1954. In both Court decisions the city was directed to release water from its reservoirs in dry periods, to maintain a certain minimum flow in the main valley.[11]

Factors That Influence the Quality of the Water

Geology. In the Westchester watersheds there are long, narrow outcrops of metamorphosed limestone, a soluble rock, but most of the area is underlain by relatively insoluble schist and gneiss. In the Catskill and Delaware watersheds most of the rocks are dark sandstones and shales, also insoluble.[12] As a result the water is soft, with only 17 parts per million of dissolved matter in the Catskill and Delaware water and 40–50 ppm in the Croton water.[13] Both home and industrial users are thus relieved of the expense and difficulties caused by hard water.

Because of the composition of the rocks in the watersheds, New York City's water contains little or no dissolved fluorides.[14] It has been widely recognized by dental and medical authorities that about 1 ppm of fluorides in the drinking water makes teeth more resistant to decay (but only if such water is drunk in early childhood while the permanent teeth are forming).

[11] For a good summary of the Court decisions and the Incodel effort here described, see Kennison, *op. cit.*

[12] C. P. Berkey: Engineering Geology of the City of New York, *in* New York City and Vicinity, *Internatl. Geol. Congr., 16th Sess., United States, 1933, Guidebook 9,* Washington, 1933, pp. 77–123. Plate 9 is a simplified geological map of the Westchester and Catskill watersheds.

[13] "The Water Supply of the City of New York [Origin and Achievements of the Board of Water Supply, City of New York]," 1950, p. 92.

[14] Anastasia Van Burkalow: Fluorine in United States Water Supplies: Pilot Project for the Atlas of Diseases, *Geogr. Rev.,* Vol. 36, 1946, pp. 177–193; see especially Plate I.

Lack of natural fluorides can easily be offset by addition of the desired amount, as has been done in many community water supplies. Whether or not New York City's water will be so treated has yet to be decided. Some groups strongly oppose this so-called "mass medication."

In the Catskill and Delaware watersheds especially, the banks of the streams and reservoirs consist in some places of easily eroded glacial clays. During heavy rains these are washed into the water and temporarily increase its turbidity.[15]

Vegetation. In the Catskill and Delaware watersheds large areas have been set aside as state parks and forest preserves, within which most of the surface is covered with trees. Because the forests retard soil erosion, and therefore siltation in the reservoirs, the useful lifetime of the reservoirs is prolonged, and there is little need to treat the water for turbidity. In Westchester a smaller part of the watershed is forested, but here, as in the Catskills, the land close to the reservoirs has usually been planted with evergreens (Fig. 3). These are used instead of deciduous trees because the thin, broad leaves of the latter would tend to blow into the water, where they would clog outlets, discolor the water as they decayed, and so on. For these tree belts a program of planting, pruning, thinning, and insect control is carried on by the Department of Water Supply, Gas and Electricity as part of the maintenance of the water-supply system.[16]

Population Density. In 1950 the population densities per square mile in the various watersheds were as follows:[17] Bronx-Byram, 184; Croton, 128; Esopus, 17; Schoharie, 26; Rondout, 17; Neversink, 19; East Delaware, 18; West Delaware, 30. Except in the Westchester area (Bronx-Byram and Croton) these densities are very low, and there is relatively little danger of pollution of the water. Where this danger exists, the city builds and operates sewage-disposal plants.

Size of the System. The large size of New York City's reservoirs, due both to nature's potentialities and to man's decisions, makes it possible for water to remain in them for a long time—in the Catskill reservoirs for as much as six months, in Kensico (the Westchester storage reservoir for the Catskill and Delaware systems) for about three weeks. This permits natural purification of the water before it finally enters the aqueducts on its way to the

---

[15] See Berkey, *op. cit.* [see footnote 12 above], p. 93.

[16] Two city agencies are responsible for the water supply: the Board of Water Supply, which develops new sources of water and builds the necessary dams and aqueducts; and the Department of Water Supply, Gas and Electricity, which maintains and operates the system built by the Board and builds, maintains, and operates the distribution system within the city.

[17] "Future Water Sources of the City of New York: Report of Engineering Panel on Water Supply to Mayor's Committee on Management Survey of the City of New York, July, 1951," p. 28.

FIG. 2—Site of the Cannonsville Dam and Reservoir (now under construction) along the West Branch of the Delaware River. Gross reservoir capacity will be about 97.4 billion gallons. The elevation is 1150 feet. (Photograph courtesy Board of Water Supply of the City of New York.)

Fig. 3—Kensico Reservoir and Dam in Westchester County, 30 miles north of New York City. The reservoir is capable of storing 30.6 billion gallons, fed to it by the Catskill and Delaware watersheds and part of the Croton watershed. (Photograph courtesy Board of Water Supply of the City of New York.)

consumers. In 1954, for example, it was found that the period of storage in Ashokan Reservoir reduced turbidity 62 per cent and bacterial count 71 per cent.[18]

Factors That Influenced the Construction of the Dams and Aqueducts

Geology. The nature and general condition of the surface materials and bedrock in which dams and aqueducts are to be built determine the kind of structure required and the cost. Geological information, gained by surface exploration and test drilling, is therefore necessary during both planning and construction. With foreknowledge of the difficulties that will be met it is often possible to plan the route of an aqueduct or the location of a dam so as to avoid some of them. Where they cannot be avoided, construction can be planned to deal with them.

Because geological advice proved helpful in the construction of the New Croton Dam, completed in 1905, the city has employed geologists on the Catskill and Delaware systems from the earliest planning stages. Their careful exploratory studies have discovered, for example, places where ground water, seeping into the tunnels in large amounts, would complicate construction; caverns in limestone that might weaken tunnel walls; masses of deeply weathered rock, along faults or in places that had been protected from glacial erosion, that would require extra strengthening of tunnels; resistant rock formations that a tunnel should avoid; thick covers of glacial moraine filling deep preglacial or glacially eroded valleys that would require tunnels to be unusually deep to pass beneath them.[19]

Elevation of the Watershed Areas.[20] The Catskill water drops from 590 feet above sea level in the Ashokan Reservoir to 295 feet at the Hill View Reservoir (the distributing reservoir for both Catskill and Delaware water),

---

[18] *Ann. Rept. New York City Dept. of Water Supply, Gas and Electricity, 1954,* pp. 71–72. See also F. E. Hale: Sanitation and Purification of New York City's Water Supplies, *Journ. New England Water Works Assn.,* Vol. 55, 1941, pp. 62–82. In spite of the naturally high quality of the water, some treatment is necessary: chlorination at least twice (but only four pounds of chlorine are needed per million gallons, as compared with 400 pounds per million gallons needed in many Midwestern cities); aeration to eliminate gases that cause unpleasant odor or taste; occasional addition of alum to precipitate sediments washed in by heavy rains. At three laboratories and in the field daily bacterial tests are made, totaling more than 30,000 a year.

[19] For detailed discussions of geological problems of this sort see Berkey, *op. cit.* [see footnote 12 above]; C. P. Berkey and T. W. Fluhr: Engineering Geology of the New York City Aqueducts, *in* Guidebook of Excursions, 61st Annual Meeting, Geological Society of America, 1948 (edited by Agnes Creagh; New York, 1948).

[20] Data in this section were taken from "The Water Supply . . . of New York" [see footnote 13 above], and Tobias Hochlerner: New York City's Water Supply to Outside Communities, *Journ. Amer. Water Works Assn.,* Vol. 37, 1945, pp. 754–764.

92 miles away, near the city line in Yonkers. Thus in the Catskill Aqueduct the water can move downhill under the influence of gravity. But since the drop is fairly slight, it was necessary to build about 80 per cent of the aqueduct with just enough slope to make the water flow. Where the surface is about at the level necessary for gravity flow, the aqueduct is a cut-and-cover structure—a channel cut into the surface and covered over with a mound of earth. In higher areas the gravity-flow level is maintained through tunnels. Where valleys cut below this level, the aqueduct goes under them in pressure tunnels.

Flow in the Delaware Aqueduct is by gravity also, and the drop from the outlet of the Rondout Reservoir, flow line 840 feet above sea level, to Hill View is even greater than that from Ashokan. However, this aqueduct is a deep pressure tunnel throughout its length, for reasons discussed below.

Incidentally, the elevation of the distributing reservoirs determines how and where the water will be delivered within the city. Catskill and Delaware water, distributed from the Hill View Reservoir, can flow by gravity to all parts of the city except the highest, where pumping is needed. In contrast, Croton water, distributed from the Jerome Park Reservoir, elevation about 133 feet, can reach by gravity flow only the parts of the city less than 40 feet in elevation. But since these consume only about one-third of the total Croton supply, the rest must be pumped to higher areas.[21] Long Island well water must always be pumped, of course.

Cultural and Physical Geography along the Delaware Aqueduct Route. The Delaware Aqueduct could have been constructed like the Catskill—a combination of cut-and-cover sections and tunnels (gravity and pressure). However, because of various conditions along the route it was built as a deep pressure tunnel throughout.[22] By the time it was built, in the late 1930's, villages, houses, roads, and other structures were much more numerous than they had been in the early years of the century, and property values had greatly increased. Building deep below the surface avoided conflict with these surface developments and eliminated the necessity of paying high taxes for surface rights of way. Only underground easements were needed. West of the Hudson the aqueduct crosses a number of deep valleys, under which pressure tunnels would have been required anyway, and a number of high ridges, under which deep tunnels were necessary (the deepest of these

[21] The Delaware Aqueduct, connected with the West Branch Reservoir of the Croton system, can now carry about 100 mgd from the higher Croton reservoirs to Hill View, which reduces the cost of pumping Croton water from the Jerome Park Reservoir.

[22] See "The Water Supply . . . of New York" [see footnote 13 above]; Lawrence Ravitz: Delaware Watershed Connected with City through 85-Mile Underground Aqueduct, *Bull. General Contractors Assn.*, March, 1948, pp. 15–18; and "More Water for New York City," *ibid.*, March, 1937, pp. 46–55.

Fig. 4—Schoharie Reservoir and Gilboa Dam. The capacity of the reservoir is 19.6 billion gallons. The elevation is 1130 feet. (Photograph courtesy Board of Water Supply of the City of New York.)

is 2500 feet below the ridge crest). A deep pressure tunnel for the entire length was therefore simpler to build, and it will have lower maintenance costs and greater safety from damage. Choice of the exact route was often guided by surface conditions. For building the access shafts (there are 31 of these) room was needed on the surface, and both for this reason and to keep down the cost of the sites the more heavily built-up areas were avoided whenever possible.

EFFECT OF THE CITY'S WATER-SUPPLY SYSTEM ON THE SOURCE AREAS

Changes in Physical Conditions

The Upland Watersheds. Most obvious among the physical changes in the upland watersheds are the reservoirs—twelve in the Croton watershed, two in the Catskill system, and four in the Delaware. These, with their borders of pine trees (another change introduced by the water system), add greatly to the scenic beauty of the areas and to their recreational facilities. By state law the city must allow boating, fishing, and ice cutting on the reservoirs, subject to reasonable regulations.[23] Ice cutting is no longer carried on, of course. But permits for boating and for fishing, from shore or boat, are available free of charge from the Department of Water Supply, Gas and Electricity.

More localized is the change in Esopus Creek, which now carries, in addition to its own water, the water from the Schoharie Reservoir (Fig. 4), diverted southward under the mountain divide by means of the Shandaken Tunnel. Because of the resulting great increase in the volume and depth of Esopus Creek, some adjacent areas have been flooded.[24]

In the spring and summer of 1950 New York City tried to change conditions in the Catskill and Croton watersheds in still another way—artificial rain making.[25] As one of its efforts to ease the critical water shortage of 1949–1950 the city employed Dr. Wallace E. Howell, a meteorologist, to seed the clouds over the watersheds with silver iodide. In 31 weeks Dr. Howell carried out 36 seeding operations. During that period the rainfall in some months was greater than average, and in the watersheds it was 14 per cent greater than in surrounding areas that had not been seeded. Whether

[23] T. De L. Coffin: Sanitation of the Croton Watershed, *Water Works Engineering*, Vol. 95, 1942, pp. 1440–1442 and 1462.

[24] "The Water Supply . . . of New York" [see footnote 13 above], p. 15.

[25] *New York Times*, Apr. 25, 1954; H. T. Orville: Weather Made to Order? *Collier's*, May 28, 1954, pp. 25–29.

the increased rainfall was caused by the seeding can never be proved, of course, since natural variations in rainfall from year to year are marked.

The Long Island Water Table. When ground water is withdrawn more rapidly than it accumulates, the water table is lowered. Many parts of the country have been damaged in this way, some of them seriously; a notable example is western Long Island.[26] During the early decades of this century the water table here dropped rapidly because of the combined effects of (1) decreased replenishment as buildings and pavements covered more and more of the surface and (2) increased use. Water was withdrawn both for public use, from wells owned by the city and by several private water companies, and for industrial use, from wells owned by the industries themselves. How great the overwithdrawal was becoming was not realized until 1933, when a detailed survey of the island's ground-water resources revealed that the water table was below sea level, more than 15 feet below in some places, in an area of more than 40 square miles, including nearly all of Brooklyn and adjacent parts of Queens. Sea water was infiltrating into the wells and moving farther and farther inland each year.

It was because of this situation that in 1933 the New York State Legislature passed a law requiring that new Long Island wells yielding more than 100,000 gallons a day and not to be used for agriculture must be approved by the state Water Power and Control Commission. When such new wells are to supply water for industrial cooling and air conditioning, the water must be returned after use to the aquifer from which it was taken. This can be done by pumping the water back through a recharge well (the method commonly used in crowded Brooklyn and Queens because it requires little surface area) or by allowing it to accumulate in a recharge basin and soak back into the ground (the method often used in the more open areas of Nassau and Suffolk Counties). The returned water has been found to be 2°–20° F. warmer than when it was first pumped from the ground and is therefore less effective for subsequent cooling; however, only where there are numerous recharge wells close together is the effect marked. Nassau County has also provided eleven recharge basins for the accumulation and seepage of storm runoff discharged into the sewers.

In spite of these conservation measures, the water table continued to drop for several years and in the late 1930's reached levels as much as 35

[26] See, for example, M. L. Brashears, Jr.: Artificial Recharge of Ground Water on Long Island, New York, *Econ. Geol.,* Vol. 41, 1946, pp. 503–516; A. H. Johnson and W. G. Waterman: Withdrawal of Ground Water on Long Island, New York, *New York State Dept. of Conservation, Water Power and Control Commission, Bull. GW-28,* 1952; N. J. Lusczynski and A. H. Johnson: The Water Table in Long Island, New York, in January 1951, *ibid., GW-27,* 1951; N. J. Lusczynski: The Recovery of Ground-Water Levels in Brooklyn, New York, from 1947 to 1950, *U. S. Geol. Survey Circular 167,* 1952.

feet below sea level. Recovery did not begin until about 1941 and was slow at first. An element of gradual change was the decrease in the number of plants manufacturing ice. As their business was curtailed by the increasing use of electric refrigerators in homes, their pumping of ground water decreased, from 18 mgd in 1936 to 4 mgd in 1947. A more abrupt change came in 1947. In that year net withdrawal of ground water in Brooklyn was reduced by more than half, because the city required the New York Water Service Corporation to stop pumping from its Flatbush wells, source of the infamous "Flatbush" water. Against this unsatisfactory public supply—brackish, corrosive, and hard—there had been public outcry for years, and the change in 1947 to Catskill water brought rejoicing. It also initiated a more rapid recovery of the water table, which by the early 1950's had been raised above sea level in the entire south half of Brooklyn. In the northwest, where there are large industrial wells that predate the conservation measures of 1933, heavy industrial use keeps the water table well below sea level. And in western Queens it stays slightly below sea level because of pumping for public supply by the Jamaica Water Supply Company and the New York Water Service Corporation.

Effects on People and Communities

Displacement of People and Their Works. To strangers driving past, the city's reservoirs may look like natural lakes. Old-timers, however, cannot forget that they are man's work, in a sense a new cultural landscape blotting out the old one they remember so well. Inundated under many feet of water are hundreds of farms, among them prosperous dairy farms in the valleys tributary to the Delaware; resort hotels and camps that drew numerous summer visitors to the mountain valleys of the Catskill and Delaware watersheds; more than 20 villages, with their homes, churches, schools, and businesses; and more than 60 cemeteries. From these last some 10,000 bodies were removed for burial elsewhere. And from the farms and villages some 6000 permanent residents have been displaced.[27]

By state law the city is allowed to acquire the property it needs through condemnation proceedings, but it is also required to pay generously. As a matter of course it must pay the value of the property, buildings, and equipment taken—and this requires a separate negotiation for each piece of property, 557 of them in the Pepacton Valley alone, for example. But in

[27] Exact figures for the areas covered by the Ashokan, Schoharie, Rondout, Neversink, and Pepacton Reservoirs are given in "The Water Supply . . . of New York" [see footnote 13 above], pp. 35 and 76. Some figures for the area that will be covered by the Cannonsville Reservoir are given in the *New York Times,* July 28, 1957.

addition the city must pay claims for business losses, loss of wages, and so on, both to those whose property has been taken and to people in nearby areas. In the Pepacton Valley there were 475 such claims.[28]

Benefits to Local Communities. To residents in the watershed areas the city water system brings several benefits: an easily available water supply if they wish to tap it; a real-estate tax income that may be sizable; and in many localities sewage-disposal plants at no cost.

By state law the city must allow communities and water districts in Delaware, Greene, Orange, Putnam, Schoharie, Sullivan, Ulster, and Westchester Counties to take water from city aqueducts or reservoirs, subject to reasonable regulation. The users must pay a reasonable rate for the water and all costs of their connections with the city system.[29] Use has been made of this privilege chiefly in Westchester, where 58 per cent of the water supplied by communities in 1957 came from the city system.[30] To these communities, and to a handful west of the Hudson, the city furnishes an average of nearly 50 mgd, for which it is paid more than $1.5 million yearly.[31]

Land owned by the city for water-supply use totals 73,000 acres, with an assessed value of about $75 million. The 1957 state, county, town, village, and school-district taxes on this land amounted to about $5.5 million.[32] In some localities the city's payments make up a large part of the total real-estate tax income—90 per cent, for example, in the little village of Olive in Ulster County, and 25 per cent even in the prosperous township of North Castle in Westchester County.[33]

By state law New York City can, with the approval of the state Health Department, set up sanitary regulations in its watershed areas.[34] This permits the city (at its own expense, of course) to improve sewage-disposal facilities on private property and, in villages with public water supplies, to build sewage-disposal plants, which it must maintain and operate forever. Such plants have been built in a number of places in all the city's watersheds, and one was built outside the watersheds at Port Jervis, N. Y., on the Delaware River, as directed by the United States Supreme Court in its decree of 1931.[35]

---

[28] "The Water Supply . . . of New York" [see footnote 13 above], pp. 4–5.

[29] Hochlerner, *op. cit.* [see footnote 20 above], p. 755.

[30] *New York Times,* Mar. 9, 1958.

[31] *51st Ann. Rept. New York City Board of Water Supply, 1957.*

[32] See the *New York Times,* July 7, 1956, and February 2, 1958, and annual reports of the Department of Water Supply, Gas and Electricity.

[33] *New York Times,* July 5, 1956.

[34] Thaddeus Merriman: Sanitation on the Catskill Watersheds: Riparian Ownership Creates Interesting Problems, *Amer. City Mag.,* Vol. 31, 1924, pp. 119–120.

[35] See Kennison, *op. cit.* [see footnote 10 above].

EFFECT OF THE CITY'S WATER-SUPPLY SYSTEM ON MORE DISTANT AREAS

Control of Volume in the Delaware and Its Tributaries

Water diverted from the Delaware headwaters for use in New York City is permanently removed from the Delaware drainage system. And yet because of the diversion the headwaters below the dams and the main valley downstream from them have more water available for use, not less, as many residents of the valley feared would be the case.[36] Without the dams the volume of these streams varied greatly, from flood stage, when there was more water than could be used, to a mere trickle in the dry summer months. The dams help to reduce the volume of floods, with their destruction and waste of water, as was demonstrated in 1955 when Hurricane Diane brought heavy rains to the region. And the dry-season volume is increased by releases of stored water from the reservoirs. For the main valley these were ordered by the United States Supreme Court in its decisions of 1931 and 1954, in amounts great enough to maintain a specified minimum flow (according to the 1954 decision, 1525 cubic feet per second at the United States Geological Survey gauging station at Montague, N. J.). This is chiefly to provide adequate water for community water supplies, navigation, sewage disposal, and pollution control; however, camps and resorts in the upper valley and the shad-fishing industry downstream should also benefit. In the very dry summer of 1957 these releases made up about two-thirds of the average flow of the river. Within New York State the minimum volume of the streams below the dams is controlled in the same way (Rondout Creek, a tributary of the Hudson, is included), in accordance with regulations of the Conservation Department of New York State and the state Water Power and Control Commission. These releases, made whether or not any are needed for the main valley, are solely for conservation of fish. As a result, the streams are kept full even in droughts. In the dry summer of 1957, for example, 1201 million gallons of water were released daily from the Pepacton Reservoir, and 345 million from the Neversink Reservoir, at a time when the natural flow in the streams would have been only 133 and 83 million gallons daily.

Control of Salinity in Delaware Bay

Salinity of the water in Delaware Bay, of great importance to the oyster

[36] Data in this section were taken from C. E. Heacox: Reservoirs vs. Drought, *New York State Conservationist,* Feb.–Mar., 1958, p. 7; "Report [to the Interstate Commission on the Delaware River Basin] on the Utilization of the Waters of the Delaware River Basin, Malcolm Pirnie Engineers, Albright and Friel, Inc., Consulting Engineers, August 1950."

industry, is affected by the volume of fresh water flowing in. The boundary line between fresh and brackish water surges upvalley at times of low stream flow and downvalley in floods. It is close to this boundary that the oysters flourish best; for there the salinity is too low for their chief enemies—oyster drills, starfish, and mussels. Some oystermen feared that New York City's withdrawal of Delaware River water would cause a permanent upvalley shift of the critical border zone, bringing saltier water to the oyster beds they were working. Instead, the decreased variation in stream volume will mean a decrease in the naturally great variation in salinity. This should benefit the oyster industry, which yields five million bushels a year here and is important to residents of both New Jersey and Delaware.[37]

The story of New York City's water supply is thus one of interactions: between various elements of the earth environment within the watershed areas; between man and the earth environment both locally and in more distant areas; between the city and individuals in the watershed areas; between the city and other political units or agencies (the United States Supreme Court, New York State and adjoining states, state agencies and departments, counties, townships, villages, school districts); and between man's resource needs and government regulations. On the one hand the amount and quality of the water available to the city have been affected by the physical and cultural geography of the watersheds and by the political organization of the main Delaware Valley. On the other hand the development of the city's water supply has affected the physical and cultural geography of the watersheds and of the Delaware Valley. In these more distant areas it has not influenced political organization, but the city's own political organization, resulting from the creation of the Greater City, may have been partly influenced by water needs and developments. And both locally (on Long Island) and in the Delaware Valley the utilization of water resources has resulted in government regulation, which in its turn has influenced the availability of water.

To understand the geography of New York City's water supply, we must know the locational facts of where the water comes from, where it is stored, and by what routes it reaches the city. And we must know descriptive facts about the source areas. But these facts, locational and descriptive, are only the raw materials of geography. From them must come an understanding of the interactions discussed above, a compound of physical, cultural, and political geography.

---

[38] "Report on . . . the Delaware River Basin," p. 56.

6

Reprinted from *Soviet Geography,* **2**(10), 57–63 (1961)

CHANGES IN THE GEOGRAPHY OF POPULATION CENTERS IN CONNECTION WITH CREATION OF THE TSIMLYANSK RESERVOIR

By M. N. Khromov

(From Izvestiya Vsesoyuznogo Geograficheskogo Obshchestva, 1961, No. 1, pp. 79-81)

(Abstract: The author discusses some of the problems involved in the resettlement of population from lands flooded by the filling of the Tsimlyansk Reservoir on the lower Don River in 1952 in connection with construction of the Volga-Don Canal.)

A substantial number of river development projects in the Soviet Union are situated in lowlands and plains. Under these conditions the creation of large dams and reservoirs usually results in the flooding of large areas and their removal from economic utilization.

The construction of large reservoirs always involves the transfer of a substantial number of population centers from the area of the future reservoir and the adaptation of the population to new areas of settlement. In the

Editor's Note: Throughout this article "rayon" means "region" or "regional." "Rayon seat," in the legend on the following page should read "regional center."

Changes in the geography of populated places of Rostov and Stalingrad Oblasts in connection with the filling of the Tsimlyansk Reservoir.

Legend:

Conventional Symbols

Cities, workers settlements and rayon seats.
Completely resettled populated places.
Partly resettled populated places.
Populated places untouched by resettlement.
Newly built populated places.
Populated places that received new settlers.
Oblast boundaries.

case of the Rybinsk Reservoir more than 600 places including the town of Mologa, were moved to new sites. In the case of the Kuybyshev Reservoir about 300 places were affected, including the entire town of Stavropol' and part of the town of Zelenodol'sk. In the area of the Bratsk Reservoir there were 238 populated places, including the old town of Bratsk and parts of the towns of Svirsk and Usol'ye-Sibirskoye. Such transfers result in the building of new population centers, usually merging the population of two or more of the old villages. Such new centers often differ sharply in their economic functions from the old populated places. Although the problems involved in changes of settlement and population geography as a result of the construction of large reservoirs are of considerable interest to economic geographers, they are seldom discussed in the literature. In the present paper the author intends to discuss some of the problems involved in the relocation of population from the area of the Tsimlyansk Reservoir.

The Tsimlyansk Reservoir is one of the largest Soviet reservoirs filled in recent years. Its area is 2,686 square kilometers; its length from the Tsimlyansk Dam to the town of Kalach is 183 km., and its width ranges from 3-5 to 38 km. Filling of the reservoir affected three rayons of Rostov Oblast (Tsimlyanskiy, Volgodonskiy and Dubovskiy) and six rayons of Stalingrad Oblast (Kalachevskiy, Oktyabr'skiy, Kotel'nikovskiy, Surovikinskiy, Chernyshkovskiy and Nizhne-Chirskiy) (see map on pp. 58and 59).

The area flooded by the reservoir was in a zone of inadequate moisture supply and bore relatively low and irregular crops. Agriculture was of the grain and livestock type. Industry was poorly developed and consisted mainly of enterprises of the rayon level.

Settlement patterns were related to the inadequacy of the moisture supply, with valley-ravine and valley-gully settlement types predominating. Because of the semi-arid conditions, the southeast part of European Russia was settled and economically developed mainly along the river valleys, including the Don and its tributaries (Chir, Khoper, Medveditsa, Tsimla and others). The settlement of the middle and lower reaches of the Don and its tributaries in the 16th and 17th centuries led to the formation of Don Cossack villages, many of which were preserved up to the time of the filling of the reservoir.

The Cossack villages, or stanitsas, of Tsimlyanskaya, Verkhne-Kurmoyarskaya, Nizhne-Chirskaya and Nizhne-Kurmoyarskaya were more than 300 years old. Out of the 48 original Don Cossack settlements of 1672, eight were in the area of the future reservoir.

The riverine character of settlement in the Don valley and along its tributaries resulted in a relatively high population density in the future reservoir zone, where the density was two to three times higher than the average rural density of 6 to 12 persons per square kilometer in Rostov and Stalingrad oblasts as a whole. The flooded zone therefore contained a relatively large number of populated places. (It is interesting to note that the same situation exists in the case of other reservoirs; see item 5 of the bibliography.) A total of 172 populated places were affected by the Volga-Don project, 159 in entirety and 13 in part.

Those that were moved entirely to new sites included the former rayon seats of Tsimlyanskaya and Verkhne-Kurmoyarskaya; those moved in part included the town of Kalach, the workers settlement of Krasnoarmeyskiy and the rayon seat of Nizhne-Chirskaya. A total of 49 new populated places were built, of which 37 were mergers of two or more of the former places. This approach to resettlement reduced the total number of populated places in the area by 113, including 39 in Rostov Oblast and 74 in Stalingrad Oblast (see map).

Most of the places were moved only relatively short distances, an average of 13 km. in Rostov Oblast and 10 km. in Stalingrad Oblast. A few places were moved considerably farther. In Rostov Oblast, for example, Nizhne-Kurmoyarskaya was moved a distance of 140 km. to the village of Ryabiche-Zadonskiy in new irrigation lands, and the village of Kulaly was moved 100 km. to Cherkasskiy. In Stalingrad Oblast, the village of Verkhne-Kurmoyarskaya was moved 70 km., and Vatazhnyy 90 km.

Most of the new populated places were built on the shores of the future reservoir at a relatively short distance from previous sites. A substantial number of flooded villages were merged with existing villages situated near the shores of the reservoir. In Rostov Oblast, 18 out of a total of 21 new settlements were situated on the shores of the reservoir, and in Stalingrad Oblast, 23 out of 27 new places. The relatively short transfer distance was due to two factors: (1) the fact that the moving of houses was not economical over distances of more than 20 to 25 km., and (2) the relative ease with which new farmland could be provided for the resettled population in the steppe zone compared with reservoir projects in the forested northern and eastern areas of the country.

The question of land availability and the possibility of creating a diversified agriculture in the resettlement areas were among the principal factors considered in the project.

The filling of reservoirs in the steppe zone usually floods only part of the land of collective farms (mainly hay meadows and pastures) and the population can be resettled on land of the collective farms that is not affected by flooding. In some cases when most of the land of a collective farm is flooded and the rest is inadequate to assure diversified farming possibilities, the population is resettled on the land of a nearby farm. This results in a merged collective farm and farm settlement.

In view of the fact that all the collective farms in the Tsimlyansk Reservoir zone had adequate land resources and, on the contrary, even suffered from a labor shortage, resettlement on the land of other farms has had a beneficial effect on the farm operation.

Altogether only 28 old populated places were merged in Rostov and Stalingrad oblasts in connection with the filling of the reservoir. In forested areas, where reservoirs tend to flood most if not all of the available farmland, resettlement of the population and replacement of the land constitute a far more difficult and expensive problem.

Another characteristic feature of the Tsimlyansk project has been the improvement of the economic-geographic situation and of transportation services of most of the new settlements as well as the old population centers unaffected by the flooding.

The construction of the Volga-Don project has greatly improved navigation conditions. Previously Kalach was the head of navigation, and even so could be reached only by small vessels at low-water stage. There were 44 large sandbars between Kalach and Tsimlyanskaya. The filling of the reservoir has greatly increased the depth and Kalach has become an important river port. Navigation has also been improved on the lower Don, with guaranteed depths of 2.4 to 2.6 meters. The settlements that were moved to the shores of the reservoir thus found themselves on one of the major waterways of the country.

Transportation conditions of both old and new settlements were also improved with the construction of the Morozovsk-Kuberle railroad crossing the Don on the Tsimlyansk dam. Construction of this line has brought many villages considerably closer to the nearest railroad station. While the old settlement of Tsimlyanskaya, for example, was situated 115 km. from the railroad at Tsimla station, the new settlement of Tsimlyanskiy is situated directly on the new line. The distance between the village of Romanovskaya and the nearest railroad has been cut from 50 to 8 km.

There were some cases, however, in which transportation conditions deteriorated. The filling of the reservoir, for example, flooded the floodplain of the Tsimla River, creating a large bay that cut off four villages -- Aksenov, Budarin, Medvedev and Pronin -- from the rest of Tsimlyanskiy Rayon. Under these conditions it was deemed best to move these villages to new sites despite the fact that they had not been directly affected by the flooding. (Similar cases occurred in the case of the flooding of the Rybinsk Reservoir; see (1), p. 135, of bibliography.)

The transfer of populated places to new sites was accompanied by complete reconstruction. The old settlements had been poorly laid out, without any planning. They were scattered chaotically over dissected terraces along the banks of the Don River and its tributaries. These defects were eliminated as a result of their removal to new sites. The Architecture Committee worked out new plans for each settlement based on its future prospects of development. Those prospects were assessed on economic grounds, such as specialization of production. An example is the new workers settlement of Tsimlyanskiy, with broad, straight streets, a fine residential area for power-station workers, and a palace of rest and culture situated on the high bank of the Tsimlyansk Reservoir. A newly built food-processing and light manufacturing industry is rapidly developing in the new settlement. After some time the settlement is expected to be raised to city status.

The government has provided assistance to the resettled population. A total of 38 million rubles was allocated alone to the population of Tsimlyanskiy Rayon. Each household received between 7,000 and 30,000 (old) rubles depending on the value of its home and private plot. In addition the sale of building materials to the new settlers was organized on a broad scale. This enabled them to expand their living space and to build three- and four-room homes instead of their old one- and two-room houses, and to provide themselves with good kitchen and bathroom facilities.

The construction of large river-development projects leads not only to the building of new population centers replacing the ones moved from flooded sites, but also to the construction of new settlements not related to resettlement but to the construction and operation of dams and power stations. In the case of the Tsimlyansk Reservoir, such settlements were the town of Volgodonsk, a transportation and industrial center on the reservoir bank, and the workers settlement of Novo-Solenovskiy. Next to Volgodonsk is the new river port of Tsimlyanskiy and one of the nation's largest factories for the production of fatty acids, with an annual capacity of 30,000 tons of fats. The factory makes it possible to release 200,000 hectares from the cultivation of oilseeds. For comparison, it might be noted that the entire area in oilseeds in Rostov Oblast amounted to 169,000 hectares in 1957.

These are some of the problems related to changes in settlement geography of Rostov and Stalingrad oblasts in connection with the construction of the Tsimlyansk Reservoir.

Bibliography

1. Bruk, S. I. "The transformation of nature and economy in areas of large reservoirs," Vopr. geogr., No. 27, 1951.
2. Gaveman, A. V. Moskovskoye more (The Moscow Sea, a reservoir on the Volga River), Kalinin, 1955.
3. Zaural'skiy. "Permanent and temporary flooding in large-scale hydraulic construction projects," Vestn. s.-kh. nauki. Melioratsiya i gidrotekhnika, 1940, No. 3.
4. Luskin, Z. D. Otvod zemel', zemleustroystvo i perenos stroyeniy. Opyt sooruzheniya kanala Moskva-Volga (Condemnation of lands, land use and removal of structures. Experience from the construction of the Moscow-Volga Canal), Moscow: Stroyizdat, 1945.
5. Meyerson, A. B. Bratskoye vodokhranilishche (The Bratsk Reservoir), Irkutsk, 1956.
6. Paplinskiy. "Moving of wooden buildings on the Moscow-Volga Canal," Stroitel'stvo, 1937, No. 14-15.
7. Fesenko, S. A. "Calculating the effects of permanent and temporary flooding," Gidrotekhn. stroit., 1940, No. 7.

7

Reprinted from *Trans. Amer. Geophys. Union,* **17**, 465–471 (July 1936)

WATER-SPREADING AS PRACTICED BY THE SANTA CLARA WATER-CONSERVATION DISTRICT, VENTURA COUNTY, CALIFORNIA

V. M. Freeman

The Santa Clara Water-Conservation District was organized in 1928 under what is known as the Water-Conservation Act of 1927, Assembly Bill No. 233, and is, therefore, a legal entity. The assessed valuation of the District is approximately $20,000,000 and the boundaries embrace 110,000 acres of lands situated in the Santa Clara River Valley and the Oxnard Plain, in Ventura County, California. The lands in the incorporated cities of Oxnard, Santa Paula, and Fillmore are not in the District. The maximum annual tax which can be levied by the District is 15 cents on the $100 of assessed valuation of land and improvements. The District was organized for the purpose of protecting water-rights and the conservation of the waters of the Santa Clara River and its tributaries. The District is dependent almost entirely on ground-water as a source of supply for domestic and irrigation purposes.

Our organization was the first agency to practice water-spreading in Ventura County and our success is due in no small part to the valued council of Harold Conkling, Deputy State Engineer, and R. H. Jamison, Senior Hydraulic Engineer, State Division of Water-Resources, regarding the proper location of our spreading-works.

Having had no previous experience in the design and operation of spreading-works and due to the fact that our funds are limited, we have felt our way along rather carefully. Percolation-tests were made at all tentative spreading-ground locations prior to construction. This procedure was made possible by the cooperation of water-companies having distribution-mains or ditches near the proposed spreading-ground locations. We operate three spreading-grounds located near the cities of Saticoy, Santa Paula, and Piru.

Saticoy Spreading-Ground--The Saticoy Spreading-Ground is located on the south side of the Santa Clara River and east of the Saticoy Bridge. Water is diverted from the Santa Clara River by temporary earth-dams. It is conveyed to the spreading-basins by 2600 feet of 60-inch reinforced-concrete pipe and 2700 feet of unlined canal. The capacity of the pipe-line and canal is 135 second-feet. The spreading-system consists of 33 basins, varying in size from 1.2 to 6.0 acres of wetted area. The total wetted area of the 33 spreading-basins is 97 acres. The top soil on which the basins are constructed has been classified as "Yolo fine sandy loam." The depth to ground-water beneath the basins at the beginning of a spreading-season has varied from 75 to 90 feet, since 1931. The lands occupied are under lease for a period of 20 years.

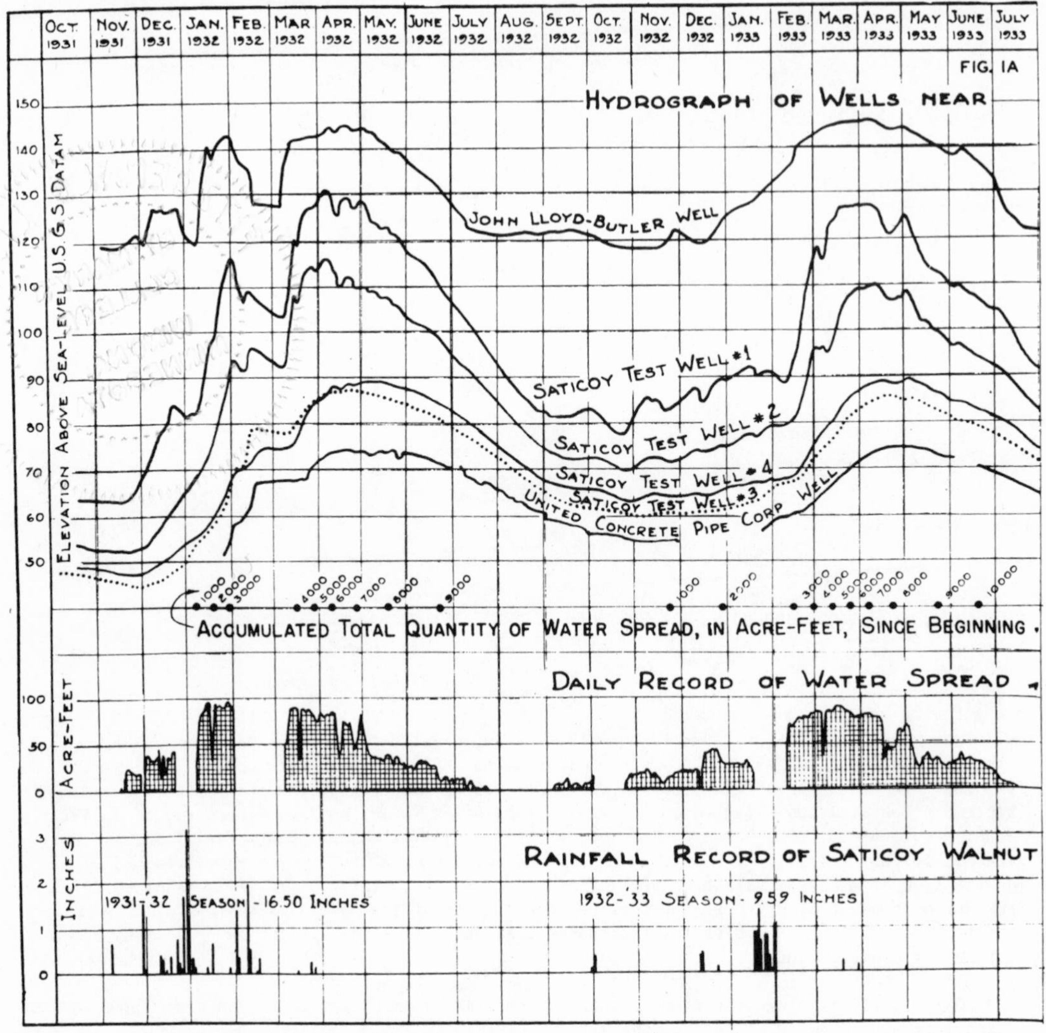

In 1931 the District drilled four test-wells adjacent to this spreading-ground. These wells were equipped with 8-day rational water-level recorders. The hydrographs of these wells are given in Figure 1 and show the fluctuation of the water-plane and the amount of water spread at the Saticoy Spreading-Ground.

In addition to the hydrographs of the four test-wells, this chart also shows the hydrographs of the John Lloyd-Butler Well and the United Concrete Pipe Company Well. The Lloyd-Butler Well is located near the upper basin and the United Concrete Pipe Company Well is located approximately 600 feet below the Last Basin. The static water-level in these wells is very sensitive to our spreading-operations and responds to any interruption or change in quantity of water being diverted into the basins. The following are ground-surface elevations in feet above sea-level at wells shown in Figure 1: No. 1, 143.09; No. 2, 140.26; No. 3, 137.25; No. 4, 143.16; John Lloyd-Butler Well, 151.10; United Concrete Pipe Company Well, 134.30.

Santa Paula Creek Spreading-Ground--The overflow-channels on the easterly side of the Santa Paula Creek debris-cone have been utilized for spreading-purposes each year since the fall of 1931. Water is diverted from the main channel of the Santa Paula Creek by means of a small rock-and-gravel dam and is conveyed to the overflow-channels by means of 700 feet of 30-inch reinforced-concrete pipe having a capacity of 25 second-feet. Ninety-seven small spreading-basins have been formed by the construction of loose rock check-dams in the overflow-channels. The total wetted area of these 97 basins has not as yet been developed. The top soil of the overflow-channels is of the river-wash type usually found on debris-cones having a fairly steep

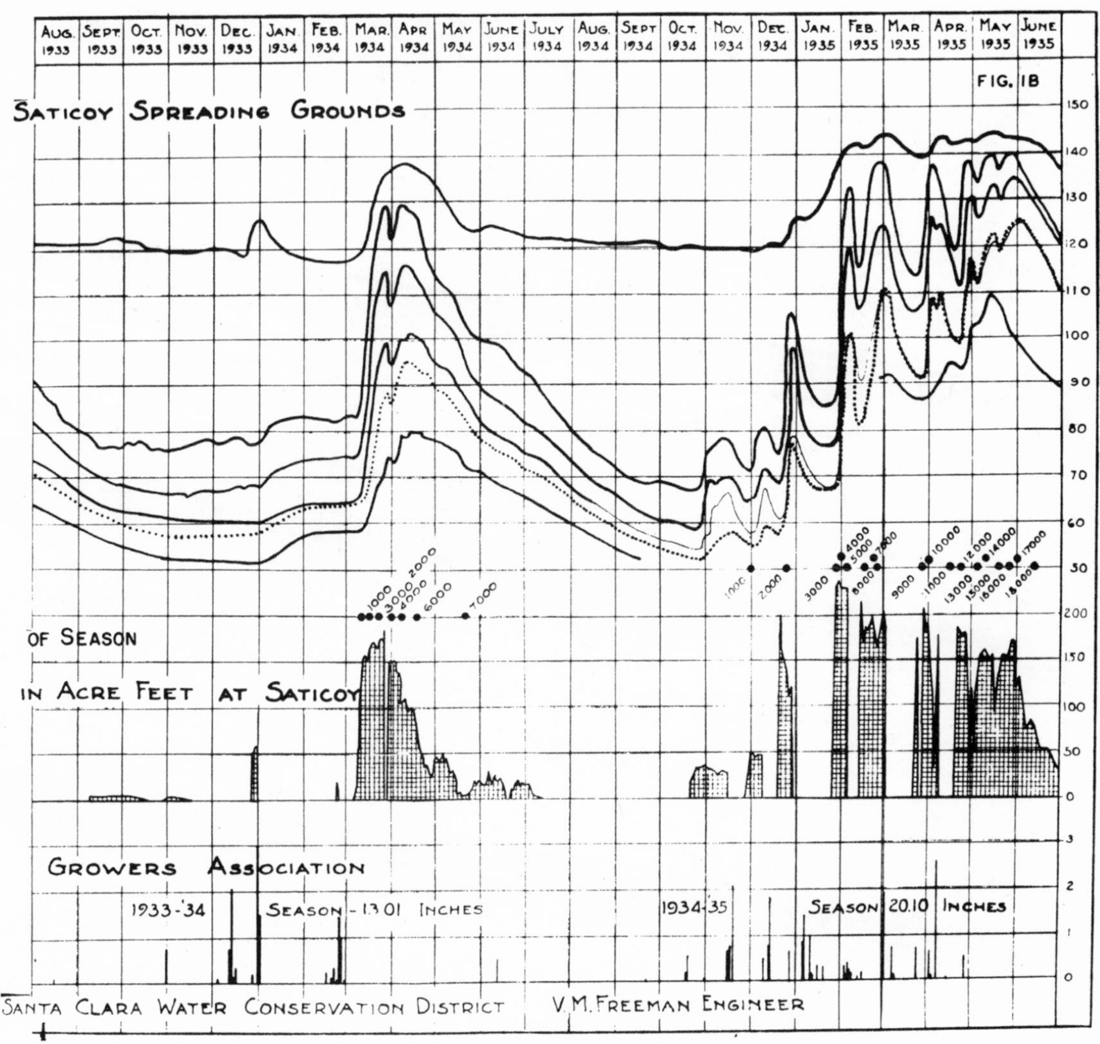

gradient. The depth to ground-water beneath the lower end of the spreading-ground is about 100 feet at the beginning of a spreading-season. The land occupied was leased by the District for a ten-year period.

Piru Spreading-Ground--This spreading-ground is located on the west side of the Piru Creek debris-cone south of the State Highway. Water is diverted from the main channel of the Piru Creek by rock-and-gravel dams of temporary construction. It is conveyed to the spreading-basins by 2000 feet of 48-inch reinforced-concrete pipe having a capacity of 80 second-feet. At the present time we have nine basins with a total wetted area of 43.2 acres. The top soil on which the basins are constructed has been classified as "Yolo gravelly fine sandy loam." The depth to ground-water beneath the basins at the beginning of a spreading-season has varied from 130 to 160 feet since 1932. The District acquired the fee title to the land occupied by this spreading-ground in 1930.

The C. S. Johnson Well located 2500 feet below the Piru Spreading-Ground was equipped with a Stevens water-level recorder, type L, October 1, 1931. The hydrograph of this Well is given in Figure 2 and shows the fluctuation of the water-plane and the amount of water spread at the Piru Spreading-Ground.

The elevation of the ground-surface at the center of the Piru Spreading-Ground is 660 feet above sea-level, and the elevation of the ground-surface at the Johnson Well is 647.8 feet. The hydrograph from September 1927 to October 1931 was plotted from occasional measurements made by

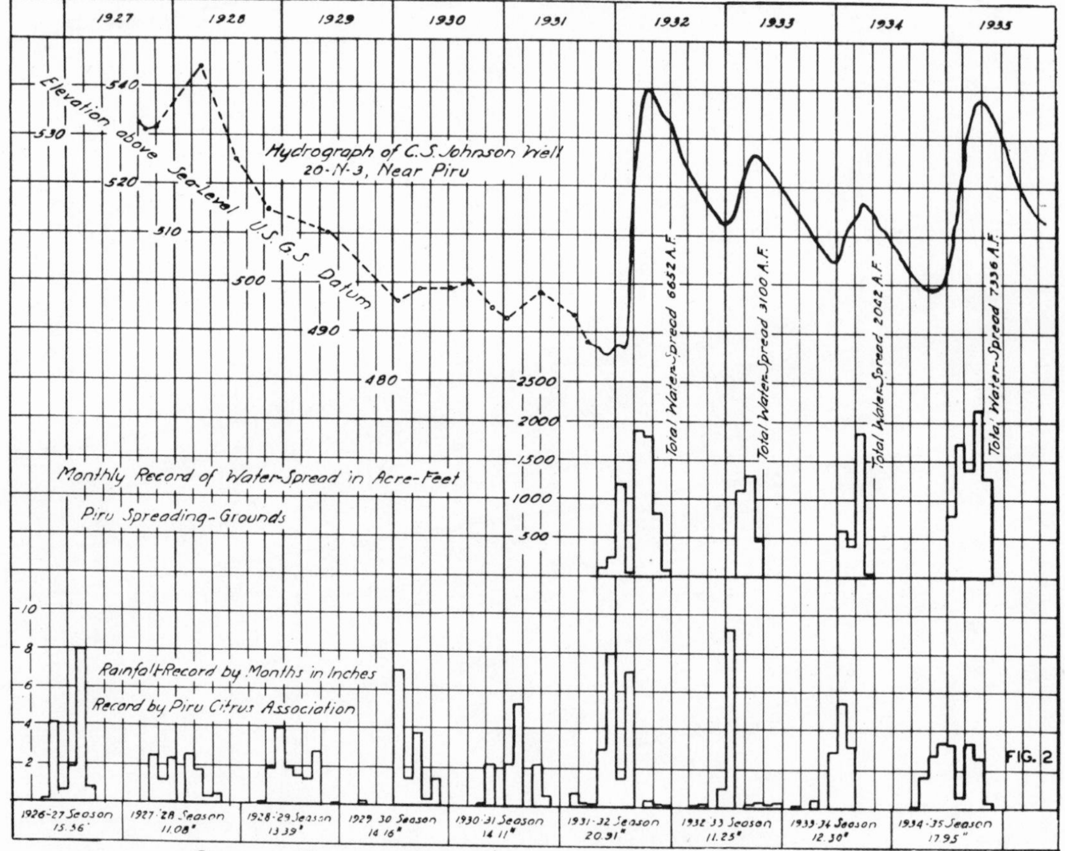

SANTA CLARA WATER CONSERVATION DISTRICT

Chart showing Hydrograph of C.S. Johnson Well, Monthly Record of Water-Spread at Piru Spreading-Grounds, Rainfall-Record of Piru Citrus Association, from 1927 to date — V. M. Freeman, Engineer

the State Division of Water Resources and the District. The fluctuation of the ground-water plane as shown on this chart should not be entirely attributed to the spreading of water at the Piru Spreading-Grounds, as a portion of it is due to natural percolation in the Piru Creek and Santa Clara River channels during storm-flows.

The following is a brief statement of our method of procedure in spreading water. The Santa Clara River and its tributaries carry large quantities of silt and suspended matter during storm- or flood-flows. No attempt is made to spread water carrying more than 20 cubic feet of suspended matter per acre-foot. Water in our streams carries as high as 5000 cubic feet of suspended matter per acre-foot during peak-flows but generally the load of suspended matter reduces to 20 cubic feet or less per acre-foot in from two to ten days after the peak. Determination of the amount of suspended matter carried by the streams is made by the evaporation-method from samples collected in pint milk bottles by means of a sampler copied from the design used by the United States Geological Survey as described in Water-Supply Paper 636B. The sampler is used with weight, cable, and stay-line similar to current-meter suspension.

The spreading-basins of the Saticoy unit have not been cultivated or subsoiled since their construction, the natural growth of vegetation being left undisturbed.

The first unit of the Saticoy Spreading-Ground was constructed in the fall of 1929. To date the basins have not been cleaned and there is no noticeable reduction in the rate of percolation at the beginning of a spreading-season.

The Piru Spreading-Ground was constructed in the fall of 1931. The upper four basins were cleaned two years later, at which time a silt-deposit varying from two to four inches in thickness was removed.

Table 1--Santa Clara Water-Conservation District: Measurements of surface-flow of Santa Clara River at a point 2600 feet above Saticoy Bridge and at Montalvo Bridge, showing increased percolation after scarifying stream-channel

Date	Discharge 2600 ft east of Saticoy Bridge	Discharge Montalvo Bridge	Perco-lation	Esti-mated natural perco-lation	Hours	Total spread	Total spread	Accumulation
1933	sec-ft	sec-ft	sec-ft	sec-ft		sec-ft	acre-ft	acre-ft
March 1 (a.m.)[a]	79.44	70.84	8.60	8.60	..	.....	......	....
1 (p.m.)	70.92	62.51	8.41	8.41	..	.....	......	....
7[b]	77.38	64.99	12.39	8.77	12	1.81	3.589	3.589
8	.....	.....	.....	....	24	9.67	19.176	22.765
9	74.68	50.49	24.19	8.47	24	15.72	31.173	53.938
10	78.48	52.91	25.57	8.90	24	16.67	33.057	86.995
11	79.58	55.04	24.54	9.02	24	15.52	30.776	117.771
12	82.50	59.03	23.47	9.36	24	14.11	27.980	145.751
13	72.77	49.16	23.61	8.25	24	15.36	30.459	176.210
14	74.92	41.93	32.99	8.50	24	24.49	48.564	224.774
15	71.18	37.64	33.54	8.07	24	25.47	50.507	275.281
16	.....	.....	.....	....	24	26.92	53.382	328.663
17	74.83	37.96	36.87	8.49	24	28.38	56.278	384.941
18	70.09	37.33	32.76	7.95	24	24.81	49.198	434.139
19	.....	.....	.....	....	24	21.49	42.615	476.754
20	61.40	36.27	25.13	6.96	24	18.17	36.030	512.784
21	63.44	33.27	30.17	7.19	24	22.98	45.569	558.353
22	60.62	36.27	24.35	6.87	24	17.48	34.663	593.016
23	59.96	32.21	27.75	6.80	24	20.95	41.544	634.560
24	57.12	34.66	22.46	6.48	24	15.98	31.668	666.248
25	55.91	30.90	25.01	6.34	24	18.67	37.023	703.271
26	.....	.....	.....	....	24	16.87	33.453	736.724
27	45.56	25.33	20.23	5.17	24	15.06	29.864	766.588
28	.....	.....	.....	....	24	15.03	29.804	796.392
29	43.71	23.75	19.96	4.96	24	15.00	29.745	826.137
30	.....	.....	20.90	....	24	16.04	31.807	857.944
31	.....	.....	21.84	....	24	17.08	33.870	891.814
April 1	40.98	18.21	22.77	4.65	24	18.12	35.932	927.746
2	.....	.....	20.14	4.48	24	15.66	31.054	958.800
3	38.07	20.56	17.51	4.32	24	13.19	26.156	984.956
4[c]	.....	.....	18.93	4.64	24	14.29	28.337	1013.293
5	.....	.....	20.35	4.96	24	15.39	30.518	1043.811
6	.....	.....	21.77	5.28	24	16.49	32.700	1076.511
7	.....	.....	23.19	5.60	24	17.59	34.881	1111.392
8	36.20	11.59	24.61	5.92	24	18.69	37.062	1148.454
9	.....	.....	26.03	6.24	24	19.79	39.243	1187.697
10	.....	.....	27.45	6.56	24	20.89	41.425	1229.122
11[d]	.....	.....	28.87	6.88	24	21.99	43.606	1272.728

[a]Measurements made before scarifying; estimated natural percolation of 11.34 per cent based on measurements made March 1, 1933.

[b]Started scarifying in river-bed March 7, 1933.

[c]Starting April 4, estimated natural percolation increased one per cent per day on account of warmer weather prevailing.

[d]Natural percolation estimated 19.34 per cent.

Water diverted to spreading-grounds is measured by means of Parshall flumes and rated canal-stations equipped with type-E, eight-day Stevens recorders.

Our field-force varies from three to five men depending upon the quantity of water being spread. At the Piru and Santa Paula spreading-grounds one attendant at each is on duty eight hours per day during the spreading-season. At the Saticoy Spreading-Grounds three men working eight-hour shifts are on duty when we are diverting 50 second-feet or more. When the head drops to less than 50 second-feet one man working 8 hours per day handles the work satisfactorily.

Another method of increasing ground-storage of water but not involving the use of basins consists of scarifying the stream-bed of the river. Current-meter measurements of the flow of the Santa Clara River from a point approximately 2600 feet above the Saticoy Bridge to the ocean

Table 2--Santa Clara Water-Conservation District: Measurements of surface-flow of Santa Clara River at a point 2600 feet above Saticoy Bridge and at Montalvo Bridge, showing increased percolation after scarifying stream-channel

Date	Discharge 2600 ft east of Saticoy Bridge	Discharge Montalvo Bridge	Percolation	Estimated natural percolation	Hours	Total spread	Total spread	Accumulation
1933	sec-ft	sec-ft	sec-ft	sec-ft		sec-ft	acre-ft	acre-ft
Dec. 19[a]	39.90	30.39	9.51	9.51	..	.....	......	....
20[b]	39.06	28.48	10.58	10.58	..	.....	......	....
21[c]	37.40	.....	15.29	11.22	24	4.07	8.071	8.071
22	35.74	.....	20.01	11.79	24	8.22	16.300	24.371
23	34.08	.....	19.08	12.26	24	6.82	13.524	37.895
24[d]	32.41	14.21	18.20	12.64	24	5.56	11.025	48.920
25	30.76	.....	17.22	12.92	24	4.30	8.527	57.447
26[e]	29.10	.....	16.29	13.09	15	2.00	3.966	61.413
1934								
Jan. 15[f]	77.40	65.30	12.10	12.10	..	.....	......	....
16[g]	71.66	63.66	8.00	8.00	..	.....	......	....
17	.....	.....	14.77	9.66	24	5.11	10.133	71.546
18	72.49	50.94	21.55	9.71	24	11.84	23.479	95.025
19	.....	.....	30.26	9.94	24	20.32	40.295	135.320
20	75.90	36.93	38.79	10.17	24	28.80	57.110	192.430
21	.....	.....	35.64	9.62	24	26.02	51.598	244.028
22	67.67	35.36	32.31	9.07	24	23.24	46.085	290.113
23	.....	.....	31.60	8.80	24	22.80	45.212	335.325
24	.....	.....	30.89	8.53	24	22.36	44.340	379.665
25	61.67	31.48	30.19	8.26	24	21.93	43.487	423.152
26	.....	.....	30.17	8.21	24	21.96	43.547	466.698
27	.....	.....	30.14	8.16	24	21.98	43.586	510.284
28	.....	.....	30.12	8.11	24	22.01	43.646	553.930
29	60.18	30.09	30.09	8.06	24	22.03	43.685	597.615
30	.....	.....	29.94	8.08	24	21.86	43.348	640.963
31	.....	.....	29.80	8.10	24	21.70	43.032	683.996
Feb. 1	.....	.....	29.66	8.12	24	21.54	42.714	726.710
2	60.80	31.29	29.51	8.15	24	21.36	42.357	769.067
3	.....	.....	29.99	8.26	24	21.73	43.091	812.158
4	.....	.....	30.47	8.38	24	22.09	43.804	855.962
5	63.39	32.45	30.94	8.49	24	22.45	44.518	900.480
6	.....	.....	30.23	8.41	24	21.82	43.269	943.749
7	.....	.....	29.52	8.33	24	21.19	42.020	985.769
8	.....	.....	28.81	8.25	24	20.56	40.770	1026.539
9	60.98	32.88	28.10	8.17	24	19.93	39.521	1066.060
10	.....	.....	26.79	7.92	24	18.87	37.419	1103.479
11	.....	.....	25.48	7.68	24	17.80	35.297	1138.776
12	55.54	31.38	24.16	7.44	24	16.72	33.156	1171.932
13	.....	.....	25.72	7.93	24	17.79	35.278	1207.210
14	.....	.....	27.28	8.41	24	18.87	37.419	1244.629
15	.....	.....	28.84	8.90	24	19.94	39.541	1284.170
16	69.97	39.56	30.41	9.38	24	21.03	41.702	1325.872
17	.....	.....	28.84	8.85	24	19.99	39.640	1365.512
18	.....	.....	27.27	8.32	24	18.95	37.578	1403.090
19	58.17	32.47	25.70	7.79	24	17.91	35.516	1438.606
20	.....	.....	.....	....	24	16.87	33.453	1472.059
21	.....	.....	.....	....	24	15.83	31.391	1503.450
22[h]	.....	.....	.....	....	14	8.63	17.113	1520.563

[a]Measured 23.84 per cent loss. [b]Measured 27.09 per cent loss. [c]Started work with tractor. [d]Measured. [e]Water spread in grounds. [f]From January 15, 1934, to end, natural percolation calculated at 13.40 per cent. [g]Started work with tractor. [h]Water turned in spreading-grounds.

Note: Storm of January 1, 1934, changed the natural percolation-factor.

show there is very little percolation in the stream-bed between these points after the peak storm- or flood-flow has passed. In order to salvage some of this water which wastes into the ocean, the District has been scarifying the stream-bed from a point 2600 feet above the Saticoy Bridge to a point approximately two miles below the Saticoy Bridge. This work is done after storms each year using a heavy road-scarifier drawn by a 20-horse-power Holt tractor. The edges of the stream and all riffles are scarified. The results of this work after storm-flows in 1933 and 1934 are shown in Tables 1 and 2. The total calculated induced percolation shown in Table 1 is 1272 acre-feet for the period March 8 to April 11, 1933. The total calculated induced percolation shown in Table 2 is 1520 acre-feet for the period December 21, 1933 to February 22, 1934.

In areas similar to that of the Santa Clara Valley, where there is a sustained flow in the streams after storms, or where stream-regulation has been provided, the writer is of the opinion that the depth to ground-water beneath a spreading-ground is as important a factor to be considered as the rate of percolation in the design and operation of spreading-works. Our experience indicates that the depth to ground-water at the beginning of a spreading-season is one of the fundamental factors affecting the capacity of a spreading-ground.

At the Saticoy location, where the ground-water plane was about 80 feet below the ground-surface at the beginning of the 1934-35 spreading-season, it was observed after spreading 13,000 acre-feet on 97 acres of basins there was a noticeable reduction in the rate of percolation per acre of wetted area. The spreading of this 13,000 acre-feet of water raised the ground-water plane beneath the spreading basins to within ten feet of the surface.

During the 1934-35 season from the latter part of October 1934 to the first of July 1935, a total of 18,917 acre-feet of water was spread at the Saticoy grounds. From the behavior of the works during the latter part of the season it is thought the capacity of the Saticoy Spreading-Works, as constructed, has a yearly capacity of about 200 acre-feet per acre of wetted area when the ground-water plane stands 80 feet below the surface at the beginning of a spreading-season.

During the 1934-35 season we spread a total of 30,411 acre-feet. The cost of material and labor incidental to the spreading-operations during the 1934-35 season varied from $0.145 to $0.203 per acre-foot with an average cost of $0.183 per acre-foot. The District's efforts have been modest as evidenced by the financial statement for December 27, 1927 to June 30, 1935. This shows total receipts from taxation of $124,633 and total disbursements of $119,208. Since its inception in 1928 our organization, up until June 1935, had spread a total of 98,166 acre-feet of water.

8

Reprinted from *Econ. Geol.*, **41**, 503–516 (1946)

ARTIFICIAL RECHARGE OF GROUND WATER ON LONG ISLAND, NEW YORK.

M. L. BRASHEARS, JR.*

ABSTRACT.

In 1933, the water table in a large area in western Long Island was below sea level, and potability of ground water was threatened by inflow of sea water. To prevent further overdevelopment, the New York State Water Power and Control Commission has required that water pumped from new wells for cooling and similar purposes be returned to the ground. During the summer of 1944, over 200 recharge wells and several recharge pits were returning water at the combined rate of about 60,000,000 gallons a day. Also in operation were several large recharge pits which return storm sewer runoff in Nassau County. The water is returned to glacial beds from which most of it is pumped, but in places it percolates into the underlying Cretaceous formations. Well drillers have developed recharge wells capable of returning as much as 1,000 gallons a minute, many of them having been in operation for over 5 years without failing. Recharge pits dug in coarse glacial gravels are capable of returning about 1,000,000 gallons a day per acre of exposed surface. The legal requirement that water pumped for cooling be returned to the aquifer has caused a gradual decrease in net withdrawal of ground water but has increased actual use. Hence a rise in water levels has occurred in the critically overdeveloped area. Water levels reached lowest stage at the end of 1941 and have recovered slowly since then. However, water levels are still far below sea level in many places, and sea water continues to move inland in areas of heavy pumping.

INTRODUCTION.

Because of the wide-spread occurrence of highly productive water-bearing material and other favorable factors, the ground water resources of Long Island have been used extensively for many years for industrial and public water supplies. Overdevelopment in the heavily industrialized and populated area at the western end of the Island caused a gradual decline of water levels and in 1933 it was discovered that the water table was below sea level in an area of more than 40 square miles and that sea water was moving into this area. The State Legislature, recognizing the seriousness of the situation, took steps to protect the public water supplies on Long Island from further overdevelopment and passed a conservation law requiring that the approval of the State Water Power and Control Commission be obtained before constructing a well having a capacity of greater than 100,000 gallons a day. In general, it has been the policy of the Commission, since the passage of the law, to require water pumped from new cooling and air-conditioning wells to be returned to the aquifer from which it is withdrawn. Since the passage of the law many new supply wells for cooling and air-conditioning have been drilled and because of the requirement of the Water Power and Control Commission

* Published by permission of the Director of the U. S. Geological Survey.

a number of large recharge basins and more than 200 recharge wells, many of which have been in operation for over five years without failing, have been installed to return their discharge to the ground. During the summer of 1944, these recharge wells and basins were operated at a combined rate estimated to be more than 60,000,000 gallons a day which represents an average ground water withdrawal for an entire year of from 15 to 20 million gallons a day. Thus, the conservation policy of the Commission has permitted the drilling of a large number of new supply wells for industrial cooling and comfort air-conditioning but at the same time has prevented further substantial over-development.

Because of its relatively low temperature during the summer months ground water is used for cooling and air-conditioning by many establishments on Long Island—theatres, restaurants, ice plants, public buildings, breweries, and manufacturing plants—having in most cases peak daily requirements of from 500 to 1,000 gallons per minute, but with some of the larger plants having daily requirements of as much as 5,000 gallons per minute. Most of the cooling plants are situated in Kings (Brooklyn) and Queens Counties (Fig. 1), and because only limited space is available in these urban areas at the western end of the Island, only recharge wells have been used to return cooling water. In contrast, recharge basins have been installed at several of the larger installations—mainly air-conditioned war plants—situated in the rural areas in Nassau and Suffolk Counties. Recharge wells having capacities of as much as 1,000 gallons per minute have been successfully constructed and as the demand at most plants is usually less than this limit, most of the cooling installations have required only one recharge well. However, at some of the smaller plants, because of unfavorable geologic and ground-water conditions, it has been necessary to construct more than one recharge well to return the discharge from only one supply well. At the larger plants, either recharge basins—capable of returning three to four million gallons a day—or several recharge wells have been utilized to return cooling water.

Depending upon the type of cooling plant, the temperature of the water returned to the ground ranges from about 2 to 20 degrees higher than the temperature of the water pumped from the ground. As shown by Leggette [1] and the writer [2] the return of warm water causes a rise in ground temperature. In some places this rise has been substantial and has decreased the advantage of using ground water for cooling purposes by causing a decrease in plant efficiency and an increase in operating costs. However, appreciable areal rises of ground water temperature have occurred only in the vicinity of centers of considerable recharge. Where wells are not closely spaced or are separated by impervious layers there has been no serious rise in the temperature of the ground water.

In addition to the return of warm water from cooling and air-conditioning plants, and occasionally from dewatering wells used during sub-surface con-

[1] Leggette, R. M., and Brashears, M. L., Jr.: Ground water for air conditioning on Long Island, New York. Am. Geophys. Union Trans., Part I, pp. 415–417, 1938.

[2] Brashears, M. L., Jr.: Ground water temperature on Long Island, New York. Econ. Geol., 26: 821–828, 1941.

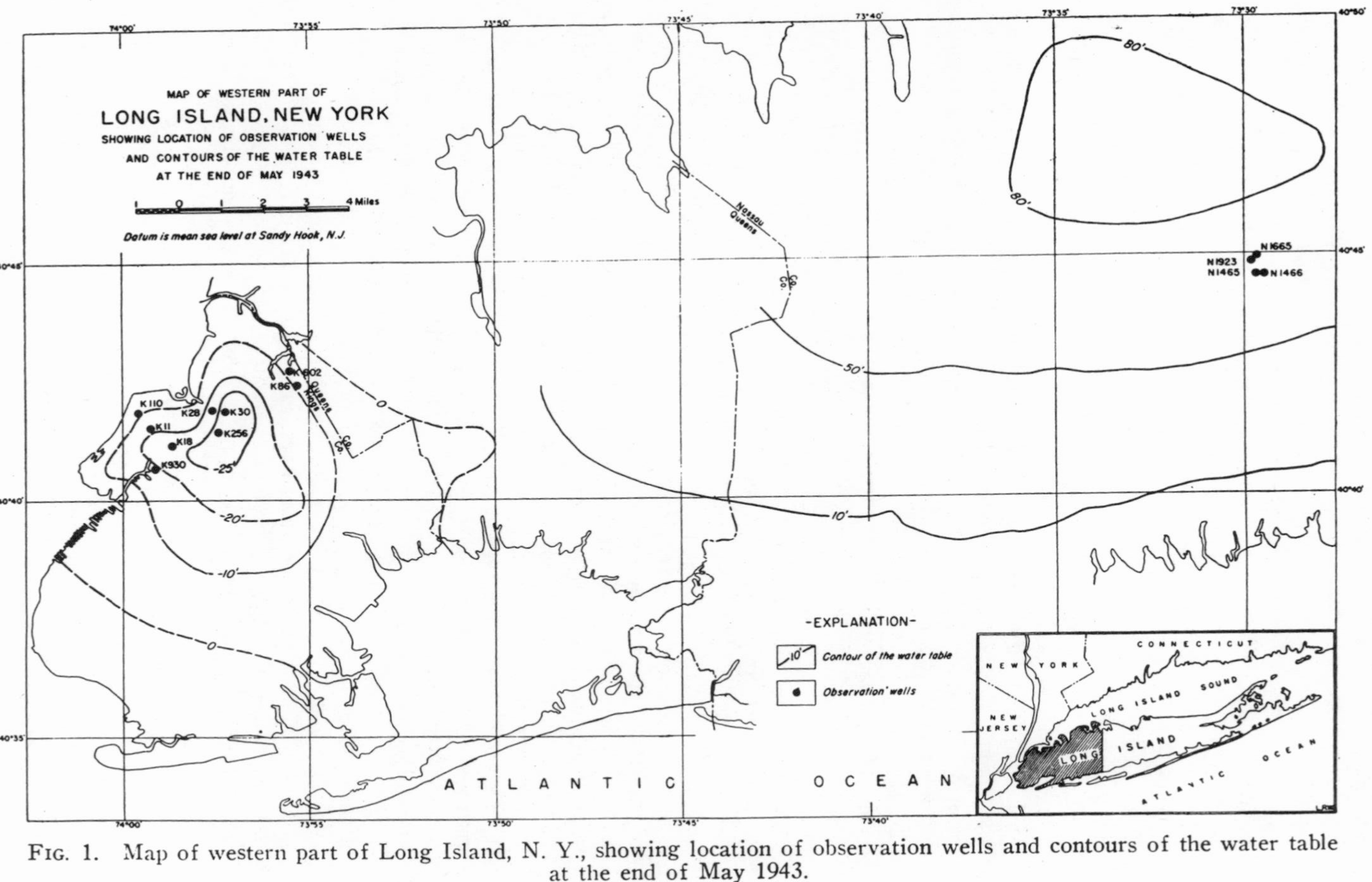

FIG. 1. Map of western part of Long Island, N. Y., showing location of observation wells and contours of the water table at the end of May 1943.

struction, a considerable amount of storm sewer run-off in Nassau County is being returned to the ground by means of water spreading. Eleven seepage basins, ranging in area from about 1 acre to 9 acres and having a combined area of about 40 acres, are being operated by the Nassau County Department of Public Works. According to reports based on general records, the average rate of infiltration in these basins is about 500,000 gallons per day per acre, with the rate of infiltration being somewhat higher immediately after the bottoms of the basins have been scarified.

GEOLOGY AND GROUND WATER CONDITIONS.

Long Island is composed of Coastal Plain sediments lying uncomformably on a floor of metamorphic rocks of pre-Cambrian and early Paleozoic age. The sediments consist of a considerable thickness of unconsolidated deposits of Cretaceous age overlain in most places by a relatively thin mantle of Pleistocene outwash and till.[3] The bedrock, which consists mainly of gneiss, slopes to the southeast at about 100 feet to the mile and crops out only in a small area in the northwestern part of Queens County, at the western end of the Island.

The Cretaceous deposits consist of a thick series of interbedded sands and clays which also slope to the southeast. The lower part of these sediments, considered to be of Raritan age, is composed chiefly of clay that overlies an extensive artesian aquifer, the Lloyd sand. The upper part of the Cretaceous, believed to be of Magothy age, consists largely of fine sand containing numerous relatively thin beds of clay. Several fairly widespread beds of water-bearing gravel occur in the beds of Magothy age, especially in the lower part just above the clay of Raritan age. The Cretaceous artesian beds are the chief source of supply of a number of Public Water supplies in the central part of Long Island, particularly along the shore lines and on the barrier beaches where the overlying glacial deposits can be readily invaded by sea water. Because they generally lie at considerable depths, and are relatively expensive to develop, the Cretaceous beds have not been utilized to any great extent for industrial or cooling purposes.

The glacial deposits rest unconformably on the Cretaceous. In a considerable part of western Long Island, the Cretaceous beds have been deeply eroded and in some areas entirely removed, and in these places the Pleistocene deposits lie directly upon the old bedrock surface. The early glacial deposits consist of highly permeable water-bearing outwash gravels—the Jameco gravel, an artesian aquifer—which are overlain by beds of interglacial clay, silt and fine sand—the Gardiners clay and the Jacob sand. The early glacial deposits are distributed around the borders of Long Island and also lie in the buried valleys that were cut in the Cretaceous deposits at the western end of the Island. The uppermost and youngest sediments on Long Island, except for minor accumulations of very recent material, are considered to be of Wisconsin age and consist chiefly of outwash and till. These beds cover

[3] Thompson, D. G., Wells, F. G., and Blank, H. R.: Recent geologic studies on Long Island with respect to ground water supplies. Econ. Geol., 32: Figs. 1 and 2, p. 454, 1937.

most of the Island and the outwash is the chief source of ground water on Long Island.

Although the uppermost beds of outwash sand and gravel are interspersed with thin layers and lenses of clay and silt that confine the ground water at some places, ground water occurs chiefly under water table conditions in these beds. The lower beds, however, are covered almost everywhere by extensive overlapping and interfingering layers and lenses of clay and silt which confine the ground water. The glacial beds are more productive and the temperature of the ground water in them is normally lower than that in the Cretaceous deposits. Because of these factors, and also because they lie at shallower depths and can be more economically tapped, most of the ground water pumped for industrial and cooling purposes is withdrawn from the glacial outwash. Likewise, most of the warm water discharged from cooling plants is returned to these beds.

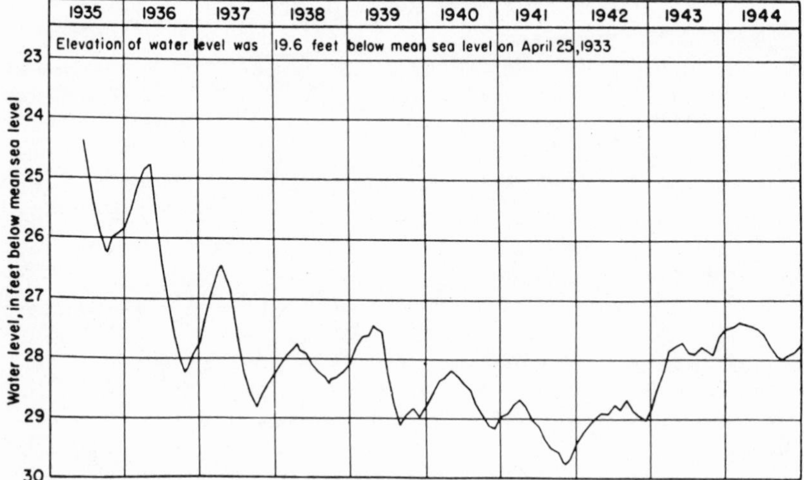

FIG. 2. Movement of water level well K-30, Kings County (Brooklyn), N. Y.

The overdevelopment of the ground water resources in the western part of the Island has caused the water table to decline considerably below sea level in most of Kings County and western Queens County and a "crater-like" depression has been formed on the water table. The area in which ground water levels lie below sea level is shown on Fig. 1, which also indicates that the bottom of the depressed area lies more than 25 feet below sea level.[4] The depth of the water table is also illustrated by the graph on Fig. 2, which shows the trend of water level since 1935 in an observation well, K-30, situ-

[4] For a more detailed statement and maps showing water levels, see Jacob, C. E.: The water table in the western and central parts of Long Island, New York State Water Power and Control Commission Bull. GW-12: 24 pp., 1945.

ated near the bottom of the "crater."[5] Elsewhere on Long Island, the water table, as shown by Fig. 1, generally slopes toward the shore and at places stands more than 80 feet above sea level.

As a result of the lowering of the water table in western Long Island, sea water from the surrounding tidal bays and estuaries has moved into the periphery of the "crater." The graphs on Fig. 3 show the chloride content

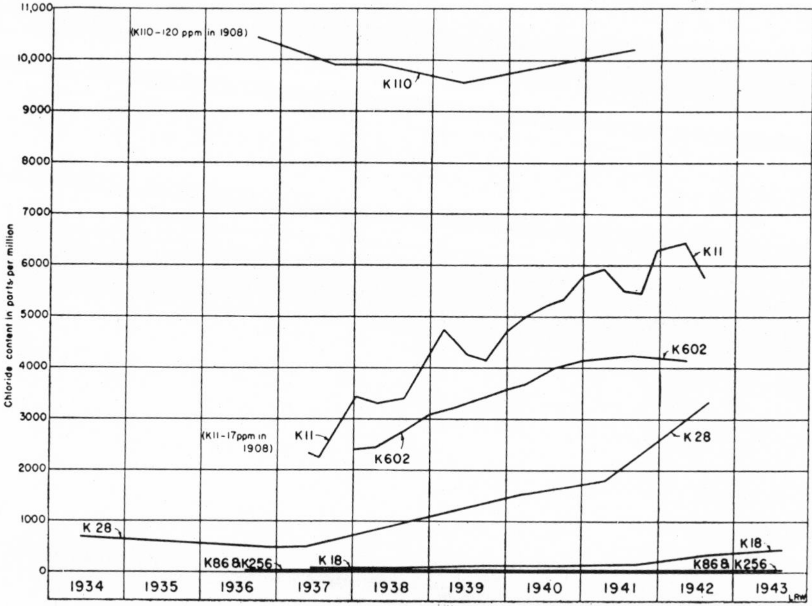

FIG. 3. Chloride content of ground water in Kings County, N. Y.

of ground water withdrawn from several wells situated around the northern part of the "crater" (Fig. 1). The chloride graphs for three sets of wells—K-110, K-11, K-18; K-28, K-256; and K-602, K-86—have been given in order to indicate the extent of the salt water encroachment and its rate of movement inland. The location of these wells, which are all used for cooling purposes, is shown on Fig. 1. Wells K-11, K-28, K-86, and K-602 are used throughout most of the year, whereas the other three wells are used chiefly during the summer cooling season. The features shown by the graphs are fairly typical of chloride conditions at other similar wells in the areas covered. The graphs for wells K-86 and K-256 indicate that the ground water in the central parts of the "crater" is relatively fresh and has not yet been invaded by salt water, whereas the graph for well K-110 shows that along the coastline the chloride content has become more or less stabilized at a high level. A single record, shown on Fig. 3, from an old well at the same plant as well

[5] For a more detailed statement of the trend of water level in well K-30, see Brashears, M. L.: U. S. Geol. Survey Water-Supply Paper 944, pp. 117–119, 1944.

K-110 indicates that encroachment had begun at this place as far back as 1908. A single record of the salinity of well K-11 in 1908 is also shown on Fig. 3. The chloride content at that time, 17 parts per million, in contrast to well K-110 in 1908, indicates fresh water conditions. Available records indicate that the chloride content of Upper New York Bay and the East River, although variable, is on the average about half that of sea water, or about 12,000 to 13,000 parts per million. It would appear, therefore, that the chloride content of the ground water in the area around well K-110 has reached and become stabilized at about the maximum possible salinity. Furthermore, it is apparent from the remainder of the graphs on Fig. 3—wells K-11, K-18, K-28, and K-602—that sea water has moved inland at a fairly rapid rate, during the past few years.

RECHARGE WELLS.

The operation of a recharge well is similar to that of a supply well except that the flow of water is in the opposite direction. When water is poured into a recharge well, the head in the well is increased. As a result, a cone of elevation is produced on the water table in the area surrounding the recharge well. The cone of elevation is similar to the cone of depression produced around a pumping well, except that the apex of the cone is above the water table. If a supply well and a recharge well are close together, as is the case at many installations on Long Island, some of the water discharged from the recharge well will be drawn into the supply well.

Various kinds of recharge wells have been constructed on Long Island but essentially all of them fall into two basic classes of construction, the so-called "dry type" and the so-called "wet type." The former consist of cased holes that end above the water table whereas the latter are screened below the water table. A few recharge wells have been constructed with the screen partially above and partially below the water table. Available records indicate that about 75 per cent of the recharge wells so far constructed are screened below the water table.

Each type of recharge well has certain inherent advantages not found in the other but, according to well drillers, the "wet type" of well is generally more successful. In the "dry type" of well, the warm water is usually discharged at a considerable distance above the water table permitting therefore some dissipation of heat as the water percolates downward to the water table. This type of recharge well is usually finished with a section of well casing into which slots have been cut whereas "wet type" wells are generally equipped with a standard well screen. Because of this factor and because they are shallower in depth, the "dry type" of well is less expensive to construct. However, excessive clogging is reported to take place in these wells because of the release of dissolved gases as the water leaves the discharge pipe and because the water comes in contact with oxygen in the air. Moreover, there are no adequate means of reconditioning these wells, whereas the same methods that are used to redevelop supply wells—surging, bailing, and acid treatment—can readily be applied to the "wet type" of well.

The construction and successful operation of each recharge well is governed in large part by local geologic and ground water conditions. One limiting factor is the depth of the water table below the land surface. If the water table is shallow-lying, as is usually the case in seaside areas on Long Island, the permissible build-up of the hydrostatic head at the recharge well will be relatively small. In such areas, it is generally possible to create in a pumping well a drawdown of greater extent than the maximum build-up that can be attained in the companion recharge well. Thus, assuming equal conditions of well construction and equal permeabilities, the maximum possible rate of return may well be considerably lower than the rate of yield of the companion supply well. Under such conditions it is necessary to construct more than one recharge well to handle the discharge from a single supply well.

The presence of silt or other particles in the water discharged into a recharge well may clog the screen openings and may even pass through the screen and be deposited in the surrounding material, and thus reduce its permeability. Even though the amount of silt in the water is small, the aggregate may constitute a large quantity. For example, if the water pumped from a supply well on Long Island, which is operated about 1,000 hours during the cooling season at the rate of 500 gallons per minute, contained only one ounce of silt in every 100 gallons, it would carry nearly 10 tons of silt into the recharge well. It is very important, therefore, that a supply well be adequately developed to remove all sediment.

Because of the limited space available in the urban areas in western Long Island, it is frequently necessary to construct recharge wells within short distances of their companion supply wells. And since the Water Power and Control Commission requires that the warm water from cooling plants be returned to the aquifer from which it is withdrawn, it is of prime importance to secure the maximum possible vertical separation between the screens of the recharge well and the pumping well in order to take advantage of any impervious zones or other irregularities in stratification between the horizons at which the two wells are finished. If only a thin relatively impervious zone is present, the rise in temperature of the water pumped from the supply well would be much slower than if no such zone were present.

The data shown on Fig. 4 show the influence of irregularities of stratification on the rise of ground water temperature at a cooling plant in Kings County, New York, and indicate the desirability of utilizing favorable geologic conditions in constructing recharge and supply wells. At this locality (Fig. 1), glacial deposits containing three separate beds of sand and gravel rest directly upon the old bedrock surface. Two wells (K-930 and K-956), capable of pumping at a combined rate of over 1,000 gallons per minute, discharge into one recharge well, K-931. In the summer of 1939, one supply well (K-956) and the recharge well were both screened in the upper aquifer whereas the other supply well was pumping water from the middle bed of sand and gravel, which is separated from the upper horizon, as shown on Fig. 4, by a relatively impermeable zone. In 1940, both supply wells were deepened and thereafter tapped the lowermost aquifer which lies beneath a

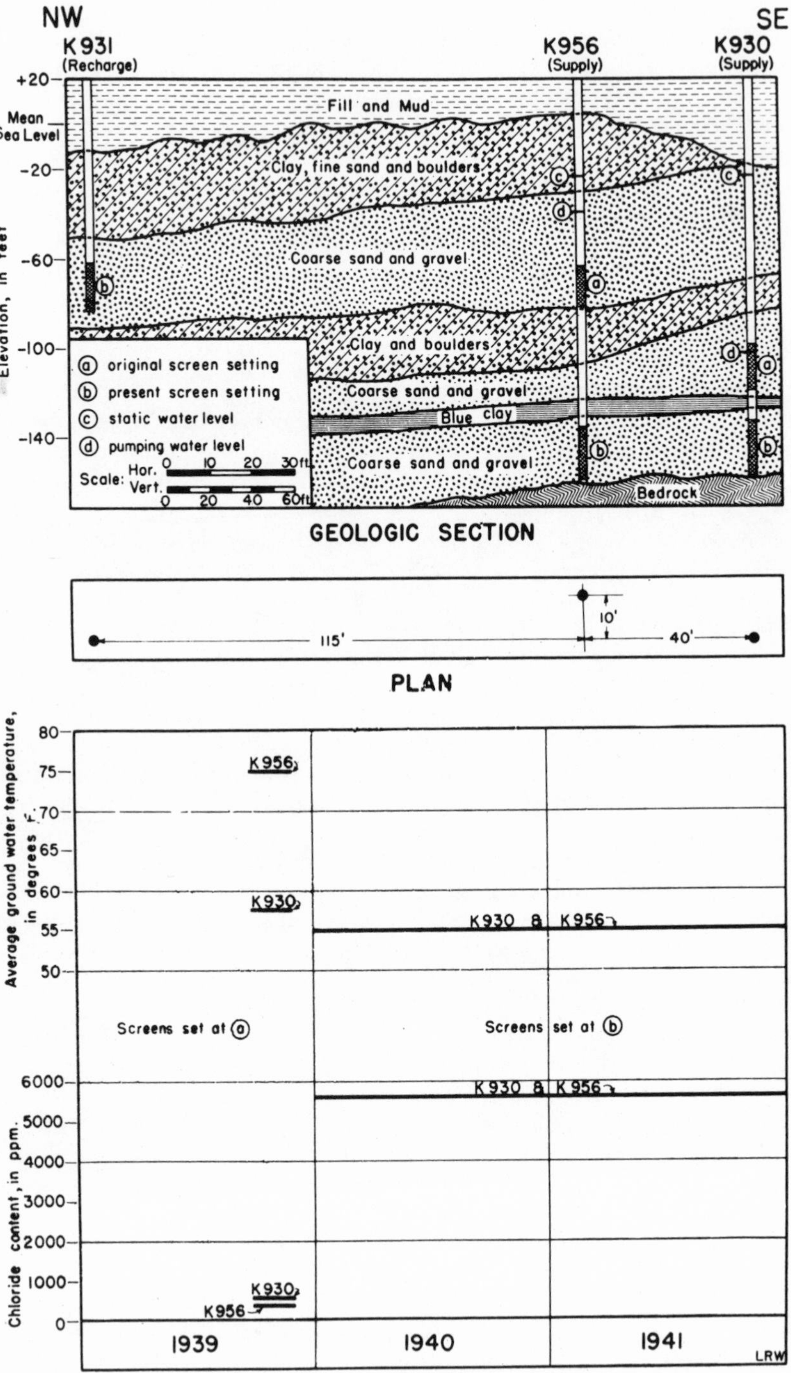

FIG. 4. Influence of geologic conditions on the fluctuation of temperature and salinity of water in wells in Kings County, N. Y.

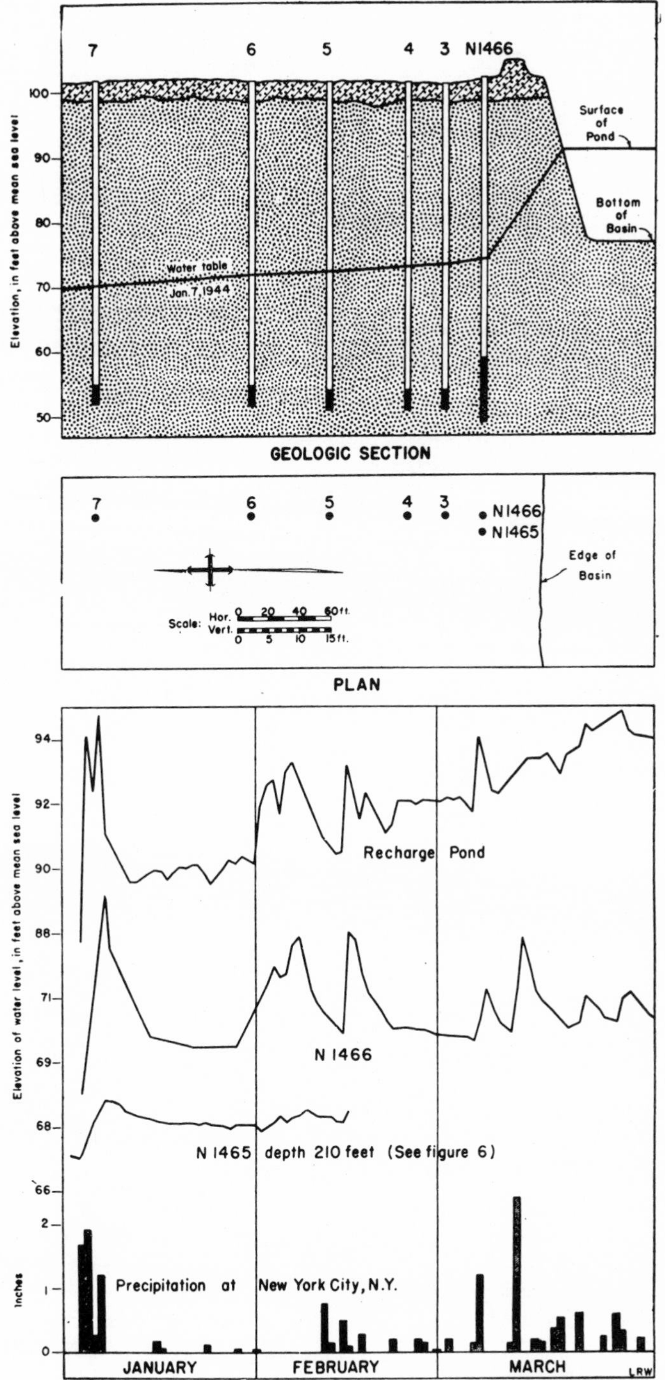

FIG. 5. Movement of ground water level in wells in Nassau County, N. Y., as result of recharge operations.

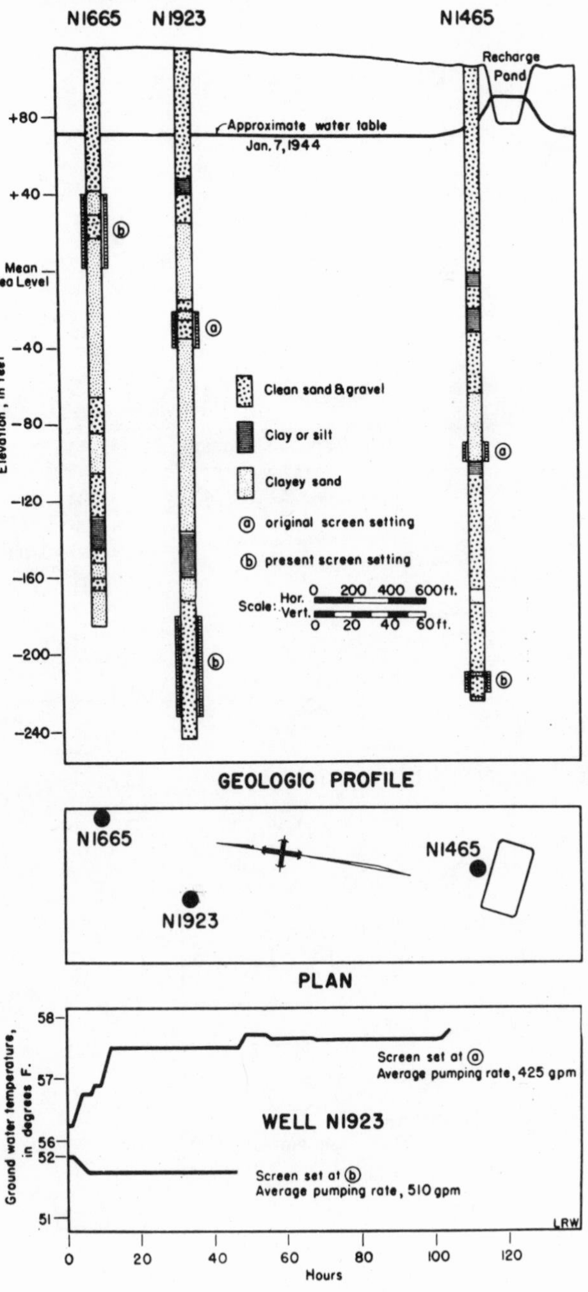

FIG. 6. Influence of geologic conditions on fluctuations of ground water temperature in wells in Nassau County.

thin layer of clay. The graphs of ground water temperature shown on Fig. 4 show the protective effect of the impermeable zones, and indicate that water pumped from the middle aquifer is only slightly affected by recharge in the upper zone and also that little if any warming occurs in the lower zone whereas the temperature of the water in the upper zone was raised about 20 degrees F. The graphs of chloride content for the two supply wells, also given on Fig. 4, by indicating differing salinities for each aquifer likewise show the hydraulic separation of the three beds of sand and gravel.

FIG. 7. View from northwest of recharge basin showing intake pipe and shelter housing water-stage recorder.

The protective effect of irregularities in stratification is again shown by the data for a large war plant in Nassau County where the water levels lie above sea level rather than below as is the case in Brooklyn. The recharge basin shown on Figs. 5 and 6 is used to return cooling water pumped from four large capacity wells (see also Fig. 1). Process water relatively high in impurities is also discharged into the basin which penetrates about 30 feet of coarse outwash and is about one acre in extent. The discharge into this basin ranges from about 300,000 gallons a day in the winter to about 3,000,000 gallons a day during the peak season in the summer. Previous to the construction of the basin, the warm water was returned by means of long, narrow trenches about 10 feet deep which were located in the vicinity of two of the pumping wells (N-1665 and N-1923). Warm water discharged from the trenches caused a rise of several degrees in well N-1665. Graphs giving the fluctuation of water level in the recharge basin, a nearby shallow observation well, N-1466, and a nearby deep observation well, N-1465, are given on Fig. 5, along with a geologic cross section and the daily precipitation. The character of the deposits penetrated by well N-1465, which consist of Upper Cretaceous beds overlain by about 50 feet of glacial outwash, is given on Fig. 6, along with similar information for two other deep wells. A view of the recharge basin is given in Fig. 7, which also shows the location of the water-stage recorder operated on the basin.

The Cretaceous sediments are composed of alternating layers of sands and clays that vary considerably in thickness and extent and it is evident from the data on Fig. 6 that the extent of the lenses of clay is limited. The overlapping nature of the permeable beds and the absence of a widespread layer of clay provide the physical setting for vertical movement of water. And as might be expected, the graphs of water level on Fig. 5 confirm the geologic evidence that all of the permeable beds are hydraulically interconnected by showing that a rise in water level in the recharge basin causes a rise of water level in the deep well, N-1465, even though its screen lies below lenses of clay and beds of clayey sand. However, the hydraulic channels through the intervening lenses of clay are tortuous and cause a roundabout vertical movement of water, thus providing a means for dissipating the heat in the warm water, a feature that is illustrated in Fig. 6.

During the drilling of well N-1923, a test screen was set in the well at a depth of about 160 feet. Later on another test screen was set at a depth of about 320 feet. As shown by the graphs of ground water temperature on Fig. 6, warm water from nearby sources entered well N-1923 at the time it was test pumped at the higher level whereas the bed of clay lying above the lower screen prevented an inflow of warm water. By utilizing these favorable geologic conditions it has been possible to recharge the deep-lying water-bearing beds without causing a rise in water temperature.

SUMMARY.

Although the conservation policy adopted in 1933 by the Water Power and Control Commission has permitted the drilling of new wells for cooling purposes, further overdevelopment has been essentially prevented since water pumped from all new wells, except a few having capacities less than 100,000 gallons per day (70 gallons per minute), is being returned to the ground. In addition, a number of large wells drilled previous to 1933, which discharged cooling water to the sewers, have been abandoned since adoption of the conservation policy. Discontinuance of pumping at such wells thus has reduced to some extent the areal overdevelopment. Although water levels in the "crater area" continued to drop at a decreasing rate for a number of years after the conservation policy was adopted, a reversal in the trend of water levels, resulting from the gradual decline in pumpage in the area, took place near the end of 1941. Since then, as shown by the graph (Fig. 2) of water level in an observation well (K-30) situated near the center of the depressed water table, water levels have gradually recovered. However, the water table near the center of the overdeveloped area was still more than

27 feet below sea level at the end of 1944 and the inflow of sea water has continued (Fig. 3). It is rather clear, however, that the conservation program of the New York State Water Power and Control Commission not only has prevented further overdevelopment but also has brought about a gradual overall improvement of conditions. As overall pumpage is further reduced, an additional recovery of water levels with a consequent reduction in rate of inflow of sea water is to be expected.

ACKNOWLEDGMENTS.

The ground water investigation which forms the basis of this paper is being conducted by the U. S. Geological Survey in cooperation with the New York Water Power and Control Commission, the Nassau County Department of Public Works, the Suffolk County Board of Supervisors and the Suffolk County Water Authority. Officials of these agencies, well drillers and well owners, furnished much information and assistance that has been helpful and the writer wishes to gratefully acknowledge their efforts in his behalf. The determination of the chloride content of well water was made at the Mount Prospect laboratory of the Department of Water Supply, Gas, and Electricity, City of New York.

9

Reprinted from *Eng. Geol. Case Histories* 7, 62–74 (1969)

Ground-Water Management in the Raymond Basin, California

JOHN F. MANN, JR.

INTRODUCTION

The Raymond Basin lies just a few miles to the northeast of the City of Los Angeles, and includes the City of Pasadena and all, or parts of, several smaller cities. The history of water development in this area is interesting and complex. The combination of substantial runoff from nearby high mountains, large alluvial volumes to absorb the flood flows, and a natural underground "dike" which forced the ground waters to the surface, resulted in perennial springs and surface flows which were utilized by early Indians. Some of these rising ground waters were developed by the padres of the San Gabriel Mission, and by white settlers in the early 1800's for such purposes as operating a grist mill, a sawmill, and a tannery, in addition to domestic uses (Blackburn, 1952). The earliest wells, just above the "dike," were artesian. As more wells were drilled in the basin above the "dike," and especially with the advent of the deep-well turbine pump, the rising waters were dried up and the artesian flows stopped. Alarmed by the progressive lowering of water levels in the basin, the City of Pasadena in 1937 sought, through the courts, to restrain pumping (Blackburn, 1961). The resulting litigation is referred to as Pasadena vs. Alhambra, or the Raymond Basin Adjudication.

From the standpoint of both physical and legal innovations, this is a landmark case. It was the first ground-water basin in California in which the Court reference procedure was used, the first in which the Division of Water Resources was appointed Watermaster to administer the decree, and the first basin in California in which essentially all the rights to pump ground water were adjudicated. Legally, the case is famous for developing the "doctrine of mutual prescription." At the time the action was filed, the pumpers consisted of true overliers who pumped their own water and used it on their own land, overlying appropriators such as municipalities and public utilities, and exporting appropriators who pumped water from the basin and transported it for use outside the basin. In the judgment, no recognition was given to priorities based on time or place of use. The trial court decreed that overdraft had existed for more than 5 years, and that each pumper had prescripted all the other pumpers. The safe yield was apportioned among the pumpers on the basis of extractions preceding the filing of the action. The judgment was affirmed by the California Supreme Court (33 Cal 2d 908), but one of the justices dissented vigorously. The shock with which some of the California legal fraternity greeted the doctrine of mutual prescription is reflected in the dissenting justice's opinion:

> I would say that the doctrine laid down in the majority opinion in the case at bar is based upon the philosophy of bureaucratic communism.

Control of ground water pumping in the Raymond Basin under the Watermaster has now been in effect for more than 20 years.

GEOLOGY

The Raymond Basin covers some 40 square miles in the northwestern portion of San Gabriel Valley, a large area of alluvial ground-water storage in the inland portion of coastal southern California. The Raymond Basin is separated from the main San Gabriel Valley by the Raymond fault which retards the southerly outflow of ground waters from the basin (Fig. 1). Those ground waters are

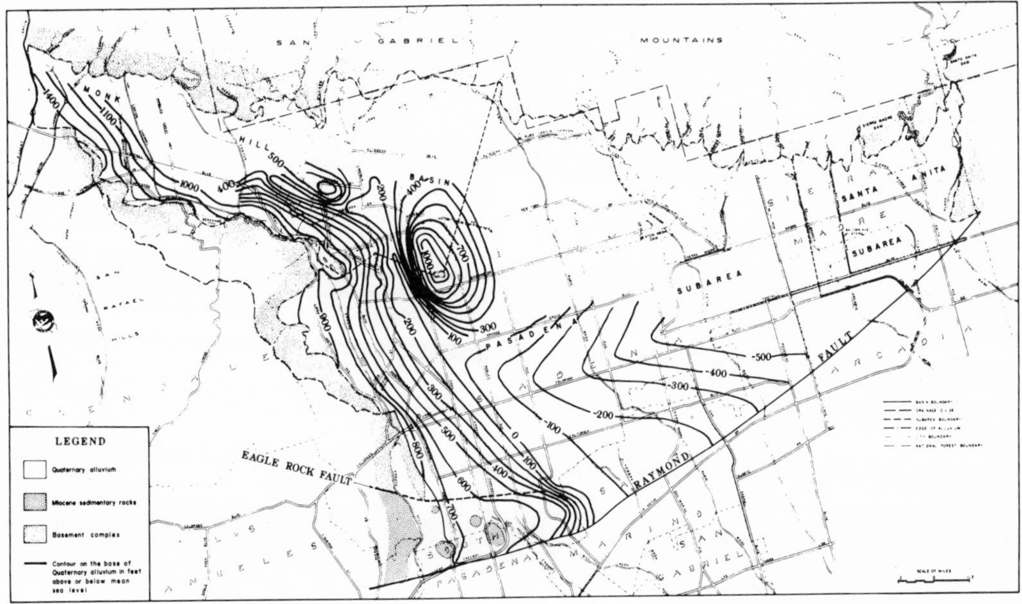

Figure 1. Geologic map and contours on the base of the Quaternary alluvium.

stored in thick alluvial deposits of fan origin which were laid down on an irregular bedrock topography.

Flanking the Raymond Basin to the north, and the source of the alluvial materials, are the high rugged San Gabriel Mountains consisting mainly of plutonic and metamorphic rocks, the so-called Basement Complex. The bold south front of those mountains is associated with the complex Sierra Madre fault zone, along which the Basement Complex has been dropped sharply. The Basement Complex is also exposed to the west of the Raymond Basin in the San Rafael Hills, which have only a few hundred feet of relief. Non-water-bearing rocks of Miocene age are exposed only near the southwest corner of the basin (Fig. 1). These consist of sandstones, shales, and conglomerates, and all have low porosity and permeability.

The Sierra Madre fault zone is one of the major zones along which the San Gabriel Mountains have been uplifted; it has been active since long prior to the deposition of the alluvial fan materials. Movements have continued through various episodes of the alluvial deposition, and near the mountain front, weathered alluvial gravels are in fault contact with the Basement Complex. The faulting does not affect the Recent alluvium.

The Eagle Rock fault forms the boundary between the Basement Complex and the Tertiary rocks near the southwest corner of the Raymond Basin (Fig. 1). To the east, the Eagle Rock fault is covered by alluvial materials, and the nature of its termination in that direction is not known. However, there is no evidence that movements on this fault have displaced any of the alluvial materials.

The important Raymond fault can be traced from several miles west of the Raymond Basin, along the south side of the Raymond Basin, and into the San Gabriel Mountains to the east (Fig. 1). Its surface trace is marked by a line of low hills, south-facing scarps, and sag ponds (Buwalda, 1940). Water levels stand 200 to 300 feet higher on the north side of the fault than on the south side. Near the southwest corner of the basin, where the up-faulted Tertiary rocks form hills 100 or more feet high, there are high dips and even some over-turning associated with the faulting. East of the Tertiary rock exposures the topographic expression of the faulting continues, but it is of a much more subdued nature. Where the active channels of Eaton and Santa Anita Creeks cross the fault, the topographic features have been removed by erosion and replaced by a featureless backfill of unfaulted Recent alluvium.

Almost the entire Raymond Basin is underlain by Basement Complex, which is completely covered by alluvium except for the small exposure at Monk Hill (Fig. 1). The configuration of the bedrock surface shown on Figure 1 was derived largely from well logs, but confirmed in critical areas by seismic surveys conducted in 1937, 1938, and 1939. One seismic profile was run westerly from Monk Hill to the San Rafael Hills to investigate the possibility that southerly underflow from the Monk Hill Basin might be prevented by a bedrock barrier (Sonderegger, 1936). Another seismic profile crossed the Monk Hill Basin about one-half mile northwest of Devil's Gate Dam. The most important features of the bedrock topography are: (1) the Monk Hill mound; (2) the large buried valley starting near the northwest boundary of the Monk Hill Basin, passing to the west of Monk Hill, then swinging easterly and reaching the Raymond fault near the eastern edge of the Raymond Basin; and (3) the sharp drop-off east of the Tertiary outcrops. The below-sea-level elevations indicate that this buried erosional surface must have been developed at a time when the Raymond Basin fault block was standing relatively much higher than at present.

The present alluvial surface shows a generally smooth slope in a southerly to southeasterly direction. Near the northwest corner of the Raymond Basin the apices of the alluvial fans are at elevations of about 1800 feet; easterly along the mountain front the fan heads become lower, reaching elevations of 800 feet near the eastern corner of the basin. Minimum elevations of the alluvial surface are about 600 feet near the Raymond fault in the eastern part of the basin. The alluvial thickness is about 1100 feet where the main bedrock valley just west of Monk Hill. Except close to the bedrock outcrops surrounding the basin, the alluvial thicknesses are generally in excess of 700 feet.

Close to the mountains, the alluvial fan materials are expectably coarse, but bouldery materials extend all the way to the Raymond fault. Sandy layers are not common. Clays, resulting from the weathering of gravels, are abundantly distributed throughout the Raymond Basin, especially in the older gravels near the mountain front, and in the fans of the minor streams issuing from the mountains. Numerous clay and peaty layers are found just north of the Raymond fault, and are probably related to high water tables, ponds, and artesian leakage.

SOURCE AND MOVEMENT OF GROUND WATER

Recharge to the ground water of the Raymond Basin is derived from the percolation of stream flows originating in the mountains to the north, deep penetration of rain falling on the alluvial surfaces, and returns from delivered water used for irrigation or discharged to cesspools.

Two bodies of ground water are recognized: (1) the Arroyo Seco-Eaton ground-water body including the Monk Hill Basin and the Pasadena Subarea, which constitute the Western Unit; and (2) the Santa Anita ground-water body (the Eastern Unit). All the mountain runoff from the extreme northwest corner of the Raymond Basin and extending for several miles to the east of Eaton Canyon is considered to contribute to the Western Unit. Big and Little Santa Anita Creeks contribute to the Eastern Unit. Ground waters in the Western Unit move southerly toward the Raymond fault, but are diverted easterly by the impermeable block of Miocene rocks (Fig. 2). Most of the underground outflow from the Western Unit crosses the Raymond fault in the easterly portion of that unit. Ground waters in the Santa Anita Subarea move directly south and cross the Raymond fault, where permeability permits, without appreciable change of direction.

The southerly boundary of the Monk Hill Basin approximates the minimum cross-section of alluvial fill in the bedrock valley just west of Monk Hill. To the north of this boundary, water levels remain at appreciably higher levels than in areas to the south, suggesting retarded underflow. Lower permeability of alluvial materials near this boundary may contribute to the slowing of underflow. The easterly boundary of the Monk Hill Basin is arbitrary; the underlying alluvial materials are fairly tight, easterly components of water-level gradients are small, and underflow is considered minor.

The boundary between the Pasadena Subarea and the Santa Anita Subarea attempts to approximate the western boundary of ground waters derived from Santa Anita Creek. There is considered to be little underflow across this line because of limited permeability and unfavorable gradients. The position of the hydrologic boundary was influenced in part by a convenient nearby street.

In its functioning as a barrier to the movement of ground water, three conditions along the Raymond fault can be recognized: (1) the tight barrier of the Miocene rocks; (2) the leaking fault membrane; and (3) overspill through Recent alluvium. The topographically high exposures of Miocene rocks between the Eagle Rock and Raymond faults form a complete barrier to southward-moving ground water. Although there are several alluvial passes crossing this block, the water-table elevations indicate that the ground water in those passes is of local origin and creates a ground-water ridge from which there is northerly and easterly flow into the central Pasadena Subarea. East of the Miocene outcrops the underflow barrier is created by reduced permeability along the fault plane itself. The Raymond fault is a reverse fault with the north block up, and the fault plane dips at a high angle to nearly vertical. The barrier is caused by gouge, by the blocking of displaced aquifers by low permeability beds, or possibly by dragged tight layers. The barrier in the older alluvial materials is not completely effective, and there is considerable

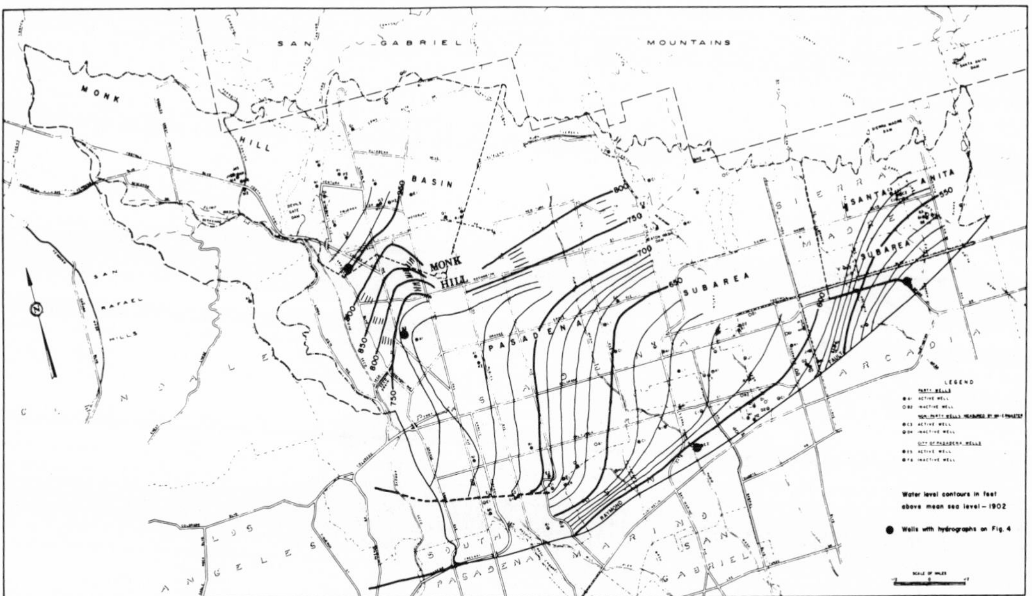

Figure 2. Water-level contours prior to heavy ground-water development.

leakage across it. At the Raymond fault, the Recent alluvium of Santa Anita Creek is about 80 feet thick, and there is opportunity for overspill through the Recent alluvium of ground water which rises because of the barrier effect in the older faulted alluvium. The Recent alluvium of Eaton Creek is so thin that subsurface overspill could only be minor.

FLUCTUATIONS OF WATER LEVELS

The general climatic trends in the Raymond Basin are shown on Figure 3. There was a general drought condition from 1916 to 1937, a wet period from 1937 to 1944, and a serious drought extending from 1944 with only minor relief through 1964. As shown in Figure 4a, the wells in the Monk Hill Basin show large fluctuations and good recoveries in wet periods. This is explained by strong recharge to the alluvium near the mountains, high rainfall (and therefore higher rainfall penetration) at the higher surface elevations prevailing in the Monk Hill Basin, and retarded ground-water outflow west of Monk Hill.

In the main Pasadena Subarea the recoveries during 1937-1944 are not so complete as in the Monk Hill Basin, and the continued recovery after 1944 is the result of the curtailment of pumping which started in 1944 (Fig. 4b). Just above the Raymond fault, where pressure conditions prevail and where local pumping, more than recharge, controls the water levels, the effect of the pumping curtailment is most evident (Fig. 4c). From 1944 to 1947 the recovery of static water levels was about 110 feet. In any year, the sharp annual fluctuations are indicative of the pressure conditions.

In the Santa Anita Subarea, the effects of direct recharge are shown as good recoveries, even in a single wet year (Fig. 4d). There was no initial curtailment of pumping in 1944, but as the drought progressed and water levels fell, a special provision of the judgment curtailed pumping in 1960-1961 and 1961-1962 (Fig. 5).

HISTORY OF THE LITIGATION

On September 23, 1937, the City of Pasadena filed a complaint against the City of Alhambra and 24 other named defendants in the Superior Court of Los Angeles County to quiet title to the water right within the Raymond Basin area. Because of the physical and legal complexities, an attempt was made to work out a "physical solution" to the problem. On January 31, 1939, most of the parties petitioned the Court to refer the matter to the Division of Water Resources as Referee for a determination of the physical facts, especially the safe yield and the annual extractions, and on February 8, 1939, such an order was made. On June 21, 1939, the Referee filed a preliminary report recommending that additional parties be brought into the action, and the Court ordered the Plaintiff to amend its complaint so as to follow that recommendation. The geologic and hydrologic studies by the Referee culminated in the Report of Referee, which was filed on July 12, 1943 (DWR, 1943). The Report of Referee concluded that the annual extractions exceeded the safe yield, resulting in a continued overdraft.

During the period of the reference the parties had been working on a proposed stipulated judgment, incorporating a water-exchange agreement. That agreement was approved by the Court on November 19, 1943. All parties but two had stipulated to the proposed judgment, and on November 24, 1943, the Court signed an order requiring that the stipulating parties comply with the terms of the proposed judgment during the pendency of the case. Following

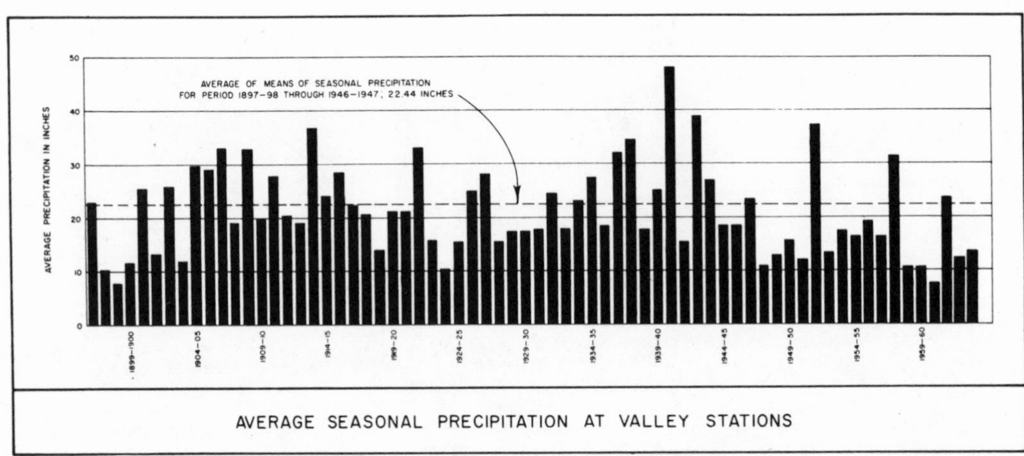

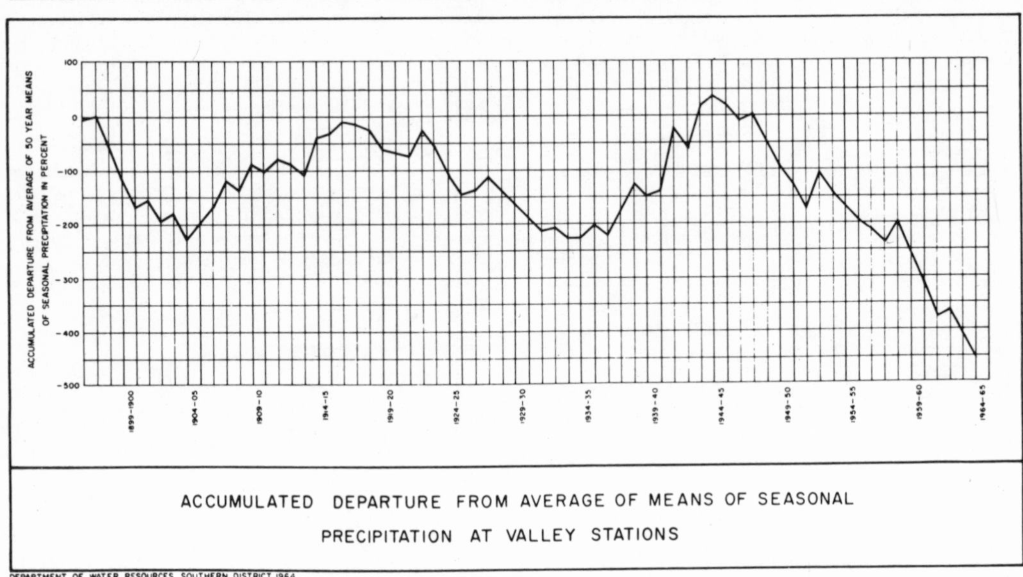

Figure 3. Average seasonal precipitation and accumulated departure from average.

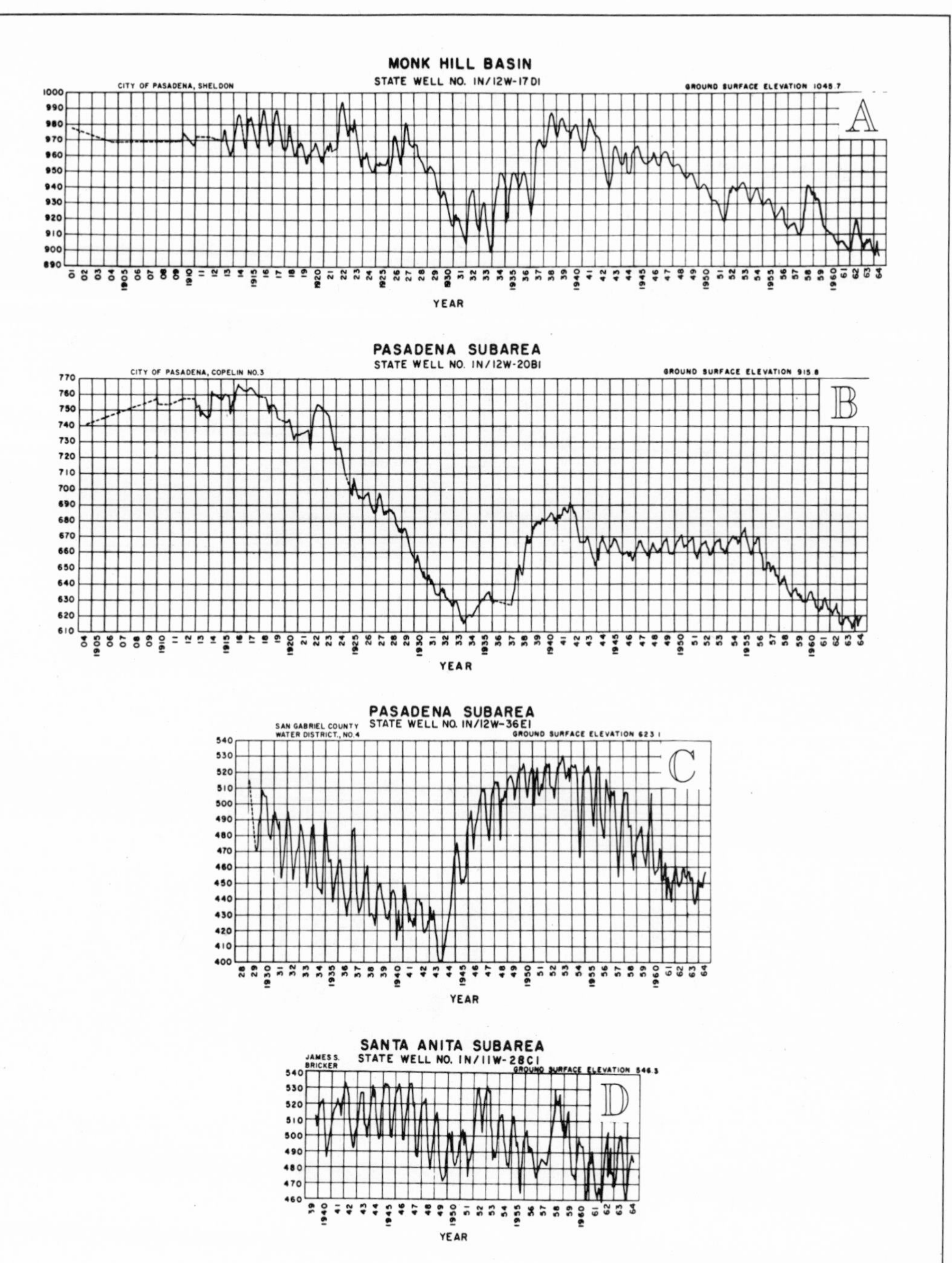

Figure 4. Representative hydrographs.

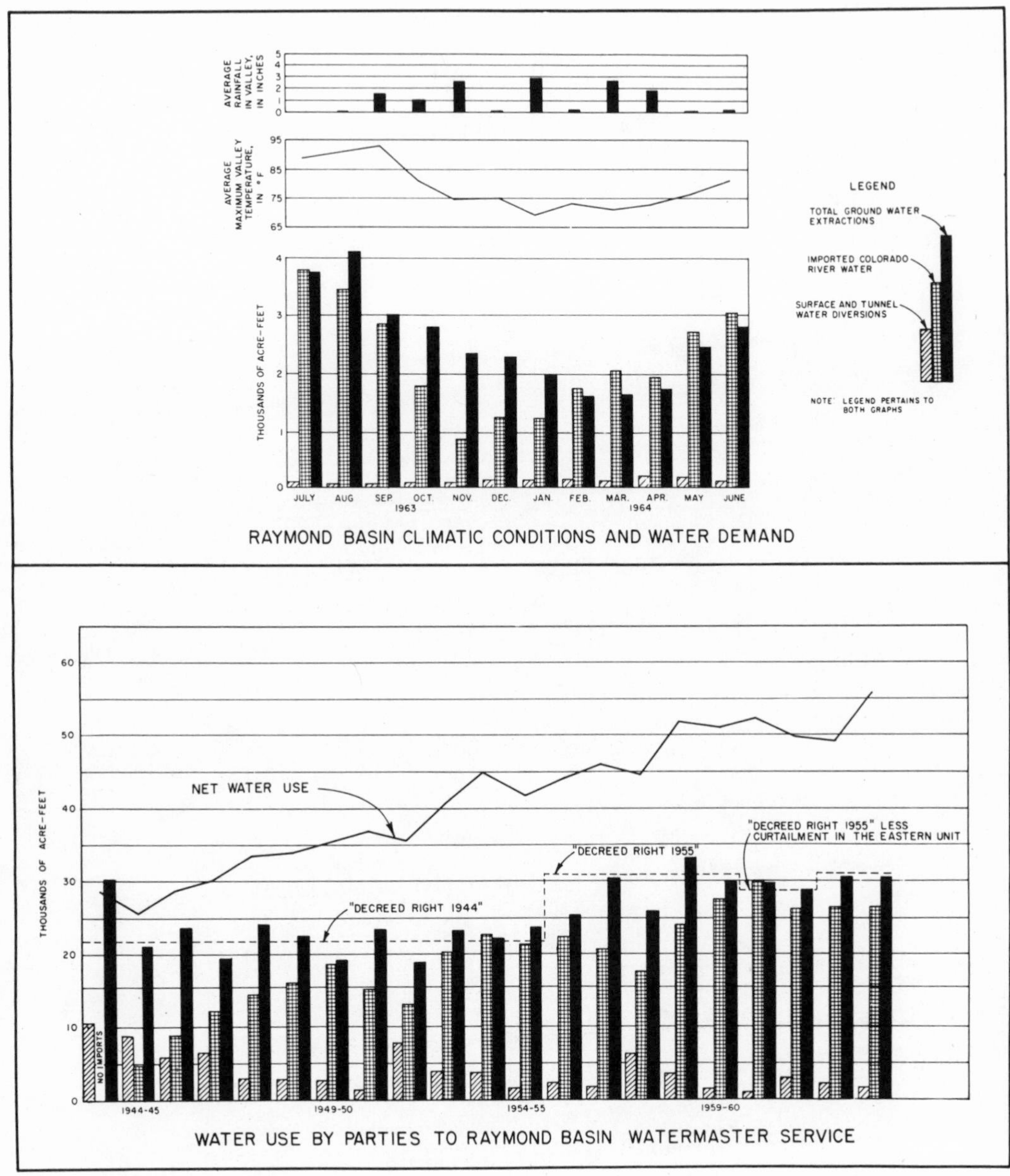

Figure 5. Climatic conditions, water demand, and water use by parties.

68

the provisions of the proposed judgment, the Court, on April 5, 1944, signed an order appointing the Division of Water Resources as Watermaster.

After a short trial, the Judgment was entered on December 23, 1944. Its most important provision was a required one-third cut-back in pumping in the Western Unit, effective as of July 1, 1944, except as to one party for whom the cut-back was to start July 1, 1945. One party appealed to the California Supreme Court, but the judgment was affirmed with minor modifications on June 3, 1949 (33 Cal 2d 908). A petition for a writ of certiorari to the United States Supreme Court was denied in 1950.

The terms of the judgment made it very difficult for the growing City of Sierra Madre, which had no source of imported water, to obtain its required water supplies. This situation led, on June 30, 1950, to the signing of an agreement between the City of Sierra Madre and the City of Arcadia, the only other pumper in the Santa Anita Subarea, which permitted the City of Sierra Madre to pump salvaged flood waters above its decreed right.

After six dry years of reduced pumping, during which water-level responses were better than expected, the City of Pasadena petitioned the Court, under its continuing jurisdiction, to order a review of the determination of the safe yield of the Raymond Basin area. On November 17, 1950, the Court appointed the Division of Water Resources as Referee for the review. The Report of Referee, filed October 5, 1954 (DWR, 1954), indicated a safe yield about 40 percent higher than the original figure, and on April 29, 1955, the Court signed a modification of the judgment which permitted increased pumping beginning July 1, 1955.

East Pasadena Water Company, Ltd., which had been added as a party Defendant in the original case and later dismissed, was not bound by the original judgment, and began pumping from one well in May 1955. The City of Pasadena, on April 26, 1960, filed a separate suit against this pumper and asked for an injunction. Negotiations were entered into and a stipulation for judgment was filed on March 26, 1965. The judgment provides for a waiver of pumping rights by the Defendant (except those that had been acquired by merger from another company with a decreed right), and an injunction against all pumping after December 31, 1966.

ORIGINAL SAFE-YIELD DETERMINATION

On June 9, 1939, the court made an Order of Reference to the Division of Water Resources, Department of Public Works, State of California for a determination of the physical facts, especially the safe yield. The resulting study was one of the earliest and most comprehensive studies of safe yield made in California (DWR, 1943).

The 29-year period from 1904-1905 through 1932-1933 was found to approximate closely the long-time mean precipitation. However, because of the many cultural changes in this urban area from 1904 to 1933, it was considered necessary to adopt a shorter, more recent period in which surface developments were much the same as in 1937, the year the lawsuit was filed. The shorter period selected was the 11-year period 1927-1928 through 1937-1938. The 11-year period had the further advantages of approximately normal precipitation, much more complete hydrologic data, and only a small net change of ground-water storage.

All inflow and outflow items were evaluated for the 11-year period and adjusted to the 29-year mean period. The Monk Hill Basin, Pasadena Subarea, and Santa Anita Subarea were handled separately. The inflow items evaluated were precipitation on the alluvial area, inflow from the mountains, and inflow from the hills. Measurements of mountain runoff went back only to 1913 and covered only 65 percent of the tributary mountain area. Correlations were used to extend and expand the existing records. Runoff from the hills was estimated from areas and precipitation. Long-time mean storm outflow from the Raymond Basin necessarily had to be related to the existing culture, and fortunately there were some gaging-station records during the 11-year period. The difference between the surface inflow and outflow was designated "local water remaining."

Detailed cultural surveys were made in 1938 and 1939, and to these acreages were assigned unit consumptive use values to determine total consumptive use. An independent study of consumptive use was based upon the differences between measured deliveries and the amounts of sewage exported from the basin or discharged to cesspools. Delivered water not derived from local wells was imported: (1) by the City of Pasadena from the San Gabriel River (since 1934); (2) a small amount from west of the Monk Hill Basin; and (3) a small amount by the City of South Pasadena northerly across the Raymond fault.

The change in storage during the 11-year period was based on water levels in 1927 and in 1938, and specific yield values. Two maps were prepared--contours of equal changes of water levels and contours of equal specific yield values averaged for depth in the zone of water-level change. The specific yield values had been developed mainly in an earlier study (DWR, 1934). Because of the complexity of underflow conditions at the Raymond fault, it was not possible to make a direct estimate of the underflow. It was calculated by taking total supply, subtracting disposal, and adjusting for change in storage.

The safe yield was determined to be 21,900 acre-feet per year, distributed as follows: Monk Hill Basin--6060; Pasadena Subarea--11,940; and Santa Anita Subarea--3900.

PROVISIONS OF THE JUDGMENT

The judgment declared that, under the then-existing conditions, the safe yield of the Eastern Unit was 3900 acre-feet per year and the safe yield of the Western Unit was 18,000 acre-feet per year. The taking by non-parties, upon whom the judgment is not binding, was declared to be 340 acre-feet per year for the Western Unit and 109 acre-feet per year for the Eastern Unit.

Diversions of surface-flow tributary to the Raymond Basin area were not treated in the same manner as ground-water pumpage. Such surface diversions, in the future, were to be limited to the maximum capacities of the diversion works as had existed at any time during the five-year period prior to October 1, 1937. Such maximum capacities for twelve specific diversion works were listed in cubic feet per second, and greater diversions were enjoined.

The most controversial and far-reaching provision is found in paragraph III:

That each and all of the rights of the parties hereto to pump water from wells or otherwise take water from the ground in said Raymond Basin area are of equal priority and of the same legal force and effect.

The "present unadjusted rights" were listed for two parties in the Eastern Unit, totaling 3791 acre-feet per year and for 26 parties in the Western Unit, totaling 25,608 acre-feet per year. The method used to calculate "present unadjusted rights" is not to be found in the judgment. However, a statement of what has come to be known as the "Raymond Basin formula" may be found in paragraph XIV of the Findings of Fact and Conclusions of Law:

. . . the highest continuous production of water for beneficial use in any five (5) year period prior to the filing of the complaint by each of the parties in each of said units, as to which there has been no cessation of use by it during any subsequent continuous five (5) year period . . .

Because the pumping of the "present unadjusted rights" in the Western Unit would have resulted in continued overdraft, each pumper was cut back proportionately to an amount designated as the "decreed right." In the Western Unit the "decreed right" was determined by reducing the "present unadjusted right" in the proportion that the safe yield of the Western Unit, less the nonparty pumping, bore to the aggregate of such rights of the parties in the Western Unit. This amounted to a cut-back of about 29 percent. Greater pumping than the "decreed right" was enjoined, except that in a single year, 120 percent of the "decreed right" was permitted, although over a 60-month period the pumping was restricted to 5 times the "decreed right." The "decreed rights" of all the parties in the Western Unit were listed in acre-feet per year, to the nearest acre-foot.

Because no overdraft was found in the Eastern Unit, there was no initial cut-back. As to the two parties, the City of Arcadia and the City of Sierra Madre, the pumping of 120 percent of the "decreed right" was permitted, but with the same 60-month reckoning. There was a specific limitation on the amount of water which could be pumped within one-half mile of the western boundary of the Eastern Unit and a further provision for reduction of the "decreed right" in the Eastern Unit from 3791 acre-feet per year to 3261 acre-feet per year in any year following a spring in which water levels were below an elevation of 500 feet in wells in a specified area near the southeastern corner of the Western Unit, and the water-table slope from this specified area was easterly into the Santa Anita Subarea.

The judgment appointed the Division of Water Resources as Watermaster, set up an advisory board of four members, and required each party to keep records of diversions, ground-water production, imports, exports, transfers, and water levels in wells. There were orders covering the responsibilities of the Watermaster, the financing of his activities, the preparation of annual reports, and appeals from Watermaster determinations. The judgment specifically denied making any determination regarding rights to imported water and intent to recapture such water after apreading. It incorporated an attached Raymond Basin Water Exchange Agreement of 1943 and gave legal protection to those parties exchanging water. An important provision was the retention of jurisdiction by the Court to review the safe yield, to protect against contamination, and to re-apportion rights forfeited or abandoned.

WATER EXCHANGE AGREEMENT

The Raymond Basin Area Water Exchange Agreement was signed by all but two of the parties during October and November 1943, and was approved by the Court on November 19, 1943. It became part of the judgment. The main objective of this agreement was to provide a means for any party to meet its needs by temporarily purchasing the rights released by another party. Each party agreed to participate in the Exchange Pool for a specified number of years--from 10 to 50. A party which offered to release water to the Exchange Pool for a certain year was required to specify the amount offered and the cost--equivalent to an average of its costs for all water (including imports). Water released in one unit could not be pumped in the other unit.

A special arrangement was made for the Monk Hill Basin. As to its taking from the Monk Hill Basin, the City of Pasadena was restricted to pumping the difference between the safe yield and the combined pumping of the non-parties and the six other parties in the Monk Hill Basin. Under certain conditions, the City of Pasadena, by virtue of this required shift of pumping from the higher Monk Hill Basin to the lower Pasadena Subarea, was allowed "undue costs" to be paid by the pumpers in the Monk Hill Basin.

Parties who desired to purchase water from the Exchange Pool were to file annual requests in advance. Requests were to be filled starting with the least expensive water offered, and the price to all Exchangees was the average price of all water taken from the Pool. Exchangors were considered to have pumped the water released and paid for. The Watermaster maintains an accounting of the water exchanged, collects from the Exchangees, and disburses money to the Exchangors (DWR, 1945W-1964W). The exchange agreement was amended in the spring of 1944 to include one additional party in the Monk Hill Basin.

SALVAGE OF WATER BY THE CITY OF SIERRA MADRE

In the Santa Anita Subarea, the only significant pumpers are the Cities of Arcadia and Sierra Madre. The City of Arcadia lies on both sides of the Raymond fault, and whereas pumping north of the fault is restricted, pumping south of the fault is unrestricted. As needed, the City of Arcadia imports ground water to its customers north of the fault. The City of Sierra Madre extends into the Pasadena Subarea, but has pumping rights only in the Santa Anita Subarea. Its rights under the judgment included a surface diversion of up to 6.0 cubic feet per second in Little Santa Anita Canyon, and a "decreed right" of 1264 acre-feet per year, which was later modified upward to 1764 acre-feet per year. However, when water levels drop and there is an easterly water-table slope from the Pasadena Subarea into the Santa Anita Subarea, the pumping right of the City of Sierra Madre is reduced to 1087 acre-feet. The reduced pumping allocation was in effect in 1960-1961 and 1961-1962 (Fig. 5) and was in effect in 1964-1965. To 1965, the City of Sierra Madre had not had available to it any imported waters.

In anticipation of future difficulties, the City of Sierra Madre on June 30, 1950 entered into an agreement with the City of Arcadia which permitted the City of Sierra Madre to spread certain flood waters within the Santa Anita Subarea and to recapture them, apart and in excess of its "decreed right." This agreement was approved by the Court on October 6, 1950, and the responsibility for calculating the net amount salvaged was assigned to the Watermaster (DWR, 1959).

The City of Sierra Madre has about 22 acres of spreading grounds on the west side of the lined channel of Sierra Madre Wash (Little Santa Anita Creek). The active production wells are just south of these spreading grounds. Water is diverted from the nearby channel of Sierra Madre Wash, from Santa Anita Creek to the east by means of a pipeline 1.2 miles long, and from storm drains carrying street runoff in the vicinity of the spreading grounds. The water is measured at the intake to the spreading grounds and at an overflow weir. The gross amount spread is reduced by two items: (1) that portion of the diversion from Santa Anita Creek which would have percolated above the Raymond fault, assuming the diversion had not been made; and (2) the increase in underflow across the Raymond fault which is attributable to the spreading.

For (1) an empirical relationship was set up relating discharge (in cubic feet per second) at the head of the percolation reach to percolation in the reach (in cubic feet per second). Data for this relationship have been obtained from streamflow measurements at both ends of the percolation reach. This water, calculated on a daily basis, is considered part of the natural safe yield. The determination of (2) involved monthly calculations of increased underflow resulting from increased water-table slopes across the Raymond fault. Deductions are taken for as long as the spread water remains unpumped. For the period 1951-1964, the City of Sierra Madre spread 11,792 acre-feet and was able to pump under a salvage credit a total of 4490 acre-feet.

In 1964, on behalf of the City of Sierra Madre, a proposal was made for the spreading and salvage of reclaimed sewage. This would involve some 1600 acre-feet per year developed by a water reclamation plant in the Pasadena Subarea. Several alternatives were suggested: (1) spreading in the Pasadena Subarea, pumping by the City of Sierra Madre in the Pasadena Subarea; (2) spreading in the Santa Anita Subarea, additional pumping by the City of Sierra Madre there; and (3) spreading in the Pasadena Subarea, pumping by the City of Arcadia there, with release of pumping rights in the Santa Anita Subarea by the City of Arcadia to the City of Sierra Madre. These suggestions are still under discussion.

REDETERMINATION OF SAFE YIELD

After a series of six dry years, during which time water levels had risen progressively, Plaintiff City of Pasadena petitioned the Court to order a review of the determination of the safe yield, and the motion was granted on November 17, 1950. This reference was also to the Division of Water Resources. The Report of Referee was completed in July 1954 (DWR, 1954).

The methods employed in the redetermination were much the same as used in the original study. Because of the availability of more complete hydrologic data, the original 29-year period (1904-1933) was replaced by a 30-year period (1919-1949), which was adopted as the long-time mean period. The original 11-year period (1927-1938), considered to represent cultural conditions as of 1937-1938, was replaced by the 12-year period 1938-1950, which more accurately reflected the cultural conditions as of 1951-1952.

The result of the redetermination was an increase of safe yield of about 40 percent (Table 1). The reasons for this increase can be seen in Table 2. The most obvious cause for the increase in safe yield is the sharp increase in imports, especially in the Pasadena Subarea. Another factor tending to increase the local safe yield is the reduction in exports, at least to the extent of the return waters. Items working in the direction of reducing the safe yield are the increases in surface outflow and sewage export. Although consumptive use remained relatively unchanged, there were greater delivery demands, with the result that a greater percentage of the delivered water got into the sewers. Furthermore, additional areas were sewered, and former cesspool recharge became sewage export. The increased surface outflow is related to the expansion of impervious areas that accompanied the further urbanization. The item labeled "decrease due to spreading" is an adjustment necessitated by the terms of the salvage agreement between the City of Arcadia and the City of Sierra Madre.

CONCLUSIONS

The Raymond Basin adjudication is but one event in a series through which the City of Pasadena sought to assure water supplies for future growth. In 1928, the City of Pasadena became one of the charter members of the Metropolitan Water District of Southern California, which was formed for the purpose of importing water from the Colorado River to coastal southern California. As early as 1923, that city had filed applications to appropriate flood waters of the San Gabriel River several miles to the east of the Raymond Basin. Those appropriations were protested vigorously by local interests and an agreement was negotiated in 1934 whereby the City of Pasadena, upon Colorado River water becoming available to it, would relinquish and abandon all rights to any of the waters of the San Gabriel River (Walters and others, 1961). The City of Pasadena imported water from the San Gabriel River during the period 1933-1941, but from 1941 to the present time all imports have been from the Colorado River.

The availability of supplemental water is a prime requisite to a physical solution of the Raymond Basin type. Where no supplemental water is available, an overdrafted ground water basin has three choices: (1) an immediate cut-back in pumping with curtailment of existing uses; (2) continued mining of water until the surface economy has to be abandoned; and (3) continued mining of water with a shift to higher water uses, such as agricultural to urban. Alternative (3) is often used in some basins with the expectation that the enlarged economic base generated by the mining of local ground water will demand (and be able to afford) future supplemental supplies.

The Exchange Pool can be a means of forcing those pumpers with growing demands to

Table 1. Comparison of 1938 and 1952 safe yields (acre-feet per year)

	Monk Hill Basin	Pasadena Subarea	Total Western Unit	Santa Anita Subarea	Total Raymond Basin
1938	6060	11940	18000	3900	21900
1952	7490	17990	25480	5290	30770
Percent Increase	23.6	50.7	41.6	35.6	40.5

Table 2. Changes in long-time mean items governing safe yield (acre-feet per year)

Item	Monk Hill Basin 1938	Monk Hill Basin 1952	Pasadena Subarea 1938	Pasadena Subarea 1952	Santa Anita Subarea 1938	Santa Anita Subarea 1952
Precipitation	12110	12100	29600	29600	4450	4450
Inflow from mountains	7720	5330	2770	2480	5680	5460
Inflow from hills	291	220	153	110	0	0
Inflow from Monk Hill Basin			5220	5680		
Subtotals	20111	17650	37743	37870	10130	9910
Surface diversions	1880	3640	1790	1780	1460	1140
Extractions	6380	6420	17570	12260	3380	2920
Imports	165	1060	2910	16400	0	810
Transfers in	0	640	4860	3530	0	0
Subtotals	8425	11760	27130	33970	4840	4870
TOTALS	28536	29410	64873	71840	14970	14780
Surface outflow	5430	6030	10980	14140	4140	4210
Exports	0	0	9520	4580	2030	0
Transfers out	4460	3010	0	640	403	530
Subtotals	4460	3010	9520	5220	2433	530
Sewage outflow	139	530	5776	8800	0	160
Consumptive use	10230	10130	25940	25050	3910	3770
Subtotals	10369	10660	31716	33850	3910	3930
Decrease due to spreading					0	200
TOTALS	20259	19700	52216	53210	10483	8670

arrange for receiving supplemental water, by making the costs of pumping quantities larger than assigned rights more than the costs of supplemental water. The Water Exchange Agreement was important in the earlier years of Watermaster operation, especially in the Monk Hill Basin. Colorado River water became available to the Monk Hill pumpers in 1955, but the quantity was somewhat lower than that of local supplies, and there was some reluctance to accept it. Under the terms of the agreement, however, a party with a connection to the Metropolitan Water District could get no water from the Exchange Pool unless undue hardship could be shown. After 1958 the Exchange Pool in the Western Unit ceased to be important; in 1963-1964, only one entity requested water from the Exchange Pool, in the amount of 30 acre-feet. In the Eastern Unit the amount exchanged in the 20 years of operation has averaged only about 100 acre-feet per year.

As illustrated by the activities of the City of Sierra Madre, the control of ground-water pumping tends to result in better conservation measures. The salvage of flood waters by the City of Sierra Madre may not exclusively involve waters that would otherwise waste to the ocean; some of those waters may have percolated to ground-water storage in San Gabriel Valley. In other ground-water basins, the proportion of water salvaged from unquestioned waste might be higher. The proposed reclamation of water from sewage completes an interesting cycle: (1) local disposal of sewage to individual cesspools; (2) expansion of sewerage facilities and connection to outfalls (tending to decrease the safe yield); and (3) local treatment of collected sewage with disposal of sludge to the outfalls, and local spreading of the effluent (tending to increase the safe yield).

In the more than 20 years that have elapsed since the start of ground-water management in the Raymond Basin, it appears that the pioneering approaches developed for that basin have been physically effective, the flare-up of water rights controversy has been minor, and the local entities are content with their solution.

In spite of the peace achieved locally, the Raymond Basin adjudication was not without external repercussions. The new doctrine of mutual prescription has brought strong reactions from supporters of classical concepts of water rights, and re-evaluations of those concepts (Towner, 1957; Hutchins, 1957; Sawyer, 1949). The Raymond Basin formula for calculating pumping rights has encouraged a race to build up prescriptive rights before adjudications are filed (Krieger and Banks, 1962). The Raymond Basin type of settlement has been completed in a second ground-water basin in southern California, it is almost completed in a third ground-water basin, and is currently being considered in several others.

ACKNOWLEDGMENTS

In the preparation of this paper, the author has necessarily drawn very heavily upon studies and reports prepared by the California Department of Water Resources in its dual role as Referee and as Watermaster. The department has kindly given permission to use Figures 3 and 5 and has made available the base maps for Figures 1 and 2, and the hydrographs on Figure 4. Through the courtesy of Duncan A. Blackburn, chief engineer and general manager of the Pasadena Water Department, access was gained to much information in the department's files.

REFERENCES CITED

Blackburn, D.A., 1952, Forty years in developing a water system: unpublished paper presented on October 29, 1952 at the California Section meeting, American Water Works Association.

________, 1961, The adjudication of the Raymond Basin: unpublished paper presented at the Southern California Coordinating Conference on November 21, 1961.

Buwalda, J. P., 1940, Geology of the Raymond Basin: private report submitted to the Pasadena Water Department.

Hutchins, W. A., 1957, California ground water: legal problems: 45 California Law Review 688-697.

Krieger, J. H., and H. O. Banks, 1962, Ground-water basin management: 50 California Law Review 56-77.

Sawyer, F. A., 1949, Water law: mutually prescriptive interests in underground water: 37 California Law Review 713-718.

Sonderegger, A. L., 1936, Report on ground-water conditions in Raymond Basin: private report submitted to Pasadena Water Department.

Towner, P. A., 1957, Mutual prescription--threat to vested rights to ground water: unpublished paper presented on December 12, 1957 at the convention of the Irrigation Districts Association of California at Long Beach.

Walters, E. H., I. R. Calvert, and M. A. Bengel, 1961, History of the San Gabriel River Water Committee, the San Gabriel River Spreading Corporation, and the San Gabriel Valley Protective Association: published by the Upper San Gabriel Valley Water Association.

The following reports by the California Department of Water Resources (and its predecessor, the Division of Water Resources) are cited as DWR, year. Watermaster reports are cited as DWR, yearW.

California State Department of Public Works, Division of Water Resources, 1934, South coastal basin investigation, geology and ground water storage capacity of valley fill, Bulletin 45.

________, 1943, Report of Referee, City of Pasadena vs. City of Alhambra, and others, No. Pasadena C-1323, Superior Court, Los Angeles County.

________, 1954, Report of Referee on a review of the determination of the safe yield of the Raymond Basin area, Los Angeles County, California. City of Pasadena vs. City of Alhambra, and others, No. Pasadena C-1323, Superior Court, Los Angeles County.

________, 1959, Report of Raymond Basin Watermaster on determinations of credit for water salvaged by the City of Sierra Madre in the Santa Anita Subarea, Raymond Basin, Los Angeles County, California.

________, 1945W to 1964W, Watermaster service in the Raymond Basin, Los Angeles County. Annual Reports.

III
Geomorphic Hazards

Editor's Comments on Papers 10 Through 17

Webster defines hazard as an "unforseen disaster." As used in geology, the term takes on two additional meanings. To qualify as a hazard, the event should be a short-term phenomenon, and the event must have created an extraordinary amount of damage or loss in lives. When interior forces within the earth are unleashed with the fury of volcanic activity or earthquakes and result in human loss, they can be truly called "geologic hazards."

> Two decades ago, the California Division of Mines began to tangibly react to the need for application of geologic principles for the public welfare by initiating interdisciplinary investigations of earthquakes. About ten years ago, the Division enhanced the relevance of its work to geologic protection of the public by entering into an intensive program of large-scale urban mapping with cooperative funding from Los Angeles County. Greatly intensified use of the environment in that metropolitan area has turned ordinary geologic processes into geologic hazards. Thus was born the Geologic Hazards program of the Division of Mines and Geology. There are no geologic hazards without people; the "hazards" arise from man's unwise, inept, and careless occupation and use or abuse of the geologic environment (Oakeshott, 1970, p. 193).

Human disasters that occur as the result of surficial processes, such as flooding and landsliding, are also geologic hazards, but more specifically *geomorphic hazards.* It is these features that are mostly emphasized in this part. There is a basic difference between geomorphic hazards and most geologic hazards: man by improper planning or disregard of natural processes may trigger a geomorphic hazard or hasten its onset. However, with some exceptions (see Volume III, Baldwin Hills, California, and Denver, Colorado), man is generally impotent to create changes in the interior forces of the earth and thus cannot be blamed when earthquakes or volcanic eruptions occur. It is not necessary that man be the initiator, because geomorphic hazards can still occur without his help, as in the case of Hurricane Agnes in 1972.

McKenzie and Utgard (1972) ask the question, "What can the geologist do about geologic hazards?"

> Working with adequate geologic knowledge he can conduct proper geologic investigations that can be used to prevent a geologic hazard from becoming a disaster. Recognition or identification of a geologic hazard at a certain locality must first be made. Once clearly identified and defined, there are several approaches to solving the problem, depending on the type of hazard. One solution is to avoid the problem by changing the proposed location of a structure such as a reservoir, nuclear power plant, or highway. This solution is often necessary in the case of naturally occurring hazards. Other alternatives are to eliminate the hazard or engineer the structure to withstand the hazard. Normally, the latter approaches are more costly than avoiding the problem. The urgency to avoid or prevent geologic hazards is a necessary outgrowth of a society characterized by increasing population and urbanization (p. 30).

The expansion of urban areas will increasingly contribute to potential danger from geomorphic hazards. The main trouble is that the hazard twins, floods and landslides, are like a two-edged sword. Cities with flat topography sprawl on and around floodplains and nonsheltered coasts, thus maximizing losses during high-water stages. Conversely, cities on rugged terrain build on slopes that easily become unstable with development, which distorts and accentuates normal gravity forces and causes increased mobility of hillslopes. Another aspect of some hazards is that the magnitude of the process and the damage it causes are entirely relative. Losses that occur are dependent upon such factors as climate and geographic location. A 6-inch snowstorm can cause havoc in Richmond, Virginia, but have negligible effect in St. Paul, Minnesota; a 3-inch rainfall can cause severe flooding in Tucson, Arizona, but do little damage in Rochester, New York. Thus the only generality applicable to all cities is that a complete assessment of the land–water ecosystem must be made and the growth of the urban area must be moderated to provide an optimum harmony with the natural equilibrium of the physical system. Further information on hazards is contained in Betz (in press).

Floods

The topic of flooding is so vast and has such a voluminous literature that the four articles selected for presentation in this section serve mainly as a summary to point the way for this popular and extremely important subject. The U.S. Water Resources Council article is an excellent review of the status of floods throughout the United States. Gilbert F. White's article provides a significant appraisal of the way flooding problems were analyzed and planned for in six U.S. cities. His work in the field of water management has received international acclaim. As Chairman of the Department of Geography at the University of Chicago from 1956–1969, he was instrumental in developing many new approaches to land-use practices that have had wide impact in policy decisions in the United States and elsewhere. White was also president of Haverford College for 10 years, and since 1970 has been Director, Institute of Behavioral Sciences, University of Colorado. To complete this section, the first chapter in Richard Bigger's volume on flooding in metropolitan Los Angeles is used and complemented by passages from Robert Carin's treatment of flooding in China.

Floods (nature's most common physical hazard) have plagued man since the time of Noah, and probably always will. In the twentieth century, problems associated with flooding have become inextricably involved with structural control devices such as dams and their impounded reservoirs. For example, the beneficial aspects of the latter are loudly championed as serving many purposes, including flood control, soil conservation, water supply, hydroelectric power, and recreation. Unfortunately, a variety of activities undertaken during the urbanization process constantly increases flood severity and associated damages, although the funds expended to "control" floods and to conserve lands and property from the hazards of flooding have also increased. It is a vicious circle. Part of the paradox occurs because of the innate feedback mechanisms that operate in the natural world, and man's acts to reduce flood damages at one point have often yielded larger damages than ever farther downstream. Although smaller floods may in part be minimized by such structural controls as dams, levees, floodwalls, and the like, when large floods occur the damages can become even greater. Such losses are sustained not only in ruined urban areas, but also on agrarian lands and in the upsets created in river channels. This latter problem of silting in reservoirs, channel incisement downstream from dams, and a rejuvenated erosion cycle in tributaries was discussed in Volume III of this trilogy. White and his group have repeatedly pointed out that part of the overall problem of floods is in their perception; they are perceived differently by different groups of people. Of course, the importance of environmental perception is not limited to flooding. In his well-documented summary and bibliographic work on environmental perception, Goodey (1971) presents the various developmental themes regarding man's values, attitudes, and concepts of urban areas. Knowledge of such parameters is fundamental because "Decision-makers operating in the environment base their decisions on the environment as they see it and not as it is, although their actions do affect the real environment" (p. 1). Typical of these attitudes are the different ways the floodplain is perceived (Whyte, 1968); residential developers, public officials, water engineers, and conservationists all differ in managerial approaches to this resource. Landscape awareness has begun to appear in many places, and suggestions for solutions of environmental decay have been widely offered, for example, in the journal *Landscape* under the leadership of J. B. Jackson; but not until the 1960s did the movement really start to take hold. Environmental perception was summed up by Mattern (1966), who introduced the concept of "landscape consciousness" and described it as "the exact knowledge of the ecological interrelationships of our environment."

Case histories have been written that describe how dams can be associated with flood tragedies. A dam failure in 1889 at Johnstown, Pennsylvania, caused 2,100 deaths. The St. Francis dam in California gave way on March 12, 1928, killing more than 350 people and destroying $10 million worth of property. The St. Francis disaster had the salutary effect of leading to the enactment of a new law in California making it compulsory to have a geologic investigation of all potential dam sites. The worst dam disaster in history occurred on October 9, 1963, at the Vaiont Dam, Italy, where landslides set up giant waves that overtopped the dam and inundated downstream areas with a wall of water that was still 230 feet high 1 mile below the dam. Loss of life exceeded 2,600, even though the dam was not structurally damaged.

The past few years have continued to demonstrate the ever-present danger of flood hazards. The year 1972 was very unfortunate for inhabitants of several floodplains. On February 26, 1972, a flood of Buffalo Creek, West Virginia, killed 118 people, destroyed 500 homes, and caused property damage of $15 million. The disaster was caused by the failure of a dam that had been constructed of rock waste from coal mining. In early June, Rapid City, South Dakota, was devastated by torrential rains that caused flooding and the collapse of Canyon Lake Dam, resulting in 226 dead, 1,000 destroyed houses, and $100 million in damages. Then on June 21 – 24, 1972, there occurred what has been described as "the most ravishing storm in U.S. history," Hurricane Agnes. It was unusual for a tropical storm of such magnitude (unleashing rainfall of 15 inches over wide areas) to travel so far inland. A total of 206 counties and 27 cities were officially designated as disaster areas. Harrisburg and Wilkes-Barre, Pennsylvania, Richmond, Virginia, and Elmira and Corning, New York, were especially hard-hit. The total losses amounted to more than $3.5 billion in property destruction, 116,000 damaged or destroyed buildings, and 130 dead. At Harrisburg, the Susquehanna River crested at 16.5 feet above flood stage. Ironically, it inundated the headquarters of the Pennsylvania Geological Survey, and destroyed 40,000 volumes in its famous library and 250,000 maps. In Pennsylvania alone these floods generated 16 million cubic yards of solid waste.

The year 1973 was hardly less severe. Heavy rains throughout the Mississippi Basin in the spring caused flooding of over 10.4 million acres, killed 30 people, left 30,000 homeless, and caused immediate damages of $193 million. Much greater ultimate loss was involved because of the long residence time of floodwaters on farmlands, which prevented spring crops from being planted. It was estimated that an 11-mile-long floodwall constructed at St. Louis in 1955 saved that city $340 million. Of course, flooding was not restricted to the United States. Floods on the Indus River in Pakistan by August 26, 1973, had affected 8 million people, flooded 2,000 square miles, damaged and destroyed 1 million homes, and ruined standing crops worth $250 million.

The term "flooding" is often used in the literature to denote inundation of land, regardless of whether the water is from a river or from lakes or oceans (Burton and Kates, 1964). For example, flood damages amounted to many millions of dollars during the 1973 spring when water levels in the Great Lakes were abnormally high and were whipped inland by a series of storms. One of the great human disasters of all time occurred in the delta region of the Ganges in East Pakistan (now Bangladesh) on November 12, 1970, when ocean waters that were driven inland by typhoon winds covered a vast region and drowned several hundred thousand inhabitants.

Flood Control and Rehabilitation

The articles on flood control and rehabilitation all have elements that indicate some of the different strategies that have been developed (see also Spieker, 1970). At this point, however, it may be helpful to consolidate many of these ideas and provide additional information to place the subject in perspective.

There are three different approaches commonly used in dealing with flood-hazard policies:

1. Structural and corrective. These are engineering controls that involve some type of construction, such as dams, levees, floodwalls, channel modification, watershed, soil and vegetation conservation, and flood proofing (special shoring of buildings).

2. Land-use management. Included in this group are such measures as zoning prohibitions, building codes, tax adjustments, and open-space corridors.

3. Absorption of loss. This involves a "do-nothing" or calculated-risk attitude in which the property owner gambles that he will have little or no loss, or can evacuate in time to prevent great loss. Or he may rely on a subsidy to meet incurred damages through some type of public relief or floodplain insurance program.

The most common approach of urban inhabitants toward flood control is to seek protection by dams, floodwalls, and levees. There has always been controversy concerning the building of dams. They have been challenged on such grounds as inability to justify the benefit–cost ratio (Haveman, 1965), questions regarding size (Leopold and Maddock, 1954; Peterson, 1954), and on conservation matters (Ackerman, 1971; Morgan, 1971). In a protest filed with the Army Corps of Engineers by the National Parks & Conservation Association against the continuing plans of the agency to construct the Meramec Park dam on the Meramac River, Missouri, the Corps was asked what value had been placed on the habitat of an endangered species and made this reply:

> . . . there is no meaningful way for placing a dollar value on the esthetic and wildlife amenities you have mentioned (National Parks & Conservation Association, 1973, p. 29).

Of course, when improperly constructed, dam failure yields even greater destruction; they also change geomorphic processes, causing imbalances in rates of sedimentation and erosion. When retaining structures in cities are breached or overtopped by floods, excessive damage may result. On May 30, 1948, the 18,700 inhabitants of Vanport City, Oregon, barely escaped in time when the protecting dike broke; within 1 hour water had destroyed the town. Much of the damage caused by the Indus River flood of August 1973 was attributed to the lack of a proper soil conservation program in the upstream watershed region. Soil erosion and control practices are covered in Volume III of this trilogy. When stream channels are altered and manipulated by man, the flooding damages may simply be transferred farther downstream. Such channels also require constant maintenance or they will revert to former patterns, and groundwater recharge can be impaired because storm runoff may rush out of the basin faster than the soils of the floodplain and stream channel can absorb it.

Although flood-control legislation in the United States can be traced back to 1849 with the passage of the Swamp Lands Act, it was not until the twentieth century that major legislation and funding became available to undertake massive conservational programs. Furthermore, many flood-control projects are justified on the basis of the protection of the urban areas where damages are generally the greatest. The Swamp Lands Act provided that the proceeds from the sale of federal swamps and flooded lands that had been granted to the states should be applied to drainage, reclamation, and flood-control projects. By 1900, the U.S. Army Corps of Engineers was actively engaged in flood-control construction, largely on the Mississippi River, and by 1925 was preparing investigations for possible work on all navigable streams and major tributaries. Not until the Flood Control Act of 1936, however, was a nationwide policy established that sought to alleviate hazards caused by flooding. In Volume III (see dams, flooding, U.S. Army Corps of Engineers, soil conservation) various aspects of flooding as related to soil erosion control measures are discussed, such as the Watershed Protection and Flood Prevention Act of 1954. The need for coordinated types of water-management programs for the control of floods is indicated by the complex array of problems that beset the metropolitan areas of southern California:

> The development of effective comprehensive flood control programs in southern California is particularly important throughout the reach of the coastal megalopolis, from San Diego to Santa Barbara. Flood control in southern California abounds in technical problems challenging engineers and geologists who must keep pace with the rapid acceleration, changing patterns and requirements of urban growth to permit the safe maximum utilization of high cost land.
>
> Flood control problems encountered in southern California [are]: 1. Uncontrolled mountain drainage runoff and siltation, with consequent loss of flood water storage capacity. 2. Mountain and foothill soil erosion and channel scour. 3. Uncontrolled mountain debris flow. 4. Uncontrolled alluvial cone runoff. 5. Uncontrolled upper valley runoff. 6. Uncontrolled lower valley storm flow. 7. Uncontrolled local street runoff. 8. Conservation of storm flow water impounded at limited surface storage facilities. 9. Beach erosion and river outlet siltation (Zielbauer, 1966, p. 289).

One of the most important tools for those who must make policy concerning land-use practices is the development of hazards maps to show areas of potential inundation. Sheaffer, Ellis, and Spieker (1969) have provided a model for hazard mapping in the Chicago metropolitan area and to identify users who can benefit by such studies. They point out that as of October 1968, 94 of the 117 Cook County municipalities located in the Metropolitan Sanitary District adopted floodplain ordinances. Only 20 of the municipalities do not have floodplain hazards, and the other three were revising ordinances that were considered unsatisfactory. The reason for nearly 100 percent adoption was that the district implemented the policy of not giving sewer permits unless the municipalities complied with the ordinance, which required such things as restriction of residential development, establishment of floodway channels, and specifications regarding flood-proofing of buildings within the flood-hazard area.

> Lands unsuited for intensive development due to flooding, unstable soil conditions, or where the provision of essential public services and facilities is difficult, should be maintained in suitable open space use. . . . Intensive urban development should be directed so as to avoid flood plains, protect ground water deposits, and preserve lands particularly suited for multipurpose resources management programs (Northeastern Illinois Planning Commission, 1968, pp. 7–11).

In a summary statement of his book White concludes:

> In seeking to reduce flood losses where this would be consistent with optimum use of flood plains, local communities can strengthen these guides by promoting: (1) basic hydrologic and hydraulic studies, (2) dissemination of resulting data, (3) flood forecasting and warning services, (4) regulation of channel encroachment, (5) knowledge of techniques of alternative adjustments, particularly through incidental adoption, (6) regulation of land use, and (7) acquisition of suitable land (1964).

Spieker (1970) also provides a series of guidelines and suggestions for assistance in the management of flood-prone areas.

> Flood plains in an urban area can be managed by identifying them, by recognizing that either their natural storage capacity or equivalent artificial capacity is needed to accommodate floods, and by planning land use accordingly. Examples of effective floodplain management include (1) preservation of greenbelts or regional parks along stream courses, (2) use of floodplains for recreation, parking lots, or other low-intensity uses, (3) use of flood-proofed commercial buildings, and (4) provision for compensatory storage to replace natural storage capacity. Results of poor flood-plain management include uncontrolled residential development and encroachment by fill into natural storage areas where no compensatory storage has been provided (p. 2).

The aforementioned management and land-use zoning programs are especially appropriate for newly emerging urban areas (see also Bue, 1967). The alternative that is now becoming increasingly popular is the idea of floodplain insurance. The Federal Flood Insurance Act of 1956 was passed after private insurance companies had refused to establish any type of universal flood-insurance program. It permitted a commissioner to set premiums and create uniform rates within entire drainage basins. However, Congress did not appropriate sufficient funds to allow the act to function. Later, new legislation was passed, the National Flood Insurance Act of 1968, by which the federal government sells insurance through companies, who then receive a part of the premium for handling the policies. Under the act, however, persons are not eligible for insurance until their communities agree to institute flood-protection measures. In November 1973, because of damages caused by Hurricane Agnes, the state of Pennsylvania filed a $1 billion suit against the U.S. government, claiming federal officials had failed to publicize properly the availability of flood insurance. The damage sought was the estimated loss suffered as a result of the federal government's failure to act. The class-action suit named as defendants the National Association of Flood Insurers, General Accident Fire and Life Association Corp., Ltd. (A Scottish company), and Zurich Insurance Co. (a Swiss Corporation).

> The Senate is expected to vote soon on S.1495, the Flood Disaster Protection Act of 1973. The bill which has already passed the House as H.R. 8449 (see Report No. 30, page 405) is drawing stiff resistance from both the home building industry and local governments. The basic concept of the Federal Flood Plain Insurance Program is to provide low cost, subsidized insurance to families and businessses already located in flood prone areas while controlling future development on these flood plains.
>
> In 1968, Congress passed the National Flood Plain Insurance Act. This set up a program, [where] those already situated in an area with a 1% or greater chance of flooding (i.e. — the 100 year flood plain) could obtain insurance against damages suffered during flooding. The special insurance costs much less than the actuarial rates, because it is subsidized by the Federal taxpayers. This program was to replace repeated disaster relief aid to such persons.
>
> Unfortunately, the program under the present law is *voluntary*. Most communities have thought only about supposed new tax revenues from new development, and have figured that if a flood strikes, they will receive Federal disaster funds.
>
> The revision of the Flood Insurance act now under consideration would make participation in the program mandatory for all communities which contain flood prone areas. Such communities must be in the program by July 1975. If not, *no federal funds* will be available for any project or program located within the 100 year flood plain. This restriction would extend to mortgages and loans from Federally backed banks, savings and loans, and other lending institutions (*Conservation Report*, 1973, p. 541).

Landslides

Specialists in hillslope mechanics classify landslides as only one of many different types of rapid mass movements on the surface of the earth. They are all gravity related and are classified by a nomenclature that describes the type of movement, that is, whether a fall, slide, or flow. Here, however, the term "landslide" will be used in the popular sense to denote all types of rapid downhill movement of solid earth materials. In the four articles reproduced for this section, emphasis is placed on landslides caused through loss of slope equilibrium by surficial processes, since other aspects of this phenomenon are covered in Betz (in press; see also Legget, 1973, pp. 423–452). The articles were selected as representative of the most important ideas dealing with landslides and human affairs. Leighton presents a generalized treatment of the problem of landslides and some of the remedies for stabilization and conservation of hillslopes. The monograph published by the Geological Survey of Canada was the first definitive investigation of the classic man-induced landslide at Frank, Alberta, an example which is so relevant that it is still used in many geology texts. The paper by C. L. So demonstrates that urban planning is needed in hilly terrain to prevent natural mass-movement hazards that can result from heavy rainfall, particularly where there is a thick saprolite. Jahns concludes this unit by providing a historic perspective of how the establishment of grading ordinances in California has become a powerful conservational measure.

Throughout the civilized world, landslides have caused vast destruction. The most devastating landslide in recorded history occurred during the 1920 earthquake in Kansu Province, China. Gigantic masses of loess were loosened from mountain sides, overwhelming a densely populated valley 3 miles long. More than 180,000 inhabitants were killed by the cataclysm. Another terrible landslide calamity caused by an earthquake in mountainous terrain occurred more recently in Peru.

> Too often we fail to realize the potential danger of building on or near steeply sloping land. A recent and tragic illustration of this human failing occurred during the 1970 earthquake in Peru, possibly the most catasrophic earthquake in the Western Hemisphere. The majority of the 40,000 deaths resulted from a tremendous, earthquake-triggered avalanche of debris that swept over, and largely buried, the cities of Yungay and Ranrahirca, along with some smaller towns (National Academy of Sciences, 1972, pp. 103–104).

Peru was also the site of mud-water avalanches which on December 13, 1941, killed 7,000 and again on January 10, 1962, killed an additional 4,000. In Santos, Brazil, heavy rains in March 1956 triggered soil and rock landslides that caused more than 100 deaths and millions of dollars in property destruction. Repeated slides every rainy season in coastal Brazil lead to further tragedies.

Man has often been instrumental in aiding nature to set the stage for disaster. For example, the destruction at Vaiont, Italy, was set in motion by a huge landslide into the

Vaiont reservoir. Kiersch (1964) attributed the cause of the landslide to (1) adverse geologic conditions in the reservoir, (2) man-made conditions where bank storage affected slope stability, and (3) man-made changes that created changes in ground-water levels. Another man-induced tragedy (Woodland, 1968) occurred October 21, 1966, in the village of Aberfan, Wales. Heavy rains lubricated the oversteepened slopes of an 800-foot-pile of spoil materials from coal-mining operations; the entire hillside smothered the village, killing 144 people (including 112 children).

One aspect of some tragedies is man's failure to heed advice and information. For example, Legget (1973) shows how a report, "The Stability of Colliery Soilbanks," written in 1959 by G. L. Watkins was available and its information could have prevented the Aberfan tragedy. The Alaskan Good Friday earthquake of March 27, 1964, produced the greatest energy of any recorded on the North American continent. It caused hundreds of millions of dollars in damages and killed more than 100 people by landslides and subsidence. The city of Anchorage was hardest hit with $200 million in damage; again a geologic report had not been heeded. In 1959 the U.S. Geological Survey had published a bulletin that covered the Anchorage area, delineated the Bootlegger Cove clay, mapped its extent, and described how landslides could be activated easily in the clay. However, the report was not used in the urban planning of Anchorage.

> The planning department was relatively new and its early problems concerned more pressing matters. The report is a general treatment and did not zone or classify the ground except by geologic map units. The map is not a document the planners can use directly without interpretation by a geologist. There were no geologists on the planning staff (Dobrovolny and Schmoll, 1968).

This example also illustrates the need to translate geologic reports into land-use planning actions. It further indicates how even catastrophies can yield by-products that are beneficial. Eckel (1970) shows how the entire town of Valdez, Alaska, was razed and rebuilt on a more stable site where better port facilities were developed. The business part of Anchorage, which had suffered intense damage, was greatly strengthened and stabilized. Various studies of the damage and of geomorphic processes have developed new dimensions in earth science knowledge and have provided a meeting ground for many diverse scientists to combine their skills to guide future decisions concerning land use. The Alaskan investigations have also provided new hydrologic information, expanded geophysical theories of the earth, and have initiated new concepts regarding the causes and movement of landslides.

In his article, C. L. So shows types of areas that can be subjected to mass movements in thickly populated Hong Kong. So is Senior Lecturer in the Department of Geography and Geology, University of Hong Kong. His Ph.D. is from the University of London, and he is a specialist in slope studies and natural and environmental hazards.

The articles by Leighton and Jahns reflect two different aspects of landslide problems in southern California. F. Beach Leighton is Professor of Geology at Whittier College, where he has taught since 1950. The material reproduced in this volume is much condensed from his longer treatise, which shows construction techniques that can be used for the prevention of landslides. The paper by Richard Jahns introduces the topic of grading ordinances, a unique legal tool used for the first time in California to minimize damage by landslides in areas that are being developed. Jahns is Professor of Geology at Stanford University, where he also serves as Dean, School of Earth Sciences. Jahns is a distinguished scientist with a notable record with the U.S. Geological Survey, Pennsylvania State University, and the California Institute of Technology. His work has been published widely in many different geology fields. Jahns is past president of the Geological Society of America. The grading ordinances are highly significant to geologists because they provide some of the earliest legal rules which specifically require that the discipline of geology be heavily involved in mapping, reporting, and inspecting decisions regarding hillside building sites. Most of these codes have clauses that are similar to the following excerpts:

> Prior to issuance of a grading permit, the Building Official may require an engineering geological investigation, based on the most recent grading plan. The engineering geological report shall include an adequate description of the geology of the site, and conclusions and recommendations regarding the effect of geologic conditions on the proposed development (Ventura County Grading Ordinance, Sec. 3170-6.3, as amended April 29, 1969).
>
> The Building Official may require sufficient inspection to assure that all geologic conditions have been adequately considered. Where geologic conditions warant, the Building Official may require periodic geologic reports. These inspections may be required to include, but need not be limited to inspection of cut slopes, canyons during clearing operations for ground water and earth material conditions; benches prior to placement of fill; and possible spring locations (Sec. 3170-16.2).

Merriam (1960) provides a case study of the notorious Portuguese Bend area in California. He shows what can happen when home developers are oblivious to landslide-prone topography. This is the site of a large residential area of expensive homes located on the south slope of the Palos Verde Hills, west of San Pedro, California. The slide has been slowly moving for many years, but became more active when home building greatly increased in 1956. By 1960, slides had caused millions of dollars in damage and many homes had to be removed to avoid complete destruction. Even as late as 1970 the slides were continuing to move about 0.02 feet per day. There are multiple causes for the reactivation of this slide, such as sewage effluent from homes which serves to lubricate the clays and give them greater mobility. In addition, Morton and Streitz (1967) show that in a lawsuit the County of Los Angeles was held accountable for producing a contributory role in damages sustained by property owners. It was ruled that highway fill at the head of the landslide had produced an unusual loading burden, which increased groundwater flow and lubrication of materials. The county had to pay damages of $5,360,000. In a very interesting study Slosson (1969) analyzed landslide damages in southern California that resulted from torrential rains in 1969. The storm caused $6.5 million in property loss at 1,400 development sites. He compared the damages that were incurred on the basis of when the development took place.

1. Of the developments from the period before 1952, when there were no grading ordinances, 1,040 from a total of 10,000 sites were damaged in the amount of $3.3 million.

2. Of the developments from the 1952–1962 period when only "semi-adequate codes with limited geology but no status or responsibilty" were in effect, 350 from a total of 27,000 sites were damaged in the amount of $2,767,000.

3. Of the developments from the 1963–1969 period when the new modern codes were instituted and geologists were required to make inspections during construction charged with legal responsibility, only 17 sites out of a possible 11,000 were damaged, amounting to $182,400.

10

Reprinted from *The Nation's Water Resources*, Water Resources Council, Washington, D.C., 1968, pp. 5-2-1–5-2-10

Floods and Flood Damages

U.S. WATER RESOURCES COUNCIL

INTRODUCTION

In any assessment of the adequacy of supplies of water to meet the water requirements of the Nation, the control of floodflows occupies a peculiar role because it deals primarily with flows that are in excess of acceptable stream levels and in excess of water requirements. However, facilities to temporarily impound excess floodflows may provide potentials for long-term storage of water for other purposes and are directly related to comprehensive plans for the control and use of water and related land resources. Furthermore, controlled use of flood plains, including flood insurance, flood warning services, channel improvement, levees and other local protection works are alternative measures for controlling or alleviating the adverse effects of floodflows. Thus, the problems of flood control and flood damage prevention are closely related to the overall management of water and related land resources.

As a means of assessing flood management procedures, this chapter provides summaries of existing flood control programs, their costs and their effectiveness in preventing flood losses, and presents appraisals of future flood management problems. The summaries consist of available information contributed by a number of Federal agencies concerned with flood control and related activities. Data obtained from these varied sources may lack consistency and uniformity owing to variations in the degree of accuracy and detail, and to the lack of uniformity of approach used in their development. For example, summaries of the upstream program include data on projects for which some measures are not yet operational and this is true to a lesser extent in the downstream program. Efforts to include projects and their effects for all flood control programs were not entirely successful, particularly in the State and local sectors and in the upstream areas. Also, investments are in terms of Federal appropriations and include funds being expended on ancillary programs, on projects yet to be completed, and, in some instances, on projects not yet started.

In the upstream area, estimates of damages prevented are based on flood prevention benefit values listed in watershed work plans developed to date. They include changed land use and more intensive land use benefits induced by the projects. In the downstream area, estimates of historical damages prevented by existing works are for major floods based on current development conditions within the protected areas.

Future flood damage potentials for the Nation are summaries of regional projections of remaining damages based on extensions of past trends in land use and economic indicators, and reflect current project conditions. For the downstream areas, present estimates of future flood damage potentials for 2020 compare reasonably well with those presented in the Senate Select Committee Report extended to 2020 ($1.2 and $1.4 billion, respectively). Future damage potentials have not been adjusted to take into account the effect of future programs for management of flood-plain use and development or for construction of future flood control works. Since background and experience on costs and effects of flood plain management activities are yet to be developed, the effectiveness of this new and important program has been treated in general terms.

Estimates contained in the chapter and in the accompanying tables and charts should be viewed as preliminary in the light of constraints and limitations therein and used with caution. The need for collecting more complete information on a consistent national basis was recognized by the Task Force on Federal Flood Control Policy in its report of August 1966, *A Unified Program for Managing Flood Losses* (HD 465, 89th Congress). Work on the program recommended in the report is under way, including action to remedy some features of the data problem.

BACKGROUND AND RESPONSIBILITIES

Although flood control in the United States began as a matter of local concern, the Federal interest in the problem has grown until flood control has become one of the major public works activities of the Federal Government. The Federal concern for flood control was first advanced in the Sacramento and Mississippi River Basins in 1917. With enactment of the Flood Control Act of 1936, the Federal Government accepted a high degree of responsibility for controlling floods throughout the Nation, in cooperation with "States, their political subdivisions and localities thereof." Flood control legislation enacted since 1936 has broadened the Federal interest from a single-purpose effort to reduce flood damages to consideration of flood control as a major element in the multiple-purpose development of the Nation's rivers and streams. In recent years, the Federal Government has recognized and fostered the concept of restricting flood losses through gathering and disseminating information on flood-prone areas. This information provides a basis for correction of existing flood problems and also for coordination and planning of useful development of these areas.

Prior to 1936, organizations such as improvement districts, conservancy districts, flood control districts, other local and quasipublic entities, and private interests assumed primary responsibility for flood control. While some still retain this responsibility for individual projects, most others participate in flood reduction measures undertaken under existing Federal flood control legislation. Local organizations help to provide lands, easements, rights-of-way, and relocations, and also provide assistance in formulating projects suitable to local needs and conditions that are acceptable to local residents. Obtaining and disseminating information on flood-prone areas is an activity assumed by the Federal Government in cooperation with State and local governments. The planning and coordination of the development of these areas are, however, primarily an activity of State and local government.

FLOOD DAMAGES

In general, the term "flood" refers to overflow or inundation that comes from a river or other body of water and causes or threatens loss of life and/or damage to goods and services in immediate and adjacent areas. Floods may be classified as downstream floods for those experienced on the mainstem and major tributaries, and as upstream floods for those experienced on creek and headwater areas. Data and information presented in this chapter have been divided into "upstream" and "downstream" categories wherein upstream refers to those streams above a point where the total area drained is 250,000 acres (390.6 sq mi) or less, and downstream refers to the stream pattern below that point.

Estimates of flood damages are used to express the economic loss caused by floods and to provide a measure of the Nation's flood problem. Flood damage surveys for major flood occurrences have been conducted on a national scale for more than 60 years and these data have been published since 1902. More recently, the Federal agencies concerned with flood control have made numerous determinations of flood damage potentials within reaches of streams and river basins and in headwater areas that would be affected by Federal or Federally assisted flood control works under study. They also have determined the flood damages experienced and eliminated below existing works. A complete inventory of nationwide flood damages has never been undertaken. In instances where the record is incomplete or lacking, reasoned estimates of flood damages are used.

Floods of the past which resulted in great loss of life and those which caused extraordinary property damage are listed in tables 5–2–1 and 5–2–2, respectively. The record indicates that while there has been a reduction of frequency of loss of life from floods, the frequency of major property damage from floods has increased. Floods causing damages of $50 million or more, based on 1966 price levels, were experienced during the period 1900–1940 on an average of about once every 6 years. Since 1940, floods causing damages in this order of magnitude have occurred on an average of once in less than 2 years. Since there is no evidence that floods themselves are increasing in magnitude and frequency, this increase in occurrence of property damage seems indicative of the expanding economy of the Nation, with the increased development and use of the flood plain made possible, in many cases, by partial protection works.

Before 1940, most of the floods causing heavy property damage also resulted in great loss of life, as shown in tables 5–2–1 and 5–2–2. But since then the loss of life caused by floods has been much less—probably a reflection of better flood and hurricane warning systems. Sixty per-

TABLE 5–2–1.—*Floods causing 100 or more deaths*

Year	Stream or place	Lives lost	Cause
1831	Barataria Isle, La.	150	Hurricane tidal flood
1856	Isle Derniere, La.	320	Hurricane tidal flood
1874	Connecticut River tributary	143	Dam failure
1875	Indianola, Texas	176	Hurricane tidal flood
1886	Sabine, Texas	150	Hurricane tidal flood
1889	Johnstown, Pa.	2,100	Dam failure
1893	Vic. Grand Isle, La.	2,000	Hurricane tidal flood
1899	Puerto Rico	3,000	Hurricane tide and waves
1900	Galveston, Texas	6,000+	Hurrciane tide flood
1903	Central States	100+	Rainfall-River floods
1903	Heppner, Ore.	247	Rainfall-River floods
1906	Gulf coast	151	Hurricane tidal flood
1909	Gulf coast—New Orleans	700	Hurricane tidal flood
1913	Miami, Muskingham and Ohio Rivers	467	Rainfall-River floods
1913	Brazos River, Texas	177	Rainfall-River floods
1915	La. and Texas Gulf coast	550	Hurricane tidal flood
1919	La. and Texas Gulf coast	284	Hurricane tidal flood
1921	Upper Arkansas River	120	Rainfall-River flood
1926	Miami and Clewiston, Fla.	350	Hurricane tidal and river flood
1927	Lower Mississippi River	100+	Rainfall-River flood
1927	Vermont	120	Rainfall-River flood
1928	Puerto Rico	300	Hurricane tide and waves
1928	Lake Okeechobee, Fla.	2,400	Hurricane tidal flood
1928	San Franciscquito, California	350	Dam failure
1932	Puerto Rico	225	Hurricane tide and waves
1935	Florida Keys	400	Hurricane tidal flood
1935	Republican R., Kans., Nebr.	110	Rainfall-River flood
1936	Northeastern U.S.	107	Rainfall, snow melt-River floods
1937	Ohio River	137	Rainfall-River flood
1938	New England Coast	200	Hurricane tidal and river flood
1955	Northeastern U.S.	115	Hurricane rainfall-River floods
1957	West coast, La.	556	Hurricane tide and river floods
1960	Puerto Rico	107	Hurricane, rainfall-River floods

cent of the floods causing 100 or more deaths were hurricane associated.

Average annual flood damages have been estimated by the Federal agencies concerned with flood control and include, as nearly as practicable, an appraisal of all downstream and upstream flood damages. For the downstream damages, the estimates were based on flood-plain areas subject to inundation, while for the upstream damages the estimates include, in addition to damages by inundation in upstream flood-plain areas, the damages due to bank erosion in upstream flood-plain areas. Based on the current status of flood control works and projected conditions of flood-plain use and development, the total annual flood damage potential for the Nation is anticipated to increase from $1.7 billion in 1966 to $5.0 billion in 2020 (fig. 5–2–1). Average annual flood damage estimates by water resources regions are listed in table 5–2–3 for 1957 and 1966, as well as projections for 1980, 2000, and 2020 of potential annual flood damages assuming 1966 project conditions and with established trends in flood-plain development. These trends do not reflect the national flood-plain management program just getting under way.

EXISTING PROGRAM

In downstream areas, the existing flood control program includes some 900 projects estimated to have cost about $7 billion. These consist of over 260 reservoirs containing over 36,000 billion gallons (110 maf) of storage space for flood control, and local protection projects providing over 6,000 miles of levees and flood walls and over 8,000 miles of channel improvement works. Projects having an estimated total cost of $6.1 billion are under construction and active projects having a total cost of about $3.4

TABLE 5–2–2.—*Floods resulting in damages exceeding $50,000,000*

Year	Stream or place	Damage (million dol.) Contemporary dollars	1966 dollars	Cause
1844	Upper Mississippi River	NA	1,161	Rainfall-River flood
1889	Johnstown, Pa.	20	84	Dam failure
1900	Galveston, Tex.	25	100	Hurricane tidal floods
1903	Passaic & Delaware Rivers	25	273	Rainfall and dam failure
1903	Missouri River basin	50	NA	Rainfall-River flood
1913	Ohio River basin	150	516	Rainfall-River flood
1913	Brazos & Colorado Rivers, Tex.	128	349	Hurricane rainfall-River-floods
1921	Arkansas River	13	64	Rainfall-River flood
1926	Miami & Clewiston, Fla.	70	130	Hurricane-Tidal & River floods
1926	Illinois River	NA	51	Rainfall-River floods
1927	New England	50	178	Rainfall-River flood
1927	Lower Mississippi	284	NA	Rainfall-River flood
1928	Puerto Rico	50	90	Hurricane tide and waves
1935	Susquehanna—Delaware Rivers	36	185	Rainfall-River flood
1936	Northeastern U.S.	221	374	Rainfall-River flood
1936	Ohio River basin	150	371	Rainfall snowmelt flood
1937	Ohio River basin	418	996	Rainfall-River flood
1938	New England streams	125	376	Hurricane tidal & Riv. floods
1938	California streams	100	294	Rainfall-River floods
1942	Mid-Atlantic coastal streams	28	103	Rainfall-River floods
1943	Central States	172	NA	Rainfall-River floods
1944	South Florida	63	117	Hurricane tidal & River floods
1944	Missouri River basin	52	NA	Rainfall-River floods
1945	Hudson River basin	24	75	Rainfall-River floods
1945	South Florida	54	98	Hurricane tidal & River floods
1945	Ohio River basin	34	61	Rainfall-River floods
1947	South Florida	60	88	Hurricane tidal & River floods
1947	Missouri River basin	178	NA	Rainfall-River floods
1948	Columbia River basin	102	226	Rainfall-River floods
1950	San Joaquin R., California	32	57	Rainfall-River floods
1951	Kansas River basin	883	NA	Rainfall-River floods
1952	Missouri River basin	180	NA	Snowmelt floods
1952	Upper Mississippi River	198	NA	Rainfall-River floods
1954	New England streams	180	216	Hurricane tidal floods
1955	Northeastern U.S.	684	879	Hurricane tidal & River floods
1955	Calif. and Oregon streams	271	405	Rainfall-River floods
1957	Ohio River basin	65	72	Rainfall-River floods
1957	Texas Rivers	144	188	Rainfall-River floods
1959	Ohio River basin	114	120	Rainfall-River floods
1960	South Florida	78	86	Hurricane tidal & River floods
1961	Texas coast	300	336	Hurricane tidal floods
1964	Florida	325	342	Hurricane tidal & River floods
1964	Ohio River basin	106	112	Rainfall-River floods
1964	California streams	173	183	Rainfall-River floods
1964	Columbia R. — N. Pacific	289	311	Rainfall-River floods
1965	South Florida	139	144	Hurricane tidal & River floods
1965	Upper Mississippi River	158	162	Rainfall snowmelt River flood
1965	Platte River, Col. — Nebr.	191	NA	Rainfall-River flood
1965	Arkansas River, Col. — Kans.	61	65	Rainfall-River flood
1965	New Orleans and Vicinity	322	338	Hurricane tidal flood

NA—Not Available

billion have not been started. Although this program is carried out primarily by the Corps of Engineers, flood control is an important feature of projects constructed by the Bureau of Reclamation and the Tennessee Valley Authority. The Federal investment and pertinent data on downstream works are shown in table 5–2–4.

In the upstream area, 1,129 watershed projects have been approved for construction. The land treatment and structural measures which are completed or will be completed within the next

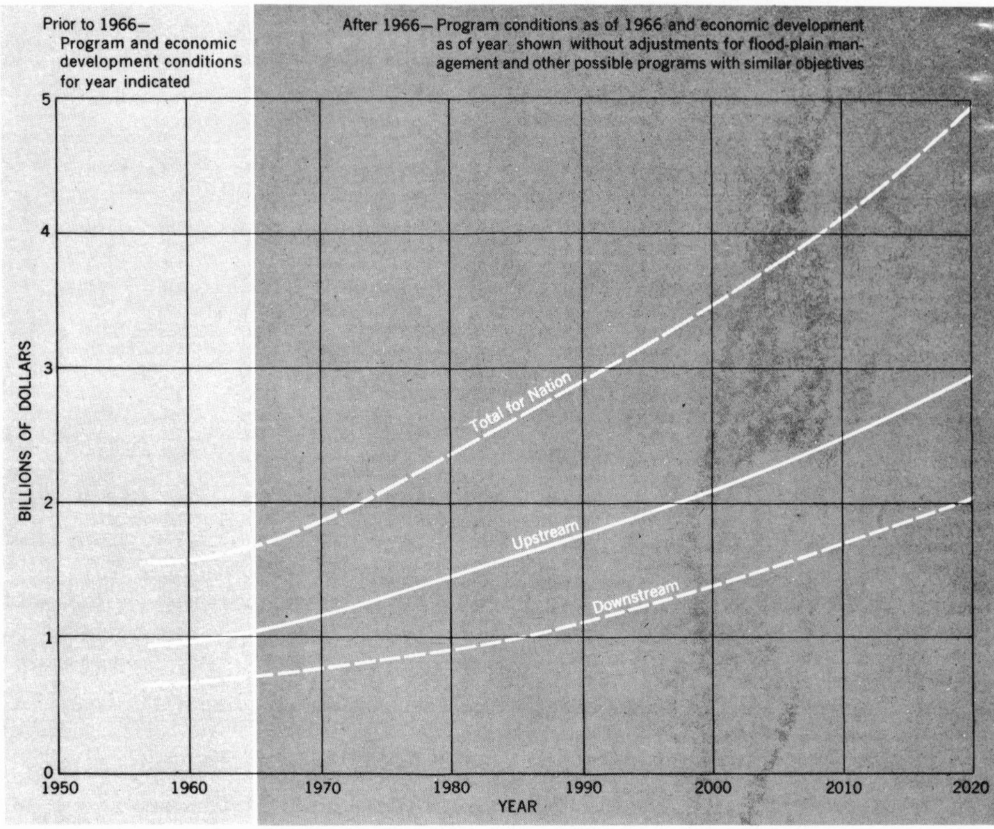

FIGURE 5–2–1.—*Projections of potential flood damages without flood plain management or new flood protection works, 1957–2020.*

6 years will cost approximately $2.1 billion of which $1.37 billion is a Federal cost. Structural measures including over 4,300 flood water retarding structures providing about 1,500 billion gallons (4.6 maf) of storage and 3,200 miles of channel improvement have been constructed in upstream areas in accordance with the approved watershed projects. Although this program is carried out primarily by the Soil Conservation Service, flood control is an important feature of small projects constructed in the upstream areas by the Corps of Engineers, Bureau of Land Management, Forest Service, and Bureau of Reclamation. The Federal investment and other pertinent data on upstream works are shown in table 5–2–5.

The Federal Government extends assistance to those endangered by an expected major flood, and to those suffering flood damages. Flood warning services extended by the Weather Bureau save lives and reduce losses of those endangered by floods. This nationwide service provides forecasts for over 1,200 communities on principal river systems. Federal expenditures for this program during 1959–1966 totaled almost $16 million.

Emergency operations for those suffering flood damages required Federal expenditures of $219 million during a 15-year period from 1951 to 1966. Those operations were administered by the Office of Emergency Planning, the Department of the Army, and the Department of Agriculture.

Further Government assistance is provided through development of information on flood plains. Data made available by participating agencies show that information on flood magnitude and frequencies, and that flood-plain maps delineating areas subject to flooding have been provided in about 170 reports for some 300 com-

TABLE 5–2–3.—*Estimated annual flood damages*

(Million dollars)

Region	1957		1966		1980 [1]		2000 [1]		2020 [1]	
	Down-stream	Up-stream	Down-stream	Up-stream	Down-stream	Up-stream	Down-stream	Up-stream	Down-stream	Up-stream
North Atlantic	64.3	62.6	63.1	70.7	75.6	91.2	89.8	120.9	116.2	163.3
South Atlantic-Gulf	46.7	109.6	44.1	123.8	55.8	183.2	74.8	267.3	90.4	383.7
Great Lakes	12.3	29.8	13.0	33.7	15.8	43.8	21.0	57.2	27.7	76.1
Ohio	78.7	49.2	73.9	55.6	99.5	68.3	151.0	90.9	237.0	116.6
Tennessee	3.5	27.3	4.9	30.9	7.6	42.6	8.3	58.3	[2]	80.2
Upper Mississippi	60.0	52.0	64.5	68.5	96.0	101.9	151.0	143.2	218.0	197.2
Lower Mississippi	66.0	38.5	86.8	43.5	117.2	55.3	164.2	73.5	224.5	100.1
Souris-Red-Rainy	5.8	13.5	5.6	15.3	6.4	18.4	7.5	24.1	8.6	32.2
Missouri	101.4	148.1	44.0	167.3	69.0	222.3	118.0	302.7	221.0	430.1
Arkansas-White-Red	48.6	129.2	50.0	146.0	61.6	184.0	90.6	245.3	127.0	330.0
Texas-Gulf	32.5	49.5	28.2	55.9	39.5	86.1	59.3	125.3	86.4	178.4
Rio Grande	12.2	10.4	14.7	11.8	14.8	19.5	15.8	30.9	18.8	44.9
Upper Colorado	0.9	16.9	13.0	19.1	19.0	27.4	30.3	42.1	57.0	62.1
Lower Colorado	5.4	25.8	10.0	29.1	20.2	59.3	42.2	93.3	96.7	141.3
Great Basin	3.0	8.4	4.1	9.5	6.7	17.5	10.2	27.5	14.1	42.0
Columbia-North Pacific	52.2	106.7	52.1	120.6	73.6	170.1	120.6	235.3	197.7	325.8
California	36.9	67.2	61.6	75.9	102.1	134.3	185.9	211.0	262.6	311.2
Alaska	3.2	[3]	4.3	[3]	5.6	[3]	8.4	[3]	12.4	[3]
Hawaii	1.2	10.6	1.8	12.2	2.2	16.8	2.8	23.7	3.6	34.0
Puerto Rico—Virgin Island	2.6	3.8	2.9	4.3	3.2	6.0	3.5	8.5	4.0	12.0
Total [4]	637	959	643	1,094	891	1,548	1,355	2,181	2,024	3,061

[1] Projected damages based on existing flood control works.
[2] Not reported.
[3] Not available.
[4] Rounded.

munities and localities covering some 5,400 square miles of flood-prone areas. These provide assistance to local interest for developing appropriate means to regulate the use of flood plains. Provision of information that local governments and their subdivisions need to enable them to put into effect zoning regulations is an important first step toward the more intelligent use of the flood plains. Federal expenditures for the program in 1966 amounted to more than $1.3 million. In connection with flood control studies of coastal or lake front areas, information is developed on the flooded area and on the degree and frequency of flooding produced by hurricanes, tidal waves, and similar sea conditions. Such information also is developed in connection with coastal mapping and charting activities.

Additional steps have been taken by the Federal Government to aid in managing flood-plain development. Executive Order 11296 directed all Federal agencies to consider flood hazards in locating Federal installations and in disposing of federally owned lands. The report of the Task Force on Federal Flood Control Policy proposed a many-pronged and coordinated attack on the flood-plain management problem.

Intensive efforts currently under way include the acceleration of flood-plain information studies, the provision of technical assistance and guidance in using the information for land use planning and regulation, research on the technical, legal and organizational problems, a gathering of more specific information about the Nation's flood problems, and studies of flood insurance proposals. One Federal agency has established flood-plain management services units in each of its field offices to work with the States and communities in more positive efforts to manage flood-plain lands. Several States are adopting flood-plain regulations or actively encouraging local governments to adopt regulations that put into effect plans for the best use of flood plains.

FLOOD DAMAGES PREVENTED

During the limited period that Federal flood control programs have been in operation, they

TABLE 5–2–4–.—*Downstream flood control works*

Region	Reservoirs			Levees and floodwalls			Channel improvement		
	Projects	Storage	Cost [1]	Projects	Structures	Cost	Projects	Improvement	Cost
	No.	*1,000 af*	*Mil. dol.*	*No.*	*Miles*	*Mil. dol.*	*No.*	*Miles*	*Mil. dol.*
North Atlantic	5	492	36.0	36	132	144.4	25	54	27.3
South Atlantic-Gulf	7	3,090	49.8	[2]	876	154.4	23	185	5.1
Great Lakes	1	377	23.4	6	7	1.3	9	28	7.1
Ohio	36	12,500	600.0	65	252	202.0	[2]	138	[2]
Tennessee	17	11,590	180.2	0	0	0	0	0	0
Upper Mississippi	14	3,020	54.0	65	861	242.0	19	70	8.7
Lower Mississippi	5	4,400	76.7	[2]	1,621	841.0	[2]	3,348	980.0
Souris-Red-Rainy	5	1,030	1.8	2	2	2.7	7	224	2.9
Missouri	56	20,700	656.0	50	1,130	193.6	7	75	22.2
Arkansas-White-Red	43	24,800	635.5	56	1,023	52.4	39	563	54.0
Texas-Gulf	20	8,600	234.2	5	128	121.4	8	106	94.4
Rio Grande [3]	4	795	31.1	5	205	7.6	7	114	10.5
Upper Colorado	3	1,500	5.5	8	5	0.2	1	1	20.0
Lower Colorado	6	12,100	59.6	2	7	3.2	1	4	0.5
Great Basin	6	386	7.4	4	33	1.6	3	23	1.4
Columbia-North Pacific	24	15,210	320.7	103	546	28.1	27	55	27.7
California	11	3,720	186.5	13	1,515	260.6	12	84	91.4
Alaska	0	0	0	2	3	0.6	1	1	0.1
Hawaii	0	0	0	4	6	0.2	4	3	0.2
Puerto Rico-Virgin Is.	0	0	0	0	0	0	0	0	0
Total [4]	263	124,310	3,158	426+	8,352	2,257	193+	5,076	1,354+

[1] Does not include cost of flood control storage in Bureau of Reclamation projects.
[2] Not reported.
[3] Does not include some facilities constructed by the International Boundary and Water Commission.
[4] Rounded.

have prevented about $14.6 billion in flood losses in downstream areas and $191 million in upstream areas. Summations of losses prevented by existing Federal flood control programs for important floods are shown on figure 5–2–2. Flood losses thus prevented should provide a measure of the effectiveness of the national flood control program. Under current conditions of project development, flood damage reduction benefits creditable to flood control works have been estimated at about $1 billion annually for downstream areas and $50 million annually in upstream areas. A major accomplishment to date is the virtual elimination of the possibility of major disasters for riverine flooding at those cities and localities where great loss of life and extraordinary property damages had previously been experienced. However, a disconcerting aspect of the flood control program is the fact that flood losses continue to increase in spite of the demonstrated effectiveness of the program to reduce floodflows and related damages.

FUTURE FLOOD MANAGEMENT PROGRAM

The Nation's flood management program can be expected to move ahead for some time to come under the impetus of the existing programs. Because of the physical characteristics of floods there is little likelihood that the structural measures used to store excess floodflows or otherwise control flows will change materially in the future. However, as potential sites for major reservoirs become more extensively utilized, increasing demands for multipurpose use of these potentials for all beneficial purposes are expected. Furthermore, as the best and least expensive of these potential sites are used, other programs to cope with the flood loss problem take on added importance. Current efforts to manage flood-plain use and development on a national basis are increasing. As the flood control program continues and becomes more complex the need for consistent basic policies becomes more pronounced.

TABLE 5–2–5.—*Upstream flood control works*[1]

Region	Projects	Watershed area	Flood prevention cost			
			Land treatment	Reservoirs	Channel improvement	Total
	No.	*1,000 acres*	*Mil. dol.*	*Mil. dol.*	*Mil. dol.*	*Mil. dol.*
North Atlantic	120	4,906	27.0	108.8	52.5	181.3
South Atlantic-Gulf	163	8,897	93.9	88.6	75.5	258.0
Great Lakes	21	879	11.3	6.4	7.8	25.5
Ohio	89	4,442	45.5	78.8	30.7	155.0
Tennessee	21	1,440	11.8	18.8	10.1	40.7
Upper Mississippi	49	2,052	10.9	23.8	8.4	43.1
Lower Mississippi	104	6,895	80.6	65.9	65.9	212.4
Souris-Red-Rainy	21	2,882	3.8	4.0	15.8	23.6
Missouri	184	4,938	118.9	176.4	31.1	326.4
Arkansas-White-Red	153	12,438	94.4	274.1	27.5	369.0
Texas-Gulf	83	14,616	65.2	113.6	24.9	203.7
Rio Grande	29	1,512	4.7	14.3	2.0	21.0
Upper Colorado	6	517	3.2	9.7	4.3	17.2
Lower Colorado	10	884	5.6	17.0	7.7	30.3
Great Basin	13	871	5.6	8.8	1.2	15.6
Columbia-North Pacific	24	768	5.7	15.0	6.8	27.5
California	31	1,402	11.2	25.7	77.2	114.1
Alaska	0	0	0	0	0	0
Hawaii	5	278	0.5	0.9	10.3	11.7
Puerto Rico-Virgin Islands	3	252	2.7	3.2	7.6	13.5
Total	1,129	70,869	602.5	1,046.8	467.3	2,089.6

[1] Existing and approved program of the Soil Conservation Service only. In addition, there have been many projects in upstream area constructed by the Corps of Engineers, the Bureau of Reclamation, and the Bureau of Land Management. Neither the totals nor regional data are available, but this construction amounted to over 1,000 projects, with an estimated cost of about $1 billion.

The greatest impact on water resources probably will result from the expansion of programs to regulate rivers and streams for all beneficial purposes, including flood control. Federal flood control legislation should be brought into harmony with the need for regulated rivers to assure that developmental systems will meet the needs for all beneficial purposes. In some regions, municipal, industrial, and irrigation demands for water have already become so great that much higher dry-season flows are an immediate requirement. A system capable of providing a high degree of regulation for all levels of flow is not only a means of reducing the adverse effects of excess flows but also a means for providing a more stable flow so that the stream will be of greater value for water supply, power generation, quality improvement, navigation, and other purposes.

At the current rate of Federal expenditure, flood protection may not keep up with the increase in flood damages that may be anticipated as a result of intensive use and development of flood plains. Federal expenditures averaging over $1 billion annually under existing flood control legislation would be necessary to reverse the trend of increasing damage for short-term periods in the future. The prospect that Federal expenditures of this magnitude may be needed in the future to meet the Nation's growing flood problem emphasizes the urgent need for modification of existing program features and authorization of new programs for regulation and management of flood-plain areas.

The land requirements of our expanding economy will be reflected in the development and use of the flood plains. The national flood-plain management program is designed to address these problems directly and, thus, will have a significant role in reducing the level of the Nation's future flood losses. However, because of the apparent economic advantages of flood-plain lands in urban areas, their use will probably intensify in the future. Hopefully, the flood-plain management program will temper the rate of such development. A blending of the control of excess flows and the managed use and development of flood plains can be expected, generally, to provide an optimum program to reduce flood losses.

The currently authorized program, which provides for additional economically justified flood

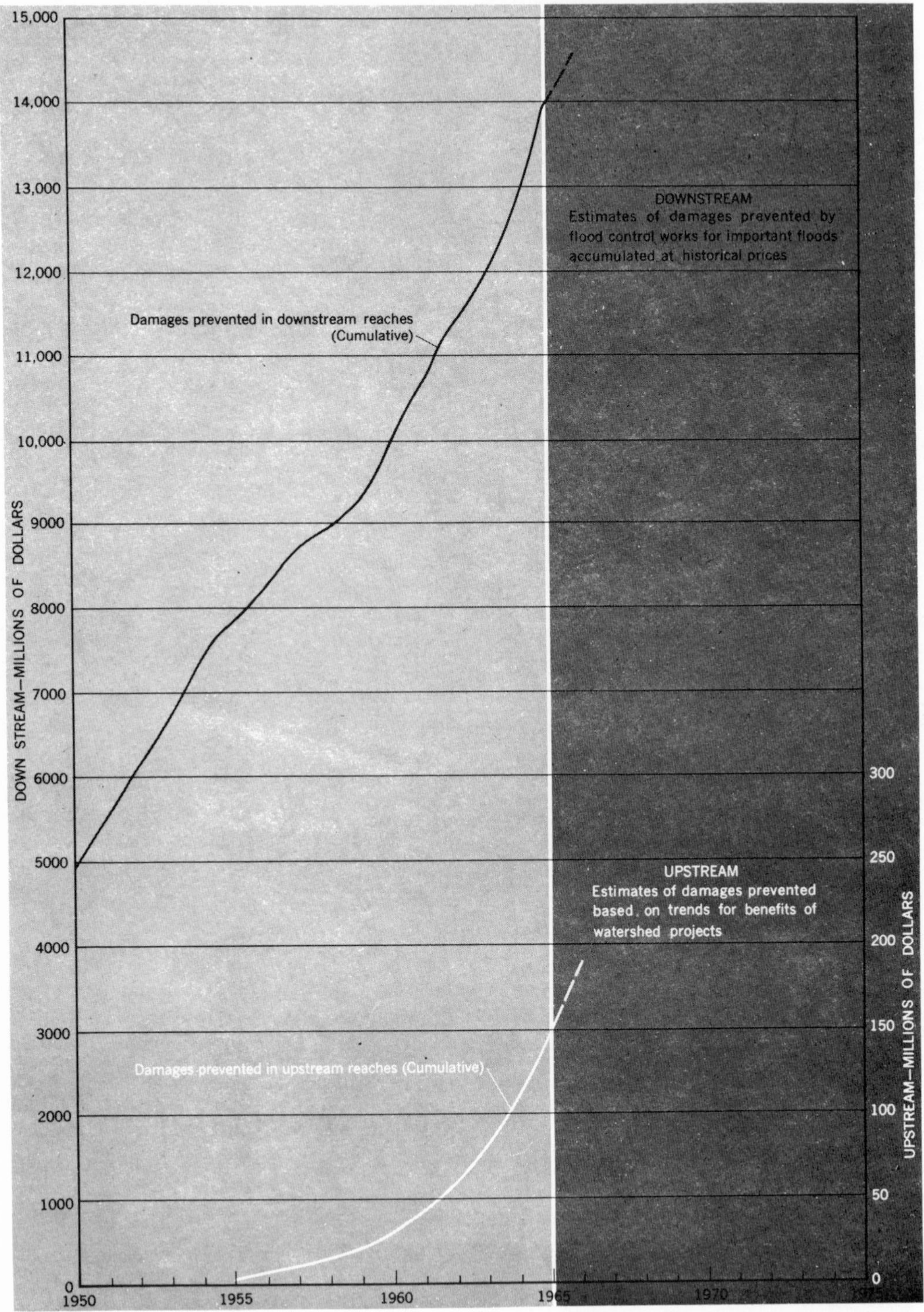

FIGURE 5–2–2—*Estimates of historical flood damages prevented, 1950–1965.*

5–2–9

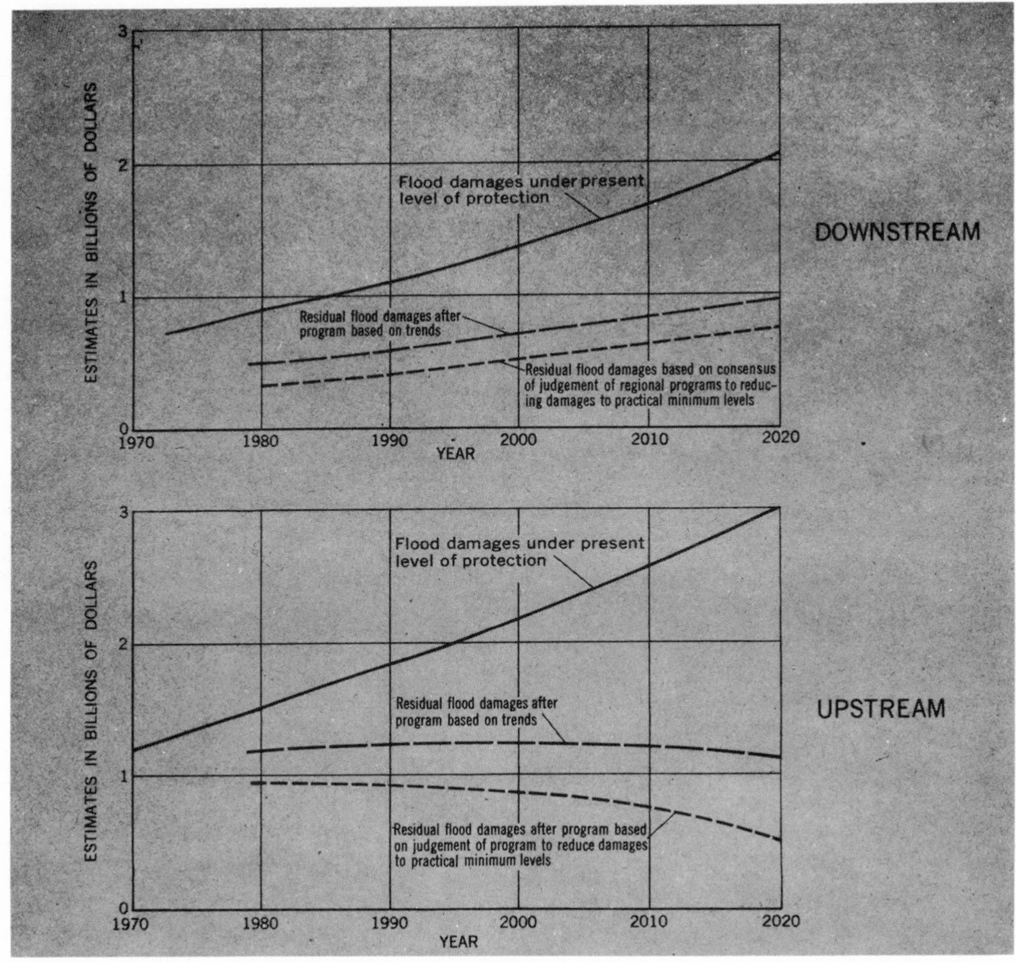

FIGURE 5–2–3.—*Projections of residual flood damages, 1980-2020.*

control projects, should continue to produce financial benefits for a long time in the future. Also storage requirements included in flood control projects are expected to place increased pressures on the diminishing reservoir resources of the Nation. Obviously, these latter requirements will need careful review to assure optimum use of the available reservoir resources. A national program to conserve these resources has been recommended.

Continuation of the existing flood control program at the current rate of expenditures is expected to reduce annual flood losses from about $2 billion to $1 billion by 2020 in downstream areas, and from $3 billion to $1.1 billion in upstream areas. Acceleration of expenditures based on regional judgment is expected to reduce annual flood losses still further to practical minimums of about $700 million by 2020 in downstream areas, and $500 million in upstream areas. Estimates of future flood damage residuals, shown on figure 5–2–3, are based on future programs reflecting past trends, and future programs based on regional judgment of programs capable of reducing damages to practical minimum levels. The effects of the flood-plain management program are omitted in both cases. However, it is anticipated that an effective flood-plain management program will permit reductions in the levels of future damages to practical minimums while permitting reductions in the extent of structural programs for flood control.

11

Reprinted from *Choice of Adjustment to Floods* (Dept. Geography Res. Paper 93), University of Chicago, Chicago, 1964, pp. 22–41

Six Partially Protected Towns

G. F. WHITE

Towns with the largest and most varied experimentation with non-conventional adjustments to floods might be expected to be those where major protection is lacking. Numerous towns have been investigated for engineering protection which has not been found to be economically feasible. Others have rejected authorized Federal protection by refusing to make local contributions in the form of costs of lands, damages, and rights of way. Still others have protection schemes recognized by local people to be inadequate or to require such a long time for completion that they face years of living with flood hazard. From earlier field studies it appears that places with protection and a belief that protection is relatively complete show little interest in alternatives, and those with early prospect for protection regard the other choices as at best a transitory substitute. There are also urban places where the hazard is regarded as so small that virtually no adjustment other than loss bearing is present. Although many flood-plain towns lack major protection works, and it has been common to describe them as "unprotected," there often is some effort at protection, however inadequate. A shoddy piece of channel clearing, a levee too weak to withstand frequent floods, or a reservoir providing only a little flood storage is believed by some of the inhabitants to offer at least slight protection.

Attention to conditions of choice therefore centers on the partially protected towns where neither the complete confidence of large-scale protection nor the complete detachment of ignorance reigns. One of these, La Follette, Tennessee, received intensive study, and five others received reconnaissance study: Aurora, Indiana; Darlington, Wisconsin; Desert Hot Springs and Cerrito Creek, California; and Watkins Glen, New York. (See Figure 3.) These six were selected so as to have certain features in common and to offer variety in physical and cultural aspects. All are towns of 2,000 to 20,000 population with no immediate prospect for protection: the Darlington government had declined to press for an engineering project while interested in a possible watershed treatment program upstream, and the others are the subject of unfavorable preliminary investigations by the Corps of Engineers. All have been studied for possible protection and in five there is partial protection of some kind. There is information on flood hazard and land use for each. In all of them the flooded area accounts for an important part of the town's activity. The Cerrito Creek bottomland is a segment of the sprawling San Francisco metropolitan area, but it has a certain local identity in terms of physical separation of lower parts of the basin from adjoining areas and in terms of having distinct commercial and industrial uses in the valley floor. There the resemblance among the six towns ends.

They were selected initially from the field of smaller towns lacking protection with a view to covering a wide range of flood frequency and magnitude and of major types of urban land use. La Follette was chosen for principal study because of the ready accessibility of data and of the cooperative attitude of local, state, and Federal officials concerned with flood problems there. The remaining five were intended to give contrast to La Follette conditions, and they turned out to be even more diversified than first suspected. As will be observed from Tables 1 and 2, the differences among them are great.

Social and economic conditions in the La Follette flood plain are well described in the companion study by Kates,[1] which also gives brief descriptions of the five other towns. As background for the findings of the present study, these descriptions will be supplemented by more precise comparison of the six towns, by further comments on the sequence of adjustments in time, and by relating their characteristics to those of other urban flood hazard places which were canvassed in 1957.

Sequence and Adjustment

Each of the towns presents a distinctive record of sequence in flood plain use and adjustment (see Figure 3).

La Follette, Tennessee.--The plan for La Follette was laid out in the 1890's on the site of a small farming settlement which had become a coal mining camp with the construction of a railroad. Lying at the base of Cumberland Mountain where Big Creek cuts its channel for the drainage of about 26 square miles of mostly wooded mountain land, the flood plain affords a flat area in a valley marked by low ridges trending northeast parallel to the mountain. The town was incorporated in 1897, and a foundry using local supplies of iron and coal was constructed in the early 1900's. Within the rectangular street grid (see Figure 4), the commercial and

[1] Kates, op. cit., pp. 31-38.

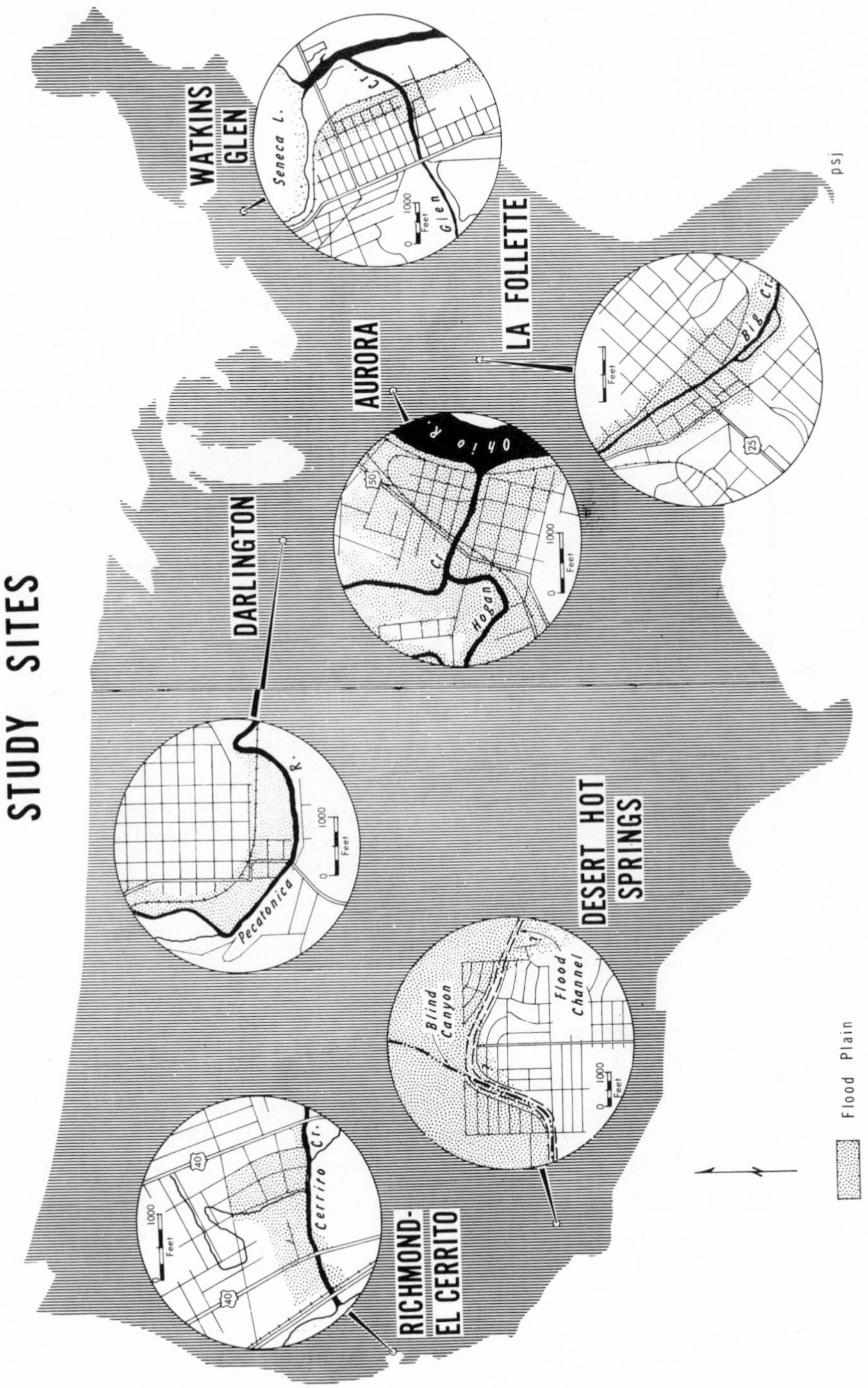
STUDY SITES
WATKINS GLEN
Seneca L.
Glen Cr.
AURORA
Ohio R.
Hogan Cr.
LA FOLLETTE
Big Cr.
DARLINGTON
Pecatonica R.
DESERT HOT SPRINGS
Blind Canyon
Flood Channel
RICHMOND-EL CERRITO
Cerrito Cr.
0 1000 Feet
Flood Plain
psj

Fig. 3.--Six study sites.

TABLE 1

PHYSICAL CHARACTERISTICS OF FLOODING IN SIX TOWNS

	Town					
	La Follette	Aurora	Darling-ton	Desert Hot Springs	Cerrito Creek	Watkins Glen
Date most recent damaging flood	1950	1961	1961	1958	1960	1935
Floods per 10 years in period of record	1.8	5.6	24	1.1	10	.3
Height of water at deepest point over-bank in feet	3	20	9	5	>2	4
Flood-to-peak inter-vals in hours	2-3	>168	6-8	<1	1-12	<2
Velocity of flood water	Low-Mod.	Low	High	Very High	Mod.	Low
Sediment load	Light	Heavy	Heavy	Very Heavy	Mod.	Heavy
Channel encroach-ments	Fill Bridges	None	Fill Bridge	Slight	Culvert Fill	Bridges
Drainage area in square miles	26	80,600	275	5.8	3	21

manufacturing uses concentrated in the flood plain. The railroad and highway penetrated the Cumberland plateau along the Big Creek valley bottom, and residential use spread up the flanks of adjoining hills.

Competition and dwindling iron supplies drove the foundry out of business in 1923. This, coupled with a sick coal industry, produced unemployment that has plagued the town ever since. While the total population of Campbell County declined in recent decades, La Follette grew in size. People migrated to it from coal mining and rural settlements. It gained some new employment in shirt-making plants and in retail trade, but lost most of its direct connection with coal mines and iron working.

Damaging floods were reported in 1897, 1901, 1903, 1920 and 1928,[1] but there was no general inundation until March 23, 1929 when virtually the

[1] Floods on Big Creek at La Follette, Tennessee (Knoxville: Tennessee Valley Authority, Division of Water Control Planning, 1958).

TABLE 2

FLOOD PLAIN USE AND ADJUSTMENTS OBSERVED IN SIX TOWNS

	La Follette	Aurora	Darling-ton	Desert Hot Springs	Cerrito Creek	Watkins Glen
Total population 1960	7,200*	4,119	2,349	3,000	25,437**	2,813
% Change 1950-1960	7	-13.8	8.0	300	41.2	-7.8
Land use in flood plain:						
Commercial	++	++	++	++	0	+
Manufacturing	+	++	+	0	++	0
Residential	+	++	+	++	++	++
Transport	+	+	++	+	++	++
Recreational	0	0	0	0	0	+
Emergency measures in practice:						
Removal	+	++	++	0	+	0
Treatment	+	+	+	0	+	0
Re-scheduling	0	++	++	0	+	0
Structural measures in effect:						
Land elevation	+	0	+	0	0	0
Pumps and valves	+	++	+	0	+	0
Building construction	+	+	+	+	+	0
Water and electricity	0	+	+	0	+	0
Protection	Channel improvement	Upstream reservoirs	None	Channel improvement	Small levees	Channel and levees
Land use regulation:						
Zoning general	City	None	Proposed	County	City	None
Special flood plain	Limited	County subdivision	Proposed	Limited	Limited	None

* Estimated for 1961 including area annexed after 1960 census.
** For town of El Cerrito. Flood plain includes parts of Richmond and El Cerrito
0 None observed
\+ A few cases
++ Common

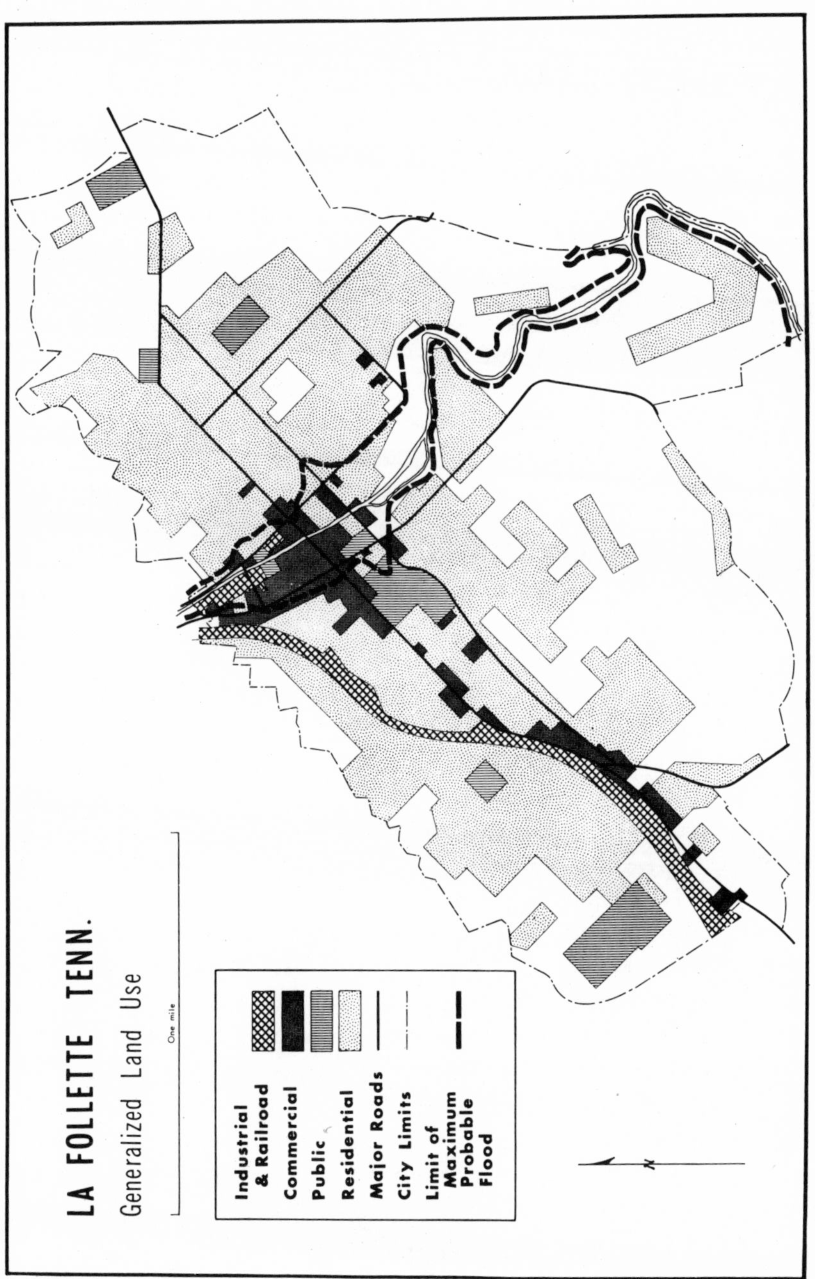

Fig. 4.--Land use in La Follette.

entire business district was damaged. At that time the areas of deepest inundation in the eastern part of town were not intensively developed, and this vacant land was the chief evidence of any other adjustment to flood hazard than bearing the loss. There were less severe floods in 1939, 1946, and 1948. Following the last of these Big Creek was deepened, particularly below the Central Avenue bridge where water piles up above constrictions from the narrow bridge openings. In 1950 a flood of about the same magnitude as 1929 hit again, causing damage estimated by TVA at more than $88,000. During the 1950 flood there was lively emergency effort by merchants to remove goods beyond the reach of water and to block off openings where water was rising. They had only a fraction of an hour's warning. Following the flood the city government deepened the entire channel a few feet,[1] which gave some local encouragement but did not in the opinion of competent engineers significantly reduce flood heights. It also requested study by the Corps of Engineers of a possible flood control and water supply project (see Figure 5). The Corps made a preliminary study and in a letter report in 1954 concluded that "there is little likelihood of economic justification for a flood control project."[2] This judgment of course involved assumptions by the investigators as to what types and degrees of protection would be worth canvassing. A request then was made through the Tennessee State Planning Commission for a report on the flood situation by the Tennessee Valley Authority and this was completed in 1958.

Except for these efforts at protection during the 1940's and 1950's the character of use and adjustment in the flood plain changed only moderately. With growth of population, there was some further building in the flood plain. At several points buildings encroached upon the previous channel and further reduced its cross section. The Aspen Street bridge washed out by the 1950 flood was replaced with a clearance slightly less than the 1950 crest. A new bridge on Beech Street was built to just clear that flow. In 1961 the Central Avenue bridge was resurfaced at the old elevation. The city built a new office building with the floor level above the 1950 flood stage, and several merchants altered the arrangement of their storage facilities to reduce flood hazard.

The TVA report led to discussions of desirable changes in regulations

---

[1] Floods on Big Creek, _op. cit_., p. 5.

[2] _Letter Report on Flood Conditions on Big Creek, La Follette, Tennessee, Tennessee River Basin_ (Nashville: U. S. Army Engineer District, 1954).

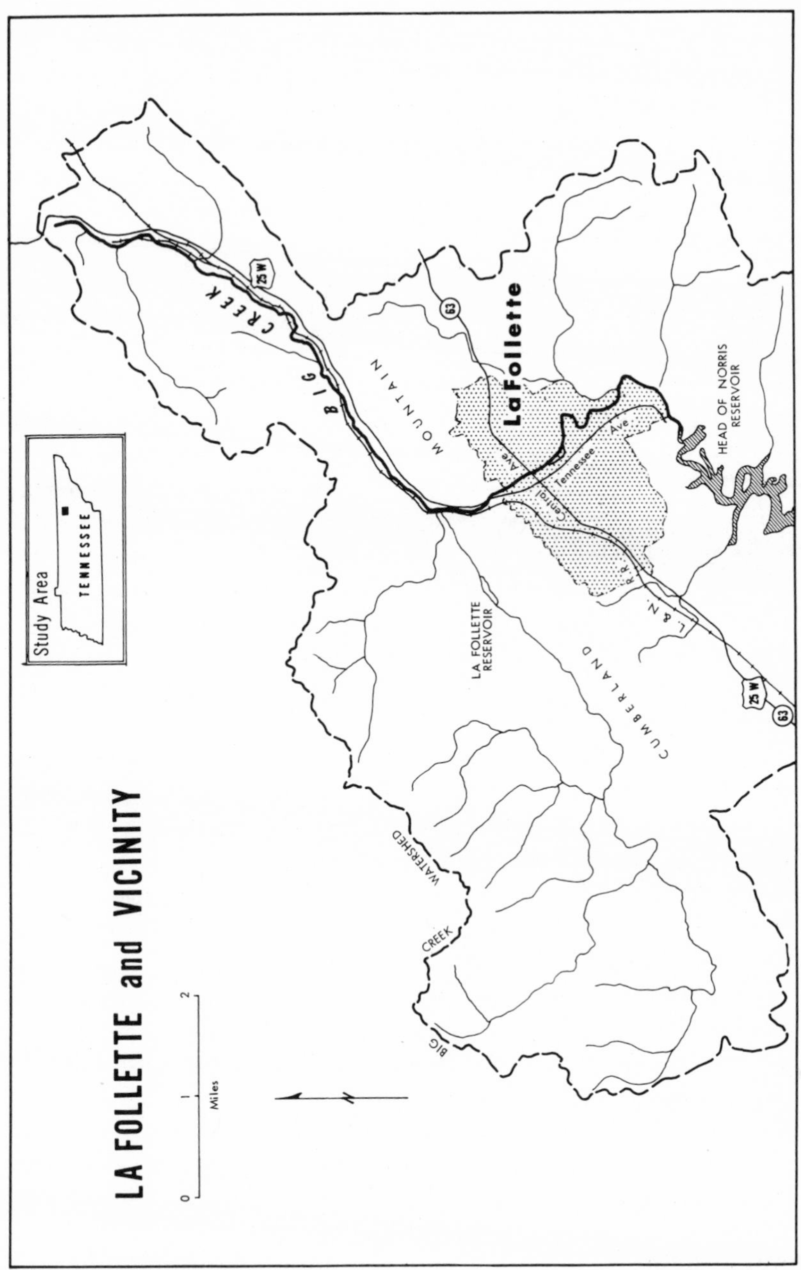

Fig. 5.--Sketch Map of Built-Up Area, Dam Site, and Flood Plain in La Follette.

of channel encroachment. A proposal was prepared by the La Follette Planning Commission with the assistance of the State Planning Commission,[1] and after two years of consideration an amendment to the zoning ordinance to regulate further constriction of the designated "floodway" was approved in 1962. In the same year the city obtained a grant and loan under the Area Redevelopment Program for construction of a water supply reservoir on upper Big Creek, but, as approved, this did not include flood-control features.

The path of adjustment in occupied parts of the La Follette flood plain thus is one of bearing the losses with some emergency removal and flood fighting as the city's commercial and manufacturing area grew slowly in hazard areas, of toying with fragmented, ineffective protection schemes, and of adopting a few structural and land use measures. The public choice has been to study protection and to enact regulation of further encroachment on the floodway. The private choice has been to depend widely upon casual emergency removal as a means of reducing losses, to adjust structural design in a few new buildings so as to reduce flood losses, and to alter a few old structures.

Aurora, Indiana.--The land platted by a development association in 1819 on the terraced flood plain where Hogan Creek enters the Ohio River from the north has remained the central business district of Aurora ever since. Records for the years following 1830 show the river overbank 73 times, with the greatest flow in 1937 when it exceeded the previous extreme of 1884 by 10 feet. First an agricultural market and grain processor related to the Ohio River trade, Aurora grew slowly during the nineteenth century. The railroad followed Hogan Creek valley westward in 1854, and highway improvements continued along the same routes. Iron works flourished and decayed, and by 1961 the major employers were a foundry, a paper container factory, and three woodworking plants. Residential uses adjoined both commercial and industrial sections.

Apparently two types of adjustments to flood hazard took root very early and are practiced widely today in preference to the loss bearing which prevails among the low-income residential managers. One is emergency action and the other is structural. Emergency action to elevate damagable goods to upper stories or to move them out of the flood plain seems to have been common practice for a long time. Both merchants and householders expect to clear their property quickly when the Weather Bureau reports show a crest

---

[1] Proposals for Adjusting to Flood Conditions at La Follette, Tennessee (La Follette: La Follette Planning Commission, 1959).

to be moving down the Ohio. Screens are placed over glass windows to prevent breakage. A furniture factory, one of the large employers, shifts its materials and machinery to upper floors. It, as well as several shops and showrooms, has had alterations in doors, stairways, and loading platforms to permit speedy removal. Both it and a bank are prepared to coat immovable machinery with grease.

These buildings, like many others in Aurora, have undergone structural changes to reduce loss. The early buildings were solid, 2-3 story brick structures which withstand damages except to floors and interior walls. Changes since then in a few buildings are installation of sump pumps, fitting of cutoff valves in sewer pipes, replacement of wooden floors with concrete, tiling of walls, and elevation of floor level above the line of more frequent floods. Because floods rise over 10 feet in parts of the business district, no efforts are made to keep out the water. The structural changes have come slowly, and it is interesting that out of 11 new buildings since 1949, 6 had floor levels above those in nearby buildings, two had no basements, and one of these had installed a concrete floor. Two buildings had no visible structural adjustment, and one had only a sewer cutoff valve. Private adoption of such measures has been spotty up to the present. A second large manufacturing plant in the flood plain has partial protection from an 8-foot private levee.

Aurora is being absorbed into the Cincinnati metropolitan complex with attendant shifts in transportation, retail commercial land use, and employment patterns. Some of the older houses are vacant; new residential building is moving from the flood plain to a location on the peripheries of the town. Within the central business district it appears that for at least a decade the deteriorated and vacant property has been most common in the lowest zones. North of Hogan Creek the lowest income, dilapidated housing is that in the lowest zone of the terrace. The neighbouring town of Lawrenceburg has greater sense of security from floods within its ring levee (although many Aurora citizens are suspicious of the danger of catastrophe from a levee break), and is suffering from similar core deterioration and peripheral growth, but has its blighted properties widely scattered in the area behind the levee rather than in lower zones as at Aurora. This is in contrast to La Follette where new buildings encroached further upon the stream channel.

Following the 1937 disaster the town fathers sought Federal protection works from time to time but these never were authorized because the benefit-cost ratios appeared unfavorable and the town felt unable to contribute heavily toward the cost. The chief public action of recent years with respect to flood hazard was enactment by the County Planning Commission in 1960 of an ordinance controlling subdivision and prohibiting subdivision of land defined by the county surveyor as subject to periodic flooding. Following the high spring flood in 1964, public interest turned to a possible scheme for relocating commercial establishments on higher ground.

Aurora through the decisions of individual managers has placed reliance until very recently upon emergency and structural measures for curbing flood losses. It has adopted a number of structural adjustments, and during recent years it has turned its growth away from the most frequently flooded zones towards outlying uplands.

Darlington, Wisconsin.--The first settlement in this farm market town was in the 1830's on a hill overlooking a narrow crossing in the Pecatonia River flood plain. After the railroad pushed its way along the river valley in 1854 the town grew down hill along Main Street to the bridge and railway station, and this four-block stretch continues to be the center of the retail shopping district. Public buildings, some shops, and virtually all of the residential use is above the reach of floods; shops, feed and lumber merchants, dairy processing, bulk oil distribution and other commercial uses are in the bottom land.

The Pecatonica goes out of bank on the average of once or twice a year in the Darlington reach at the foot of a steep valley. Spring freshets caused by melting snow, sometimes aggravated by ice jams, cause low flooding almost annually. Intense rain at any time of year can bring floods, and accounted for the highest of record in July 1950. These disturbances must have encouraged the progressive elevation of Main Street four feet above its old level during the period from 1850 to 1880. Merchants built above the more frequent floods and they seem to have expected to take emergency steps when higher waters lapped at their doors. The catastrophe of 1950 caused severe damage in excess of $2,000,000 and stimulated three shifts in both public and private positions toward flood hazard.

One response was to look to Federal engineering agencies for protection. The Corps of Engineers made a favorable finding on both a proposed levee project and an upstream detention dam, but the city initially decided not to offer local contributions for either. Opposition stemmed partly from unwillingness to accept Federal investment. In the case of the levee it centered especially on the effect of running an embankment across the lower section of Main Street. With the dam it involved reluctance to take valuable farm land out of cultivation. There was more sympathy for an S.C.S.

longer-term watershed improvement scheme which placed less emphasis upon dam construction. As a government and as a community, Darlington consciously decided not to look to the traditional engineering solutions.

The town reversed its position in 1962. It then agreed to pay the non-Federal costs of $182,000 for a local protection project having a total cost of $1,052,000.[1] Average annual benefits were estimated at $45,100 and annual charges at $43,100. In effect, the community decided it would be willing to pay about $8,470 annually for value of land in project works and $3,230 for maintenance and operation in return for losses to be prevented. The project was authorized in the Flood Control Act of 1962. While the net social gain by such improvement was slight, the town gained both in reduction of losses and in reduction of uncertainty. It thus consciously determined not to continue its reliance upon emergency action.

The earlier attitude had combined with the unexpectedly heavy losses in the 1950 flood to foster improvement in arrangements for emergency action. A county flood warning committee was organized to issue forecasts and to aid in taking steps to reduce damage after receiving the warning. This has proved an effective system thus far and has functioned on a wholly voluntary basis about 30 times since 1950. Emergency removal and treatment became the prevailing adjustment.

At the same time, interest quickened in structural adjustment by land elevation and building design. New buildings in the flood plain, including a city office addition and a sewage disposal plant, were designed to stand above the 1950 flood level, and a supermarket was constructed in 1961 on a three-foot fill with special piling to protect against undercutting by high velocity flood waters. Channel cross-section thereby is reduced. This supermarket is located on land sold by the city from a large block it holds north of Main Street along the stream channel. Although there was no zoning ordinance in 1961, one was in preparation which would zone this strip commercial with a restriction upon those uses, such as bulk oil plants, involving fire danger. Having depended chiefly upon emergency action and loss bearing, the city first looked to further commercial development of the flood plain at elevated floor levels with continuing flood warning service, and then shifted over to reliance upon protection works.

---

[1] U.S., 87th Congress, 2d Session, Pecatonica River, Illinois and Wisconsin, House Document, No. 539 (Washington: U. S. Government Printing Office, 1962), pp. 46-47.

Desert Hot Springs, California.--This is a fast-growing resort town on the desert south flank of the Little San Bernardino Mountains. The path of adjustment has been primarily one of loss bearing.

Unlike its larger and more prosperous neighbour to the south, Palm Springs, Desert Hot Springs has not reached the position of a commercial center for adjoining areas, it has not incorporated, and it is off the main axis of urban growth that stretches along the highway at the foot of the San Jacinto mountains. Thus, the activities of its present population are linked almost wholly with the servicing of older year-round citizens who account for more than half of the total, and of short-term visitors who patronize its motels and vacation apartments. There are retail service shops, but not a single wholesale commercial or industrial establishment.

Desert Hot Springs' functional orientation is wholly toward residential locations, taking advantage of the high winter temperatures, long rainless periods, dry air, warm mineral water, and arid mountain scenery. The arrangement of land use follows a largely rectilinear pattern reflecting the system of subdivision which began in the 1940's and has moved at an accelerated pace since the mid-1950's. The business uses cluster along the two main streets near their intersection, and the residences and guest houses spread out from there in a rough rectangle. Considerations of highway paving, city water mains, and property price and ownership apparently have been more influential than esthetic ones in affecting the direction of expansion; some scenic outlooks have remained free of new construction.

The town not only lacks records of flood frequency, but also suffers uncertainty as to where the flood plain is at any given time. This is because of its location on an alluvial fan, with an average slope of five per cent, over which two tributaries are actively moving. There are no satisfactory records of stream flow out of either Blind Canyon or the larger Marongo washes to the west. Estimates of flood recurrence must be taken from aggregated experience for similar areas in the Coachella Valley. Moreover, the very short tenure of virtually all of the residents means that they characteristically are unaware of events of more than a few years past. The major part of the town is on a cone which is drained at rare times of intense rainfall by Blind Canyon and its Cactus Creek branch. These flowed off to the west into Little Marongo Wash at the time of the last heavy flow, their courses having been channeled and confined by works constructed by the Riverside County Flood Control and Water Conservation District in 1952. A serious flow in 1950 stimulated this channel improvement. Floods are flash events, rising to crest in less than an hour, and rushing out of the canyon mouth to spread over the cone and then roar down the wash. Velocities and sediment loads are high.

As shown on the sketch map (Figure 3) the present channel makes a sharp turn at the point where it reaches 8th Street and flows down that asphalt channel to the Wash. Given the rough estimates as to expected flows and the limited capacity of the channels, it is possible that the next major flood would break into new paths, leaving untouched some areas of recent damage and bringing a violent flow of mud and boulders across other property. Few parts of the town on the fan could be considered wholly free from this danger. Capacity of the improved channel has been reduced in recent years. The judgment of engineers in the County office is that short of large-scale detention reservoir construction in the upper part of Blind Canyon, no complete regulation of the shifting stream will be achieved.

Much the same situation applies to the lands bordering the Marongo washes. While their last course is known, the sedimentary evidence of earlier channels and the habits of desert streams suggest that they could wander disastrously. They are not confined at present. The County does attempt by zoning to prohibit dumping refuse in them.

County zoning classifies most of the area as suitable for residential and commercial construction. The more vulnerable beds of the washes are classified so as to prevent building without permit and to curb further constriction of the channel.

With rapid population growth, quick turnover in land ownership, and infrequent floods, the prevailing adjustment since the first subdivision has been bearing the infrequent loss. Following the 1950 flood County authorities also pushed investigation of a reservoir project judged by the Corps of Engineers to be not feasible, and they supported zoning regulations to prevent outright invasion of flood channels. The paved roads are designed with high curbs to carry flows of 6-8 inches. While technicians know that a flood larger than the 1950 flow could cause heavy losses, few citizens are aware of a flood hazard and no conspicuous action is taken by them to reduce losses when the next stream of water, mud, and boulders disgorges on the cone.

Cerrito Creek, California.--The 55 acre flood plain of this creek where it flows out from its steep upper basin onto the Bay shore along the south border of Richmond has been settled slowly as metropolitan San Francisco has engulfed it, and still has about one-quarter of its area vacant and zoned for residential or industrial development. Sharp peaked floods of short duration came with less than an hour's warning on the average of once a year until 1958. Stage occasionally is increased by high tide in the Bay. The lower, bayside portion of the flood plain is in Richmond, the upper part is in El Cerrito, and the lower stream is the northern boundary of Albany. Hazard thus is the concern of three municipalities from which settlement has moved into the valley bottom.

During the 1920's and 30's a few small manufacturing plants located in the Richmond section near the traversing railway and highway on land which was elevated by fill from the adjacent Albany Hill. The stream channel was shifted south to permit more space. About the same time a few residences were constructed in what is now the El Cerrito section. These were frame buildings of the "Sacramento" type with garages and basement on the ground floor. The brief floods rarely exceeded one or two feet in depth, and, other than the residential design, loss bearing was the prevailing adjustment until relatively high floods in 1955 and 1958 spurred new approaches to flood hazard. El Cerrito authorities then sought unsuccessfully for a Federal Flood control project, but at the same time they built up a one- to two-foot levee along the creek, began cleaning the channel regularly, and required new buildings to have floor levels above the elevation of the levee.

In Richmond, a pump company set out to flood proof its plant in 1958. Drawing in part upon experience with its plant on the Mississippi flood plain in St. Louis, this manufacturer built a three-foot retaining wall, installed emergency bulkheads on all major doors, permanently elevated all damageable material stores at least four feet high, built an interior drainage system for both water and oil, installed permanent sump pumps at low spots, and deployed sandbags and portable sump pumps at strategic places for quick use. It regularly drills employees in the use of this equipment and annually reviews preparations, experience, and new problems.

Construction of the Eastshore Expressway across the plain upstream probably reduced hazard at this plant and increased ponding above it. One of the smaller manufacturers, an aggregate plant, believes that with a somewhat elevated site its losses in time of flood would not be serious. Another, a mill and lumber company, went into bankruptcy in 1961 for reasons apparently having nothing to do with flood. The remaining small manufacturing and commercial establishments bear flood loss without other adjustment. New apartment buildings and scattered houses in the El Cerrito section have adhered to required floor elevations but no doubt will be subject to heavy losses from floods rising higher than the 15- to 25-year frequency events of 1955 and 1958.

The course of adjustment throughout the flood plain has been gradual invasion by loss bearing occupance with early structural adjustments by residential builders. Emergency and structural measures have their most intense application in the Richmond pump plant without public stimulation. Structural measures and minor protection have been adopted under local government pressure in El Cerrito.

Watkins Glen, New York.--This small, shrinking town was the scene of disaster in 1935 when a flow far greater than an estimated "maximum probable" rushed down from the steep scenic uplands of Glen Creek and broke out of a agraded and debris-clogged channel across most of the built-up areas. This spurred a Federal project of three silt reservoirs, channel dredging, and levees which was completed during 1938-1959. The levees are now recognized as possibly subject to failure in the event of a larger flow of 10,000 c.f.s. A greater degree of protection has been judged by the Corps to be economically unwarranted. Hydraulic conditions are exceedingly complex. Engineers are reluctant to assign a recurrence interval to the 10,000 c.f.s. flood. It is difficult to state with certainty more than that if a very rare flow were to occur in the right circumstances a failure in the reach above the railroad tracks would cause flooding in a strip about one block wide adjoining the tracks and in a wider lowland downstream.

It therefore is not unreasonable that the citizens of Watkins Glen consider themselves free from flood. Many acutely remember the right of July 7, 1935 when their only remedy was to wade for their lives, but they look with confidence at the channel works, and they do now what they did before 1935--nothing to prevent further loss if and when the rare event occurs.

Chief source of employment in Watkins Glen is salt refining. Recreation based on the rugged Glen Creek gorge state park and on Seneca Lake boating draws some trade, and the town is a retail and public service center for Schluyler County. It also provides dormitory residential space for workers in nearby towns. The area likely to be flooded by a rare flow is chiefly vacant and residential with a few commercial establishments in converted houses. Most of the buildings are two-story with ground-floor elevations about two feet above the surface. If the town were to grow in industry it might expand into the lower plain, but growth is not threatening, and increase in none of the four current sources of employment would promise intensification in the flood plain. A reported small amount of overbank flow in 1950 did not arouse anxiety as to the future.

Watkins Glen resembles numerous places having partial protection and the confidence of assumed complete security. The time and place of failure seem so indefinite that no other adjustment than "protection" and loss bearing seems credible.

Other Towns with Flood Hazard

When compared with the more than one thousand towns identified in 1957 as having flood problems, these six places show an interesting range of characteristics.[1] They can be compared according to both individual conditions and associations of characteristics.

Some of the more significant aspects of the national distributions are given in Table 3. With the exception of Cerrito Creek and La Follette, the towns fall in the lower quartile of all places having flood hazard when arranged according to population. These two more nearly approach the national median than the others. The rate of population change in 1930-50 in the six towns ranges from losses of 15 per cent to gains of several hundred per cent. By comparison with the national distribution they have a larger proportion of declining and slowly growing towns. A larger proportion of them have substantial amounts of commercial, manufacturing, and residential land use in the flood plain than the mean of the towns in the national canvass, but the distribution of types of uses is similar to the national average.

In terms of flood occurrence, they represent extreme quartiles of less than 1.7 floods and more than 6 floods per 10 years, but do not include the modal condition of about 2 to 3. La Follette frequency comes closest to the mean of the larger group of towns. The maximum height of water at the point of deepest overbank flow embraces the national range but lower heights are better represented than larger ones, and La Follette,while theoretically subject to waters rising to first-floor ceilings, has not in its history experienced more than 3 feet. The flood-to-peak interval for five of the towns is much shorter than the national mean of 30 hours: only Aurora has such a long period that duration of flooding is measured in days rather than hours. La Follette has at best two to three hours warning from the time waters reach bankfull, the Desert Hot Springs and Watkins Glen intervals are even shorter, Cerrito Creek varies from one to 12 hours according to hydrologic conditions, and Darlington averages 6-8 hours with the flood waters receding rather rapidly. Velocities of flood waters in the six towns span the possible range from low to very high, and so too do their sediment loads. Inasmuch

---

[1] White, et al., op. cit., pp. 33-48.

TABLE 3

COMPARISON OF FLOOD PLAIN CHARACTERISTICS
IN SIX TOWNS AND IN 1957 CANVASS

Characteristics	Six Towns Range	Urban Places in 1957 Canvass			
		Number of Places	Lower Quartile	Median	Upper Quartile
Population size	2,000-26,000	1010	-4,000	-15,000	25,000 -
Size of drainage area in square miles	3-80,600	560	0-35?	250?	800 -
Floods per 10 years of record	.6-20.0	496	0-1.7	3.0	6.0-
Height of water at deepest point over-bank in feet	2-30	534	0-5?	8.0?	11 -
Flood-to-peak interval in hours	1-168	3.16	0-10?	30	100 -
Per cent with following use accounting for 20% or more of total land use in flood plain:		875		Mean of 875 towns	
Commercial	83			70	
Manufacturing	66			43	
Residential	100			84	
Transport	33			20	
Recreational	0			5	

as size of drainage area is a readily calculated parameter of flood conditions, this measure also is given in Table 3.

A sense of urgency linked to the date of the most recent damaging flood may have some bearing on the timing of public decisions affecting flood adjustments. The six towns include places that had not suffered flood in 26 (Watkins Glen) and 11 (La Follette) years but four of them had experienced overbank flow within the three years preceding the study.

The association of land use characteristics may be compared with those for other towns studied in 1957.[1] A simple classification of 732 of those

[1]White, et al., op. cit., pp. 44-45.

places showed that about 40 per cent have basic manufacturing on the flood plain and 40 per cent have their central business district subject to flood. In 30 per cent a key transport artery crosses the flood plain. Roughly a third had only peripheral areas on flood zones. Only 15 per cent were entirely on the flood plain. Among the six towns, only one may be considered to be wholly in the flood plain, four have important industrial uses, four have their central business district in the path of floods, and all have important traffic arteries subject to interruption.

A factor analysis suggests that about half of the total variation in 24 variables in these cities could be accounted for by four patterns of correlation.[1] These findings are difficult to relate to the present study because they do not distinguish degrees of protection and contain no data on alternative adjustments.

The six towns thus are moderately representative of the range in land use, water velocity, and sediment load found in places of less than 20,000 having flood problems. Their conditions differ from national distributions chiefly in having a smaller proportion of fast-growing towns, of towns with flood occurrence of 2 to 3 years in 10, of towns with high inundation depths, and of towns with long flood-to-peak intervals. The towns are not highly representative in a statistical sense. Inasmuch as the great bulk of the damage potential for the United States is located in larger towns, the six towns can not be taken to accurately reflect conditions in the damage centers.

The types and paths of adjustment which they have adopted are nevertheless similar to those in cities which have been studied at other times. Probably La Follette and the five other towns offer less promising opportunities for alternative adjustments to floods than many larger towns with greater damage potential. They depart from the national distribution in ways that would appear to make them less suitable than larger towns with different population, frequency, depth, and flood-to-peak interval characteristics. It will be shown in the next chapter that the bias inherent in the six towns is against conditions favorable to solutions other than protection and loss bearing. The findings therefore underestimate rather than exaggerate the opportunities for alternative adjustments.

---

[1] Wolf Roder and Brian J. L. Berry, "Associations between Expected Flood Damages and the Characteristics of Urban Flood Plains. A Factorial Analysis," Papers on Flood Problems, pp. 45-58.

12

Reprinted by permission of the Regents of the University of California from *Flood Control in Metropolitan Los Angeles* (Univ. Calif. Publ. Pol. Sci.), University of California Press, Berkeley, Vol. 6, 1959, pp. 1–10. Originally published by the University of California.

FLOOD CONTROL IN METROPOLITAN LOS ANGELES

BY

RICHARD BIGGER

THE FLOOD PROBLEM

Deluge, 1914

Rain began to fall about 12:30 A.M. on February 18, 1914, throughout the area of Los Angeles. For four days the sodden skies soaked the cities, the farms, the beaches, and the mountains. By February 21 more than 19 inches of water had fallen in parts of the San Gabriel Mountains, 3 or more inches along the coast. In one hour, on the night of February 18, 1.5 inches of rain descended on the city of Los Angeles.[1]

Runoff from almost barren mountain slopes, from city roofs and streets, and from farms began almost immediately. Two weeks of general precipitation in the preceding month had thoroughly soaked the ground; its absorptive capacity had vanished.

With little warning, water, laden with tons of debris, poured out of the steep mountain canyons, rushed quickly down the creeks and washes, into the Los Angeles and San Gabriel rivers. Near the center of Los Angeles, the flood discharge of the Los Angeles River reached 31,140 second feet, about the normal flow of the mighty Colorado River. That of the San Gabriel in the foothills of the San Gabriel Valley was 26,620 second feet. Discharge rates from smaller tributary mountain canyons sometimes approximated one-half of those of the larger streams.[2]

Water and debris gushing out of the canyon mouths and flashing into the rivers swept over the highly unstable wash and stream banks and into the built-up areas in the foothills and plains. Four million cubic yards of silt were emptied into the harbors of Long Beach and Los Angeles. Hundreds of people became temporary refugees, and many were injured. Between February 18 and February 24 there was practically no communication with the outside world. Telegraph messages to San Bernardino, 60 miles away, were sent via Chicago. Long Beach was an island, cut off on all sides by the fiercely rushing waters. Rail traffic was entirely suspended.[3]

When the waters finally subsided and the debris was removed, the damage caused by the flood was reckoned at $10,000,000,[4] including wreckage in bridges, roads, rail lines, buildings, agriculture, industry, and public utilities. In addition, the Army Engineers estimated that $400,000 would be needed to dredge out the deposit of silt at the harbors.[5]

Organized flood control was born out of the fears and losses sustained in this catastrophe. Today, the ultimate cost of the flood-control program, begun in a small way at that time, is reckoned at over three-quarters of a billion dollars. It is also a vast intergovernmental venture requiring the coöperation of federal, state, and local governments. One of the most striking elements of the Los Angeles flood-control story is the way in which many agencies at different levels have meshed planning, operations, and finances. This, in fact, is perhaps the main thread of the story to be told in this study.

In order, however, to be conversant with the governmental problems and programs of local flood control, it is necessary to outline the flood and conservation problems in Los Angeles County. That is the purpose of the remainder of this chapter.

The Flood Hazard

The metropolitan region of Los Angeles County has probably been subject to a greater potential flood hazard—mainly from flash floods—than any other area of similar size and population density in the United States. Almost half of the 1,568 square miles in the combined metropolitan drainage basins is subject to overflow. This includes almost half of metropolitan Los Angeles County. Danger areas are the flood plains fanning out from main stream and tributary channel banks and from canyon mouths.

Before 1889, periodic floods, although causing extensive inconvenience, did not bring about any general demand for remedial measures. This was largely owing to the fact that economic development had not progressed to any great degree. The region's population in 1890 was only 100,000.

Between 1889 and 1914 a great industrial and agricultural expansion took place, and immigrants poured in. By 1914, about 700,000 persons lived in the area, and assessed value of property (less than one-half actual value) had increased to $804,119,007,[6] almost fourteen times the valuation of 1890.

The metropolitan region has continued to grow tremendously. The 936,000 population of 1920 became 2,208,000 in 1930, and over 5,000,000 by 1954. More than fifty cities, including sprawling Los Angeles, lie within the area. Agriculture, industry, and commerce developed rapidly. By 1955, assessed valuation of taxable real property in the metropolitan region reached $6,166,750,900.[7] The latter area is predominantly urban, although value of the produce from its agriculture is larger than that of any other county in the state. The Long Beach–Los Angeles harbor area provides one of the world's largest ports, and in the metropolitan region there is a huge investment in petroleum, aircraft, motion pictures, automobile assembly, and other industries.

Many of these economic resources, as well as residences and commercial property and utilities, have lain—and continue to lie—in the path of floods. Probably more than two million people live in areas believed subject to flooding. Assessed valuation of real property on the menaced lands is certainly over three billion dollars—actual value being more than seven billions. Growth of the region since 1914 has made intensive and organized efforts to control the rushing waters an ever more pressing imperative.

Lack of foresight has helped to bring about the tremendous need for added protection against the inevitable flood. Periods of time between floods are sometimes long, whereas memory of man is short. Lands which historically have been seriously menaced were purchased by those—especially newcomers—who thought that the climate of Los Angeles was all sunshine and warmth. They farmed or built industries and homes in the foothills at mouths of canyons, along the low river banks, and even in the dry stream beds.

Metropolitan development has meant that property damage and loss of life from the periodic inundations have become successively more disastrous. The flood of 1914 caused some $10,000,000 in destruction of property, although official records do not show any loss of life. The lesser deluge in 1916 brought $4,000,000 in property damage; again no one was killed by the swirling waters.[8] In 1934, a flood descended on the small La Canada Valley in the foothills, carrying out of the mountains over 600,000 cubic yards of debris. It devastated buildings, citrus groves, vineyards, villages, and highways; the reported damage exceeded $5,000,000. Forty persons were counted dead.[9] The last great flood—in March, 1938—affected almost the entire flood-hazard area. Damage to property was estimated at over $62,000,000; fifty-nine lives were lost.[10] Regular transcontinental transportation was halted for nine days, normal telegraphic and telephonic communication stopped for a period of three days, and public health was jeopardized by breaking of sewage lines.[11]

Floods have struck Los Angeles twenty-one times during the 143-year period between 1811 and 1954.[12] Magnitude of the floods before 1938 is unknown, but has been estimated by recourse to whatever historical and geological records are available. Weather Bureau rainfall records date only from 1876, therefore an estimate of flood frequencies is difficult to determine with any degree of exactness. Only the memories of witnesses in an 1889 court case give a clue to dates and magnitude of floods before 1878.[13] On the basis of the scanty information available, it is believed that a "great" flood, approaching the probable maximum, covering the entire flood plain, will occur once in a hundred years; a "large" flood, inundating all low-lying valley areas and sections of the coastal plain adjacent to stream channels, may occur six times in one hundred years; and "moderate" floods may come about once every decade.[14] These figures are averages; in actuality, time between sizeable inundations has varied from one to twenty-three years. There is no certainty as to when a flood will come, or as to its destructiveness; there is certainty that a flood will sometime strike, and that it may be devastating.

Flood Causes

Flood control and the complementary water-conservation problems in southern California are contained primarily in watershed areas of the rivers which drain southward and westward from the crest of the coastal ranges to the Pacific. They are found principally in the coastal plains, tributary valleys, and mountain foothills. Within the Los Angeles area generally, the drainage basins include those of the Los Angeles and San Gabriel rivers and Ballona Creek in Los Angeles County, and that of the Santa Ana River in Orange County, southwestern San Bernardino County, and northwestern Riverside County. A minute portion of eastern Los Angeles County is drained by San Antonio Wash, a part of the Santa Ana system, which courses down the border between Los Angeles and San Bernardino counties. This has its origin in mountainous areas of both jurisdictions. Coyote Creek, at the southeast limit of the San Gabriel watershed, follows the lower border of Los Angeles and Orange counties, draining a very small part of both.

Los Angeles County, for our purposes, may be divided into three general areas. The coastal region, an alluvial plain with tributary valleys, is bounded by the Pacific Ocean on the south, the San Gabriel Mountains on the north, and the Santa Monica and Santa Suzanna ranges on the northwest. It is comprised of 1,000 square miles of flat and hilly land, and stretches eastward and in part southward into neighboring Orange, Riverside, and San Bernardino counties. The region beginning at the edge of the southern foothills of the coastal ranges and extending to the crest of the latter, which is 30 to 50 miles inland, consists of approximately 700 square miles of rough, mountainous territory. The remainder of the county lies north of the mountain crest; it contains nearly 2,400 square miles of rugged terrain and desert plateau, and is only thinly populated. A good share of the mountainous area is a federal forest reserve, the Angeles National Forest.

The metropolitan region of the county is located primarily in the coastal area—the coastal plain and its two large tributary valleys—but upper portions lie within the foothills of the mountain ranges. The vast coastal plain occupies the southwestern part of the county; San Fernando Valley lies to its north, cut off from it by a spur of the Santa Monica Range extending inland from the west; San Gabriel Valley is in the east, partly divided from the plain by two ranges of rolling hills. West and east of San Fernando Valley, and north of San Gabriel Valley, lie the foothills and the mountains.

All of the county's metropolitan river systems may take the offensive against life and property. The Los Angeles River, arising in northwestern San Fernando Valley, winds in a semicircle through the lower edge of the valley, through the center of Los Angeles, and through the coastal plain, emptying at length into the ocean at San Pedro Bay. Except for the upper reaches in western San Fernando Valley, and for mountain tributaries, the entire Los Angeles River system flows through built-up residential, commercial, industrial, and port areas. The San Gabriel River, formed in the southeastern part of the San Gabriel Mountains, flows southerly across the San Gabriel Valley, and through the coastal plain into Alamitos Bay, about 6 miles east of the mouth of the Los Angeles River. A short distance below the foothill city of Azusa, deposits of sand, gravel, and boulders have divided the channel into two branches. The western branch is known as the Río Hondo, and it becomes tributary to the Los Angeles River. The San Gabriel and Río Hondo systems drain through areas largely suburban and agricultural in character, although the southernmost portions of the channels flow through industrial and residential developments near the city of Long Beach. Small Ballona Creek and its tributaries drain the area on the western edge of the Los Angeles River basin, between the southern slopes of the Santa Monica Mountains and the Pacific. Practically all of Ballona Creek overflow region is occupied by residential and industrial development.

The crest of the coastal ranges where the river systems have their origin is at most 50 miles inland from the Pacific. Elevations rise from sea level on the plains to above 10,000 feet in the eastern mountains, decreasing to about 3,000 feet in their northwest part. Mountain slopes are extremely steep; land slopes in the valley areas are also high. The coastal plain is relatively flat. These facts mean stream gradients are steep except in the coastal plain, and drainage lines are exceedingly short. The total length of the Los Angeles River is only 50 miles; that of the San Gabriel River is 58. Channels of tributaries and of Ballona Creek and the Río Hondo are also short.

River banks are low and courses unstable, owing, among other causes, to the building up of deltalike fans of debris brought down from the mountainous areas by rushing waters of the past. For the most part, the main streams and even tributaries are dry during the greater share of the year. It is only during periods of fairly heavy precipitation—in the wintertime—that they carry an appreciable amount of water.

The precipitous slopes of the mountains and canyons are composed principally of disintegrated igneous rock, which is readily erodible where not protected by forest covering. The thin soils of these areas and lack of rainfall during the greater part of the year limit vegetation to a sparse growth consisting mainly of live oak and chaparral. Much of this region is not so protected. During dry months there is a dangerous fire hazard in the mountain and foothill forest and brush areas. After a burn, the denuded soil is exposed to heavy water erosion. From three to five years are required for a new growth of brush cover.

Climate of the area is subtropical and semiarid. Average annual precipitation varies from about 10 inches near the coast to 40 inches near the crest of the mountains. However, in some years there is almost no rainfall; in others, much more than average. About 80 per cent of the precipitation, most of it rain except in the very high mountains, falls during the four-month period from December to March. The rainfall picture is further complicated by an erratic series of wet and dry cycles, a single cycle extending sometimes over a period of several years.

Practically all storms, moving in from the Pacific, are trapped by the semicircular ranges enclosing the coastal area, and the entire rain crop falls upon the southern mountain slopes and the valleys and plains. Normally, rainfall from light or evenly spaced storms would be absorbed into the vast underground basins underlying the coastal plain and the valleys, or trickle safely down the river systems into the ocean.

But the region is subject to frequent torrential winter storms. They are violent, erratic, and usually of short duration, passing by in a few hours. Often several may descend upon the area during a period of days, separated by perhaps intervals of lighter rain. At one mountain station 1.17 inches of rain fell in five minutes during such a turbulent storm. On the plains, a record of .42 inches was established for a similar period. Precipitation rates have been known to exceed 2 inches per hour in the San Gabriel Mountains, and 1.5 inches per hour on lower lands nearer the coast.[15]

Torrential downpours occurring within extended periods of precipitation are responsible for the violent flash floods. Almost all major floods of record have been preceded by about 8 inches of rainfall within a period of a few weeks.[16] The thoroughly soaked ground is then unable to absorb subsequent heavy outpourings. With little impediment, water rushes down the steep, sparsely covered mountain slopes, down the canyons, over the alluvial fans at canyon mouths, through the larger creeks and into the rivers. The descent of runoff to valley floors takes place in a matter of hours at most, and sometimes in only a few minutes. Since almost none of the precipitation falls in the form of snow, practically all of it becomes part of the flood.

Discharge of water from the mountains is heavily laden with silt, sand, and fine gravel, accumulating more such debris as it rushes through the erodible foothill and upper valley areas, and even the plains. Rapidly moving sludge of this kind may carry fifteen- to twenty-ton rocks along with it.[17] Intensity of the torrential flow from the mountains, transporting the debris and boulders, increases astonishingly whenever the mountain watershed is denuded by forest fire.

Instability of stream beds has meant that the rampaging waters and debris may quickly overflow river banks and flood the flat, low-lying areas in valleys and plain. They may also cut new channels and inundate land previously thought immune to floods. Within the past eighty years the two principal rivers in Los Angeles County have changed course materially in this way.[18]

Urbanization—roofs and paved streets—has increased amount of runoff and its rate perceptibly. Development of farming and farm drainage systems has tended to bring about the same result in agricultural areas. Lands that could be safely inundated and could hold back, at least for a time, the rushing water, or on which some portion of the runoff could percolate underground, have been taken up by subdividers for more intensive use.

The floods strike violently, almost without warning. Some may be small and localized. Others, less frequently, devastate the entire menaced part of the metropolitan area. To protect the region from this looming terror, measures must be taken long before a flood is in the making; there is no time after it has begun.

Wasted Waters

The threat to life and property caused by the rushing flood waters is a source of fear to local inhabitants. A deeper sense of frustration sets in as they realize that thousands of acre-feet of precious water are being lost to the sea. Even in years of normal rainfall, the loss to the sea is great; in flood years, it is prodigious.

With less than 1 per cent of the state's water resources, arid Los Angeles County supports two-fifths of California's population. A stable and increasing water supply is therefore essential to the growing urban population and to the farms, most of which would produce almost nothing without irrigation.

Before 1913, inhabitants relied entirely on indigenous sources, which were sufficient for the small population of that era. Subterranean ground water basins tapped by wells provided the bulk of the water. Huge deposits of porous sands and gravels form cones at the canyon mouths and fill valley and coastal basins, sometimes to depths of more than 2,000 feet. Runoff from the mountains and valleys percolates into these reservoirs, which provide usable storage capacity estimated in excess of 3,636,000 acre-feet.[19]

As the region developed, these local supplies became quickly overtaxed. Agricultural, industrial, and domestic needs all meant a more intensive use of the underground reservoirs. The year-round flow of the rivers, originating in the underground basins, had dried up shortly after the 1880's owing to the draft from the first spate of artesian wells. Additional thousands of wells were then sunk for irrigation purposes and for urban needs. The rate of extraction was too much, and the water table dropped alarmingly, spurred on by the abnormal lack of rainfall between 1894 and 1904, as well as by subsequent dry cycles. The hundreds of artesian wells, the major source of water between the 1880's and early 1900's ceased to flow. Meanwhile, the number of pumped wells grew.[20] Lowering of the water table became increasingly evident after 1916, and by the 1930's levels were dropping from 2 to 20 feet a year.[21] It was estimated that the underground basins had been depleted by 2,300,000 acre-feet between 1914 and 1930.[22] The yearly overdraft in the area, exclusive of the city of Los Angeles, was roughly between 116,700 and 162,750 acre-feet.[23] This is from one-fourth to one-third of the dependable annual yield of the region's water resources.[24]

By 1905, the prospective water shortage had become very alarming to the city of Los Angeles. Between that year and 1913 the city constructed an aqueduct system to tap the Owens Valley in the High Sierra. By 1940 this had been expanded to secure additional supplies from the Mono basin not far away. These sources can probably yield some 240,000 acre-feet annually.[25]

Needs of the developing region, however, soon required importation of more water. Between 1923 and 1941, the resources of all southern California were thrown into the building of a system to bring water from the Colorado River. The Metropolitan Water District, which operates this system serving eighteen constituent cities and water districts, estimates that its capacity is about 1,000,000 acre-feet per year.[26]

In the fiscal year 1950–51, the city of Los Angeles delivered about 398,869 acre-feet of water to its urban and agricultural citizens.[27] Twenty-two per cent (87,751 acre-feet) came from local sources, and about 1.5 per cent from the Colorado River.[28] During the same period of time the Metropolitan Water District sold 165,472.6 acre-feet to its members and other purchasers, about one-fifth of the capacity of its aqueduct. Approximately 55,000 acre-feet of this was consumed in Los Angeles County.[29]

In 1951, some 3,076,000 inhabitants of Los Angeles County, out of a total population of 4,125,000, were dependent in part on water brought in from Owens Valley or from the Colorado. These consumers received about 453,900 imported acre-feet in 1950–51, and they obtained an additional 255,200 acre-feet from local sources, largely from the underground basins.[30] The remainder of the county's population, nearly 1,000,000 urban and agricultural users, relied entirely on the local sources. The total load placed thereby on the valley and coastal basins is unknown, but it was certainly prodigious. Lowering of the water table in some parts of the county continues apace, particularly in the western coastal plain, the central coastal plain, and in the basins close to the foothills,[31] whereas near the coast, pressure from the sea on the almost depleted underground reservoirs has led to serious salt-water intrusion, which has ruined much agricultural land.

The local water crop, no matter how well conserved, could never supply more than part of the region's needs, but it is certain that every bit of water saved is of value to the area's inhabitants. Just how much of the annual runoff can be conserved, over and above what percolates naturally into the soil, is pretty largely a matter of conjecture. The rainfall picture is complicated by an erratic series of wet and dry cycles. In addition, rapid flood runoff from heavy storms and from hard-surfaced roads and roofs of the growing built-up area decreases the amount that can seep into the underground reservoirs.

The Los Angeles County Flood Control District, in 1930, estimated that on an average, over 100,000 acre-feet of wasted water could be conserved each year, perhaps as much as 150,000 acre-feet in flood years.[32] If the average daily consumption of water is 150 gallons per capita, this would be enough to supply from 600,000 to 900,000 people, no mean saving. It is felt that the best way to conserve the runoff is to let it percolate into the vast storage space of the many underground basins in the foothill, valley, and coastal plain areas from surface-retarding reservoirs and other permanent flood-control works.[33] The costly projects can thus be valuable in both flood years and years of less rainfall.

Thus conservation ranks as a major interest of the flood-control authorities in Los Angeles, although it is secondary to protection against floods. It was perhaps a more important issue in the decades between 1910 and 1940, before arrival of water from the Colorado River. That event took some pressure from the local sources, and, perhaps more important, allayed the anxious thoughts that lack of water would bring the growth of the metropolitan region to a dead end. At the present moment, southern California is not starved for water, although those areas that depend entirely on the underground basins are not too well off. However, continued phenomenal growth of population may require additional sources in the not too distant future. Some authorities estimate that this date will arrive earlier than 1970.

The amount of water which can be obtained by conservation of most of the region's annual runoff is by no means as great as that which might be made available from other sources, such as the abundant rivers of northern California. But it is sufficient to provide a part of the growing needs of Los Angeles County. Interest in conservation has lagged, but it is still an element in the thinking of flood-control officials.

13

Reprinted from *River Control in Communist China* (Communist China Prob. Res. Ser. EC31), Union Research Institute, Hong Kong, 1962, pp. 87–92, 97–99, 122–124

River Control in Communist China

ROBERT CARIN

Defects and Mistakes

While, with denuded mountains existing in many areas, soil erosion, flood, drought and sandstorms assume such serious proportion as to hinder the development of agricultural production,[437] certain defects and mistakes have been manifested in water conservancy work. Take the defects in 1950, for instance:

> Firstly, there was the excessive ambition for doing too many construction works thereby neglecting the proper emphasis. Some of the plans were so colossal and big that they were beyond the existing manpower and material capacity. Some of the plans were based on those of the Japanese and puppet regime, and no careful study of revision had been undertaken. Some even proceeded with the work without a full set of plans . . .
>
> Secondly, there was an insufficiency in study and investigations, and there were insufficient systematic checks, with the result that problems could not be found out in time . . .
>
> Thirdly, no minute estimate of the benefits of the construction works had been made, thus causing many losses . . .
>
> Fourthly, no sufficient preparations had been made prior to construction, and during construction, organization and administration had not been properly carried out . . . For instance, during the undertaking of winter repairs in East China, there was not enough preparation for foodstuffs, tools, housing and supplies for workers in such *hsien* as Ssuhung and Wuwei of North Anhwei. In these places, civilian workers having come up to the dykes would just eat, without doing any work; and because there was no lodging, they just walked away after eating, thus wasting foodstuffs up to 1,000,000 catties . . .
>
> Fifthly, the fiscal organization of agencies of all grades was not strong enough, and in some specific districts there existed the conception of placing emphasis entirely on construction, with utter disregard of expenses.[438]

Although special administrative organs were set up at all the important water conservancy projects throughout the nation, after the criticism of the Ministry of Water Conser-

Editor's Note: A row of asterisks indicates that material has been omitted from the original article.

vancy in 1953 on the erroneous ideology of giving no importance to its administration after a project has been built,[439] there was not much improvement. Evasively, Fu Tso-yi said:

> . . . the defects and mistakes in work (during 1956) . . . were caused mainly by our lack of overall analysis of the objective situation, and our comparative emphasis on the favorable side of things, paying too much attention to the activism of the masses, and under-estimating certain objective difficulties and problems, making insufficient efforts for the prevention of possible deviations, while our technical guidance also did not keep pace with the development of our work. As a result, the defects and mistakes at the lower levels were inseparable from the subjectivism and bureaucratism of our leadership . . .
>
> There is also the defect of constant changes to the capital construction and surveying-designing plans of the Central Government and the various provincial authorities.[440]

However, Fu Tso-yi had to admit that there still existed many questions in capital construction, and a prominent one was the question of the quality of surveying and designing work. Fu then pointed out:

> In the capital construction projects already started, instances of the suspension of work, repetition of work, wastage of efforts, and even the failure of the finished projects to assume the role planned for them, may often be traced fundamentally to defects in designing work. In the work of designing and planning, clarified ideological guidance and technical guidance were often lacking and some key problems could not be discovered in time or could not be solved in time. As a result, the designing personnel at the lower levels became confused and lost their sense of direction. The designs and plans produced under such circumstances often resulted in a lot of work being done on the secondary issues, whereas on the decisive issues there was a lack of earnest surveying work at the work sites and penetrative studies and comparisons of alternative plans. For example, during the first stage of the comprehensive plans for the Haiho basin and the lower reaches of the Yellow River, repeated revisions on paper were made on the irrigation systems and composition of crops, and detailed work was carried out on these matters. Earnest and repeated comparative studies of the major conservancy pivotal projects, and the choice of major navigation channels, were not carried out, however. These important issues were decided too early.[441]

The *People's Daily* reported that in the organizational work for the plan on the comprehensive utilization of river basins, the Peking government also had not yet made any clear-cut stipulations, with the result that duplications and incoordinations appeared in the work of the various departments concerned. The poor planning work was also apparent:

> . . . the plan for the comprehensive utilization of the Huai River basin (is) aimed at the solution of flood and drought disasters and providing for establishment on the river's tributaries of four water reservoirs, the Futzuling, Hsianghungtien, Motzutan and Lianghokou. It is noted that the Pi River basin

> on the upper stream of Lianghokou measures only 4,280 square kilometres and that its average volume of flow for quite a number of years in the past is 3,100,000,000 cubic metres. But the total capacity of the four reservoirs is as big as 7,500,000,000 cubic metres which requires an investment of Yuan 360,000,000 . . . The plan suggests establishment of Linhuakang system control on the main stream of the Huai River. This according to an estimate reported, measures 100 kilometres long, necessitating the evacuation of 500,000 inhabitants, the inundation of 1,500,000 to 1,500,000 *mow* of arable land, and an investment of Yuan 400,000,000. The purpose is to control the possible menace of a flood that appears about once in every 300 years. But the plan provides as measures for flood drainage on the arable plain guarantees against only those damages that result from torrential rains appearing once in every ten or twenty years. In fact, when the once-in-300-year flood does come, most of the area will be inundated by water-logging and while the reservoirs are set up for the prevention of floods, they will not be effective in draining water.[442]

Criticizing a number of persons who solely depended on the state's investments to build water conservancy works and neglected mass types of works, the *People's Daily* said:

> . . . they have not thought of the state's actual conditions when they consider the question of investment. The Huai River report suggests an investment of Yuan 5,400,000,000 in the immediate future and the Haiho report calls for an investment of Yuan 7,200,000,000. Investments on mass work are excluded. Such a large expenditure on agricultural water conservancy construction in a given area seems to be unsuitable for our national economic conditions in the near future.[443]

So, there were still points in the planning that had to be deliberated upon.[444]

Water-Logging

Owing to the neglect of drainage works, water-logging became frequent and serious in China.[445] Fu Tso-yi said:

> Though we began to pay attention to water-logging, we had not done enough in the field. During the past few years, water-logging had been responsible for a great share of our flood calamities, and the masses in different areas had created many new experiences in fighting water-logging. But we had not done enough in the timely summing up and interchange of these experiences.[446]

In an attempt to cover up the neglect of drainage works as well as the incompetence in flood prevention projects, the *People's Daily* drew the attention of Chinese people to water-logging in these terms:

> Flood is understood to include deluges and water-loggings. In certain areas and years, water-loggings were worse than deluges in disastrous effect. Take for example Hopei Province in the years, 1949 to 1954. Water-logged land accounted for 66 per cent of its flooded area. On the Huai River plains, damages done by water-logging were almost equal to those by deluges. Of the 5,000,000 *mow* of arable land in the Tungting Lake area, some 1,000,000 *mow* are perpetually water-logged and unfit for production. Water-logging is frequent in 13 provinces including Hopei and in the Northeast, and East and Central China. In a normal year, the area vulnerable to water-logging totals 90,000,000 *mow* in which the area in Hopei, being the largest, fluctuates between 25,000,000 and 450,000,000 *mow*.[447]

Holding the Kuomintang responsible for water-logging, Chen Lien in the *Planned Economy* writes:

> . . . water-logging disaster means that farmland is inundated by excessive rain water; flood disaster means that loss is caused by breach of river embankments . . . Embankments were in dilapidated condition and were of poor quality. The condition was made worse by the Kuomintang reactionary government. The draining capacity and flood-prevention capacity of all the rivers were very low. Whenever there was a heavy rainfall, river embankments were burst open and vast areas were flooded, making it difficult to distinguish flood disaster from water-logging disaster. It frequently happened that river embankments were burst open before excessive rainfall caused water-logging. Flood and water-logging were easily confused.[448]

In China, large water-logged areas are found in thirteen provinces—Hopei, Shantung, Honan, Anhwei, Kiangsu, Liaoning, Kirin, Heilungkiang, Hupeh, Hunan, Kiangsi, Chekiang and Kwangtung. Among these provinces, water-logging is most frequent and serious in Hopei, Shantung, Honan, North Anhwei and North Kiangsu, as indicated in the accompanying table:[449]

Table 1. Unit: 10,000 *mow*. *Hopei, Shantung, Honan, Anhwei and Kiangsu*

Year	Total area flooded in China	Flooded area	Water-logged area included in flooded area	Percentage of Water-logged area
1949	12,787	9,430	8,212	87.1
1950	7,005	6,492	6,133	94.5
1951	2,214	1,164	1,164	100.0
1952	2,766	2,500	2,500	100.0
1953	4,797	3,645	2,916	80.0
1954	16,958	12,446	11,513	92.5
1955	4,009	3,383	3,079	91.0
1956	16,487	12,670	10,972	86.6
1957	8,502	6,270	5,470	87.2

In the case of Heilungkiang, there are some marshlands and about 1,000,000 hectares of arable land susceptible to water-logging:[450]

> The output for the past few years has dropped: 17.51 billion catties (including soy beans) for 1952, 14.17 billion catties for 1953, 14.06 billion catties for 1954, 16.39 billion catties for 1955, 15.8 billion catties for 1956. The output of 1956 dropped by 1.7 billion catties compared with that of 1952. Much wasteland has been reclaimed in this province during the past few years and the situation would be worse if more wasteland were reclaimed. The main cause for this is: serious water-logging (around 10 million *mow* affected in 1956) . . .[451]

In the course of emphasizing water-logging, the drop of food-grain production over the past years as a consequence of floods and drought is disclosed as follows:[452]

(Unit: 100 million catties)

1949	114	1953	150
1950	52	1954	177
1951	63	1955	128
1952	—	1956	244

In spite of the fact that water-logging can do widespread damage to agriculture, the flood problem in China is still a knotty point. Chen Lisu said that before flood is brought under proper control, it is difficult to understand correctly the serious character of water-logging and, even if it is correctly understood, it is impossible to tackle the water-logging problem independently without tackling the flood problem.[453]

Instability of Policies

In the course of flood prevention, the Chinese Communists appear to have shown instability in their policies. For instance, after the propagated belief that the problem of preventing flood in the major rivers of China would inevitably have to be solved by big reservoirs,[454] more than 20,000 small size reservoirs, some with dams as high as more than 20 metres, have been built in all parts of the country, since October 1955. It is, however, disclosed that according to inspections carried out in different areas, about 20 percent of these reservoirs are not of good quality.[455] Citing Shaoyang, Hsiangtan and Hengyang Administrative District of Hunan as an example, Fu Tso-yi put it this way:

> . . . an inspection was carried out to determine the quality of 698 newly completed small reservoirs. It was discovered that about 20 percent of the reservoirs were not properly constructed. Some of them were defective because they did not have any spillway or because of a miscalculation of the area covered by the reservoir for drawing water therefrom, or because of a miscalculation of the amount of heavy rainfall.

Others were defective because the foundations were not laid properly, the piles were not securely driven, the sides of the reservoir were too steep causing the danger of total collapse, some of the underground water ducts leaked, measures were not taken to prevent the destruction of the lower parts of the water ducts or spillways by heavy torrents, or, in a small number of cases, the water could be drained away through holes in the crags of the reservoir.[456]

* * * * * * *

Future Problems

It has been stated that as far as river control is concerned, China's general water conservancy plans have been or are being drawn up only for most of the larger and medium-sized rivers. So, problem one arises:

> . . . as technical planning documents, they (general water conservancy plans) fail to reflect the actual conditions of the national economy in river basins and areas, and fail to reflect in their entirety the changes which have occurred in agriculture, water conservancy construction, and electric power industry.
>
> The point is that in the rural areas, vast changes have occurred in the conditions of direct flow as a result of the energetic construction of mass water conservancy projects, and that major amendments, therefore, must be made in the existing general water conservancy plans in respect to the hydrological calculations and water conservancy calculations. In the existing general water conservancy plans, these calculations make no allowance for the decrease in water quantity, and the change in the equilibrium of water quantity which is taking place now and will continue in the next two to three years.
>
> At present, the plans for the use of many reservoirs for flood prevention, irrigation, and electric power generation are seasonally regulatory. This is so especially in the case of medium-sized and small reservoirs. During the years of abundant water or normal water quantity, seasonally regulatory reservoirs have to let out large quantities of water into rivers and thence into the sea. Thus, under the condition of water shortage generally speaking, seasonally regulatory reservoirs cannot store up all the water, and a large quantity of water is thus wasted . . .
>
> The problem lies in the fact that small reservoirs and even medium-sized reservoirs are built with materials which are locally available . . .
>
> It should also be borne in mind that many accidents have occurred owing to the destruction of flood overflowing opening of the medium-sized and small reservoirs.[472]
>
> Under the circumstances, problem two crops up:
>
> Though a large amount of flood prevention work has been carried out already, the prevention of floods and water-logging still remains an outstanding task.
>
> And then, comes problem three:

> There are now a large number of hydraulic engineering structures in the country. Large water conservancy projects built in 1958 alone total 547, and 3,303 medium-sized and several hundred thousand mass small water conservancy projects were also built . . .
>
> Because the problem of management was underestimated, many projects did not adequately play their economic role in flood prevention and irrigation expansion. Because management was improper, many projects met with accidents, damaging the materials of the people and of the state . . . the success of all water conservancy projects lies not only in designing and building but in managements, and . . . the final results of designing and building have to depend entirely on management . . .[473]
>
> Finally, problem four:
>
> Industrial development, for instance, often leads to contamination of water. In the northeast, the water of some small rivers (in Shenyang area) has been contaminated and rendered useless by industrial waste water. The fish in the rivers are killed, and the water cannot be used for irrigation for it will kill the crops it irrigates. Unless waste water is properly disposed of, the future industrial development will contaminate to a greater extent the river water and the underground water. The bitter experience of the Soviet Union and many other countries in Europe has proved this . . . There is of course no hurry in enacting water laws. But . . . comprehensive study should be made of this problem.[474]

All told, flood and drought calamities in China have not been completely controlled and many areas are still menaced by flood and drought.[475] The Chinese Communists say that they have large numbers of rivers and rich water and soil resources in our country. They have not yet had much time to harness the rivers, and a gigantic program to eliminate calamities and to get more benefits from their rivers has just begun.[476]

In view of the foregoing situation, conclusions may be drawn from several outstanding issues.

Now the Chinese Communists are obviously aware of the difficulties in river control. One aspect of the difficulties is limitations of financial and material resources. Another aspect, in some ways more formidable, is that the Chinese Communists have overestimated the geography of their water resources. This is probably due to their slender technical basis as well as their inadequate understanding of the hydrologic cycle in the country. Consequently, a number of water conservancy projects are ineffective in flood prevention.

Besides, the Chinese Communists have overemphasized the role of reservoirs in the middle reaches of rivers. There is little to show that they have shaken out of this unsophisticated preoccupation to pay more attention to the upper and lower reaches of rivers.

There are also indications that, owing to construction of water conservancy projects at random, the Chinese Communists have wrecked the hydrologic balance in the country. This has so far created a severe crimp in their plans for the exploitation of river basins. Meanwhile, it has greatly aggravated the flood menace.

After more than a decade, river control in China presents the peasant masses with a bundle of worries. Millions of them these days are still pushed around to build or repair water conservancy projects.

Whatever the development may be, river control in the country depends principally on the reliable plans, the accuracy of hydrologic data, the quality of projects and the conservation of water and soil.

But China's water conservancy projects are generally built for flood prevention. Not until this has been achieved and the safety for agricultural production has been insured, can dreams of river control in the country be cherished.

* * * * * * *

References

437. "CCP and State Council Joint Directive on Afforestation Program", (dated April 7, 1958), *NCNA* Peking, April 7, 1958.
438. Ref.[30].
439. "Ministry of Water Conservancy Calls National Water Conservancy Administration Conference", (held in Peking on May 18–26, 1956), *NCNA* Peking, June 1, 1956.
440. Ref.[9].
441. *Ibid.*
442. Ref.[351].
443. *Ibid.*
444. *Ibid.*
445. Ref.[35].
446. Ref.[9].
447. "Water Conservancy is Soul of Agriculture", *People's Daily,* December 22, 1957.
448. Ref.[35].
449. *Ibid.*
450. "High Tide of Water Conservancy Construction Reached in Heilungkiang", *NCNA* Harbin, November 14, 1957.
451. Wang Kuang-wei, "Some of the Ways to Agricultural Development", *Study,* No. 17, September 3, 1957.
452. Ref.[445].
453. Ref.[35].
454. Ref.[163].
455. "Strengthening of Leadership Over Flood Prevention Needed in Southern Provinces", (a "responsible official of the Central Flood Prevention Headquarters issued a statement to *NCNA*" on May 20, 1956), *NCNA* Peking, May 20, 1956.
456. Ref.[1].
457. Ref.[351].
458. Yu Wei-nung, "Further Develop the Role of Water Conservancy Projects", *Red Flag,* No. 24, December 16, 1960.
459. "Inspection Completed of Work in Preparation for Flood Period of Lower Reaches of Yellow River", (inspection group, organized by the Ministry of Water Conservancy and Electric Power and the Yellow River Water Conservancy Commission "in the middle of April" 1958, concluded the inspection on May 8 of the year), *NCNA* Peking, May 13, 1958.
460. "Directive of CCP Central Committee and State Council on Water Conservancy and Fertilizer", (dated October 24, 1959), *NCNA* October 24, 1959.
461. "Carry Out Preparations for Flood Prevention As Soon As Possible", *People's Daily,* June 13, 1960.

462. "Store Up Water to Prevent Drought", *People's Daily* editorial, September 28, 1960.
463. "Great Soviet Aid in Our Agriculture and Water Conservancy", *People's Daily,* April 17, 1957.
464. Ref.[103].
465. Chou En-lai, "Report on the Work of the Government", (delivered at 4th session of 1st National People's Congress on June 26, 1957), *NCNA* English, Peking, June 26, 1957.
466. "Decision of 5th Plenary Session of CCP Kweichow Provincial Committee on Expulsion of Kang Chien from Party", ("unanimously passed on February 12, 1958"), *Kweichow Daily,* Kweiyang, April 29, 1959.
467. Yeh Yung-yi, "The Question of Building Buffer Reservoirs on the Lower Reaches of the Yellow River", *Water Conservancy Bulletin,* No. 2, April 23, 1959.
468. Fu Tso-yi, "Achievements in Water Conservancy and Power Development", (delivered at 1st Session of 2nd National People's Congress on April 23, 1959.)
469. Huang Ou-tung, Second Secretary of the CCP Liaoning Provincial Committee, "New Task for Liaoning Province on the Agricultural Front", *People's Daily,* February 1, 1960.
470. "Excerpts from Deputy Chao Wen-fu's Speech at NPC Meeting on How the Masses of People in Honan Province Fully Expanded the Superiority of People's Communes to Defeat the 250 Days of Dry Spell and Drought and Reaped a Bumper Yield of Crops", *NCNA* Peking, April 5, 1959.
471. "Furious Typhoon and Rain for Seven Days and Nights in Swatow Administrative District", *People's Daily,* July 9, 1960.
472. Kao-erh-nieh-fu (transliteration), Chief of Team of Soviet Water Conservancy Experts, "Problems Concerning Future Development of China's Water Conservancy Work", (speech delivered at the National Conference of Water Conservancy and Electric Power in 1959; no date revealed), *Water Conservancy and Electric Power,* No. 4, February 20, 1959.
473. *Ibid.*
474. *Ibid.*
475. Ref.[466].
476. "It Is Very Good to Build Water Conservancy Projects on Extensive Scale", *People's Daily* editorial, September 7, 1959.

14

Reprinted from *Engineering Geology in Southern California,* R. Lung and R. Proctor, eds., Association of Engineering Geologists, 1966, pp. 149, 151–152, 155, 157–159, 178–179, 183–187, 189–192

Landslides and Hillside Development

F. B. LEIGHTON

INTRODUCTION

The Landslide Problem

Mariners never embarked upon more uncharted seas than the hillside builder in southern California who meticulously blueprints everything down to the last stud and nail only to overlook the "terra firma". If "terra firma" in southern California could be frozen in solid rigidity, the approach could be different. But concentrating in hillside areas on the part of the dwelling above ground to the exclusion of the "terra firma", is like concentrating on the waves at sea in an area of subsurface mines.

In one storm period during 1962, landslide disasters in the Greater Los Angeles area took two lives and forced the evacuation or prevented the occupation of over 100 hillside homes. Millions of dollars of property damage occurred to hillside structures and

149

Editor's Note: Most of the plates and several sections of text have been omitted from the original article (omissions are indicated by a row of asterisks). The limitations of space force us to omit material that is not central to the purpose of the volume.

appurtenances -- garages, swimming pools, retaining walls, patios, utilities, etc. Litigation fees that follow these disasters can amount to as much as the actual property loss itself. As noted by Jahns (1958), "it also is well to note that everyone ultimately pays the piper in numerous indirect forms, including increased tax, insurance, utility rates, and, in many instances, lowered property values".

Invariably, the landslide victim believed that "it could happen on other hillsides, but never on this one". Landslide insurance was once available but not now; and it is little solace to recall that the neighbor's slope was cut at a steeper angle and is stable. The city inspector may believe that the existing slide has temporarily restored equilibrium to the slope; yet to the homeowner this has been a home slide, not a landslide, and it has destroyed, not restored, equilibrium. The slide might not have occurred had proper attention been given to the condition of the slope prior to building.

With 7.5 million dollars damage inflicted upon the City of Los Angeles during the rains of 1951-52, City ordinances were passed that required the application of geology and engineering to residential development. Admittedly, the single residential family did not have the financial or maintenance resources of a highway department in the repair of landslides and severe erosion. Whereas a man will prudently drive past a landslide or even walk on one, he does not relish camping with his family for 24 hours, day in and day out, in an unstable area. His family and home represent his major investment.

Why not remove the gamble and the guesswork? Why not eliminate the undesirable consequences? From such questions the present grading ordinances were born. They were designed to withhold building permits from hillside building sites until conditions were shown to be safe by the geologist and civil engineer. This was easier said than done.

Flatlands provide a more static environment than hillsides, yet are themselves no assurance of foundation stability, as demonstrated by failures of structures built on or over expansive soils, old peat bog areas, loose and unconsolidated sediments, old uncompacted fills, "quick" clays, limestone caverns, "mined-out" areas, active fault zones, and areas of subsidence caused by withdrawal of petroleum and water. All of these unfavorable conditions have been reported in southern California flatland.

Flatland problems become amplified in hillside areas, particularly the drainage problems. In addition, a new dimensional concern is introduced by landslides and associated mass movements. For this form of nature's exercise, we owe a debt to the urging of gravity, and to a new physical dimension, slope.

Slope, including its underlying material, is the most important geologic and engineering element in hillside development. In terms of slope stability, high moderate to steep slopes are generally the most problematic. Nevertheless, it is well to remember that the reason many slopes are gentle is that the underlying materials are very weak.

It is common to devote less attention geologically to foothill areas and isolated low hills than to major hillsides. Despite their tame appearance, these areas can actually be zones of weakness between the lowlands and the hills, or can be isolated belts of weakness within the lowlands. Similarly, valley floors and table-like summits within hillsides cannot be overlooked and must be treated as integral parts of hillside development. Sea-cliffs and river bluffs must be evaluated for building purposes the same as hillsides (Figure 1). Because hillside stability problems do not respect artificial boundaries, these boundaries must be treated as transitional.

The role of landsliding in southern California has been underestimated by the general public and by engineers and geologists alike. Landslide hazards have not been widely recognized nor appreciated, because of limited hillside development, because of the early development of preponderantly stable areas, because of the relative obscurity of most old slides and potential slides, and because of still-prevalent, widespread myths which suggest that the number of active landslide areas can be counted on one's fingers and that landslides are restricted to some of our cliff-side coastal communities (as displayed in Figure 1).

One of the deans of engineering geology, Charles P. Berkey, wrote prophetically in 1937, "I am convinced that the question of landslides is a matter of much larger importance than is usually assumed. Recent experience leads to the belief that it is of special significance in connection with many practical problems, particularly those connected with engineering projects. In my own case, some of these features were for a long time overlooked, and it is clear that a better understanding of them would have been useful." (Personal communication from C. P. Berkey to C. F. Stewart Sharpe, March 31, 1937.)

Probably nowhere else in the continental United States is to be found such a myriad of complex geologic problems related to urban development. In southern California this situation stems from the marked contrast in topography, geology, climate and vegetation. As aptly put by Mc Gill (1964), "The Los Angeles area provides an outstanding and instructive example of the growing importance of urban geology. As on the national scene, the importance is the result of the activities of man impinging on the natural environment, but in this megalopolis of southern California, both elements are notoriously unpredictable."

Examples of complementary and paradoxical terrain features in hillside subdivisions are those where stable, near-vertical cliffs, adjoin gentle, low slopes that are unstable; where strong rocks are interspaced with fracture zones; where sound and durable rocks contain one weak link in the form of a subtle clay seam of knife-edge thickness. Viewseekers and sea-enthusiasts delight in the shoreline bluffs of southern California and the protection from the sea below that they offer, unmindful that there are strong, steep bluffs and that there are weak, steep bluffs, unmindful that many existing prehistoric landslide areas are like dormant volcanoes, asleep but not dead (Figure 1). Reactivation of many of these old slides has been periodic. On the other hand, some slide areas are reasonably safe to build upon because of their combined old age, dense consolidation, and stable position (Figure 12).

On the basis of subsurface exploration, geologists have determined that many puzzling structural features are now ascribable to a landslide origin. (Instances of the reverse are also true!) For example, certain rupture plates of bedrock formerly considered to be fragments of thrust or gravity fault plates, are more likely remnants of landslides. Many of the chaotic breccias in southern California appear to have accumulated in large part as mudflows and debris flows (Jahns, 1954). The PRELIMINARY MAP SHOWING LANDSLIDE LOCATIONS IN A PORTION OF SOUTHERN CALIFORNIA (in pocket) when compared with geologic maps of a decade or two ago furnishes further testimony of evolution in mapping and interpretive studies.

Hillside Development -- A Team Project

In the frontier days of hillside development, one man served concurrently as topographer, engineer, draftsman, geologist and meteorologist. Today hillside development recognized as a complex endeavor calling for extraordinary teamwork, a fluid approach and imaginative foresight from a battery of specialists (and staffs) that commonly includes a developer, lender, land-planner and design engineer, architects, soils engineer, geologist, legal and financial adviser, grading and building contractors, and one or more governing agencies.

The specialists in this team operation are like the manager on a professional baseball team who can ruin a good ball club and who can't help a poor one. Each specialist is only one of a number of important links that demand both individual tenacity and collective forging to form a durable chain. Each has an obligation within the realm of the aesthetic, economic, ethical, legal and safety aspects that cannot be shifted to the shoulders of others, but must be borne by each and held accountable by all. And yet each specialist must be "mission-oriented", reflecting a mutual respect for the potential contributions of all the specialists and a dedication to the creation or enhancement of useful, attractive and safe surroundings - with a high net value to the developer.

Slope instability caused by landsliding is only one of the many potential geologic and civil engineering problems of hillside development. Other problems include ground-water seepages, expansive soils, erosion and deposition by running water and wind, active faulting, tectonic creep, and subsidence-settlement.[(1)] These problems are enumerated in Table 1. This collation emphasizes the interdependency of geology and civil engineering. Each of the problems cited demands the proper blend of the two disciplines, the exact proportions differing in nearly every case. Quick or easy solutions to these problems are rare and yet are commonly expected when execution of grading operations cannot be postponed.

One of the basic problems of hillside development in this area is its newness and uniqueness, combined with explosive hillside-tract sprouting. This requires revision of approaches and techniques, redefining of specialist roles, retraining and requalification of specialists in the integration of specialties, and redoubling of efforts -- all without the benefit of very much hindsight or past research investment. Nor is there little time for the human evolutionary processes of adaptation and new understanding.

Types of Landslides

Landslides [(2)] in this chapter will refer to true slides, those landslides that have a definitive slip surface or definitive rupture zone. They can be further divided into bedrock slides (chiefly block glides) and overburden slides (chiefly slumps and slump-flows). The basal slip surface or rupture zone of bedrock slides occurs within bedrock.[(3)] Overburden slides occur within overburden or along the boundary zone of overburden and the underlying bedrock. Overburden slides can in turn be subdivided into fill-failures (artificial) and soil-failures (natural). In engineering parlance, the terms "slope-failures", "slip-outs", "scab-failures" all are variants of true slides.

In typical southern California fashion, true slides come in all sizes, shapes, rates of movement, material components, and disaster proportions (Plates 1, 2, 3). Their periods of incubation may be hundreds of years or may be represented by a second-hand's movement. Their total duration of movement may be a minute or two or they may continue to creep for years. They may move as rigid blocks or behave like custard pudding.

Historical Perspective

Landsliding is responsible for the bulk of the material moved from valley sides and from sea cliffs in southern California (Plate 2 and Figure 1). Its importance as a sculpturing process exceeds that of direct erosion of these areas by running water and the waves. In the sea cliffs shown in Figure 1, landslides affect about 60 percent of the length of the sea cliffs, as computed from geologic maps, and a high percentage of the cliffs of the principal stream-deepened canyons. The retreat of the frontal faces of both sets of cliffs is controlled largely by the landslide process.

True landsliding has been a dominant process of landscape sculpture both above and below sea level. As natural phenomena, landslides in southern California have accounted for inversions of relief; obliteration of terrain features such as river bluffs, fault scarps and sea-cliffs; burial of features such as old soil profiles, beaches, plant communities, stream and lake sediments; initiation of new drainage reentrants, blockage and

---

(1) For more comprehensive checklists of potential geologic problems the reader is referred to treatments by Mc Gill (1954) and Jahns (1960).

(2) The term <u>landslides</u> includes those slides artificially produced, as well as those naturally produced, because the types of landslides are the same in both cases. This is reflected by the time-honored classifications of landslides (Ladd, 1935, Sharpe, 1937, and Varnes, 1958). (See Table 3.)

(3) The term <u>bedrock</u> means much more than hard, resistant rock that has to be drilled and blasted. Shales and siltstones are mapped by the geologist as bedrock but can have the engineering characteristics of overburden. Bedrock underlies overburden which refers to all types of surficial deposits such as soil, fill and alluvium.

filling of old drainage channels, diversion of stream waters and derangement of stream courses and the formation of ponds and lakes. Landslides have left some areas more erosive, others less erosive; they have subdued topographic features and in some other areas have created bolder topographic features. They have altered native plant selectivity and natural plant associations. Landslides have created at least minor earthquakes, generated seismic waves in bodies of water, produced floods by removing natural dams and by creating unstable natural dams. They have provided both barriers and avenues for the percolation, collection and emission of ground water, petroleum and gas.

Landslides have commonly developed a peculiar but typical undulating and disordered topography that commonly includes wide benches, scarps, closed depressions, trenches and ridges as well as chaotically jumbled debris. Deposits formed by landsliding include tongues, cones, fans and aprons in channel bottoms and on basal slopes.

The landslide process above sea level dates back to the time when each set of southern California coasts and hills periodically and progressively emerged above sea level. Rather steady emergence along the coast has been continuing for more than 300,000 years. This uplift is still occurring in a number of hillsides at an imperceptible but measurable rate.

Nearly every segment of most hillsides has at some time slid, each older slide mass being progressively removed by other erosional agents (as illustrated by Figure 2), establishing landslide conditions for the succeeding cycle of emergence and erosion. Events of this sort would be left to imaginative speculation if it were not for evidence in the form of uplifted remnants of stream channels, buried fossils found in the sediment, relics of freshwater lakes and older valley profiles. Most slides which are shown on the PRELIMINARY MAP SHOWING LANDSLIDE LOCATIONS belong to the most recent geologic cycle of hill genesis. Many may be directly related to the last wet glacial age. Still older slides are difficult to recognize because they commonly have been subject to uplift and erosion rather than burial and preservation.

In southern California the human historical perspective of hillside development covers a 200$^{\pm}$ year span, a fleeting geologic instant in the succession of landslide events--- so short a time that the geologic historical perspective is easily lost.

The Grading Process

It took many tens of thousands of years to produce many of the hillside areas in southern California, but only within this century has man acquired the tools to grade them. With modern engineering and grading practices and appropriate financial incentive no hillside appears too rugged for future development. No hillside material can withstand the concentrated assault by grading, tunnelling, and blasting activities. Man has become a geologic agent capable of sculpturing the hillside as pervasively as a grinding glacier, a torrential stream or an erupting volcano. He can convert overnight (geologically) a peak into a series of flat lots and roads. This tampering and molding of our landscape can either harness the destructive forces of nature and create more pleasant and useful settings, or it can upset nature's equilibrium and create unexpected hazards (see Figure 3).

Every conventional building structure must rest on the earth as its foundation. The supporting earth may be the natural ground surface (Figure 4) or the graded (man-made) surface (Figure 3). Figure 4 shows three general ground conditions for establishing safe structural foundations on natural slopes. The flatlands are largely the province of the soils engineer[4] where bearing capacity and expansiveness are the chief soil problems.

---

[4] With respect to present hillside development in southern California, the civil engineer has come to mean the design engineer of the tract; soils engineer is a civil engineer with a soil testing laboratory. The design engineer commonly supervises hillside tract grading; the soils engineer controls the placement of all compacted fill and handles other matters summarized in the Appendix.

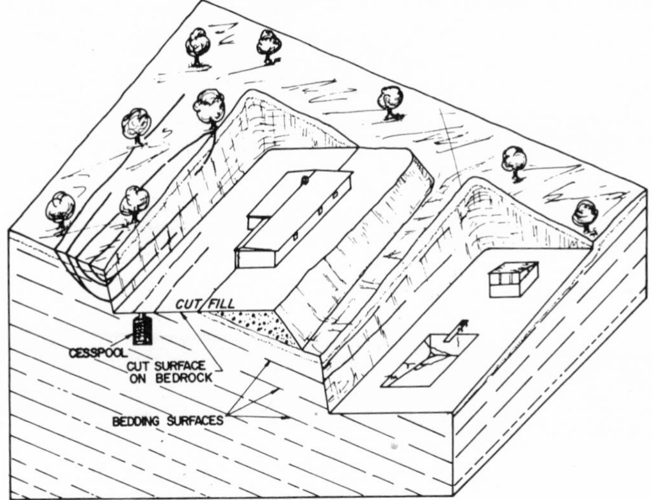

Figure 3. DEVELOPMENT OF MAN-MADE BEDROCK LANDSLIDES (modified from R. H. Jahns). Hundreds of landslides in southern California are traceable to this general situation. This problem, as much as any other, has led to the adoption of grading ordinances. A naturally stable "dip-slope" has been made unstable by removing the support from bedding planes which resemble the surfaces between a tilted deck of cards. The cracking shown is one of the early signs that a landslide is imminent.

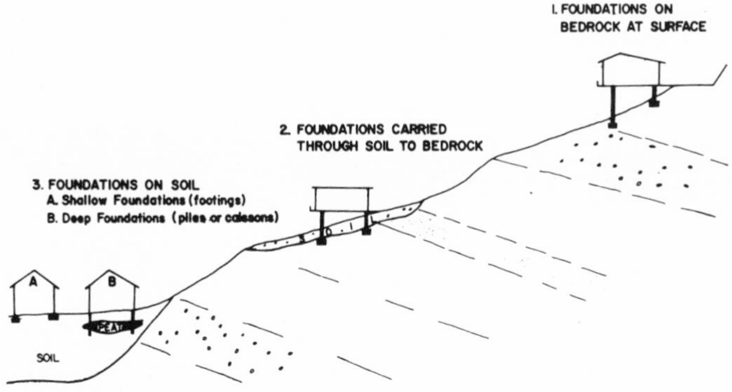

Figure 4. THREE GENERAL GROUND CONDITIONS FOR ESTABLISHING SAFE STRUCTURAL FOUNDATIONS ON NATURAL SLOPES.

CASE 1. Stable bedrock exposed at ground surface or close to it; foundations can be shallow.

CASE 2. Stable bedrock lies below deposits of unconsolidated soil; foundations are carried through the soil which might be remnants of a soil failure or an old stream or marine terrace; other alternatives are stabilizing the soil and placing shallow foundations or removing the soil in the process of building a multi-level house.

CASE 3. Stable bedrock lies too deep to reach economically with foundations; foundations needed might be shallow as in House A where high bearing strength has been determined by soils engineer, or deep as in House B where poor soil conditions exist because of an old peat bog.

Note: Cases 1 and 2 require the benefit of both geologic and civil engineering consultation whereas Case 3 is essentially a soils engineering problem.

Grading a hillside development may alter any fractional part of the natural landscape. It generally involves excavation of the high places and transportation of these earth materials to low-lying places, commonly creating in the process flat lot pads (Figures 3 and 5). Excavation in southern California has reduced peaks by as much as 100-200 feet; filling has elevated canyon bottoms as much as 300-400 feet.

These cut and fill operations are analogous to nature's leveling operations of erosion and deposition. In both sets of operations a general balance must exist between the amount of material removed and the amount of material deposited elsewhere. In nature this balance respects no land boundaries, but on a specific hillside property the balance between cut and fill material must be engineered in advance of grading. Otherwise, the earthmoving contractor may complete the project with 10,000 cubic yards of surplus material or with a deficit of a similar amount. He must use this surplus material or export it at additional expense; with a shortage of material, he must either excavate new material or import it at additional expense. In some cases redesign can eliminate this expensive imbalance.

The prime requirement for the stability of slopes is that they be graded at a safe angle. It is apparent from Figure 5 that by grading at a 1:1 slope angle rather than at a 3:1 slope angle the lot depth is increased by 100 feet. This gain in flat lot space by steepening the slope angle can be used to increase the number of lots (lot yield) in the subdivision, but can reduce net profits where stability is a problem. Stable fill-slope angles commonly range from 1.5:1 to 2:1 and stable cut-slope angles run the gamut from 1:1 to 3:1 and even flatter! The geologic basis for determining slope stability will be treated in a subsequent section.

Fills are called controlled fills if compacted and tested properly under the supervision of a qualified soils engineer and uncontrolled fills if not compacted and tested properly under the supervision of soils engineers. A controlled fill such as the canyon fill illustrated in Figure 6 must be placed in accordance with the sequence of steps shown (A, B, and C) in order to prevent rising seepage, settlement of the fill and damage to the buildings. Post-mortems from experienced soils engineers reveal a number of causes for settlement failures of uncontrolled filles, namely (1) placing fill on natural slopes from which the existing vegetation, compressible soils, or trash materials have not been removed, (2) placing the fill in layers that are too thick and cannot adequately be compacted and (3) placing the fill without providing adequate subdrainage of ground water which can result in saturation of the fills and even seepage on the surface of building sites.

To prevent these failures, foundation studies are essential prior to grading. Each potential fill placement area commands the attention of the soils engineer. The geologist can render valuable aid where geologic problems such as fault-controlled seepage are suspected or detected, or where the fill will be placed above a natural slope as in Figure 7 or above a cut-slope as in Figure 8.

The geologist can also reconstruct for the soils engineer the recent canyon history. Here his detective kit consists of old vertical aerial photographs. When viewed through a stereoscope, overlapping pairs of aerial photographs appear in 3 dimensions, much as if the viewer is hovering in a helicopter directly over the property. Study of old photographs has revealed such features as an old abandoned clay quarry with tailing piles for which there was no evidence on the overgrown ground surface; an oil derrick where no oil well had been recorded; an old garbage dump site, now buried but containing thousands of cubic yards of unsuitable trash; old slide areas now buried with fill; the existence of former dwelling sites which had utility lines and old septic tank-cesspool systems; old slope-failures now eroded and camouflaged; the boundary limits of old uncontrolled fills; the former existence of a decadent citrus grove and hence deep root systems that require removal and proper filling of the cavities; an old drainage course recently rerouted. Thus, features affecting stability can be detected in unexpected places, and can usually be stabilized without undue cost to the new developer and future residents.

Portions of hillside topographic maps are constantly being rendered inaccurate and obsolete by modern-day massive grading operations.

* * * * * * *

PREVENTION AND CURE OF LANDSLIDES

The chief objective in the solution of geologic problems in hillside development is to secure enduring stability in the most effective and economical manner. Unique opportunities exist for the application of geologic and soils information to prevent and cure landslides. Excitement in this pursuit lies partly in the knowledge-frontier aspects of the work and partly in the eventual utility value of the work.

Preventive Medicine

The backbone of prevention is prediction. Hillside stability problems not only will yield solutions if present geologic and engineering capabilities are fully utilized, but the common types of landslide hazards are predictable in advance. Supported by adequate subsurface investigation, the geologist can predict potential landslides on the basis of deep-seated structural flaws and weaknesses in the three-dimensional geometry of earth materials. Gauged by its ability to predict, geology can be eminently successful in this area of operation.

Emphasis in hillside development has gradually shifted from correcting landslide ills to preventing landslide ills. This has come about as a combination of many factors, namely: (1) the urban explosion into more and more hillside areas, (2) the growing realization that landslides can be located and diagnosed in advance of development, (3) the gradual discovery that most residential landslide disasters have been man-made or man-initiated, (4) the increasing demand by the public and their agencies for greater hillside safety, (5) the legal precedents set by the Portuguese Bend Slide case and other cases, and (6) the growing appreciation by the builder that every dollar invested in thorough and competent investigation before construction saves many dollars during construction. Nevertheless, success in preventing landslide damage has come about largely in response to painful experience.

The Property Purchase Stage

Geologic investigations should precede rather than succeed other phases of hillside development, because the characteristics of earth materials underneath a hillside can significantly influence the most effective and imaginative use and design of the land. As indicated by the list of types of geologic reports in Table 2, the realistic starting point for the developer is to secure a geologic feasibility report before he purchases hillside property. This consensus conclusion is based not only on a consideration of the safety aspects, but on environmental and resource aspects that can limit or bolster residential development.

The most successful hillside property owners and developers are those who have sought professional advice prior to the purchase and development of a parcel of hillside property. Those who have been unsuccessful -- and here the list is long -- include those who have not sought nor received sound professional advice.

The Planning and Design Stages

A geologic program prior to hillside planning can reveal geologic problems and resource areas and can contribute key ideas that will influence zoning, road access, storm drainage, sewage disposal, earthwork and other basic planning interests. The planning phase is often one of the most difficult to finance and yet the most critical stage in safe and financially sound development. Forward-minded first-phase planning will draw from the geology available and will probably head off redesigning, regrading, and rebuilding.

Geologic factors for some areas can have little or no bearing on land use; in other areas they can limit land use and tract design; they can even practically dictate land use in still other areas. The multiplicity of natural and man-made terrain factors makes each hillside area a habitat of its own, a habitat where conditions on adjoining building sites can be extremely misleading and where guessing can be regretfully expensive.

The nature of the preliminary design can profoundly influence the scope of succeeding geologic studies. A general rule of thumb is that if there are no natural hillside stability problems, plans that call for minimum of landscape alteration are generally the safest and least expensive. However, revised designs may be needed to counteract geologic and soils problems. In this respect, it should be remembered that the greater the number of design revisions, the greater the number of reviews in light of the geology. If a number of such revisions are needed (and this is common), human nature is no longer on the best of terms with Mother Nature!

Treatment of Existing Natural Landslide Areas

Leaving the hillsides natural and developing safe stilt-type houses or multi-level houses on the sloping surface is possible as illustrated by Figure 4, but this approach is no stability panacea. In fact, where stability problems exist it can be fatal. Quick reference to the PRELIMINARY MAP SHOWING LANDSLIDE LOCATIONS IN A PORTION OF SOUTHERN CALIFORNIA supplies evidence enough that many naturally unstable areas can pose residential development problems until remedial measures are undertaken. These remedial measures may be costly, but leaving the slopes in a naturally unstable state can be even more disastrous to both future residents and builders.

Few natural hillsides are incurable of landsliding. However, a small number of massive landslides exist in southern California that are too large to be economically stabilized by normal control methods. They can probably be utilized as land-fill areas, green belts or for other forms of non-residential use.

Massive grading has proved to be the most economic means of correcting most lesser landslide ills. This correction involves either reducing the driving force or increasing the resisting force, or both. Any remedial process that utilizes the natural approach of achieving slope stability by elevating the topographic lows and excavating the topographic highs can overcome many landslide problems.

The vital questions in the control of old existing landslides are at least threefold. Can the slide move downslope again once proposed grading is completed? Will the slide area be subject to significant differential settlement once grading is completed? What provisions for installing subdrains within or underneath the slide area should be made?

Answers depend upon the geometry of the slide in relationship to both existing topography and final graded topography. For example, Figure 14 shows that some bedrock slides are superposed slide blocks and that others consist of juxtaposed slide blocks. Superposed slide blocks commonly require more slide removal than juxtaposed slide blocks because they are more difficult to restrain.

Large-scale blocks of compacted earth fill may have to be designed by the soils engineer to provide lateral support for these unstable masses. These blocks are called buttress fills or just buttresses. Examples of buttress fills are shown by Figures 11 and 14 and the two cases summarized in the Appendix. Removal of the entire slide is not always justified, as in Figure 11 where the slide can be adequately restrained.

Shear keys are large trenches excavated in creep or slide areas below the disturbed zones and then backfilled with compacted fill. They are designed by the soils engineer to add shear strength and provide lateral support to unstable upslope masses. An example is shown by Figure 14.

Fresh slide debris is usually loose and subject to differential settlement. Not so for some old prehistoric slides. Homes are being built on the old intact juxtaposed slide blocks in Figure 14, because the bearing capacity of the blocks has been found adequate by soils testing.

Figure 17 shows a case history in which the more youthful lower slide mass had to be completely removed prior to placement of fill. Most of the upper slide block was left intact because it consisted of slide material that had essentially the bearing capacity of bedrock except where debris and soil filled the pre-existing gap at the head of the slide. Thus, some slides may be divided into segments which are treated individually.

Proper subdrainage of most slide areas is essential. This prevents blockage of normal avenues of ground-water circulation, saturation of fills, buildup of seepage forces within or underneath the old slide area and the subsequent emergence of seepage waters onto lot pads at lower elevations.

Treatment of Destructive Residential Slides

These slides are the type that all grading ordinances and all preliminary geologic and engineering investigations are geared to prevent. Today they occur chiefly in hillside districts developed before the advent of full-fledged soils and geologic investigations.

Fresh slides in residential districts run the gamut in slide types and sizes. Each represents a different degree of personal and financial loss. Homes may be damaged beyond repair as in Plate 1, or they may only be partly damaged or the slide may threaten but not affect a home as in Figure 11.

For the sake of simplification, the following discussion presumes that these slides are of similar size and of similar type as the block glide in Plate 1 or the slump as in Figure 11. By comparing the angle of the adjoining unmoved slope to the angle of slope within the slide and by comparing the inclination of slide features to the inclination of the same features outside the slide, the amount and direction of rotational movement can at once be determined. If there has not been appreciable rotation as in Plate 1 it is a block glide. If there has been appreciable rotation as in Figure 11 it is a slump.

The geologist may reach the slide scene after the principal slide movement has occurred, or he may be called in when the cracks and gaping fissures that herald major movement have appeared (Figure 3). By studying the pattern of fractures prior to sliding and relating these to the geologic setting it may be possible to predict the magnitude of future sliding and damage. Mapping features prior to sliding also permits a clearer picture of slide geometry. Careful geologic mapping in one case showed that several homes ready to be evacuated could not be involved in the future slide, and that one home not under surveillance should be evacuated. Basic precautions for suspect homes include disconnection of all utilities and keeping the slopes as dry as possible.

Plastic "raincoat" sheets are commonly used to protect the slopes in wet weather. Automated devices that provide warnings of slide movement and continuous records of slide movement have been developed and used to advantage.

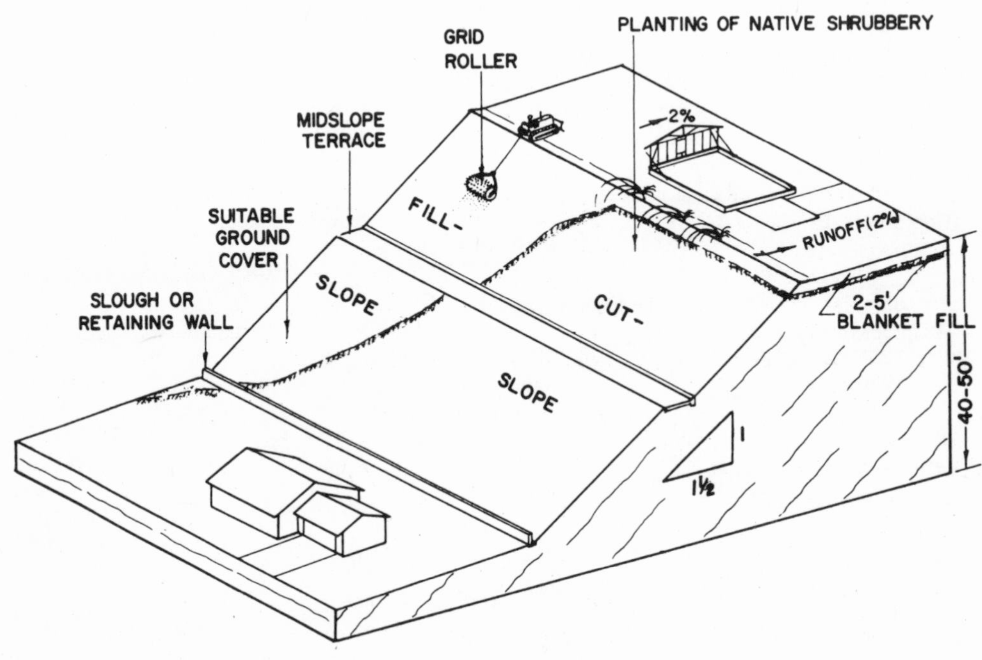

Figure 20. DEVICES TO PROTECT AGAINST SEVERE EROSION BY RUNOFF AND LOCAL MASS MOVEMENTS ("SLOUGHING"). These consist of (1) "impermeable" blanket fill on the top lot pad, (2) a sufficient slope to conduct surface and roof runoff away from the major slopes and to a street or drainage device, (3) a sprinkler system to water trees and shrubbery on an erosion-susceptible cut slope and an erosion-preventive ground cover on the fill slope, (4) a fully paved, reinforced and keyed midslope terrace to carry slope runoff, control erosion and add to overall slope stability, (5) a slough or retaining wall 2 to 4 feet high with weep holes to retain eroded and sloughed materials, (6) grid rolling of the fill slopes to tamp loose surficial soil and retard erosion, (7) sufficient foundation setback of building structures from top of slope to allow for future gradual slope retreat and sufficient setback of building structures at base of slope to allow cleanup and maintenance. Note trace of former canyon slope that now separates cut from fill.

The geologic objective in the slide investigation is to determine the geometry and origin of sliding so that proper remedial measures can be devised. Again the geologist commonly uses the same general plan of attack as in the mapping of a prehistoric slide or as in the investigation of a residential property before and during development. Notes scribbled in a geologic notebook while 50 feet in a bore hole studying the rupture surface, and measurements after picking the mud coating from each vertical inch of the 75-foot hole aid in deciphering the contributing factors to sliding.

Three prominent factors that can limit a comprehensive examination are the overriding threat to public safety, legal restrictions, and lack of room for equipment access or operation. Otherwise, a geologic investigation requires as much latitude and freedom as possible in order to make it detailed and comprehensive. Because each fresh landslide case is an emergency case, some phases of study such as inspection of old aerial photographs may have to await field measurements needed to determine both the severity of sliding and the temporary expedients that might be invoked to protect life and limb.

Temporary expedients, as utilized in the case of Figure 11, may involve placing a fill load at the toe of the slide to restrict future slide movement and supporting the vertical headwall at the top of the slide with earth anchors drilled back into the slope and tied to steel soldier beams. The latter expedient is supervised by a civil engineer and is analogous to pinning down a shingle roof with nails.

Following a destructive slide it is common practice to bring in bulldozers for clean up and safety purposes. Obliteration of portions of the slide can not only aggravate the slide hazard, but can obscure slide features critical in the evaluation of remedial solutions. Perhaps, as in the case of Figure 11, the toe area can be mapped first, concurrently with the call for a bulldozer to place fill at the toe and prepare drill sites.

Geologic surveying procedures are used to map the slide, normally on a scale of 1 inch equals 10 to 20 feet. Stakes placed astride the slide, marks made on both sides of cracks and special string used to connect points on the slide with points off the slide can be used to give warning of impending movements and to measure renewed slide movement. Gradual creep of the slide mass and sloughing of small unsupported sections within and at the boundary of the slide block are normal adjustments that will probably not alter the geologic mapping significantly, providing the mapping is accomplished after major slide movement and during one continuous stage.

Drill hole information is usually necessary to confirm the slide geometry as plotted on maps and cross sections. It also enables the soils engineer to secure strength parameters within and at the base of the slide for purposes of stability analysis and design of retaining devices. In this regard geologic mapping sheds light on the number, depth and location of drill holes needed. If the mapping can be done early and in detail, it furnishes a three-dimensional picture that will be altered only slightly by data obtained from drill holes. This geologic detail is important as some of the drill holes may not be safe to enter. On the other hand, entering the holes may be the only way to determine geologic conditions beneath the slide and to distinguish earlier episodes of sliding.

Treatment of Cut Slope Stability Problems

One of the most common cut slope stability problems is the dip slope problem illustrated by Figure 18. Once an excavation has been prepared which removes support from a dip slope, it is too late to put the material back and too hazardous in residential areas to leave the slope permanently untouched. Temporary and piecemeal expedients such as hardening of the soils, guniting the slope, planting deep-rooted plants, sandbagging the toe of the slope, covering the slope with plastic sheeting will help to delay slope failure but will not be effective in preventing slope failure.

The bygone approach to such major cut slope problems was to handle them during grading as they came to light. Unfortunately, many of these problems never came to light until it was too late. And many proved so costly and inconvenient to remedy at a late stage that the next logical question was, "Can't these problem slopes be detected prior to

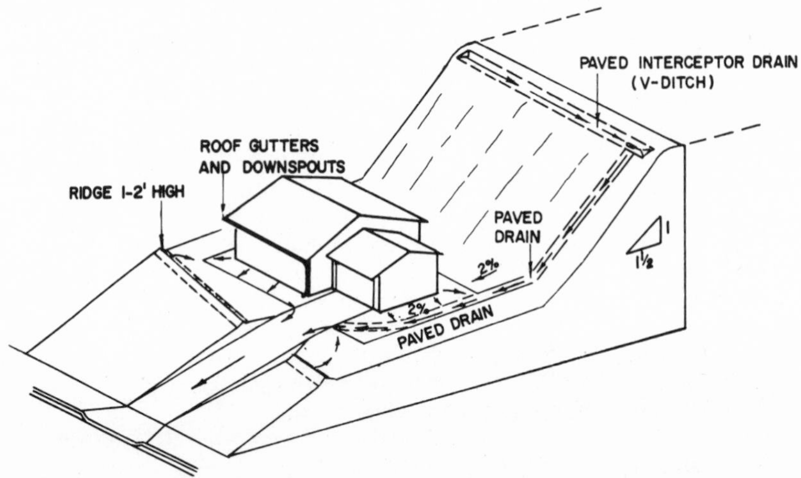

Figure 21. GOOD CONTROL OF SURFACE RUNOFF. Slopes drain properly and it is assumed that the slopes are well planted as in Figure 20. Good maintenance includes upkeep of gutters and downspouts, minimal and timely irrigation of native plants, planting bare spots in the slopes, periodic cleaning of debris from paved drains and behind slough walls, periodic rebuilding of small ridges (berms) at top of slopes, elimination of any closed depressions where water can pond, removal of perched boulders in the slopes.

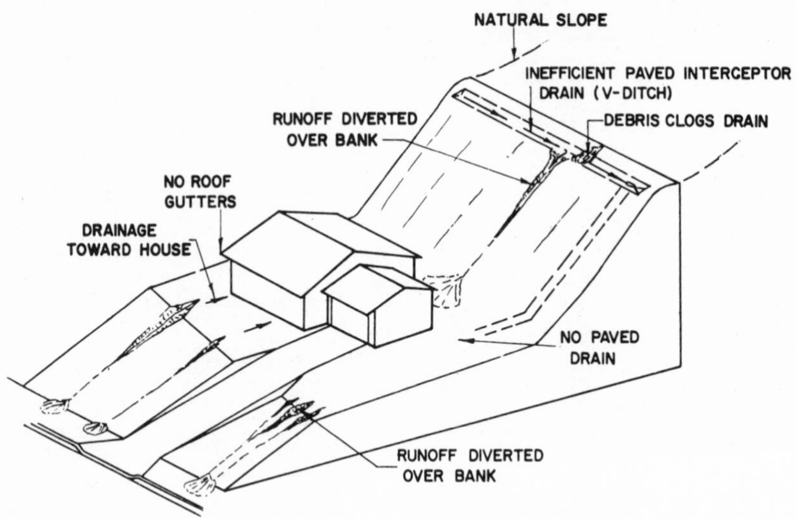

Figure 22. POOR CONTROL OF SURFACE RUNOFF. The drainage conditions shown above can result in accelerated erosion and deposition, ponding and flooding of surface runoff, settlement of foundations, local mass movements and even landsliding.

grading?" The majority of problematic major cut slopes over 10 to 12 feet in height can be identified in advance of grading. Only a small percentage may have to await full geologic evaluation until early phases of grading operations.

Figure 18 shows three different remedies to the common cut slope stability problem, namely (A) flattening the slope to the dip angle (2:1 in this case); (B) providing a designed retaining wall with properly compacted backfill, and (C) providing a designed buttress fill with proper subdrainage. Solutions B and C are generally carried out under the supervision of the soils engineer. It is, however, the responsibility of the geologist to provide clearcut and meaningful geologic parameters for design purposes.

By providing alternative recommendations of this type for cut slope problems, the geologist finds that the best alternative is less likely to be overlooked. Here again each situation is different. One approach commonly feasible is to divide a large cut slope into as many segments as there are geologic conditions. A different remedial solution can then be considered for each segment. Compound cut slope angles are an illustration of this approach. For example, cut slope angles might change laterally from 1.5:1 to 2:1 over a transition interval that averages 1.75:1. Or geologic conditions might suggest changing from 1.5:1 at the top of the slope to 2:1 within the problem area.

Large fills placed above cut slopes must be evaluated by the soil engineer for their load effects and by the geologist for adverse geologic conditions in the cut slope portions. There is not much point in carefully benching and keying a fill into bedrock if a stability problem lurks in the cut slope underneath, as illustrated by Figure 8.

Buttress fills represent the most common remedial alternative selected by the tract engineer and developer for rendering support to unstable cut slopes. Even though extra earth material has to be excavated and compacted, net costs are usually less than with other remedial alternatives, providing the buttress is designed prior to emplacement and thus the slope does not have to be cut twice, once to evaluate whether a buttress is needed and again to fabricate the buttress.

Buttress fills can be appraised as being economically feasible, economically marginal or economically unfeasible. The geologist shares a prime responsibility for indicating where larger than standard buttress fills might be needed (Figure 16). Early redesign or avoidance of these areas may increase the net value of the development, particularly if the buttress is to cost more than the value of the three or so lots to be stabilized.

Subdrains are an integral part of a buttress. That many subdrains will never deliver water from their outlets is a foregone conclusion. They are needed as safety valves to prevent the down dip migration of surface water and the buildup of seepage forces which might arise during prolonged wet seasons or prolonged irrigation periods. Some subdrains have proved conspicuously effective in this regard. For additional protection against the infiltration of surface waters into pervious bedrock, compacted-fill blankets are commonly placed on the lot pad areas that lie above the buttresses.

Some corrective measures have notably failed to do the job expected of them, but in no case on record in southern California has a designed and completed buttress failed of its own accord. The common failures in buttressing occur during the excavation of the buttress key and benches (Figure 18, Step 1). The back face of the buttress excavation is commonly cut much steeper than the angle of the bedding dip in order to conserve the amount of earth moved. Figure 19 shows a slide that developed after steep headwall benches had been cut and bedding planes were left unsupported. Failure of the slope necessitated removal of all slide debris but reduced the size of the buttress finally needed. Sliding of some buttress faces has removed all of the unstable earth material that was to be buttressed. The designed buttress then becomes a replacement fill.

The hazards of these slides during buttressing are short-lived but can be minimized by excavating at a flatter angle, by constructing the large buttresses in segments, and by avoiding buttress operations during the wet season (officially designated by a number of agencies as from November 15 to April 15). Even then many excavations for buttresses are calculated risks until the buttress is in place.

No case of buttressing is more distasteful to the developer than where he must blast with explosives the buttress excavation. "Why buttress a cut slope that is so resistant that it can't be ripped by the most powerful bulldozer?" Two "case histories" in the Appendix reveal that this apparent paradox can actually exist. In both cases bedded volcanic tuffs and bentonitic seams were interspersed with resistant volcanic rocks that required blasting. Fortunately, these conditions had been diagnosed prior to grading.

Treatment of Erosion and Sloughing Problems

Intense rainfall produces large amounts of surface runoff that accelerate processes of erosion and deposition. Material is washed down to choke downslope areas with a chaos of debris and muck. These processes must be combatted in hillside developments by the drainage devices shown in Figures 20 and 21. A generous amount of weakly bonded clay in the slopes can necessitate, from a viewpoint of erosion, flatter slopes than those shown at 1.5:1.

Of utmost importance once rough grading of hillside residential lots has been completed is the protection of raw cut and fill slopes from erosion. Terraces and interceptor drains can be ineffective and even dangerous until they are paved and properly completed. Plantings are of limited value until irrigated and established. Fresh fill slopes are commonly loose at the ground surface and readily susceptible to erosion and sloughing (local mass movements). These slopes must be grid-rolled or excavated back to well-compacted material. Lot pad areas must have the proper gradient so that runoff does not become ponded or diverted over cut and fill slopes.

Established root systems that bind the soil and a continuous cloak of vegetation that reduces runoff are the best means of protecting slopes against erosion. Plants serving this purpose can be obtained that are both fire-resistant and drouth-resistant. Leaving the forests in a natural state during residential development of mountainous areas is one of the keys to preventing soil and debris flowage.

Maintenance of hillside lots is the basic responsibility of the homeowner. With lot owners insisting upon building in closed topographic depressions, along canyon bottoms and at the base of talus slopes, it is obvious that some do's and don'ts for hillside owners might be helpful. These are available from governing agencies in generalized form. Such suggestions should be tailored to the tract, or even to the individual site. More and more developers are responding to this need by calling on their staff of specialists for such lists.

Poor maintenance of a lot is illustrated by Figure 22. This is commonly expressed by poor drainage and standing water on lot pads. Laxness in promoting efficient drainage is more than a matter of producing unsightly rills and gullies, and clogging drainage ways with debris. It may lead to gross failures of slopes and even to landslides (Figure 10).

The As-Built Geologic Map

The culmination of geologic work in a hillside subdivision is the As-Built Geologic Map (Figure 23). This map is generally prepared for those subdivisions where the hillside geology is complicated and problematical -- conditions that seem to apply to most of the hillside territory in southern California. It is an instrument of detailed geology in support of the geologist's final stamp of approval of the grading and an indication that all geologic problems have been fully recognized, evaluated, and treated. In addition, the map can be of value in the event of future foundation investigations, redesign or redevelopment.

Geologic information acquired during rough grading is transferred to a final as-graded engineering map that shows both pre-graded and as-graded topography. It is possible in some cases to distinguish both pre-graded and as-graded geology by color or symbol patterns. Excavation of the ridges during grading can eliminate some earth materials shown by earlier geologic maps; filling of the canyons can bury other earth materials. Thus, the colored as-graded geology will differ from the pre-graded geology even though there is a close match in the geometrical mapping of earth units. Cross sections commonly supplement the map and show the degree of removal of unsuitable materials, such as slide debris.

Special contours can be used on the map as in Figure 23 to show the position of the old slide rupture surface. This commonly conveys that all slide debris has been removed during grading. Other special symbols on the map show existing slope angles, positions of subdrains and geologic measurements now buried by fill.

Some as-built geologic maps will show restricted use areas. These are graded or ungraded portions of lots not suitable for conventional development in their present condition. Restricted use areas can have their restrictions lifted once corrective measures have been approved by professional consultants. Generally, removal of restrictions is sought when a house addition, swimming pool or guest house requires that the extra lot space be used.

As-built geologic maps are probably a little more static than earlier geologic maps. However, as further modification of the hillsides occurs, the maps will be subject to change. But they will always provide useful records of the geology at the close of rough grading and therefore a measure of the extent of landscape modification since that time.

SUMMARY STATEMENT

Preventive geology and preventive engineering lie at the heart of safe hillside development. Their practice can bring about substantial economies. The field geology of hillside projects generally proceeds in 4 stages: (1) a stage of planning and reconnaissance, (2) a stage of detailed mapping, (3) a stage of subsurface exploration, and (4) a stage of in-grading inspections which combines all elements of the earlier investigations. Where all of these steps are taken diligently and by competent investigators, geologic stability of hillside slopes can be attained. Some of the problems will be easy to solve; others will involve such complex sets of cultural and natural factors that they will challenge the most able team of specialists.

Until a greater number of detailed landslide investigations are undertaken and the public becomes more aware of landslide hazards and their potential prevention, man and the hillsides may have to occasionally part company rather than reaching a state of harmonious equilibrium. Landslide ills in residential subdivisions testify that we can foretell the consequence of poor detection and planning, but we can't always forestall them, notably where older homes reside in unstable hillside surroundings. Nonetheless, behind the scenes of the small number of publicized landslide ills and larger number of unpublicized landslide ills, there has been the quiet triunph of hillside stability in some of the most landslide-prone terrains. These bright achievements have been attained by scientific studies undertaken from the dual viewpoints of geology and soil mechanics.

How can a hillside homeowner feel confident that his selected homesite is a safe one? At least three primary safeguards or cornerstones are available: (1) a check that thorough and detailed geologic and soils investigations have been conducted prior to development and during development, and that all of the recommendations made by these professional consultants prior to grading, during grading, and after grading have been fully implemented and approved by them and local agencies; (2) a check that the hillside community has a strong building and grading code, either Chapter 70 of the Uniform Building Code or some variation specially tailored to the needs of that community; (3) a check that information is available from the developer or agency regarding the proper maintenance of stability and drainage control devices on the property, with recognition that significant modification of his landscape without professional advice can create new stability and drainage problems.

The prospective homeowner or developer must keep in mind these facts:

1. No matter how strong the superstructure of the hillside building structure, it can fail because of unstable terrain.
2. Existing and potential landslide areas can be distinguished in advance of construction, many in advance of purchase of the property.

3. No real insurance program has been available that will cover terrain failures. The best insurance therefore is a comprehensive investigation by professional consultants.

The day of the pseudo-scientist and pseudo-engineer who give quick answers (guesses) to complex field problems is rapidly disappearing. However, many slides are still too often dismissed as "quirks of nature" and belonging to the "mystic realm". Today, in new hillside subdivisions, landslides are excusable only where they have no appreciable effect on human life or domestic economy. Only time will tell how widely applicable this statement will be in the future.

REFERENCES ON SPECIFIC LANDSLIDE AREAS IN SOUTHERN CALIFORNIA

Allen, Chas. W., 1949, Structure of the northwestern Puente Hills, Los Angeles County, California: Unpub. Caltech master's thesis. (Includes description of landslides in this area.)

Bock, C. G., and C. W. Schmidt, 1961, Geology of the Fort Rosecrans landslide, Point Loma, California: Abstract, Ann. Mtg. Cordilleran Sec., Geol. Soc. America, San Diego, p. 19.

Bureau of Standards, 1958, Progress Report, Pacific Palisades Landslide Investigation, Department of Public Works, City of Los Angeles.

Elysian Park landslide, November 26, 1937: Eng. News-Record, 1938, vol. 120, p. 273. (Smaller slide occurred south of here in 1958 and blocked part of Pasadena Freeway for one week.)

Glendora Volcanics Landslide areas: First mentioned by Rollin Eckis, 1934, Calif. Div. Water Res. Bull. 45, p. 74, "Geology and ground-water storage capacity of valley fill." And by J. S. Shelton, 1955, G.S.A. Bull., vol. 66, "Glendora volcanic rocks, Los Angeles Basin, California." (Involves more than two square miles of landslides between Dalton and San Dimas Canyons.)

Hill, R. A., 1934, Clay stratum dried out to prevent landslips: Civil Eng., vol. 4, p. 403-407. (Discusses 2 landslides at Santa Monica in 1932 and the gas furnace network used to dry out the clay.)

Jahns, Richard H., Dec. 1958, Residential ills of the Heartbreak Hills of Southern California: Engineering and Science, Caltech Alumni Magazine, vol. 22, p. 13-20. (Excellent popular treatment.)

Jahns, Richard H., and George Cleveland, in press, Geology related to Engineering, Palos Verdes Peninsula, California: Calif. Div. Mines and Geology Bull.

Jahns, Richard H., et al, 1954, Geology of Southern California: Bulletin 170, Chapters 1, 2, 4, 5, 6, 7, 10, Geologic Guides, 1, 2, 3, 4, and 5, Map Sheets 4, 5, 6, 8, 9, California Div. Mines and Geology.

Jennings, C. W. and Bennien W. Troxel, 1954, Geologic Guide No. 2, Ventura Basin <u>in</u> Geology of Southern California, Bull. 170, California Div. Mines and Geology, 63 p. (Brief discussions, with photos, of Elysian Park and Ventura Avenue Oil Field Slides.)

Kiessling, Edmund, 1963, A trip to Palos Verdes Hills: Mineral Information Service, vol. 16, No. 11 (November), California Div. Mines and Geology, p. 9-14. (Brief discussion of the landslide including a map.)

Leighton, F. Beach, 1962, Concentration of epigene slope failures, northwestern Puente Hills, California: Abstract, Ann. Meeting Cordilleran Sec., Geol. Soc. America, Los Angeles, p. 46.

Leighton, F. Beach, 1963, Geology of San Diego Freeway cuts in Santa Monica Mountains: Report to City of Los Angeles and Calif. Div. Highways for litigation.

Livingston, Jr., Alfred and Putnam, William C., 1933, Geological Journeys in Southern California: Los Angeles Junior College Publication No. 1.

Mc Gill, John T., 1959, Preliminary map of landslides in the Pacific Palisades area, City of Los Angeles, California: U. S. Geol. Survey Map I-284. See also abstract in Bull. Geol. Soc. America, vol. 68, Dec. 1957, p. 1836.

Merriam, Richard, 1960, Portuguese Bend landslide, Palos Verdes Hills, California: Jour. Geology, vol. 68, p. 140-153. (Sliding occurred in 1929, 1936, 1940, and 1965.)

Miller, W. J., 1931, The Point Fermin landslide: Sci. Monthly, vol. 32, p. 464-469.

Moran, Proctor, Mueser and Rutledge, 1959, Final Report Pacific Palisades Landslide Study, Volume 1: Department of Public Works, State of California.

Noetzli, F. A., 1927, Multiple Arch Retaining Wall Damaged by Slip: Eng. News-Record, vol. 98, p. 146; also Cahuenga Pass Arch Retaining Wall Continues Slipping, vol. 99, p. 681.

Putnam, Wm. C. and R. P. Sharp, 1940, Landslides and earthflows near Ventura, Southern California: Geogr. Rev. vol. 30, p. 591-600.

Roth, E. R., 1959, Landslides between Santa Monica and Point Dume: Unpub. master's thesis at Univ. So. Calif., 184 p.

Sharp, R. P. and L. H. Nobles, 1953, Mudflow of 1941 at Wrightwood, Southern California: Geol. Soc. America Bull., vol. 64, p. 547-560.

Shreve, Ronald, 1959, Geology and mechanics of the Blackhawk Landslide, Lucerne Valley, California: Ph.D. thesis, Caltech. Abstract in 1960 Cordilleran Section Meeting of Geol. Soc. America, p. 41.

Slosson, J. E., and B. A. Celwick, 1965, Parson's Landing landslide, Santa Catalina Island: Effects of eustatic sea level changes on coastal stability: Abstract, Ann. Mtg., Assoc. Engineering Geologists, Denver, p. 32. (Partially active three-quarter square mile slide to be used as golf course.)

Woodring, W. P., M. N. Bramlette and W. S. W. Kew, 1964, Geology and paleontology of the Palos Verdes Hills, Calif.: U. S. Geol. Survey Prof. Paper 207, 145 p. (Slides described as down dip on slippery shale and water-soaked bentonitic tuff.)

Yerkes, R. F. and R. H. Campbell, J. E. Schoellhamer and C. M. Wentworth, 1964, Preliminary geologic map and sections of parts of the Topanga, Malibu Beach, and Pt. Dume quadrangles, Los Angeles County, California: U. S. Geological Survey cooperative field mapping program with the Los Angeles County Engineer's Office.

SELECTED GENERAL REFERENCES ON LANDSLIDES

Baker, Robert F. and Robert Chieruzzi, 1958, Regional Concept of Landslide Occurrence, Bulletin 216, U. S. Highway Research Board, Washington, D.C.

Cleaves, A. B., 1961, Landslide investigations: A handbook for use in highway location and design: U. S. Dept. Commerce, Bureau of Public Roads. (U. S. Govt. Printing Office, Washington, D.C. 30¢.)

Eckel, Edwin B. and others, 1958, Landslides and engineering practice: Highway Research Board Special Report 29, Washington, D.C., 232 p.

Emery, K. O., 1960, The Sea Off Southern California: J. Wiley and Sons, Inc., 366 p.

Forbes, H., 1947, Landslide investigation and correction: Trans. ASCE, vol. 112, p. 377-442.

Highway Research Board, 1958, Landslides and engineering practice: Special Report 29, 232 p.

Jahns, Richard H., May 1949, Desert Floods: Engineering and Science, Caltech Alumni Magazine, p. 10-14.

Kiersch, Geo. A., 1964, Vaiont Reservoir disaster: Civil Engineering, vol. 34, no. 3, p. 32-39. (An excellent discussion of the slide which caused the failure).

Ladd, G. E., 1935, Landslides, Subsidences and Rock-Falls, Proceedings of the American Railway Engineering Association, vol. 36, p. 1091-1162.

Mc Gill, John T., 1954, Residential building-site problems in Los Angeles, California: Calif. Div. Mines and Geology, Bull. 170, Chapt. 10, p. 11-18.

Terzaghi, Karl, 1950, Mechanics of landslides, in Application of Geology to Engineering Practice (Berkey volume), p. 83-124.

Turtle mountain, near Frank, Alberta.

15

Reprinted from *Report of the Commission Appointed To Investigate Turtle Mountain, Frank, Alberta* (Canada Dept. Mines Mem. 27), Government Printing Bureau, Ottawa, 1912, pp. 9–11, 13–18, 21–26, 30–34

TURTLE MOUNTAIN, FRANK, ALBERTA.

REGINALD A. DALY, W. G. MILLER, and GEORGE S. RICE

HISTORICAL SUMMARY.

Report of Landslide of 1903.

Under date June 12, 1903, Messrs. R. G. McConnell and R. W. Brock of the Geological Survey of Canada, acting as a commission appointed by the Honourable the Minister of the Interior, submitted a report on their examination of the Frank landslide which took place on April 29, of that year. The slide entailed the loss of about seventy lives of people in the town of Frank, together with the destruction of much property, including nearly 7,000 feet of the Crows Nest railway.

In their report, Messrs. McConnell and Brock say that the slide was due, not to a single cause, but to a combination of causes, among which the opening up of large chambers in the mine, situated under the base of the mountain, may have been a contributory cause. Speaking of the North peak and shoulder of the mountain overlooking the town, they say "the closing of the chambers in the mine, after the coal has been withdrawn, perhaps long after the inhabitants of the town have lost all dread of another disaster, may precipitate it suddenly in a second destructive slide. Since this possibility must always overhang the town, it certainly seems advisable that it be moved a short distance up the valley beyond the reach of danger."[1]

More Recent Observations.

Since the report was published, officers of the Geological Survey have visited Frank from time to time and have examined the mountain. From several examinations he has made of the mountain, Mr. Brock has decided that cracks have formed in that part of the mountain overlooking the town, and that one or two cracks in the vicinity of the north shoulder have gradually widened

[1] Extract from Part VIII, Annual Report, 1903, Department of Interior, page 17

Editor's Note: Most of the plates and several sections of text have been omitted from the original article (omissions are indicated by a row of asterisks). The limitations of space force us to omit material that is not central to the purpose of the volume.

during the last two years. Moreover, he has decided that the extraction of coal within a certain zone, which he has called the "zone of extreme danger," is likely to precipitate a landslide that would destroy the town. In the Summary Report of the Geological Survey for 1909, he calls attention to the danger which, in his opinion, threatens the town.

The following quotations from letters written by Mr. Brock in 1910, show the views he holds concerning the danger that he considers would arise were coal extracted from certain parts of the mine.

'Of the various causes which were responsible for the big slide there can be no question but that the mining of the coal was a prime one.

'In the report on the Frank slide we expressed our conviction regarding the connexion between mining and the catastrophe. It was not considered necessary to emphasize this point at that time, for the Company had had no means of knowing that its operations were a menace to public safety. Now the case is otherwise. If the mountain is further disturbed by mining operations and a slide occurs the Company would certainly be held responsible.[1]

'Turtle mountain is in a more threatening condition now than last year. This opinion is concurred in by Mr. Boyd. The north shoulder is, of course, the dangerous portion of the mountain. After the slide it was carefully examined and it has been closely watched since then, but until last year I saw no signs of movement or, apart from its structure, of weakness on this north shoulder. Last year I detected two cracks as shown on the sketch map which I sent you last spring. They were so slight, however, that it would not have surprised me if their existence had been questioned. This year, however, they were very marked. The cracks between this shoulder and the North peak also show development during the year. These cracks are significant as indicating movement and unstable conditions. It is true that in some cases the block severed by the crack is not large enough in itself to cause much damage if dislodged, but as the joint planes along which the cracks develop dip towards the face of the cliff, giving the block the form of an inverted wedge, only those near the face can open, the weight of a large block tending to keep the break closed. As the top surface is covered with shingle, only a gaping crack makes itself visible on the surface; hence a dangerous break back from the face, the break along which an enormous slide might take place, might not be detectable on the surface, even at the time the slide was about to occur.

[1] Letter dated May 12, 1910, addressed to the Canadian Coal Consolidated Limited, Frank, Alta.

11

'The cracks on the north shoulder prove that its solidity is not to be relied on, and the recent movements indicated by these cracks may very well be ascribed to the disturbing effect of mining that has recently been done in the neighbourhood of the foundation of this shoulder.

'In the face of such facts, I cannot evade the conclusion that mining is too dangerous to be continued. It is my firm opinion that no more liberties can safely be taken with this mountain.

'A large slide would cut off all railway communication and close the mines west of Frank. It might permanently close the pass. The town of Frank would be wiped out with a fearful toll of life. These are some of the risks that are being taken by tampering with the foundation of this mountain. It was unsafe to do what has recently been done in the way of mining. This was pointed out before this work was started and the present unfavourable condition of Turtle mountain as compared to that of last year shows that the opinion then expressed was well founded. No further mining of the seams near the base of Turtle mountain can safely be done."[1]

* * * * * * *

[1] Letter dated, Ottawa, Nov. 3, 1910, addressed to John Stocks, Esq., Deputy Minister, Department of Public Works, Edmonton, Alta.

INTRODUCTION.

The question whether there is danger of one or more destructive slides in the future involves two sets of considerations. Its investigation obviously implies an inquiry into the existing natural conditions. Are those conditions such as to warrant belief in practical danger to the town of Frank? Secondly, is the stability of Turtle mountain of such a low order that continued mining at its base would essentially add to the danger? As to the advisability of keeping the town in its present situation, these two problems are not of equal importance. If it can be shown that reasonable prudence should counsel the evacuation of the town-site because of the present natural condition of Turtle mountain, the question as to the influence of continued mining on the Frank coal seam becomes distinctly subordinate. Since your Commission believes that nearly all of the town-site is in danger of being overrun by one or more great slides, quite irrespective of the mining operations, the evidence bearing on this essential problem will first be stated.

A. Probability of a Great Slide due to Existing Natural Conditions.

The grounds for your Commission's affirmative answer to the question regarding danger of catastrophe because of the present state of the mountain, may be reviewed under five heads. These are: (1) The special, local conditions favouring such a slide. (2) The general conditions favouring a slide. (3) The similarity of conditions to those preceding the great slide of April, 1903. (4) The weakening of the North peak through the fall of rock in 1903. (5) The existence of new cracks showing incipient movement of the large block culminating in the North peak.

(1) Special Conditions Favouring a Landslide of the First Order.

After a careful study on the ground, your Commission has been forced to conclude that Turtle mountain presents a number of peculiarities which together form a highly special combination leading to continued destructive falls of rock from the North peak and its vicinity. Perhaps nowhere else in the entire Rocky Mountain system is a similar combination of features to be found. It is certain, even without further detailed examination by geologists, that this combination of features is not likely to be exactly paralleled in any other mountain mass of Álberta or of British Columbia. In the present case the form or topography of the mountain, its somewhat complicated structure, the nature of its constituent rocks, and the internal stresses developed within the mountain mass at the time of its original upheaval, all conspire to make the stability of its eastern slope extremely doubtful.

(a) *Topography of the Eastern Slope of Turtle Mountain.*

The notable steepness of the mountain side throughout the part of it which overlooks the town-site is obvious to any observer on the ground. The same quality is apparent to any topographic expert who studies the admirable contour map made under the direction of Mr. Boyd for the Dominion Geological Survey (see Map of Turtle Mountain and Vicinity). A quantitative idea of the average and maximum steepness can also be obtained from an inspection of the profiles (Figures 2-10), taken at regular intervals along the general slope. Finally, the steep quality of the eastern flank is illustrated in the accompanying photographs (Plates II and III), as well as in the cardboard model (Plate IV) herewith submitted.

The following table shows the average angles of slope (measured from the horizontal plane) for 400 foot vertical intervals on each of the profiles (here respectively numbered 1 to 9) shown in Figures 2-10:—

Contour Interval.	1	2	3	4	5	6	7	8	9
7000–6600	....	......	....	.....	56°	67° (200 ft.)	66° (220 ft.)	62° (360 ft.)	55° (500 ft.)
6600–6200	......	......	......	61°	47°	51°	59°	45°	46°
6200–5800	....	......	52°	58°	44°	39°	38°	34°	36°
5800–5400	51°	58°	40°	45°	50°	34°	31°	33°	30°
5400–5000	46°	56°	45°	42°	35°	32°	30°	31°	30°
5000–4600	52°	40°	34°	30°	27°	24°	26°	24°	20°
4600–4200	34°	31°	22°	19°	18°	22°	23°	22°	13°

The measured angle of rest for the coarse rock-debris in the longest talus slope of Turtle mountain (eastward from a point near the South peak), is just thirty degrees. If a plane of complete scission should be developed in the mountain, and if the inclination of that plane to the horizontal should exceed thirty-two degrees, the block overlying the plane of scission must instantly slide down along that plane. Actual experiment shows that thirty-two degrees is somewhat more than the maximum or limiting angle of inclination for the plane of scission if the mountain is to remain stable in spite of the scission.

Bearing in mind this outside value for the limiting angle, an inspection of the profiles in Figures 2-10 and of the foregoing table will suggest the maximum amount of rock matter which could fall from Turtle mountain. It is safe to conclude that much of Turtle mountain lies above a possible plane of scission inclined eastward at the critical angle.

(b) *Geological Structure of the Mountain.*

If Turtle mountain were composed of homogeneous granite or non-jointed limestone, the foregoing calculation would have no practical value; the strength of such rock would be such as to make absurd any reference to the critical angle above defined in connexion with the problem of the mountain's stability. But Turtle mountain is peculiar in possessing a structure which forbids our placing an estimate of an absolutely safe angle for the eastern slope at much greater than thirty or thirty-five degrees. By this, your Commission does not mean to imply that all of the rock bounded by slopes greater than about thirty-five degrees is in danger of sliding before the ordinary processes of erosion have lowered such slopes. Such a danger is, in their opinion, remote, except in a limited area where structural weakness is combined with steepness of slope in a manner to threaten disaster to the town.

Much additional work needs to be done before the geology of Turtle mountain is understood in all its details. The officials of the Dominion Geological Survey have, however, elucidated the structure to an extent sufficient for the needs of the present problem. So far as it has had opportunity in the field to test the main conclusions of the government geologists, your Commission is in agreement with these gentlemen. The structure of the mountain is indicated in the section, Figure 5, which has been adopted from their reports. This section is taken along the accurate profile No. 4 constructed for the Commission by Mr. Boyd.

In brief, Turtle mountain is an erosion remnant of a great block of Palæozoic (chiefly Carboniferous) limestones overthrust eastward upon the western limb of a syncline of Mesozoic (chiefly Cretaceous) shales, sandstones, and coal-beds. The average dips of the beds in these two primary divisions of the mountain are

14447—4

shown in Figure 5. The thrust-plane is located in the section with fair accuracy, but its exact inclination to the horizontal plane is not apparent in the outcrops. It is the opinion of the government geologists that the thrust-plane is highly inclined and accordingly it has been so drawn on the section.

From the river flat to the lower contact of the limestone (that is, the outcrop of the thrust-plane), the mountain slope is underlain by soft shales, interrupted by coal-seams and by some interbeds of sandstone. The whole is an unusually weak mass of rock; yet forms the basal abutment which is to-day helping to sustain the heavy limestone forming the upper half of the mountain.

Weak as this lower member is, it might continue to hold up the entire slope if it were not for the inherent weakness of the limestone itself. The latter is composed of rapidly alternating beds of contrasted nature. Some of them are thick, massive, and coherent, and, if the whole upper member were constituted of similar material, the chance for a destructive slide in the future would be greatly lessened. But very many other beds are flaggy, easily split along the bedding-planes and, therefore, far less strong than the beds just mentioned. On this account alone the average strength of the whole limestone member is much below that of many, perhaps most, of the great limestone formations of British Columbia or Alberta. In addition, the total strength of the member is seriously lessened by the presence of two zones of crumpling within the mass. These zones are diagrammatically shown in the section, Figure 5. It should be carefully noted that the lower edge of the mass which fell in April, 1903, coincides with one of these contorted zones. That event actually illustrated the profound weakening of the mountain structure because of the presence of these zones. Another source of weakness is found in a band of soft shales, which breaks the continuity of the limestone (See Figure 5).

However, the chief reasons for concern as regards this matter of rock strength, are the heavy jointing of the limestone and the relation of the joints to the eastern slope of the mountain, the side facing the town. As is so often the case with sedimentary rocks, very abundant joints occurring in several systems are developed nearly or quite perpendicular to the bedding. The dip of the bedding is always westward and varies from 65° to 50°. At the North and South peaks, and for a considerable distance north of the North peak (that is, the part of the mountain opposite the town), the average dip is about 50° to the west. This means that many of the joints mentioned dip directly eastward at an angle of 40°. Other systems of these joints dip towards the northeast and southeast quadrants at still higher angles. The relation of the easterly dipping joints to the topography is illustrated in Figure 5. The diagram is intended to make clear this highly important cause for instability in the mountain. If the dip of the bedding were notably *steeper* than 50°, the easterly dips of the joints would be correspondingly flatter, and the danger of bodily slipping along that joint system would be materially less than under the present conditions. If the dip of the bedding were notably *flatter* than 50°, the easterly dips of the joints would be correspondingly steeper and continued spalling of small blocks along those joints would have produced a steep but stable profile for the mountain in prehistoric time. The actual dips of the bedding and joints are almost ideal for the production of great intermittent slides from a mountain with the steepness of Turtle mountain. The slipping on joint-planes during the slide of 1903 is illustrated in Plates V and VI.

The joints are thus of profound importance as they so seriously affect the strength of the limestone and, by their attitude, furnish potential slipping planes, which threaten to become actual slipping planes if a heavy jar or a disturbance of the basal abutment should occur. Moreover, joints are the favourable channels for the seepage of ground-water which tends slowly to enlarge them and also to wet the rock, increasing the danger of sliding *en masse*.

As a result of the 1903 slide, many profound fissures were opened on the North and South peaks, and in the part of the summit area between the peaks (Plates VII-XII). These are partly due to a powerful pull exerted by the huge rock prism as it fell outward and downward. These fissures are as noteworthy for depth as they are for extent along the surface. In general, they run nearly parallel with the edge of the main eastward-facing escarpment, i.e., that overlooking the town. They not only show movement of vast masses of rock towards the brink, but they also represent deep openings into which surface water from rain and heavy snow must run, and at certain times of the year be frozen at the bottom of each fissure. It is impossible to say exactly what effect this action may have in the future, but there is evident danger of the wedging out of huge prisms of rock through frost action. That displacement may directly cause considerable falls of rock or so disturb the delicate mechanism of the mountain as to initiate slipping on master-joints, and thus even a landslide of the first order.

* * * * * * *

B. Influence of Mining on the Stability of Turtle Mountain

THE PROBLEM.

As shown on a preceding page, Messrs. McConnell and Brock, in their report on the great slide of 1903, considered that the mining operations conducted at the base of Turtle mountain might have been a contributory cause of starting that slide.

In the summary reports of the Geological Survey of Canada for 1909 and 1910, the Director stated that continuance of mining within certain areas, termed danger zones, might cause further land slides which would endanger the town of Frank.

The limits of these danger zones formed the subject of correspondence between the Director and the representatives of the Alberta government; and the Director indicated on a map of the mine the limits of the zones.

Your Commission has carefully weighed the evidence presented in the reports mentioned and also such informal evidence and suggestions as have been given by those who had knowledge of the mine and of the condition of Turtle mountain, both before and after the great slide of 1903. We have also entered and studied accessible parts of the two mines at the base of Turtle mountain.

The relation of the mining to the past and present danger of landslides from Turtle mountain may be considered under two heads:—

(1) What effect might mining have had in causing the slide of 1903?

(2) Is it probable that continuance of mining will cause other great slides?

The latter is a vital question, but it is necessary to consider the former in order to determine, as far as possible, how nearly the present conditions surrounding mining are analogous to those prior to the slide of 1903.

LOCATION OF THE FRANK MINES.

There are now two mines operating along the foot or east base of Turtle mountain, a shaft mine and a drift mine. Both belong to the Canadian Coal Consolidated, Limited, and formerly belonged to the Canadian-American Coal and Coke Company.

The drift mine was started in 1901; the shaft mine was not begun until several years after the landslide.

The drift mine enters the outcrop of a nearly vertical coal seam at a point 27 feet above the present level of the Crowsnest (Oldman) river. The strike of the seam is nearly north and south, parallel with the general axis of Turtle mountain, though not with the base of its easterly slope, which trends to the west of north. In going south from the mouth of the drift mine the outcrop line crosses an easterly spur of the South peak of the mountain, rising to a height of twelve hundred feet above the mouth of the drift. In a northerly direction from the mouth, the outcrop traverses the relatively flat valley of the Crowsnest river. Thirty-eight hundred feet from the mouth of the drift this seam, or possibly a parallel one, is opened by the hoisting and air shafts of the new mine. Twelve hundred feet north of the shaft the north edge of the valley is reached, and the outcrop rises rapidly on the flank of Bluff or Goat mountain. A level enters this part of the outcrop about 20 feet above the valley; it is connected underground with the shaft-mine workings. The shaft mine and the original drift mine are not connected underground; there is a distance of 2,700 feet between their nearest workings. The relative positions of the various mine workings are shown on the vertical, longitudinal profile along the outcrop of the coal seam, in Figure 11.

COAL SEAM DEVELOPED BY THE MINES.

It is not known whether the two mines are in the same coal seam. That opened by the drift mine is from ten to fifteen feet thick, has a hard sandstone roof and a hard, thin-bedded shale floor, which through overturning have become the foot and hanging wall respectively. Forty feet below this seam stratigraphically, there is a two-to-four-foot dirty seam, which is unworked.

The dip of the seams is from 82° to 90°, with an average of 85°, to the west; the seams, therefore, dip towards Turtle mountain.

The coal developed by the shaft mine is thinner, six to ten feet thick, and it is said to have a higher content of volatile matter, but the roof, floor, and other characteristics are the same.

There are said to be other seams both above and below the main seam, but they have not been definitely exposed by prospecting. It is thought that the Hillcrest mine, which lies immediately south of the Frank mine, may be operating on a different seam. At the Bellevue mine on the opposite side of the valley of the Crowsnest river and on the east limb of the syncline, four seams are known, two of which (in some places a third) are workable. The existence of other workable seams at Frank is of importance, for if it is conceded that mining operations in one seam may favour slides, it must be admitted that operations in additional seams above or below would increase the risk. In the absence of definite knowledge, the discussion must be confined to the operations in one seam only.

RELATION OF OPERATIONS IN THE DRIFT (No. 1) MINE TO THE LANDSLIDE OF 1903.

At the time of the landslide of 1903, the workings in the drift mine consisted of the level gangway, driven in 5,500 feet on the strike of the seam, a level for drainage and ventilation immediately below the gangway, and a series of chambers or breasts driven directly up the raise. According to the 1903 report of Messrs. McConnell and Brock, the chambers were from 60 to 150 feet in width, separated by pillars 40 feet in width. Witnesses before your present Commission stated the average width of chambers was 100 feet, and of pillars 30 feet. Manways and timber chutes four or five feet square were made alternately in the pillars. As the chambers were filled with broken coal, which was drawn off from time to time, the whole mass sliding, no propping between the foot and hanging wall was possible. The series of chambers commenced at or near a point 1,200 feet in from the mouth of the mine. Beyond a point 3,500 feet from the mouth, chambers had merely been started.

A profile of the outcrop and gangways was made from data furnished by the recent Dominion government survey (see Figure 11). This indicates that, if the chambers between the 1,200 foot point and the 3,500 foot point extended to or nearly to the outcrop, they varied in height from 200 feet to 500 feet.

Witnesses appearing before the former Commission stated positively that a squeeze of the walls of the seam was apparent prior to the landslide. Certain persons who appeared informally before the present Commission confirmed this, and one who had been engaged in timbering said that the gangway and manways had to be retimbered several times, the timbers giving way by squeeze from the walls. He also stated that certain manways driven up to the outcrop had been condemned on account of the impossibility of keeping them timbered. A number of the witnesses have stated that for a couple of months before the slide, coal had been drawn rapidly from the chambers and that falls from the walls had taken place. In this their testimony agreed with that of others interviewed by the 1903 Commission. Considering the unusual width of the breasts and the impossibility of retaining props ten to fifteen feet long between the nearly vertical walls in a mass of moving coal, it is not surprising that there should have been falls from the walls when the support given by the loose coal was withdrawn.

One witness before this Commission stated that he had investigated the breasts of some of the chambers and found that so much rock had fallen from the hanging wall (west wall), that this wall was undermined or "undercut" to a considerable distance.

The Department of Mines of Alberta reports the following out put from the drift mine:—

1901.	15,000 tons.
1902.	160,000 "
1903.	101,591 "
	276,591 "

The figures for the individual months are not available, but it is reported that the mine prior to the landslide of April 29, 1903, was putting out from 1,000 to 1,100 tons per day. It is also stated that little coal was mined in 1903 after the mine was re-opened, late in that year. Taking into account the rock removed from the mine and the coal lost in the process of loading outside the mine, of which there would be no record, it is safe to say that the excavation prior to 1903 was equivalent to over 276,591 tons of coal, or 245,000 cubic yards. The chambers, in which most of this excavation was done, extended for 2,300 feet immediately under the slide.

To give due consideration to the influence of excavation in this area, it is desirable to estimate its amount for the region above the level of the gangway. The volume represented in the gangway outside of the area in question, plus the number of cubic yards in the water level, is about 9,000 cubic yards. The amount of excavation in the newly started chambers beyond the 3,500 foot point is conjectural, but, from descriptions of witnesses, it probably does not exceed 10,000 cubic yards. Making these deductions from the total estimated yardage, gives a net of 226,000 cubic yards of excavation immediately under the landslide. In this area, including everything from gangway level to outcrop, if the average thickness of seam is assumed to be 14 feet, there are 536,000 cubic yards.

On the foregoing assumptions we must conclude that 42 per cent of the original volume was mined. It is probable from the observations of witnesses that this percentage is an under estimate of the yield. It is, therefore, on the safe side.

This is equivalent to an average shrinkage of six feet over the entire area involved in this calculation, but as broken rock occupies about 1½ times the space of solid rock, the net shrinkage may be considered to be not over four feet. Eventually, however, the broken rock would be crushed together by the weight of the strata, as has been found in driving through old long-wall packs in operations in various mining districts; so the entire shrinkage in time would be six feet. To be on the safe side we will consider only the more immediate settlement. It is not contended that there was a sudden settlement of four feet over the whole area of a length of 2,300 feet and average depth of 450 feet, but the evidence of witnesses is that a squeeze had started about six months previous to the landslide; and it probably continued for a long time before the final compacting took place.

It is difficult to determine what was the exact result of even a portion of such settlement upon the unstable original North peak, but your present Commission agrees with the findings of the Commission of 1903, that the movement of the walls was instrumental in weakening the supports of the peak and possibly was directly responsible for the landslide. The fact that the part of the mountain which fell in 1903 was exactly opposite to, and corresponded in length with, the area of large chambers, cannot be dismissed as merely a coincidence.

* * * * * * *

Danger in Continued Mining in the Drift Mine.

The present position of the mine entrance involves decided danger both to the mine and the miners. It was covered by the landslide of 1903, and the surface works were swept away. Many loose rocks on the slopes above threaten destruction. This entrance should be permanently closed and a new entrance should be made either at the extreme southern end of the mine, southeast of Turtle mountain, or else entrance should be obtained underground from the shaft mine at sufficient depth to be below possible buried water-courses. The levels should be driven in such a way (for example, with the safeguard of advance drill holes) as to receive the sanction of the representatives of the Alberta government.

This conclusion of your Commission, as to the present dangerous position of the drift mouth, is apart from considerations affecting future mining operations within the mine itself.

Influence of Continued Mining in the Drift Mine in Causing Slides.

The Director of the Dominion Survey pointed out in correspondence with the Alberta mining officials, as already noted, that there was an area of what he termed "extreme danger," and so marked it on a map of the mine submitted by these officials.

In this area he considered that any mining would be likely to precipitate a landslide. The northern limit of the "extreme danger zone" he placed at a point 1,400 feet north of the drift mouth in territory not yet entered by either mine. He placed the southern limit at a point not less than 3,500 feet south of the mouth, and thus coincident with the south edge of the great slide, but he made a note on the map that "south of this point mining not altogether safe."

Your Commission fully agrees with this conclusion as to the danger of causing slides from continued mining in this area, at least if done by the ordinary methods.

Hydraulic Packing.

The only method known to your Commission that would insure against appreciable subsidence is that of hydraulic packing with sand. This method is increasingly used in Germany, and with the greatest success in preventing the subsidence of the surface where there are expensive buildings. The settlement after packing with ordinary sand is less than five per cent; with granulated slag settlement is inappreciable, as it probably would be with sharp, clean sand.

The use of loam and sandy clay, ashes or crushed shale is less successful, the settlement with such material being from 10 to 15 per cent.

It does not appear possible to employ sand filling under ordinary commercial conditions in the Turtle Mountain district. There are no large bodies of clean sand close at hand. The only available source from which material could be obtained in sufficient quantities would be the sandstone at the base of Bluff (Goat) mountain. This would have to be quarried, crushed, transported to, and flushed into the mine. The cost with the high labour costs that prevail in Alberta, plus repairs, renewals, and capital charges, would add not less than $1.25 per ton of coal extracted, even if done on a considerable scale. The cost of installing the necessary plant would also be great, so that the system appears commercially impossible under the competitive conditions of coal production in that district.

Dry Packing.

While the use of dry packing would probably lessen the amount of subsidence, the experience with the long-wall method of mining both in America and Europe, where dry packing is employed, indicates that a settlement of 40 to 60 per cent of the thickness of the seam must be expected. It takes several years to reach the full settlement, but any portion of such settlement might cause disastrous slides.

If coal pillars are left, this merely serves to delay the process, for under the great pressures due to depth, shales such as here constitute the hanging wall will "flow" and seal all openings.

C. Conclusions.

Danger from Mining.

Your Commission, therefore, concludes that under present commercial conditions it is not possible to mine within a certain area without incurring the danger of precipitating a great landslide. We place the north limit of this area at the present south limit of the

14447—8½

shaft-mine workings, and the south limit of the area at a point five thousand feet south of the mouth of the No. 1 mine. The latter limit has been placed so far south on account of the possibility that mining operations should cause a landslide from the South peak, which in turn might cause one from the North peak, thus endangering the town, and the tracks and equipment of the Canadian Pacific railway.

The only conditions under which mining should be carried on in the danger area above described are: (1) The townsite should be abandoned and the risk to the property of the Canadian Pacific railway assumed. (2) The present entrance to No. 1 (drift) mine should be abandoned and the mine should be operated by deep levels from the shaft mine or from an opening at the extreme southern end of the property in the vicinity of Hillcrest. (3) Unusually heavy pillars should be left throughout the danger area, particularly in the upper levels, and not more than 50 per cent of the coal should be extracted. (4) The excavated areas should be packed.

DANGEROUS NATURAL CAUSES.

Taking into account: (*a*) the steepness of the eastern slope of Turtle mountain, (*b*) its peculiar structure, and especially the attitude of the joint planes (planes of scission), (*c*) the possibility of internal stresses, inherited from the period of original upheaval, (*d*) the effect of highly possible jars on the delicate mechanism of this particular mountain (jars of a moderate earthquake, like that of 1901 in this region, or slight settlement of the mine workings might precipitate a slide of the first order), (*e*) the strong similarity of the conditions now to those immediately preceding the slide of 1903, (*f*) the special danger to the stability of the North Peak block induced by the 1903 slide, (*g*) the evidence of the recent development of fissures in the North peak, and (*h*) the difficulty of forecasting the exact course of the threatened slide or slides—your Commission is agreed on the following conclusions, namely:—

Irrespective of mining operations and because of existing conditions only, there is danger of a disastrous landslide from Turtle mountain. We are agreed that danger exists from what has hitherto been called, in this report, the North Peak block. The size and position of this block is indicated on the "Map of Turtle Mountain and Vicinity showing Danger Area." The limits of the block have been roughly marked thereon by paying due attention to the analogy of the block which fell in 1903 (Figure 29, showing the *splay* of this slide), and to the attitude of the joint-planes in the mountain. In our opinion, the lower limit of this threatening block occurs at the outcrop of the zone of contorted beds in the limestone member (see Plate XV).

We are further agreed that the area likely to be overrun by the debris of this slide is shown with practical accuracy (as the "area endangered") on the "Map of Turtle Mountain and Vicinity showing Danger Area." In tracing the limits of this danger, your Commission has used the analogy of the 1903 slide and has allowed a fair "margin of safety," necessitated by accidental factors that might influence the course of the threatened slide.

Excepting the North Peak block, the South Peak block, and the fissured area between them, we believe that the danger of heavy slides into the Frank valley cannot be classed as imminent. Yet it should be carefully noted that, in the opinion of your Commission, both the estimate of the size of the threatening block and the area likely to be devastated have been conservatively estimated and so indicated on the "Map of Turtle Mountain and Vicinity showing Danger Area." It is impossible to deny the existence of danger to the part of the valley at and north of the mine shaft. We believe, however, that the new Rocky Mountain Sanatorium lies outside the zone of practical danger.

As already noted, we believe that there is danger of heavy slides from the South peak and from the fissured region just to the north. We have not mapped their probable course, since this would lie practically altogether in the already mined and now uninhabited area overrun by the 1903 slide.

On account of the dips of bedding and joints in the limestone of Bluff (Goat mountain, as locally named), we are of opinion that there is no practical danger of a first-order slide from that mountain in its present condition (See Plate XIX).

Abandonment of the Town-site.

The present shaft and mine buildings surrounding it, also the row of houses to the northwest of it, appear to be reasonably safe from the effect of a slide from Turtle mountain. Practically all the rest of the town-site should be abandoned. In the opinion of your Commission this should be done whether the mine is operated in the danger zone or not, on account of the unstable condition, from natural causes, of the North and South peaks.

Whatever the report of this or other Commission, the town can never be an important one on its present site, since there will always remain the dread of another calamitous slide like that of 1903. In spite of undoubted individual hardship, caused by abandonment of the present site, the town, on a new and safe site, might prosper as never before.

Reprinted from *Trans. Inst. Brit. Geographers*, **53**, 55–65 (1971)

Mass movements associated with the rainstorm of June 1966 in Hong Kong

C.L.SO
(*Lecturer in Geography, University of Hong Kong*)

Revised MS received 17 November 1970

ABSTRACT. The disastrous mass movements associated with the 1966 rainstorm in Hong Kong call attention to the susceptibility of slopes to deformation in the humid tropics. Locally, the predominance of igneous rocks with well-developed jointing facilitates sub-surface weathering and mass wasting. The mass movements occurred in areas both with and without a vegetation cover. Their distribution suggests that the vegetation plays only a limited part in stabilizing slopes. There is a need for a reappraisal of the function of vegetation in mass movements.

MASS MOVEMENTS associated with heavy rain have been increasingly studied since the pioneer work of C. F. Sharpe.[1] Many studies have stressed the importance of events leading to slope failure, but in them the relative role played by vegetation has not always received sufficient attention. Mass movements associated with the rainstorm of June 1966 in Hong Kong were widespread and occurred under different types of vegetation. Previously there has been only general and indirect reference to mass movements in Hong Kong,[2] in works dealing primarily with other physical aspects of the area.

Mass movements during and following the severe rainstorm of June 1966 in Hong Kong were the most disastrous ever recorded in the area. Accompanied by floods, they resulted in a death toll, within a few days, of sixty-four, made more than 2500 homeless and forced over 8000 to be evacuated, apart from playing havoc with communications, isolating some areas and causing severe damage to property. The magnitude of the disaster stemmed basically from the fact that so many people live, out of sheer physical necessity, on and in front of steep slopes, especially in the twin cities of Victoria and Kowloon. While such a rainstorm may be considered a climatic accident and a rarity by local standards, less persistent downpours and less impressive mass movements are frequent in the wet season from April to September. Past events have shown that the cumulative effect of several of these minor mass movements at short intervals may be no less than that of a major movement once in a long period. The events of June 1966 in Hong Kong are also very relevant to studies of tropical geomorphology in general.

PHYSICAL SETTING

Hong Kong consists of a dissected upland rising to over 900 m (Fig. 1). Much of the former sedimentary and volcanic cover has been removed by erosion to expose widespread outcrops of granite (Fig. 2). Because of recent uplift, steep slopes abound; lowland of any appreciable extent is confined to an alluvial plain in the extreme north and north-west and to the narrow floors of some partially infilled coastal valleys. An analysis of slope gradients confirms that most of the land with gradients of less than 1 in 5 is in the northern and the north-western

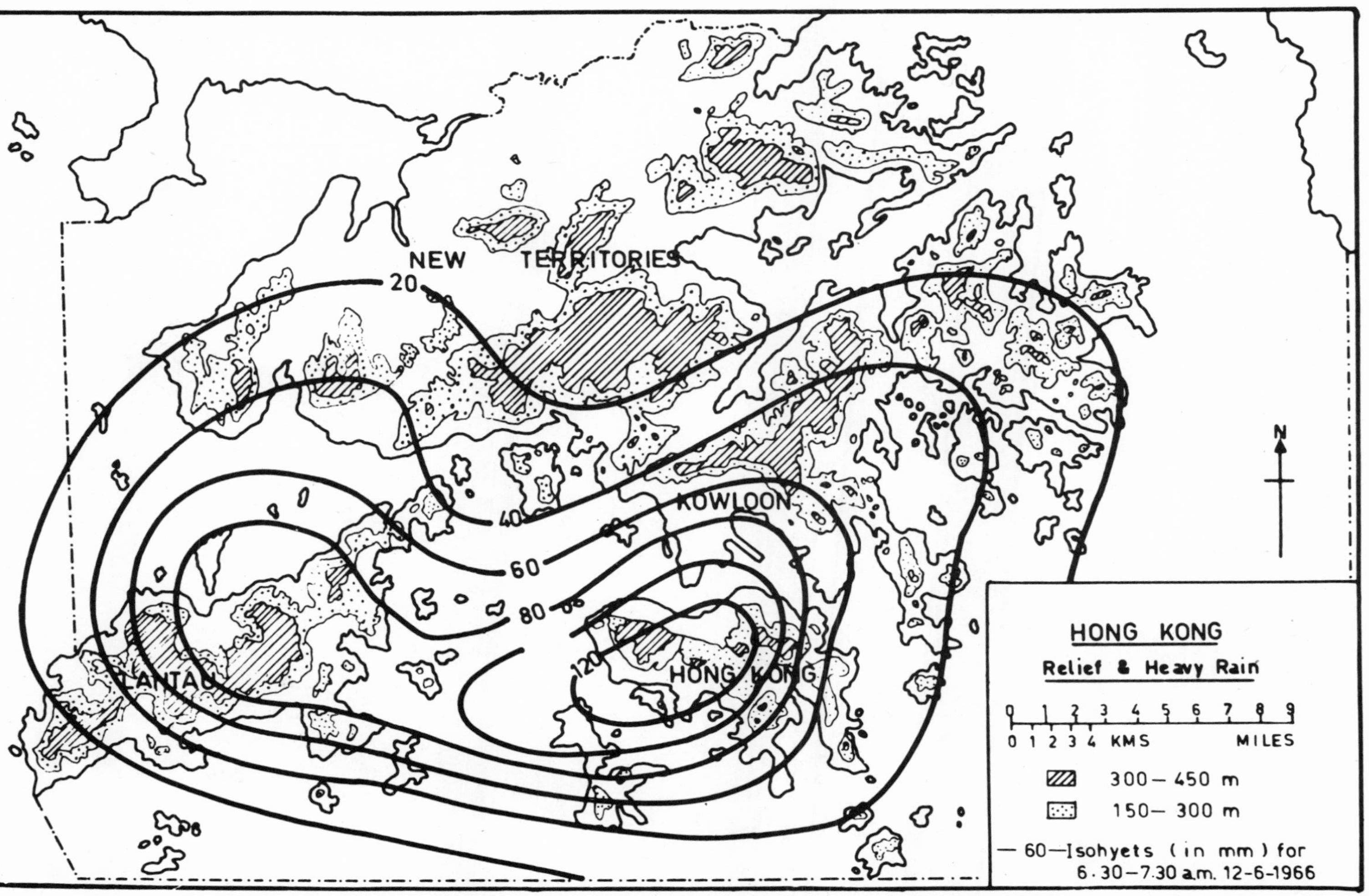

FIGURE 1. Relief of Hong Kong and distribution of heavy rain in the morning of 12 June 1966

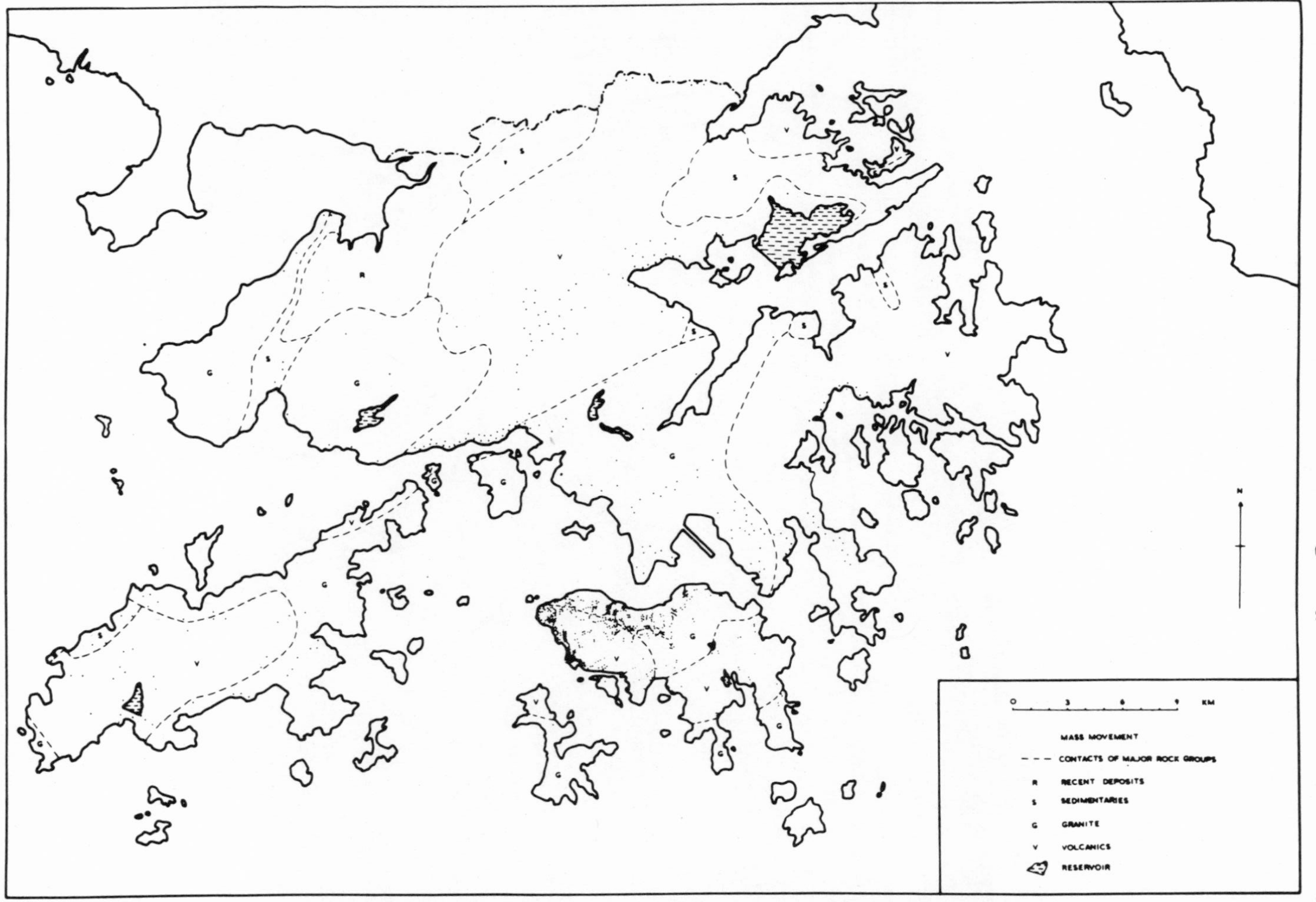

FIGURE 2. Distribution of mass movements in relation to major rock types, Hong Kong

parts, while much land, including some marginal land for agriculture and urban development, reaches gradients between 1 in 5 and 1 in 3. Steeper land with gradients up to 1 in 2 or more is also extensive.

Intensive weathering has taken place in a climate characterized by hot wet summers and cool dry winters. Weathered debris, moving by creep or other forms of slopewash, has modified the bedrock slope-forms. It often spreads out over the lower slopes at the contact between granite and volcanics. Around the harbour, for example, hills of weathered granite are often capped by the more resistant volcanics. The volcanic outcrop forms a steep, scarp-like upper slope overlooking the lower concave part built by slope-wash in the form of a fan. On some slopes, especially those in decomposed granite, gullying has occurred.

The mean annual rainfall of Hong Kong is 2168 mm but variations between 120 per cent and 45 per cent of the average amount have been recorded. The rain tends to be concentrated in the period from April to September (especially in the mornings), and over the hilly parts. Tropical cyclones which bring spells of bad weather with strong winds and heavy rain several times a year may account for 20 per cent of the annual rainfall.[3] Showers are usually heavy and frequent when tropical cyclones are centred to the west or north-west, but they never quite reach record intensities.[4] The most intense rainfall that occurs in Hong Kong is associated with thunderstorm clouds of great vertical extent. It is most prolonged when a trough of low pressure extends along the South China coast in June and August.

THE MASS MOVEMENTS

In June 1966, an active trough of low pressure persisted for an exceptionally long period along the South China coast. On the first few days of the month it migrated southward across Hong Kong and remained just to the south for several days. By 8 June it shifted northward but it moved south again on the 10th, so that on the following days until the 14th it was overhead at Hong Kong almost all the time. Then it moved north, returned and remained overhead at Hong Kong again on the 22nd and the 23rd before it disappeared. The trough thus crossed Hong Kong no less than five times and remained very near it or directly overhead frequently in the first half of the month. As a result, rain was recorded every day during the first 2 weeks, with a daily total well above 25 mm for several consecutive days during the period. Thus before the downpour of the 11th and 12th, a rainfall of 314 mm was already recorded for the month as compared with an average amount of 137 mm for the same period. Then in the 24 hours ending at noon on the 12th, a total of 401 mm of rain was recorded, this being equivalent to the normal rainfall for the whole month. The greatest fall occurred in the southern part of Hong Kong Island where 157 mm was recorded between 6.30 a.m. and 7.30 a.m. at Aberdeen. Figure 1 shows the isohyets for this period. Although in the afternoon of 12 June the rain slackened, the day ended with rainfall reaching ten to fifteen times its normal intensity in many parts of Hong Kong Island, Lantau Island and other parts of the New Territories. The bad weather, heavy cloud and intermittent rain persisted for the next few days, bringing the total for the first half of the year up to 1657 mm against an average of 963 mm.

The landslides largely started on 12 June and appeared to be localized in time and in place. They were concentrated in those hours immediately following the height of the rainstorm at 6.30–7.30 a.m. with the most disastrous occurrences around noon, especially on Hong Kong Island. By the afternoon, numerous movements were reported in other parts,

FIGURE 3. Landslips in a series, Pokfulam, Hong Kong Island

although the rain had already slackened, and on the days following until the last week of the month, minor movements and secondary falls of weathered debris took place.

The most disastrous and spectacular mass movements were generally large-scale and deep-seated landslips involving rotational shearing and slumping. They were accompanied by the emergence of much sub-surface water which also helped to erode the slopes below. The mass movement at Magazine Gap on Hong Kong Island was a case in point. Where several mass movements occurred together, a scalloped hillside with alternate depressions and shoulders developed (Fig. 3). Of a total of 702 movements identified, mapped and studied, 558 of them belonged to this type (Table I). The remaining 144 were but small surface washouts which, accompanied by water in sheets, included debris avalanches, boulder falls and rock slides. Where the area directly affected by the movement was small and weathered debris fell vertically downwards by gravity instead of fanning out, scars were seen to taper downwards and to hang loosely on hillsides. Many of the landslips and the washouts were associated with road sections and slopes artificially modified through construction and cultivation.

TABLE I

Number of mass movements

	Washouts	*Landslips*
Natural	26	187
Anthropogenic	118	371

METHOD OF STUDY

The study was based on morphometric analysis, photographic work and field survey. Vertical and oblique air photographs and ground photographs were used to compare the appearance of the sites before and after landslipping. In recording individual mass movements in the field, their associated rock type, weathered debris, slope gradient, vegetation

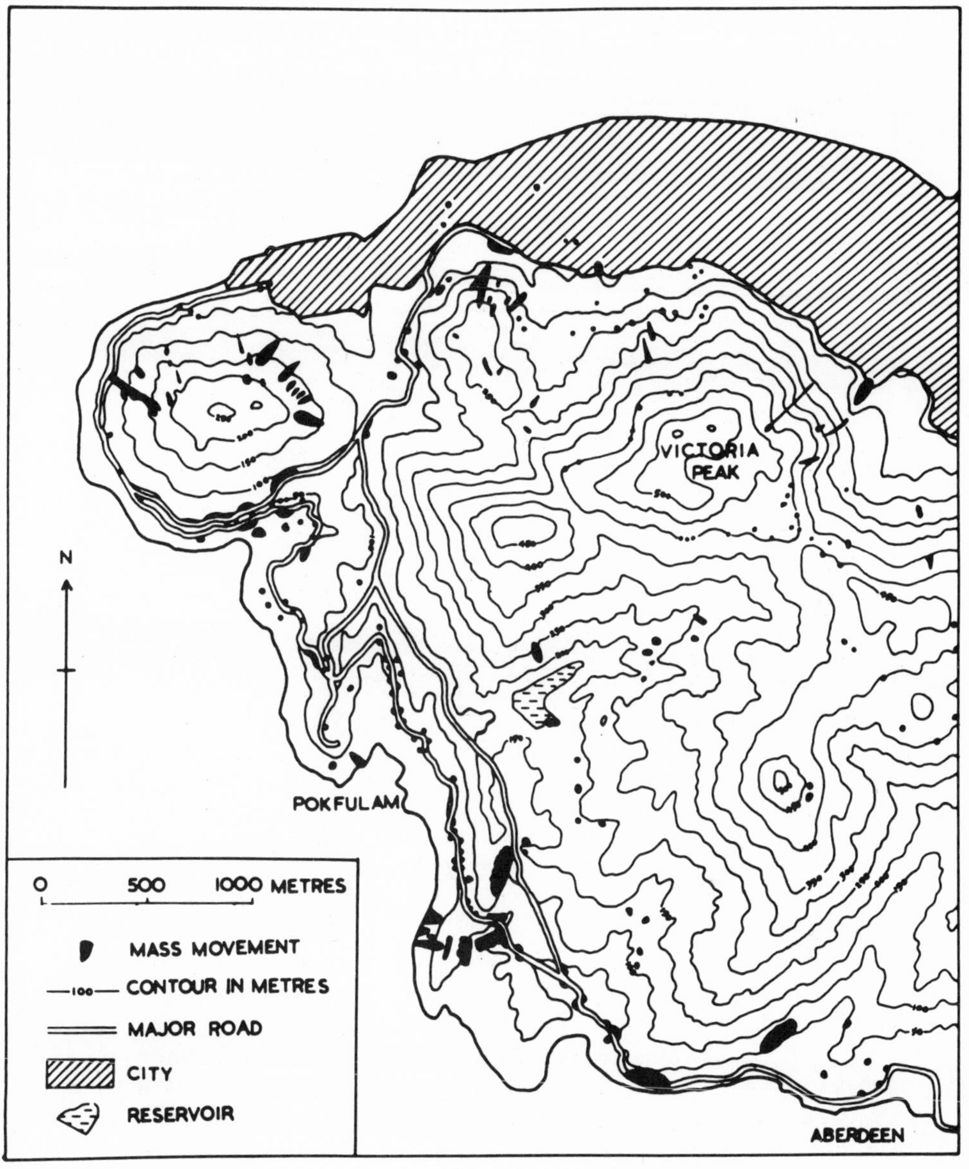

FIGURE 4. Distribution of mass movements, western part of Hong Kong Island

type and vegetation density were recorded.[5] In the course of mapping, heights of landslip scars were determined with an Aneroid surveying barometer. Slope angles were measured with an Abney level.

DISTRIBUTION OF LANDSLIPS AND WASHOUTS

The mass movements showed a marked concentration on Hong Kong Island which, with an area less than one-tenth of the total, recorded two-thirds of the mass movements (Fig. 2). They were especially numerous on the north-facing and the west-facing slopes in the western half of the island (Fig. 4). Elsewhere they were marked in the north-western part of

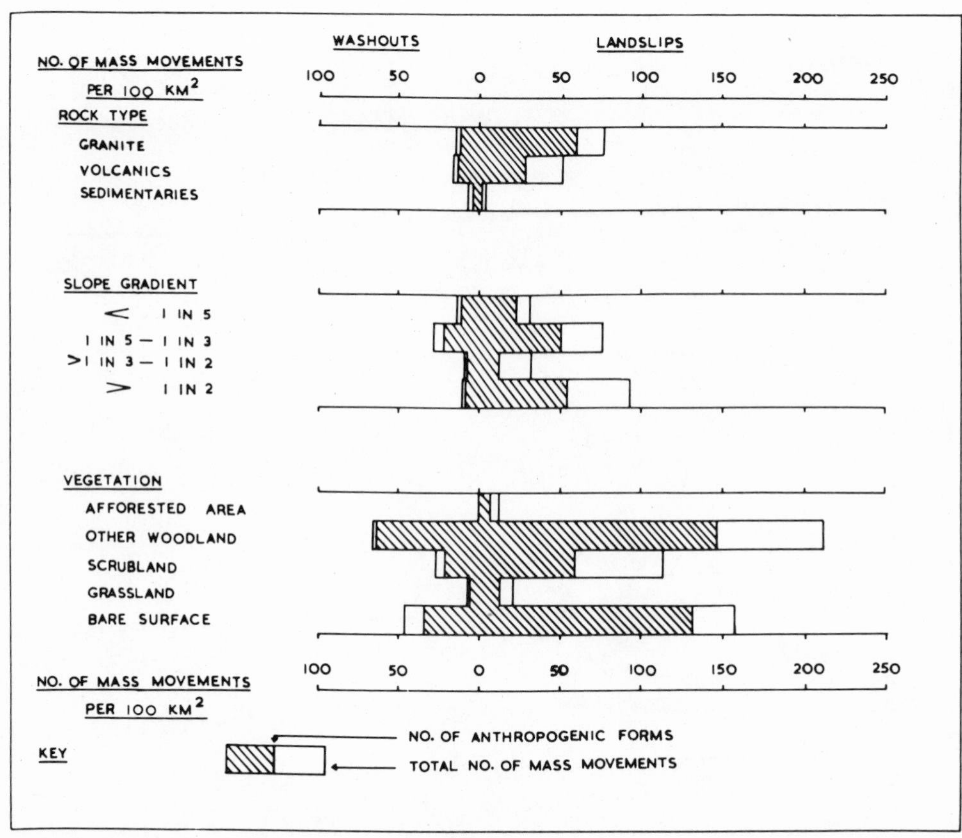

FIGURE 5. Frequency of mass movements in relation to major rock type, slope gradient and vegetation

Lantau Island, the north-western shore of Tolo Harbour and Tai Mo Shan, the highest peak (Fig. 2). While washouts were often associated with man-made features, hollowing out or undercutting built-up areas, landslips affected mainly slope deposits and the contact zones between major rock groups. These contact zones on Hong Kong Island happen to be located in the residential strip of the city of Victoria at mid-level.

The mass movements occurred in areas both with and without a vegetation cover. Detailed field mapping revealed that 34·8 per cent occurred in woodland, which was defined as land with a continuous cover of shrubs and trees over 2·5 m in height with interlocking canopies, although woodland covered only 8·4 per cent of the whole area. Similarly 36·5 per cent of the mass movements occurred on scrubland (a fairly continuous cover of shrubs and bushes from 0·3 m to 2·5 m in height) which covered 17·4 per cent of the land. The number of mass movements in afforested areas was 0·8 per cent of the total and forestry plantations covered 4·8 per cent of the land. Grassland (with grass and scrub generally 0·3 m high and covering 41·7 per cent of the whole area) was affected by only 16·8 per cent of the mass movements. On bare slopes, including badlands which often develop in granite, 11·1 per cent of the mass movements took place in an area amounting to 3·7 per cent of the land. The relative frequencies depicted in Figure 5 thus confirm that, of the various types of vegetation under consideration, woodland was affected by the greatest number of mass movements. This was followed by bare surfaces and scrubland. Grassland, with a comparatively thin cover of vegetation, was far behind in the relative frequency of mass movements. Whether the discrepancies in the distribution of the mass movements are statistically significant or not can be determined by the chi-square test on each type of mass movement and on all the mass movements taken together. Results of such tests, shown in Table II, indicate that in all cases there is a less than 0·1 per cent probability that the frequency

TABLE II

Chi-square tests

	Values of chi-square		
	Rock type	*Slope gradient*	*Vegetation*
Washouts			
Natural	52·3	28·2	32·2
Anthropogenic	4·7	21·0	207·7
Landslips			
Natural	67·2	68·3	170·7
Anthropogenic	63·5	95·1	410·0
All mass movements	70·2	141·9	688·1
Degrees of freedom	2	3	4

distribution could have arisen by chance. In other words, there is some preferential location of mass movements in relation to the various types of vegetation.

The mass movements were generally more deep-seated and disastrous in volcanic rocks than in granite. Although the number of overall mass movements *in relation to area* is greater in granite, the total number of natural landslips is greater in volcanic rocks. The fact that the latter generally support a better cover of natural vegetation than in the case of granite points to the association of these mass movements with the vegetation cover. The high rate of occurrence in volcanic rocks becomes even more significant in view of the fact that volcanic outcrops are the largest of the three major rock groups, covering 51·4 per cent of the land. The small number of mass movements in sedimentary rocks is less significant because their outcrops extend over only 8·8 per cent of the area. Results of chi-square tests (Table II) also point to a non-random distribution of the various types of mass movement with respect to rock-type with the exception of washouts related to artificial features.

Of the mass movements identified, 40·1 per cent occurred on slopes with gradients steeper than 1 in 2 which covered 26·1 per cent of the land. Smaller relative frequencies were associated with gradients of 1 in 5 to 1 in 3 (Fig. 5). However, the movements became distinctly fewer on gradients of 1 in 3 to 1 in 2 and gradients under 1 in 5. This shows that they were more numerous on the very steep slopes as well as on the gentle, concave slopes of wash and fan materials which generally support a vegetation cover. The differences in distribution with respect to angle of slope have also been found to be statistically significant (Table II).

Examination of air photographs confirmed that there was a substantial cover of vegetation before movements occurred. It also showed some cases in which adjacent slopes, with similar structure, slope profile and other local conditions were affected by mass movements even in those parts with a relatively thick vegetation cover. The evidence suggests that the long-term ability of vegetation to stabilize slopes must be questioned.

DISCUSSION

Works which ascribe slope failure to the combined effect of many factors sometimes ascribe a central role to vegetation in determining the rate and type of degradation and of slope form.[6] The changing landscape is said to be associated with the changing vegetation cover, but the manner in which this takes place and the part actually played by vegetation in the development of mass movements have still to be explained.

In Hong Kong, the shallow washouts of June 1966 represented the removal of materials already loosened and set in a critical state by the heavy downpours. The deep-seated movements were tantamount to slipping on slopes which had been structurally weakened, possibly through spontaneous liquefaction following a rapid rise in the water table during the prolonged downpour. The earth tremors recorded at noon on 12 June could hardly have acted as a trigger because of their low intensity and the fact that they were partly preceded by the mass movements. The timing of the mass movements on Hong Kong and Lantau Islands, evidently related to peaks in the unusual downpour of the morning of 12 June, emphasizes the effect of the abrupt increase in rainfall and indicates that the excessive water content reduced the effective shearing resistance of the ground. The abundant rain water also appears to have reduced the angle of repose of the weathered mantle on the slopes. Although the role of slope angle must not be unduly emphasized, as additional water could have served equally well to upset slope equilibrium by bringing about changes in frictional resistance and pore-water pressure, it certainly accounts for many mass movements related to artificial features. In this connection, the greater sand content in weathered granite than in volcanics is likely to have reduced liability to slumping by speeding the seepage of ground water and by increasing the friction angle of the weathered mantle, thus explaining partly the greater number of deep-seated landslips in areas of volcanic rocks.

Excessive water penetrating the weathered mantle thus upsets slope equilibrium. In this process vegetation makes a significant contribution by holding back any superficial movement of loose weathered particles owing to rainwash. This allows a thicker weathered mantle to develop; subsequently, it may thicken to such an extent that the slope becomes less stable. Long-term observations of the changing scars of past mass movements indicate that, where the vegetation cover was restored, subsequent recurrence of mass movements was largely confined to those parts with a particularly luxuriant vegetation cover. Thus many slopes at Tai O, made up largely of slope-wash materials from rock faces above, support and sustain a vegetation cover but have frequently been subjected to mass movements. In

June 1966, there was severe slipping of those parts where a vegetation cover had been restored after previous mass movements. Moreover, the vegetation cover also reduces run-off and encourages percolation, especially on a debris-laden slope. This in turn aids weathering; furthermore, in clay materials, the increased supply of ground water not only serves to diminish the cohesion of particles but also leads to alternate swelling and contraction of the clays with the absorption and release of moisture. The resultant shrinkage cracks and fissures not only render the formation more susceptible to shearing and crumbling, but also facilitate further penetration of rain water. When downpours and periods of dry weather alternate, these effects become most marked. This explains why in June 1966, many mass movements still occurred towards the end of the month and after a few dry and sunny days.

The character of the bedrock is also important in the percolation process. With a well-developed system of rectangular jointing in three sets, granite allows water to penetrate readily through it, leading to rotting and decomposition of the rock. It is often weathered to a depth of more than 60 m.[7] Although the weathering profiles of the volcanics show more variation, partly owing to lithological changes and partly to differences in jointing and other minor structural features, the rock also shows a tendency towards sub-surface wasting. The weathered mantle tends to thicken where two sets of jointing are moderately prominent. Its higher clay content allows better water retention and a better vegetation cover than in the case of granite, and this makes it even more liable to develop deep-seated mass movements.

CONCLUSIONS

A study of the mass movements shows that, although they were triggered off by weather anomalies, other factors affecting slope stability must also be considered. These factors include the long-term cumulative effects of weathering, sub-soil development and vegetation growth. Their combined effect may set the slope in a critical state so that, once the equilibrium is upset, rapid change ensues. In such a situation, the luxuriant vegetation cover and its rapid growth in a humid tropical environment can be misleading. Its presence often imparts to the slope it covers a temporary measure of stability; it serves to hold back creep, but in doing so it may set the stage for subsequent large-scale slope deformation. In Hong Kong, where some of the steep, vegetation-covered slopes provide sites for an important residential zone and a back stage to the congested city, over-reliance on the vegetation cover for stabilization of slopes may turn a mere accident in nature into a great man-made disaster.

ACKNOWLEDGEMENTS

The author thanks Professor D. J. Dwyer of the University of Hong Kong for advice and help with the preparation of this paper. He is also grateful to the Director of Public Works, the Director of the Royal Observatory and the Director of Agriculture and Fisheries, Hong Kong, for allowing him to consult records in their possession. The University of Hong Kong made a grant towards the cost of the illustrations.

NOTES

1. C. F. SHARPE, *Landslides and related phenomena* (1938)
2. S. G. DAVIS, 'Geological problems in relation to building sites and foundations in Hong Kong', *Proc. Engng Soc. Hong Kong* 8 (1955), 177–202; L. BERRY, 'Superficial deposits of the Hong Kong harbour area', *Hong Kong Univ. Engng J.* 21 (1957), 38–50; L. BERRY and B. P. RUXTON, 'The evolution of Hong Kong basin', *Ann. Geomorph.* 4 (1960), 97–115; P. LUMB, 'Effect of rainstorms on slope stability', *Symposium on Hong Kong soil* (1962), 73–87
3. L. STARBUCK, *A statistical survey of Hong Kong rainfall* (1950)
4. P. PETERSON, *The rainfall of Hong Kong* (1957)

5. The classification of vegetation follows that in *Land Utilization in Hong Kong* (Hong Kong Government 1967) and takes into consideration both density and type. For further relevant details see S. T. DUNN and W. J. TUTCHER, *Flora of Kwangtung and Hong Kong* (1912); *Check list of Hong Kong plants* (Hong Kong Government 1967)

6. F. W. FREISE, 'Erscheinungen des Erdfliessens in Tropenwaldes, Beobachtungen aus Brasilianischen Kustenwalden', *Z. Geomorph.* 9 (1935), 88; F. W. FREISE, 'Inselberge und Inselberg-landschaften im Granit und Gneissgebiete Brasiliens', *Z. Geomorph.* 10 (1938), 137–68; J. GIFFORD, 'Landslides on Exmoor', *Geography* 38 (1953), 9–17; L. C. KING, 'Canons of landscape evolution', *Bull. geol. Soc. Am.* 64 (1953), 721–51; P. H. NYE, 'Some effects of natural vegetation on the soils of West Africa and on their development under cultivation', *Proc. Abidjan Symp.* (1961), 59–67; R. COMMON, 'Slope failure and morphogenetic regions' in G. H. DURY (ed.), *Essays in geomorphology* (1966), 53–81

7. B. P. RUXTON and L. BERRY, 'Weathering in granite and associated erosional features in Hong Kong', *Bull. geol. Soc. Am.* 68 (1957), 1263–92

RÉSUMÉ. *Mouvements en masse associés avec l'orage de pluie en juin 1966 à Hong Kong.* Les mouvements en masse désastreux associés avec l'orage de pluie de 1966 à Hong Kong nous font remarquer la susceptibilité de pentes à la déformation sous les tropiques humides. Localement, la prédominance de roches ignées avec des joints bien developés facilite l'usé de la sous-surface par les intempéries et perte en masse. Les éboulements de terre se passaient dans des zones tant avec que sans une couverture de végétation. Leur distribution démontre qu'on n'a pas toujours éprouvé la capacité stabiliteuse de végétation. Il exige une réevaluation de la fonction de végétation dans les mouvements en masse.

FIG. 1. Relief de Hong Kong et distribution de forte pluie pendant le matin du 12 juin 1966
FIG. 2. Distribution de mouvements en masse relatif aux types majeurs de roches, Hong Kong
FIG. 3. Éboulements de terre dans une série, Pokfulam, île de Hong Kong
FIG. 4. Distribution de mouvements en masse, partie à l'ouest de l'île de Hong Kong
FIG. 5. Fréquence de mouvements en masse relatif aux types majeurs de roches, inclinaison de pentes et végétation

---

ZUSAMMENFASSUNG. *Massenbewegungen mit dem heftigen Regenguss von Juni 1966 in Hong Kong assoziert.* Die verheerende Massenbewegungen mit dem heftigen Regenguss von 1966 in Hong Kong assoziert lenken die Aufmerksamkeit auf die Empfänglichkeit der Steigungen für Formveränderung in den feuchtigen Tropen. Im Gebiet, das Vorwiegen der Eruptivfelsen mit gut entwickelten Querspalten erleichert die Verwitterung des Untertags und des Massenverschleiss. Die Erdrutsche und Bergstürze fanden sich statt bei Zonen beide mit und ohne einem Vegetationsbelag. Ihre Verteilung beweist, dass die stabilisierende Eigenschaft der Vegetation nicht immer gefühlt würde. Es erfordert eine Wiederabschätzung der Funktion von Vegetation in Massenbewegungen.

ABB. 1. Hochbild von Hong Kong und Verteilung heftiges Regengusses am Morgen von 12 Juni 1966
ABB. 2. Verteilung der Massenbewegungen in bezug auf Majorfelsentypen, Hong Kong
ABB. 3. Bergstürze in einer Serie, Pokfulam, Hong Kong Insel
ABB. 4. Verteilung der Massenbewegungen, Westlicher Teil von Hong Kong Insel
ABB. 5. Frequenz der Massenbewegungen in bezug auf Majorfelsentypen, Steigunggefälle und Vegetation

---

17

Reprinted from *Proc. Geol. Hazards and Public Problems Conf.*, Government Printing Office, Washington, D.C., 1969, pp. 283–295

SEVENTEEN YEARS OF RESPONSE BY THE CITY OF LOS ANGELES TO GEOLOGIC HAZARDS

Richard H. Jahns
Professor of Geology and Dean
School of Earth Sciences
Stanford University
Stanford, California

A short time ago I was talking on the telephone with a city official who has long dealt with elements of land development in Los Angeles. After we had touched on the subject of current academic problems, I asked him, "How would you like to be a university president these days? Beset on all sides, bucking the burgeoning budget, repeatedly threatened with reduced support unless certain dissidents are thrown off the campus, warned of serious legal and emotional repercussions if such is done, spending time and energy in responding to non-negotiable demands from people who claim immunity from normal rules of conduct because they are 'morally right,' listening to faculty opinion that is consistent only in covering the entire spectrum, and confronted by miscellaneous characters who demand immediate action on issues they have not carefully investigated but about which they feel strongly." There was a long pause at the other end of the line, then, "Well, friend, now you can see how it's been with us for the past seventeen years!" There is indeed the substance of truth in this implied parallel, for many people with contrasting interests and conflicting views have been involved in both situations. And even though the scenes and the problems have been quite different in most respects, basic complexity shows through as the common denominator.

Lest the title of these remarks become misleading, it should be pointed out that geologic hazards were not ignored in Los Angeles prior to 1952. Damaging floods, including especially severe ones in 1884, 1890, 1914, 1916, 1934, 1938, and 1943, have required periodic cleanup and repair within the city since early days of settlement. Nor have the unpleasant results of landsliding and other types of ground failure gone unnoticed over the years. And the Long Beach earthquake of March 1933, which caused serious loss of life along with widespread destruction and hardship, was an effective reminder of another, less frequent kind of geologic hazard. Along with direct responses to such unwanted occurrences have come increasingly effective measures for mitigating their effects. The County of Los Angeles, for example, has long been a leader in developing controls for flood runoff and the State of California a leader in establishing specifications for earthquake-resistant construction.

THE GRADING ORDINANCE OF 1952

It is in the context of prevention and control that the year 1952 was so important historically for the City of Los Angeles. The post-World War II period of increasing population and land development was then in full flower, and hillside terrain was being modified with heavy earth-moving equipment on a scale unknown in earlier times. The immediately preceding years had been relatively dry ones, but during the winter season of 1951-52 the heavens seemed to open up. One severe storm during the period January 13 - 18 yielded 7.5 inches of precipitation in downtown Los Angeles and substantially greater quantities in some of the adjacent hills, with results that were locally devastating. Fresh cuts and fills were scoured and deeply gullied, enormous volumes of rock, mud, and coarse debris were mobilized, and various mixtures of water and solid matter invaded lower areas where they clogged existing drainage facilities and occupied much settled land. An estimated quarter of a million cubic yards of debris was subsequently removed from city streets alone, and property damage amounted to approximately $7.5 million.

The citizenry, long-time residents and newcomers alike, were aroused by this sudden disaster and many of them demanded protective regulations for the development of hillside land. Fortunately, there was a man ready, able, and willing to accommodate them. Gilbert E. Morris, Superintendent of Building and Safety, responded very promptly--so promptly, indeed, that some observers suggested that this farsighted engineer must have had appropriate legislation in his coat pocket, ready for activation at the first promising opportunity! Within a short time Los Angeles adopted the Grading Ordinace of 1952, the first regulatory measure of its kind, and thereby assumed a pioneering role in controlling man's modification of natural urban terrain. In both its original and subsequently modified forms, this ordinance has been emulated by cities and counties in several parts of the State. The results have been salutary, but more on this later.

When regulatory measures of this kind are put into effect, the real complexities of the situation are soon thrust onto center stage. What is hillside terrain, and what are the significant distinctions between it and other kinds of ground? At first these basic questions were addressed somewhat tentatively, and an arbitrary identification of certain hillside areas was made. Control of grading in such areas was placed under the jurisdiction of a newly-established Grading Section in the Department of Building and Safety. Permits were required for cuts and fills, and provisions were made for inspection of projects in the field. The somewhat generalized ground rules, as set forth in the new ordinances, were based mainly upon then-current engineering practices of highway departments within the State. Numerous improvements in these rules have been made since 1952, some of them in response to knowledge rather painfully gained from the results of later severe rainstorms.

EARLY OPERATIONS OF THE GRADING SECTION

In the beginning, the city was confronted by the task of selecting and training a new group of specialists, the grading inspectors. This was done with surprising speed, and with results that were immediately and continuingly useful. By no means, however, was it a simple exercise! Through its inspectors, the Grading Section acted upon its responsibility for appraising the ground stability of hillside works; when a judgment of potential instability was made, the developer was required to obtain a report from one of several soil testing laboratories approved by the city. Further question as to whether a geological study should be required also was raised from time to time, but there was little early activity in this area. The question was understandably difficult for the field inspector, whose operational approach necessarily was that of an engineer.

Fortunately for all concerned, the Grading Section was headed by William E. Milburn, an able engineer with an unusual understanding of related geologic problems. He was aware during the early fifties of a need for useful geological input at many sites, but there was no geologist on his staff. Moreover, few practicing geologists in southern California were then engaged or experienced in detailed and penetrating site appraisals of the kinds appropriate to the complex natural conditions. And it was yet to be widely appreciated that the most firmly compacted fill is no more stable than the ground beneath it, the best engineered cut no more stable than the ground in back of its face.

The situation came into public focus via the customary disaster route, this time during a violent two-day rainstorm in January 1956. The resulting damage, some of it attributable to oversight or neglect of geologic factors, prompted the city to establish an ad hoc Geological Hazards Committee comprising specialists in several geologic and engineering fields. This group, in exploring the complex area within which developers and residents should operate in concert with planners, geologists, and engineers, fortified some of the Milburnian concepts that had received little earlier attention. Of special importance were the expressed views that geologic maps and sections often are basic necessities for recognition and appraisal of unstable or potentially unstable ground, and that the design engineer, the soils engineer, and the engineering geologist have a common stake in insuring safe modification of hillside terrain.

In a sense this marked another beginning that included a broadened attack on the problem of ground management and a corollary appearance of some new problems. From diverse sources came strongly worded suggestions that all land within the city should be classified according to general categories of "geologic risk," a kind of proposal that undeniably is attractive in principle. It has been revived from time to time during succeeding years, but thus far the Department of Building and Safety and its technical advisers have widely avoided this approach on the grounds that it is premature.

Within much of Los Angeles the interrelationships among geologic features, topography, and both surface and subsurface drainage are formidably complex, and they also tend to differ considerably from one another over surprisingly small areas. Translation of geologic knowledge into reliable estimates of risk for major parts of the city must await data and interpretations not yet at hand. Were a "hazards map" of Los Angeles to be prepared now rather than two or three decades hence, it would be necessarily generalized and of doubtful net value. Areas identified with relatively high risk almost certainly would include much ground that later detailed study would show to be quite safe, and, equally important, some extremely hazardous ground probably would be hidden away in areas identified with low degrees of risk. The city therefore has maintained a currently more realistic policy of concentrating on the case approach, i.e., requiring appraisals of individual properties, in terms of geologic factors respectively pertinent to them, as arrangements are being made for their development.

THE ENGINEERING GEOLOGISTS QUALIFICATION BOARD

Beginning in January 1956, the city required geologic reports prior to issuing grading permits for hillside tracts and, in some instances, individual hillside lots. Several restrictions also were added to the grading requirements during that year, but it was the call for geologic reports that precipitated a new set of operational difficulties. Within the Department of Building and Safety there was yet no geologist to review such reports and judge upon their quality and soundness of conclusions (if any!), nor were there effective means for distinguishing those geologists with competence in this rather challenging field. It soon became evident that most of the reports submitted were not fully responsive to geologic problems already recognized, inferred, or suspected by staff in what had by now become the Grading Division, in part because they were too general in scope, too preliminary in view, or too constrained geographically, and presumably in part for other kinds of reasons. In sum, the situation cried for early correction.

On February 10, 1958, the Department of Building and Safety established an Engineering Geologists Qualification Board. This group of engineers and geologists, appointed from outside the structure of city government, assumed responsibility for judging the qualifications of geologists, in terms of their respective training and experience, for submitting reports on private hillside land to be developed for residential or business purposes. Also involved was responsibility for evaluating the quality of some reports. Reaction from the geological fraternity was mixed, as might have been anticipated. Among the criticisms were scattered cries of "closed-shop tactics," "conflicts of interest," and "the blind leading the blind." Even more corrosively worded remarks were offered by some persons who failed to pass the Board's examination. Not a few applicants were puzzled by the expectation that they be familiar with the city's grading code and with the kinds of geologic features and processes pertinent to development of local hillside land. Despite the discomfiture and static, however, the roster of certified geologists grew to substantial size over the following years.

A few more words now about the reports submitted to the Grading Division, many of which also came to the attention of the Qualifications Board. Frankly, they ranged in length from one-page letters to short monographs, in flavor from pertinent to platitudinous, in style from woolly to cryptic, and in content from original to full-scale borrowings from the published record. Some included excellent maps and sections, others consisted of textual treatment only, and still others presented little more than photocopies of already published cartographic materials, generally on a scale too small to be useful. Some devoted much space to extended but not overly helpful discussions of geologic history, i.e., the "seas came in and the seas went out" approach, and many revealed no conclusions of value to the engineer or developer. Among those in which definite and potentially useful conclusions were reached, some also closed with statements disclaiming any legal--and presumably professional!--responsibility for either conclusions or attendant recommendations. In short, some of the reports were almost sparklingly good, some were awful, and too many simply did not meet the challenge of the job. Perhaps most alarming was the appreciable number of small-property reports that reflected investigations by men seemingly afflicted with tunnel vision; such treatments bespeak the disquieting notion that the geologist needn't look beyond the property line, even if a major fault or large landslide might well be near at hand!

Recognizing that the wide variations in coverage and quality of reports were partly ascribable to the lack of specified guidelines, the Qualifications Board prepared an outline of desired contents of geological reports submitted to the City of Los Angeles. Issued as a bulletin in May 1960, it was intended to serve as a general guide and checklist for those persons preparing and using the reports, rather than as a rigid framework of requirements. It was noted that certain geologic interpretations cannot be firm or complete, at least in advance of grading operations, but that the reviewer should expect full and clear presentation of all kinds of pertinent geologic data in order effectively to consider the interpretations and recommendations. Further, the Board reaffirmed the view that physical conditions differ markedly from place to place within the city, and hence that corresponding geologic studies can be expected to differ somewhat from one another in scope, length, and organization.

THE GRADING ORDINANCE OF 1963

The grading code of Los Angeles, with its increasingly stringent provisions, was noted with more than casual interest by public stewards elsewhere in the State. By 1962 it had served as the model for codes successively adopted by the Cities of Beverly Hills, Pasadena, Glendale, Burbank, San Francisco, and San Diego, and by the Counties of Los Angeles and Orange. Yet it was not wholly adequate, despite its growing reputation as the toughest set of grading regulations in the world. The repeated testings of experience demonstrated that some fundamental shortcomings remained to be dealt with, especially in the area of enforcement.

Overly generous contributions of rainfall came once again in February 1962, when 8.0 inches fell during a five-day period. As measured in terms of extent, severity, and monetary loss, damage was an order of magnitude less than that from the "milestone storm" of a decade before--and this despite the construction of more than 40,000 new homes during the intervening years. Nonetheless, the nature of the damage provided new insight into the desirability of additional regulations, and in 1963 a new Grading Ordinance was adopted. It incorporated all earlier elements of the code, and it tightened up the specifications for cut and fill slopes, compaction or fill materials, and provisions for surface drainage. Further, a highly significant resolution outlined additional responsibilities for the design civil engineer, soils engineer, and engineering geologist with respect to grading activities.

This resolution, adopted simultaneously with the new ordinance, called for periodic inspection during the course of the grading, and for final certification by the soils engineer that "he has inspected all cuts and fills and that in his opinion they meet the requirements of the design as governed by the requirements of stability as determined by the science of soil mechanics." Similarly, the geologist was directed to submit a report of his final inspection, certifying that "he has inspected the grading and that in his opinion all excavations are made in accordance with the design and are stable as determined by the science of engineering geology." Certification of an as-graded plan by the design civil engineer was specified as the final step toward insuring that originally approved intentions are properly translated into reality.

An accompanying resolution set forth new requirements for subsurface exploration by the soils engineer and engineering geologist at sites where ground stability would be lessened by proposed grading, or where any of several specified physical conditions are discovered, inferred, or projected. Guidelines were included, with closing statements that the exploratory work must be sufficient to support the findings, and that the "depth of exploration shall be adequate to reveal weaknesses in the soil or underlying bedrock which will affect the proposed grading." As clearly implied by these statements, the city was adding a highly important dimension to required understanding of ground conditions. This constituted the first formal response to the recurring problem of landsliding along surfaces below the levels of exploration ordinarily employed at that time.

In critical retrospect, the Department of Building and Safety can be credited with an impressive series of accomplishments during what could well be called a decade of learning. Most of the lessons from nature came as disagreeable fare, but it was ingested and absorbed gulp by gulp; doubtlessly, more gulps remain to be taken. And they will be taken in part by geologists, for the Department's staff now includes such scientists led by a man of unusual expertise. In their present form, the regulations are severe--too severe in the judgment of some. Yet there is adequate provision for appeal where conditions might seem to justify some relaxing of regulations. The land developer and his professional associates assuredly are confronted by a complex of onerous constraints, but these are hardly inappropriate when measured against the more basic constraints imposed by nature.

THE BUREAU OF STANDARDS

Though its role in the development of private land has received principal attention here, the Department of Building and Safety has not been alone in dealing with unstable ground in Los Angeles. The Department of Public Works, with responsibility for the design, construction, and maintenance of facilities on public property, also has been active in this area for many years. Some of the functions of its Bureau of Standards in effect have been complementary to those of the Grading Division, but these two units have operated according to philosophies, regulations, and procedures that have been developed independently. This understandably reflects a basic distinction between public and private land that underlies their respective responsibilities and administrations.

During the fifties the Bureau of Standards began to grapple with the task of controlling grading activities in more systematic ways. These efforts encountered essentially the same difficulties, complications, and frustrations as those noted earlier in the context of private land, but the Bureau did have some operational advantages. It was less in the public eye than the Grading Division and hence was able to establish new rules and procedures under somewhat lesser pressures. Nor was it making so many judgments on work to be done at the expense of private individuals and organizations. In addition, its staff included geologists at an early stage, which permitted a more direct approach to many of the problems encountered.

The Department of Public Works also is responsible for certain kinds of surveying and mapping, which opened the way for a pilot project of special interest. Early in 1962, the Bureau of Standards began to prepare geologic maps of about 75 square miles of the Santa Monica Mountains, in part through compilation of existing data and in part from the results of new field work. The products of this effort, the first of its kind for one of the City's departments, should be continuingly useful. The maps already demonstrate how unrealistic it would be if one area or one geologic formation were identified as uniformly hazardous or uniformly free from hazard, thereby providing additional support for an already-noted basic policy of the Department of Building and Safety.

A distinction is readily drawn between public and private property, and hence between the respective jurisdictions of Public Works and Building and Safety as long-established city agencies. Nonetheless, some overlap in their operations has been unavoidable, and properly so. Considerations of ground stability do not necessarily heed boundaries between private lots and dedicated streets or other public easements. Inevitably, therefore, some duplication of effort in applying and enforcing their ground rules has characterized the work of these agencies. In many instances the land developer has been confronted by contrasting sets of standards, styles of procedure, and kinds of inspection, with attendant delays and confusion. Toward resolution of such difficulties, which became increasingly serious after adoption of the Grading Ordinance of 1963, the City Council took specific action in March 1966. The Departments of Public Works and Building and Safety were directed to effect improvements in their communication, and to cooperate actively in situations of mutual interest and concern. Competition, duplication, and conflict appear to have lessened considerably during the past three years, a fortunate trend in the light of the formidable problems with which these departments must contend.

INFLUENCE OF OTHER ORGANIZATIONS

The response of Los Angeles to geologic hazards, as measured by regulatory measures and their enforcement, hardly has been arbitrary or provincial. From the beginning, the pattern instead has been one of seeking outside counsel and assessing the results of experience elsewhere. In formulating and improving the grading code, advice and recommendations from the American Society of Civil Engineers have proved to be especially helpful over a long period of time. Useful input also has been repeatedly drawn from other professional groups, from builders and homeowners associations, from ad hoc committees, and from individual engineers, geologists, land developers, builders, and additional interested citizens. The formal response to date thus amounts to a distillation of ideas, data, and interpretations from many sources.

The Association of Engineering Geologists, Southern California Section, has actively contributed to improved understanding of the physical environment, and to improved methods for dealing with it. For example, the Building Codes Committee of this organization devoted four years of effort to developing a composite code that could be used as a model for establishing or improving grading regulations, and versions of this model have been adopted by several cities since it appeared in 1964 as Chapter 70 of the Uniform Building Code. It outlines the contrasting kinds of professional supervision needed in connection with grading activities, defines the types of professionals that should be involved, and spells out the respective responsibilities of these people.

In July 1965, Mayor Sam Yorty requested the American Institute of Professional Geologists to appoint a special committee charged with a study of how "the City of Los Angeles may with the best prospects of success protect its residents from risks caused by geologic hazards," and how City government "can ensure the competent practice of geology within this city where the public interest is at stake." The seven geologists who served on this committee focused their attention upon the practice of geology as applied to private and public development of land within the city, rather than upon identification and analysis of geologic hazards per se. Their report, submitted in August 1966, included a review of the City's role in regulating surface development of land in consonance with geologic factors, a summary of criticisms that had been directed from many different sources toward various aspects of the City's operations in this area, and a general conclusion that future problems lay less with the soundly conceived Grading Code than with some of the procedures under which it was being applied.

Few persons disagreed in principle with this conclusion or with others concerning general areas of professional and organizational responsibility, additional staff in the Departments of Public Works and Building and Safety, further improvement in working relationships among geologists and engineers, streamlining and coordinating some of the City's work in reviewing land-development plans and enforcing regulations, and desirability of better informing the public about the local geologic environment. A stir, however, was caused by some of the specific recommendations, notably those that called for shifts of responsibilities within City government and ultimate dissolving of the Engineering Geologists Qualification Board in favor of statewide certification or registration of geologists. Assignment of geological responsibilities to one organizational unit was specially recommended and was subsequently argued at length. Such a move finally was judged to be impracticable, but lively public discussion of the possibility may have had beneficial effects on relationships among the geological activities of different City departments. And now that State registration of geologists has become a reality in 1969, it seems likely that the Engineering Geologists Qualifications Board at least will be faced by fewer challenges than have come its way in the past.

During the period 1965 - 1967 another special committee devoted much effort to a searching study of the landslide problem in Los Angeles. Gross sliding had occurred repeatedly in several parts of the city, with results ranging from bothersome to devastating, and the opinions of critical observers differed widely as to whether location and timing of such activities could be predicted. Public concern became widespread in June 1965, when a major ground failure in the Pacific Palisades area became so serious that it led to official proclamation of a state of disaster by Governor Edmund Brown. It also prompted Mayor Yorty to order the formation of what soon became known as The Mayor's ad hoc Landslide Committee. This group had an extraordinarily broad base that included numerous representatives of the professions, industry, homeowners associations, and City government.

Over a period of many months the committee members focused their attention upon technical, financial, and legislative aspects of the problem. Results of their work are embodied in a report, issued as a thick volume in March 1967, that could be reviewed with real profit by every citizen and prospective citizen of Los Angeles. It qualifies as a primer on landslides and related phenomena, and it includes excellent brief descriptions of several major slides within the city. Also provided are discussions of factors that cause landslides, procedures for recognizing potentially unstable ground and forestalling failure, regulations and procedures employed by the city in control of grading operations, methods used in repairing landslides and means for financing repairs, and the troublesome problem of landslide insurance. Thoughtful recommendations were made in areas of administration, the grading code, maintenance of records, improving the safety of hillside development, repair of landslides, fixing of responsibility for landslides, and landslide insurance. To borrow from a prediction made by the Committee Chairman, actions based on these recommendations should be expected to "advance the orderly, stable development of the hillside areas of the City, correct existing scarred areas, and prevent new landslides in some of the already developed areas."

The need for upgrading basic information on Los Angeles geology has not gone unnoticed by other organizations. The United States Geological Survey, for example, has contributed superbly detailed geologic maps of ground in the Pacific Palisades and Baldwin Hills areas during recent years. The California Division of Mines and Geology has been engaged in similar activities elsewhere in hillside terrain and currently is working with the city under a cooperative program. And the local universities, in addition to training increasing numbers of people qualified for encounters with complex geological problems, have been adding to the information base through the mapping programs of faculty and graduate students.

Finally, a special acknowledgment is appropriate for that large number of persons who, acting as concerned individuals, have participated in the "seventeen years of response." Some have served the city in a direct and formal way as consultants or board members. The Department of Building and Safety, for example, has long relied upon the judgment of such people on its Engineering Geologists Qualification Board and Board of Grading Consultants. Others have served less formally but with great effectiveness in a host of ways. The number of opportunists seeking little but personal advancement in times of trouble and confusion has been remarkably low, the number of unselfish contributors satisfyingly high.

PAST AND FUTURE RESULTS

The foregoing historical summary relates to the fundamental problem of distinguishing the naturally safe locality from the naturally unsafe one, and of identifying those proposed actions of man that could convert a naturally safe locality into an unsafe one. How far the struggles of the past seventeen years have led toward solution of this problem in Los Angeles is not easily judged, as efforts have been aimed primarily at protection and prevention.

Most experts nonetheless would agree with the conclusion of the American Institute of Professional Geologists ad hoc committee that a very large number of occurrences of ground failure has been forestalled, even in the face of rapidly increasing development of hillside terrain.

Since adoption of the Grading Ordinance of 1952, more than 60,000 hillside sites have been graded for residential construction within the city's boundaries. During the same period of time fewer than 50 dwellings were totally destroyed because of unstable ground, and more than half of these either were built prior to 1952 or were built on land that was graded prior to 1952. Damage due to erosion, flood waters, flood debris, and more localized ground failure has been far more extensive and costly than destruction during the past seventeen years, but unquestionably it has amounted to only a small fraction of what could have been expected in the absence of grading controls progressively imposed by the city.

The accompanying table provides some indication of progress that has been made. Effects of the 1952 rainstorm on a city essentially unprotected by grading regulations stand in sharp contrast to those of the major storms of 1956 and 1962, which occurred after such regulations had been established. Even if the indicated estimates of damage are regarded as no more than first approximations, the differences are impressive. The extremely severe pair of storms in January 1969 not surprisingly inflicted a somewhat higher order of misery, but here it is interesting to note that structural and interior damage to buildings was only a fraction of that accompanying the lesser storm of 1952.

The disquieting levels of exterior property damage in January 1969, which were increased by additional rainfall during the following month, in large part reflected countless "skin failures" on cut and fill slopes. Scab-like masses of topsoil and immediately underlying materials all too commonly peeled away such slopes and migrated downward onto adjacent settled property. These shallow failures pointed up the need for still more attention to slope compacting, planting, and drainage. Perhaps there is need to re-examine the specifications for slope planting, and certainly the individual property owner must consider more carefully the cumulative effects of his own landscaping and maintenance activities.

The heavy storms early in 1969 could well be a foretaste of things to come, if long-term trends in past rainfall are continued into the future. We tend to become preoccupied with the record of individual storms and individual years, whereas a scrutiny of shifts between lengthy periods of accumulating rainfall deficit and periods of accumulating rainfall surplus can be much more revealing. On this score, records of precipitation in southern California during the past century in effect have been extended back in time by means of tree-ring studies, with results that demonstrate a cyclic pattern over many centuries. During the most recent five and one-half centuries, the average length of dry periods has been 16 years and that of wet periods 13 years.

The latest dry sequence, which began in 1945 as a background for man's tearing away with new vigor at Los Angeles ground, was a relatively long one interrupted by only four years of above-average moisture. Yet a shift to prevailingly wetter conditions was indicated by the record of preceding climatic cycles. This shift evidently began about four years ago, but early stages of the new wet sequence have been partly masked by one very dry year and by another of about average precipitation. Rainfall during the past winter season of 1968-69, however, increases the immediate credibility of a lengthy wet period! We probably can anticipate a time of accumulating moisture surplus lasting at least into the mid-seventies, and with it additional storms of unusual severity.

Any upswing in the cyclic moisture curve inescapably promotes increased mobility of the terrain. The grading code of Los Angeles thus is almost certain to be further tested in many ways, not only by individual rainstorms but also by the more subtle long-term influences of wet-period conditions on works built under dry-period conditions. Too, it should not be forgotten that during the past seventeen years the city's ground has not been shaken by a major earthquake. That some of nature's other warnings during this same period did not go unheeded will prove to be increasingly fortunate.

IV
Landscape Abuse

Editor's Comments on Papers 18 Through 25

The twentieth-century city has created an unusual stress on the natural land–water ecosystem, and problems have become alarmingly magnified during the second half of the century. In earlier parts of this volume the particular problems of urban floodplains and hillslopes were examined. The purpose of this part is to emphasize those aspects of man's degradation of the urban environment that were not previously covered in detail. Five additional classes of terrain destruction will now be analyzed, including urban sprawl, hydrologic system distortion, derelict land, waste disposal, and coastal modification. These features of man's molestation of the landscape are closely related and in general reflect a vastly changed living style, which was ushered onto the scene in the 1900s.

The principal reasons for the physical deterioration of lands in urbanized areas are related to cultural causes and technological changes. These two factors have often reinforced each other and by their combination have vastly accelerated urban geomorphic processes. The impact of new ideas in the realm of the socioeconomic–political sector has profoundly influenced patterns of living, which have often had a detrimental effect on the environment. By the early 1900s there had begun an exodus from rural regions to the city where there were more jobs, comforts, facilities, entertainment, and action. The old adage applies, "How do you keep them down on the farm after they have seen Paris?" Of course, it was the new technology that was making this possible, such as motorized farm equipment and the development of new fertilizers that allowed fewer farmers to grow more produce. Several minirevolutions were also occurring in the cities. The automobile and the accompanying highway networks made possible the commuter, who could now forsake his place in the inner city, move to the fringes, and consequently set in motion the phenomenon of urban sprawl. The greatly increased use of concrete and the new wonder material asphalt "blacktop" caused cities to become paved over, thus altering the hydrologic regimes. (It is interesting that petroleum products made possible both cars and roads.) The development of radio and television, when coupled with other communication media such as newspapers and magazines, fostered new horizons for advertisers to control the buying habits of a nation. The

"Madison-Avenue Era" was ushered in and the public was deluged with clever ads that extolled the virtues of "keeping up with the Jones," and the imagined necessity of owning two cars and every other contrivance imaginable. A planned obsolescence program by manufacturers, plus the advent of the throw-away concept—because of clever, but wasteful, packaging in hard-to-destroy containers—has created a massive disposal problem for the discarded items of modern civilization. Furthermore, the prodigious amounts of energy necessary to run the wheels of industry and the modern home are rapidly exhausting nonrenewable resources. Finally, a somewhat insidious attitude has prevailed in many quarters, which view nature as an enemy and antagonist that must be "controlled." This battle against nature has been strenuously waged in many segments of society (see, for example, Corps of Engineers, 1964), and only recently has there been any attempt at moderation and to perceive nature in the total ecological setting with a will to accommodate and work with her (see Glacken, 1970). This complex array of factors had produced by 1974 a startling group of statistics, which included (1) a severe energy crisis and shortage necessitating fuel cutbacks of more than 15 percent, (2) consumption of new lands for cities exceeding 1 million acres per year, (3) production of solid urban wastes that annually costs more than $4.5 billion to process, and (4) erosion–sedimentation rates in developing areas that are more than 1,000 times greater than natural rates.

The paucity of publications on these subjects prior to the 1950s indicates both a lack of general awareness of the emerging physical problems of cities and that up until then they had not reached alarming proportions. An interesting jargon has been developed as descriptive of some of these phenomena. The haphazard and random development that heralds urban sprawl (a new concept in itself) has yielded such terms as "slurbs" instead of suburb, and McHarg comments that, instead of most cities having greenbelts, they have "greed belts." California is often cited as the epitomy of a desecrated environment, and other areas that suffer from the same stigma are referred to as "californicated."

> The cradle of slurban civilization is Los Angeles, California, but its offspring have found congenial soil in the New York region and elsewhere (Little, 1968, p. 12).

Urban Sprawl

The stage was set for the topic of urban sprawl in Part I, where the rapid conversion of rural lands into nonagrarian use was discussed. The environs of cities are gobbling up land as if there will be no tomorrow. Many people seem to be heeding the comments of Will Rogers who said "Buy land. They ain't making any more of it." Although land prices continue to rise, there seems to be a never-ending list of buyers for new real estate near cities. In a single year, 1972, property values in the Tokyo area, Japan, increased 30 percent, and prices for raw acreage outside Munich, Germany, have risen 900-fold since 1953. Land prices continue to escalate throughout the world at rates that are much in excess of standard increases caused by inflation. The housing shortage after World War II was instrumental in providing industry with a huge potential for the development of new residential areas. The Levittowns are the typical example of this type construction, such as on Long Island (1947) and in Pennsylvania (1951) and New Jersey (1958). Here entire new towns mushroomed overnight. In addition there were many smaller housing tracts and more isolated homes that were built in contiguous areas, until there was an entire agglomeration of units in all sizes and descriptions. This was the representative suburbia, also called the rural – urban fringe, until the term "urban sprawl" started to be used in the late 1950s.

> In terms of rapid population growth the outstanding area of the metropolitan region is not the dominant central city nor the satellite suburb but the unincorporated countryside. In forty-three of the largest metropolitan districts, the unincorporated area increased 14.5 times more rapidly than the central cities during the priod of 1930 to 1940 and 9.5 times faster than the incorporated suburbs. During the 1930's the rate of suburban growth was actually not as much as during the 1920's. In the case of the Standard Metropolitan Areas, the central cities increased 13 per cent between 1940 and 1950 as compared with a 34.7 per cent increase of population in the outlying areas. Population residing outside these metropolitan areas increased by only 5.7 per cent during this period (Martin, 1953, p. 3)

Martin calls this area of unmeasured forces and blurred or obscured patterns the rural–urban fringe. The development of these initially small communities detached from but dependent upon the larger city is new only as far as transportation facilities (if any) are new. Such communities often function as a dormitory or bedroom for the city. The U.S. urban – rural fringe population of 157 cities of more than 50,000 inhabitants in 1950 was about 7,900,000, not including those in incorporated places of 2,500 or more.

William H. Whyte's abridged comments are very properly reproduced for this section inasmuch as he was instrumental in popularizing the concept of urban sprawl. He was assistant managing editor of *Fortune* magazine in the 1950s when a series of articles was produced on problems in the suburbs and, later, on urban areas. Whyte is also the author of several books, including *Is Anybody Listening, The Organization Man,* and *The Last Frontier.* He is currently a freelance writer. The second article on urban sprawl, by Gary A. Soucie, illustrates that even desert areas are not free from this phenomenon. Mr. Soucie has been associated with various conservation groups for the past several years and is now a freelance writer and field editor of *Audubon*, the magazine of the National Audubon Society.

Urban sprawl is the rapid expansion of suburban development without complete planning for the optimum control and utilization of water and associated land resources. It is invariably haphazard and random without concerted concern or attempt at regional management with zoning ordinances that consider natural processes. Commonly, urban sprawl consumes seven times the area of land as compared to planned communities.

> . . . in the 1960's in many, if not most, large American cities, the city heart had deteriorated, and the core city was characterized by deteriorating housing or slum conditions in which minority ethnic groups were crowded. The metropolitan edge had deteriorated by the unplanned spread of suburbs, most of which offered a minimum of environmental amenities; by the spread of unplanned highway strip towns; and by a fringe area, neither farm nor city, but of neglected land in transition from one state to another (Dasmann, 1968, p. 300).

> Ringing every city is a belt, ten, twenty miles or more wide — chaotic, undisciplined sprawl . . . [whereas] cities can consume less open space, or have more room for parks . . . [and] have some grip on their future, the flung out suburban jurisdictions are a crazy patchwork of microgovernments. Washington Governor Daniel Evans wonders how anything gets done in King County, the largest district in his state containing Seattle when it includes over one thousand units of local rule. He calls it an "ill-disguised form of government by legal anarchy." And a study of metropolitan areas has noted that King County is not unusual: Chicago's Cook County has 1,113 localities; Philadelphia, 871; Pittsburgh, 704; and New York, 551.

> Major obstacles, then, to land use planning in the suburbs are built into its very structure. The failure of planning is perhaps most obvious here because, unlike cities, these outskirts have plenty of natural, undeveloped land remaining to be ruined. It is not a question of restoring or repairing misused environments. Frantic and random growth into these lovely places trickles away unchecked, out of control. Land speculation is one result (Saltonstall, 1972, p. 154).

Many cities could be used as examples of urban sprawl, but the classic cases occur in southern California and are described by Nelson (1959) in an excellent paper on the spread of an artificial landscape. The prime example is the Los Angeles metroplitan area where in 1972 one third of the entire city area was devoted to sustaining vehicles—highways, parking lots, sales and maintenance shops, and the like. The automobile has become the main villain in urban areas, causing them to become so diffuse and to consume three times as much land as was required in city areas in the 1920s.

> . . . the rich potato farm lands of Nassau County, just beyond the eastern limits of New York City, have been transformed by tract houses, shopping centers, neon strips and drive-ins. Today the county is 96% fully developed, and the old distinctions between town and country are completely blurred in the semiurban mess (*Time*, eds., 1973, p. 95.

Urban sprawl is generally considered to be detrimental for a great variety of reasons (see Advisory Committee on Intergovernmental Relations, 1968). The leapfrogging technique over the countryside destroys natural open space; urban sprawl causes upsets in hydrologic patterns, with accompanying increases in floods, erosion, and sedimentation; it initiates higher costs for public service, sewer, and water lines; and frequently it destroys any possibility for the planned construction of an efficient and economic mass-transit system.

Clawson (1962) summarizes the case against sprawl by pointing out:

> (1) A sprawled or discontinuous urban development is more costly and less efficient than a compact one. . . . (2) Sprawl is unesthetic and unattractive. (3) Sprawl is wasteful of land since the intervening land is not specifically used for any purpose. (4) Land speculation is unproductive, absorbing public gains. . . . (5) It is inequitable to allow a system in which the new land occupier is required to shoulder such a heavy burden of capital charges or debt merely for its size costs—costs which in large part are unnecassary and avoidable (p. 108)

It must be pointed out, however, that other writers indicate sprawl may be a form of normal growth that occurs at a particular point in time. Such "scatterization" may actually provide flexibility in urban development and encourage efficient adaptation to change. It is argued that uniform compactness of development ". . . should no longer [be] . . . accepted unquestioningly as a planning ideal and scatter . . . no longer categorically rejected as a device of the devil" (Lessinger, 1962, p. 159). In addition, McBride and Clawson (1970) show the caution that must be used in making too many generalizations about urbanized areas. They examine three common notions which seem to have become firmly entrenched in many people's mind and show that there is another side: (1) the concept, especially popularized and expounded by Gottman, that U.S. metropolitan areas on both coasts and around the Great Lakes are growing together and little opportunity is left for introducing order in the chaos, (2) that farmers are being pushed off the land by a few large home builders, who call all the shots, and (3) that local officials play a passive role in the process because of the limits of local governments. For example, in Montgomery County in the Washington, D.C., metropolitan area, they show that 81 percent of the land is classified as "vacant, forest, and agriculture," and in Prince Georges County, 77 percent, in Fairfax County, 69 percent is classified as "vacant."

Several paradoxes occur within residential areas adjacent to cities. For example, Amato (1969) showed how the twentieth-century outward migration of the elites from Bogota, Colombia, was not haphazard or scattered, but willful and purposeful. They settled in areas of generally more favorable environmental conditions — at higher elevations, in areas with better climate, higher soil fertility, greener areas, and best served by transportation and other service facilities.

> The elite residential areas are comparably less humid, cloudy, and damp. Moreover, the areas of elite residences are away from low lands and areas subject to flooding. They are located at generally higher elevations near the eastern mountain ranges bordering the city. The preferred elite locations also correlate closely with superior edaphic conditions. They lie in the direction of the rich farm lands and away from barren areas. . . . Not only

> have they influenced the patterns of land use development in the city through their own residential actions, but they have further reinforced this trend in Bogota by the systematic exclusion of other groups through the passage of exclusive zoning and housing ordinances and regulations (p. 99).

His findings reinforce earlier work done in 1939 by H. Hoyt in American cities. In outlying districts of cities where high developmental costs exist because of rugged or difficult terrain, there may be a bimodal distribution of income types—either rich, because only they can afford to pay for the appropriate and required services, or poor because they haven't money to pay for better-type land.

Hydrologic System Distortion

Man's defacement and scarification of terrain during urbanization profoundly affects all aspects of surface runoff. Since this is such a vital and all-pervasive topic, certain components are included elsewhere in this volume. Additional information will now be provided concerning the role that urban sprawl and construction play in amplifying morphologic disfigurement of the watershed. All aspects of this system need consideration — floods, erosion, sedimentation, channel form, and stream recharge. For example, in studying the effects of urban sprawl on flooding in southern California, Rantz (1970) points out:

> The floods of January 1969 in south-coastal California provide a timely example of the effect of urban sprawl on flood damage. Despite recordbreaking, or near recordbreaking, stream discharges, damage was minimal in the older developed areas that are protected against inundation and debris damage by carefully planned flood-control facilities, including debris basins and flood-conveyance channels. By contrast, heavy damage occurred in areas of more recent urban sprawl where the hazards of inundation and debris or landslide damage have not been taken into consideration, and where the improvements and development of drainage or flood-control facilities have not kept pace with expanding urbanization (p. 1).

He further shows that most of the 92 persons killed and $62 million in damages were localized where urban sprawl was not matched with zoning or development plans that prohibited occupance of lands in the hazard zones. The peak discharges occurred in areas where natural plant cover had been destroyed and where slopes had been undercut by grading during development.

Johnson and Sayre (1973) provide data for Houston that relates flood severity to urbanization, and publications by Robinson (1973a, 1973b, and 1973c) show increases in flooding incidence in New York due to occupance of high-risk localities. For example, 260 or 79 percent of the 330 communities with population greater than 2,500 have flood and drainage problems because of building on and adjacent to floodplains. Flooding in the Rock Creek drainage of suburban Washington, D.C., has been greatly aggravated because less than 27 miles remain today of the 63 miles of natural stream channels present in 1913. In one of the earliest analyses of urban growth and water regimen, Savini and Kammerer (1961) discuss a wide range of effects, which include floods and drainage, erosion, sedimentation, channel geometry, and subsidence.

> As a city or residential community builds, much of the cover of natural vegetation is removed, numerous excavations are made, natural drainage is restricted and eliminated entirely in many places, roads and streets are cut across the natural drainage patterns, and the biological balance within the soil is disrupted, causing the natural erosion processes to be accelerated, especially during periods of construction.
>
> Appraised in terms of general damage, 4 of the most severe floods in the Chartiers Creek Valley (Pa.) have occurred within the past 15 years. The severity of these floods may be attributed, in part, to heavy residential development in sections of the watershed (pp. 34–35).

Of course, urbanization has had similar effects in other countries, such as Japan. Tokyo is one of the most densely populated cities of the world. The Syakuzii River flows on a broad plain in the newly developed communities of Tanasitown, Hoya Town, Itabasi-Ku, and Neirima-Ku. Prior to urbanization the catchment area was primarily rural with only scattered houses dotting the countryside. Since 1958 population growth in this area has greatly accelerated, and damaging floods have occurred where flooding had previously been rare. The Department of Public Works Institute, Ministry of Construction, in Tokyo made studies of the flooding and concluded that damages had been the result of the impervious ground caused by urban development, which increased flood discharge and peak flow duration while decreasing groundwater recharge.

Three articles have been selected to provide details of these geomorphic changes that result from the urbanization process. The papers by Wolman and Schick and by Guy show the tremendous influence that construction exerts in urban areas in eroding and depositing earth materials. Hammer emphasizes changes that occur in channel morphology. M. Gordon Wolman is the son of Abel Wolman and it is a genuine pleasure to honor this father–son team, which has been internationally influential in hydrology investigations. Gordon Wolman achieved an outstanding record during the 8 years he served as geologist with the U.S. Geological Survey. He has been a professor at Johns Hopkins University since 1958 and is currently Chairman, Department of Geography and Environmental Engineering. He has served on many governmental boards, been advisory editor for several science journals, and published widely in various fields associated with water resources. Harold P. Guy is a hydrologist with the U.S. Geological Survey publications. Thomas R. Hammer is a geomorphologist with the Regional Science Research Institute of Philadelphia.

The research performed by Wolman and Schick represents some of the earliest quantitative studies to document the magnitude of man-induced erosion – sedimentation changes in urban areas. Guy extends this work and provides a broad-based overview of the problems, along with suggestions in the field of government and education for their remedy. In an associated study, Vice, Guy, and Ferguson (1969) show that in suburban Fairfax County, Virginina, 197 acres undergoing highway construction over a 3-year period contributed 37,000 tons of sediment to a local stream. The highway construction was limited to 11 percent of the Scott Run basin, but the construction contributed 94 percent of the total sediment yield during the period. In Montgomery County, Maryland, more than 4,500 tons of soil were eroded during construction of 89 houses on a 20-acre site during a 5-year period. During excavation some material can maintain stable walls until the construction is completed, and remain stable as long as they are dry. But water from rain, overland flow, or shallow groundwater may lubricate clayey elements enough to cause caving and sliding, which may eventually lead to landslides. Some of the earliest records of building-construction landslides were from Bath, England, in 1790 and 1799. In alleviating these hazards, William "Strata" Smith, father of geology in England, received fame for his remedial work, which consisted of tunneling into the hill to intercept the groundwater. Thorough drainage of the landslide area and the development of public gardens have prevented further sliding. Although landslopes are 12 to 15 degrees, they remain stable as long as properly drained and not overloaded (Kellaway and Taylor, 1968).

The U.S. Department of Agriculture is also very interested in the control of erosion at building sites and in a number of publications (1970b) has developed guidelines designed to improve planning procedures and minimize the detrimental effects of erosion – sedimentation during construction activities.

> Erosion and sedimentation can be controlled effectively, and at reasonable cost, if certain principles are followed in the use and treatment of land: (1) using soils that are suited for development, (2) leaving the soil bare for the shortest time possible, (3) reducing the velocity and controlling the flow of runoff, (4) detaining runoff on the site to trap sediment, and (5) releasing runoff safely to downstream areas. In applying these principles various combinations of the following practices have proved effective:
>
> 1. Selecting land where drainage patterns, topography, and soils are favorable for the intended use.
> 2. Fitting the development to the site and providing for erosion control in the site development plan.
> 3. Using for open space and recreation those areas not well suited for urban development.
> 4. Developing large tracts in small workable units on which construction can be completed rapidly so that large areas are not left bare and exposed for long periods.
> 5. Grading at a minimum and removing only undesirable trees wherever possible.
> 6. Controlling runoff and conveying it to storm sewers or other outlets so it will not erode the land or cause offsite damage.

7. Protecting critical areas during construction with mulch or temporary cover crops and with mechanical measures such as diversions and prepared outlets.
8. Constructing sediment basins to detain runoff and trap sediment during construction.
9. Providing for safe offsite disposal of runoff, including the increased runoff resulting from construction.
10. Establishing permanent vegetation and installing erosion control structures as soon as posssible (pp. 9–10).

Hammer documents the widening of stream channels because of the urbanization process. Additional aspects of channel morphology are involved when streams flow through congested areas. The channels are commonly constrained by floodwalls, their beds are armored with concrete, and bends are straightened. Some of these aspects are covered in Volume III [see Daniels in Coates (1973)]. It is unfortunate that when man engineers new channels he frequently fails to accommodate streams to their natural morphologic behavior patterns. For example, the laws of hydraulic geometry as developed by such workers as Leopold, Maddock, Wolman, and Fahnestock are commonly ignored, and the normal ranges of meandering are changed. Failure to heed natural laws results in both upstream and downstream terrain changes by the watershed feedback system, causing additional costs and damages.

> Channel widening, artificial impoundments, dams and the whole list of hydrological maneuvers available provide at great cost what Mother Nature usually provides free of charge if left to her own devices (Little, 1968, p. 16).

Derelict Land

"Derelict land" is a very descriptive term first used in England to characterize terrain that has been ravaged by mining and industrial activity. These effects are experienced in many parts of the world and the United States has more than its share of such areas, as described in Volume III of this trilogy (e.g., in the iron mines of Minnesota, the placer gold mines of California, and the coal strip mines). The building trades consume fantastic amounts of surficial earth materials, and it has been estimated that in the next 25 years in the United States 100 billion tons of sand, gravel, and stone will be removed for these purposes. This section is largely concerned with derelict lands that are contiguous to urban areas, and K. J. Hilton provides a particularly apt example. The other article reproduced is from the Civic Trust of London and gives additional insight into the problem with some of its solutions. K. J. Hilton is at present the Secretary of University College, Cardiff, Wales. Between 1960 and 1965, he directed a multidisciplinary research team into the causes and effects of industrial despoilment in the Lower Swansea Valley. Here fumes from coal-burning industries were instrumental in causing devegetation that resulted in 1.5 million tons of soil materials being eroded to depths of 30 to 36 centimeters over an area of 2 square kilometers. Additional landscape damages were caused by killing the vegetation and creating terrain blight from waste products. The Hilton study was one of the early investigations of industrial environmental degradation and has influenced subsequent governmental policies and action in England to remedy the problems. Before 1960, K. J. Hilton served in Nigeria and Ghana in the Colonial Administrative Service and at the West African Research Office, Accra.

Waste Disposal

A thorough discussion of pollution is beyond the scope of this volume, but a few brief comments are necessary to place the problem of waste disposal in perspective. Although the United States contains less than 6 percent of the world's population, it consumes about one third of the world's production of energy and natural resources, and produces almost half the world's pollution. Urban areas alone produce 500,000 tons of sewage daily. Most experts agree that the price tag to abate the creeping wasteland would cost at least $100 billion in the next 5 years. Urban areas need $10 billion to meet current water-quality standards and an additional $6 billion to build and repair sewer lines under the streets. If municipalities were to take the additional step of separating sanitary sewers from storm sewers (in many cities thse are combined in a single conduit), another $35 billion would be required. Wolman's article in Part I contains further information on this topic.

The commentary in this section will concern itself with what might be termed *planned-fill sedimentation*, the deliberate deposition by man of earth materials that changes terrain configuration. Such human-induced deposition is different than "anthropogene sedimentation," a term in wide use in Europe for any type of sediment related to man's activities. For example, river fill (alluvium) in Germany that began to accelerate around 2500 B.C. because of Bronze Age deforestation and the use of cloven-hoofed domestic animals can be clearly differentiated from early Holocene sediments. In this volume two types of planned-fill sedimentation will be emphasized: solid-waste disposal systems and the filling of wetlands. Certainly, the entire urbanization process is one of sedimentation whereby man deposits roads, houses, industrial plants, and office buildings on top of virgin terrain, but we deal here with planned fill. The sedimentation previously discussed was not premeditated or purposeful, but instead the result of inadequate planning and control systems.

Solid waste is known by a variety of terms, such as garbage, refuse, junk, rubbish, trash, and litter. These are by-products of civilization and the residue from the metabolism of the city. Huge amounts of materials are imported into the city for consumption, and the residuals that have outlived their usefulness must in some manner be exported from the city. A major difference exists between modern civilization and earlier ones. Ancient cities commonly built on their own debris, and in archeological digs it is not unusual to find as many as a dozen earlier cities built on top of each other. In contrast, modern cities usually deposit their materials outside the city, which raises the topographic surface of the perimeter. A natural analog would be the manner in which inselbergs are drowned by their own sediments. In the United States, cities generate 250 million tons of solid waste each year, of which sanitation departments export 190 million tons, with the remainder disposed of by users or left behind to clog the cityscape. The National League of Cities in a report states that 46.5 percent of cities are so smothered by wastes that they will run out of dump sites in the next 5 years. Solid waste is growing five times faster than the population. The average city inhabitant creates about 6 pounds of trash a day (1 ton per year).

A typical ton of municipal waste contains 920 pounds of paper, 440 pounds of food and yard waste, 200 pounds of glass, 160 pounds of metal, 140 pounds of wood, and 140 pounds of miscellaneous items such as cloth, rubber, and plastic. Disposal costs for these solid wastes are more than $4.5 billion a year—one of the most costly duties in city government, exceeded only by expenditures for schools and roads. Nearly 75 percent of the nation's total solid waste is still being discarded in open dumps. Of the 14,000 land disposal sites only 13 percent are being operated within recognized sanitary landfill standards, which require earth coverage of all deposits each day and prohibition of burning. This concept and technique for "sanitary" landfill did not emerge until about 1940, but by 1945 almost 100 cities were using the practice, and by 1960 more than 1,400 cities had adopted this policy.

Man's extravagant use of raw materials and the products of industrialized society leads to depletion of natural resources, large expenditures of energy, and disposal problems that are costly and counterproductive to the land – water ecosystem. The California Water Pollution Control Board (1961) provides a series of documented case histories of environmental damage caused by leachates at solid-waste disposal sites. Schneider (1970) also discusses these problems:

> One well-documented case is that of pollution from about 650,000 cubic yards of refuse deposited in a garbage dump near Krefield, Germany, over a 15-year period in the early 1900's. High salt concentrations and hardness were detected in ground water about a mile downgradient from the site within 10 years of operation . . . [and] wells near the dumping site were still contaminated 18 years later.
>
> In Schirrhof, Germany, ashes and refuse dumped into an empty pit extending below the water table resulted in contamination of wells about 2,000 feet downstream. The contamination occurred 15 years after the dump was covered.
>
> In Surrey County, England, household refuse dumped into gravel pits polluted the ground water in the vicinity. Refuse was dumped directly into the 20-foot-deep pits where the water depth averaged about 12 feet. Maximum rate of dumping was about 100,000 tons per year over a 6-year period, and this occurred during the latter part of the period of use (1954 – 60). Limited observations on water quality extending less than a year after the

closing of the pits showed chloride concentrations ranging from 800 mg/l at the dump site, through 290 mg/l in downgradient adjacent gravel pits, to 70 mg/l in pits 3,500 feet away.

In the United States the Solid Waste Disposal Act of 1965 marked the first significant interest shown by the federal government in the management of solid wastes, and the Resource Recovery Act of 1970 amended the legislation to provide a new focus for the recycling and recovery of valuable waste materials. Several states have passed their own legislation concerning disposal sites, and others provide special technical help in the location of suitable disposal areas. The Pennsylvania Solid Waste Management Act of 1969 (and its accompanying rules and regulations) is of particular interest because it was the first legislation of this type that specifically required geologists to make site investigations and provide reports before any site could be officially designated for purposes of landfill disposal.

> . . . A soils, geologic and groundwater report of the characteristics of the proposed site shall be included as satisfactory to the Department. This report shall be based on a geological investigation and on a published standard soil survey. . . .

There are many additional ramifications to the disposal problem that also affect groundwater conditions, such as contamination by road salting, pollution from septic-tank effluent (prevalent on Long Island), and the loss of groundwater recharge to streams by pavement waterproofing, thus causing abnormally low base flow to streams and requiring low-flow augmentation from other water sources to dilute properly sewage effluent.

Coastal Modification

The coastal zone is becoming an increasingly popular locale for developmental projects by man. Many of the world's great cities are on coasts and in positions where shoreline terrain makes possible good harbor facilities. Industry is also attracted to coastal settings because transportation costs can be minimized. Although beaches have provided recreational sites for many years, their utilization since World War II has been vastly accelerated. The construction of entire new communities and the rush for second homes at the seashore has put a premium on coastal real estate values. Since it is in built-up areas that man concentrates his modification of coasts, such a topic is appropriate for this volume on the physical changes in urban areas.

A great paradox often emerges because of man's attempts to manipulate coastal areas in the name of conservation and preservation. His very acts to conserve this environment often result in greater environmental destruction than ever. The second law of thermodynamics is once again upheld; thus, when man tries to accomplish a perceived beneficial act (invariably short-term), nature always reacts. As Dolan points out in his article, man's attitude of considering nature as an antagonist, thereby making it necessary to fight and control her, can lead to very sad results (see also Godfrey and Godfrey, 1973). Robert Dolan is Professor and Chairman, Department of Environmental Sciences, at the University of Virginia. He has published numerous works on beaches and coasts. As a consultant with the National Park Service, he has been influential in searching for policies that reduce man's distortion of the coastal area. His article on the artificial sand-dune system in the Outer Banks of North Carolina illustrates the type of natural backlash that can occur.

Groins and jetties have also attracted much attention from conservationists because, in case after case, there is clear demonstration that they distort the natural balance of coastal systems, and cause increased erosion rates in down-drift areas.

> The construction of harbor jetties is an even more important cause of beach erosion. If the longshore current is predominantly in one direction, sand will build out on the upcurrent side of the jetties, often making the beach on that side too wide, as at Santa Barbara. On the downcurrent side, the beach is cut away by winter storms, but the ordinary replenishment that would come in summer is not possible because the sand is stored on the other side of the jetties. As a result, many downcurrent beaches have been destroyed. This is particularly true in Southern California where most harbors require jetties. Examples of erosion on the East Coast due to jetty building are found at Cape May, New Jersey, and at Ocean City, Maryland. South Cape May has virtually disappeared during the past 50 years due to the jetties to the northeast and to the southerly current. Assateague Island has been eroded at least 1,500 feet because of the Ocean City jetties (Shepard and Wanless, 1971, p. 548).

Groins produce much the same effect. For example, groin fields at Westhampton Beach and Ocean Beach on Long Island have caused adjacent property damage, and have contributed to a fivefold rate of accelerated erosion in downdrift areas. The extensive groin fields of Miami Beach, Florida, were started after the 1926 hurricane but have not served their purpose of beach stabilization or of prevention of sand movement by littoral drift.

Man's use of other types of construction has been equally damaging to the coastal environment. A pass was cut through the Bolivar Peninsula in Texas. The presence of the pass changed the water circulation pattern in Galveston Bay and East Bay so that erosion was accelerated by the new configuration, and in 1961 Hurricane Carla was able to erode more than 900 feet from the peninsula, which otherwise would have been naturally protected. Breakwaters can also cause abnormal upsets and damages, such as at Redondo and Santa Barbara, California:

> In 1929, against the advice of the Corps of Engineers, Santa Barbara, California, erected a breakwater to shelter small craft and attract tourist income. The basis of the Corps' concern immediately became evident.

> Above the breakwater beach frontage ballooned out some seven hundred feet. Within the breakwater sand began shoaling up at the rate of eight hundred cubic yards a day. Below the breakwater the shore receded as much as two hundred forty-five feet. Ten miles downstream a row of beach homes slumped into the sea. The breakwater that cost less than a million dollars to build caused twice that amount in property damage (Marx, 1967, p. 36).

Inman and Brush (1973) also discuss man-made beach changes. Silver Strand Beach in southern California has no natural inland sources of sediment since Rodiques Dam was completed in 1937. The beach has had to be artifically maintained by replacing 22×10^6 cubic meters of sand in the period 1941–1967. In some areas, the "mining" of beach sand is an important industry. During 1970, 21.3×10^6 tons of sand and gravel were dug from beaches, river beds, and coastal dunes in California. The same year, 112×10^6 tons were excavated in Great Britain, of which 13.2×10^6 tons were dredged from offshore banks, many of which provide essential protection to the coastline from wave erosion. A classic case occurred in Devon in 1894, when 500,000 tons of gravel were dredged offshore near the village of Hallsands. The village suffered severe damage and was almost obliterated by waves whose energy was no longer dampened by the shallow topography.

The following references are recommended for providing additional geomorphic information on coastal areas: (1) *general:* Burton et al., 1969; Corps of Engineers, 1971a, 1971b, 1973. (2) *damages:* Nichols and Marston, 1939; Tannehill, 1938. (3) *sand-dune changes:* Chapman, 1949; Davis, 1957; Jagschitz and Bell, 1966; Savage and Woodhouse, 1969; Van der Burgt and Bendegom, 1949; Woodhouse and Hanes, 1967. (4) *reclamation:* Constandse, 1967; Darby, 1956; Spits, 1970; Van Veen, 1962. (5) *beach nourishment:* Vesper, 1961, 1965, 1967.

The last class of planned-fill sedimentation that will be discussed concern's man rapacious schemes to fill in wetlands for the purpose of new development and sprawl. It is difficult to single out one particular element of the environment where man's desecration has been the worst, but certainly his destruction of the ecology and morphology of wetlands would rank very high on the list. The term "wetland" has come into usage in a descriptive sense to aid in dispelling older perceived uncomplimentary attitudes often associated with such terms as swamp, marsh, and bog. Wetlands occur in both coastal and fluvial environments, but are united by virtue of their delicate balance, which is easily destroyed, their importance in the entire ecological chain of life, and their cushioning and absorptive qualities for minimizing storms and flooding damages. For example, one particularly damaging flood in eastern Pennsylvania washed out hundreds of bridges, but bridges of similar type that were in the path of floodwaters in Cranberry Bog, a natural area that had been preserved, were left undamaged. Wetlands also provide important oxidation and sedimentation basins where urban runoff can escape and be intercepted, and where nutrients can be used in the local ecosystem instead of creating damages farther downstream.

Man's willful, diabolical, and imprudent obliteration of wetlands has reached alarming proportions throughout the world. Of 27 million acres of U.S. coastal wetlands that are important to fish and wildlife habitat, Niering (1970) shows that 570,000 acres have already been eradicated. The greatest losses occur in California and Florida. In New York, New Hampshire, Connecticut, and New Jersey about 15 percent of total wetlands have been destroyed. When considering all American wetlands, 650,000 acres were lost by filling and dredging in the 1950 – 1969 period.

> Although the nation's marshes, swamps, and bogs are among the most productive landscapes in the world, these liquid assets have suffered greater destruction and abuse than any other natural habitat manipulated by man. As a result of draining, dredging, filling, and/or pollution we have in the conterminous United States reduced the nation's wetland asset to 70 million acres, slightly more than half the original acreage (an estimated 127 million acres). And the destruction is continuing at an accelerated pace of 1 per cent or more per year, favored by the pseudo-socio-economic concept that conversion of these habitats into other land-use patterns results in the highest and best use.
>
> In the urban – suburban complex the remaining wetlands are engulfed by some 140 million Americans crowded onto less than 5 per cent of the land. Yet cattail marshes, wooded swamps, and fringing tidal marshes can still persist if given adequate proteciton from the environmental stresses of urbanization. Unfortunately, to the average urban dweller such areas appear to have little relevance to daily life (Niering, 1968, p. 177).

Not all wetlands are contiguous to cities, of course, but the following example from Boston illustrates the prevalent attitude that such areas are low on the priority list for preservation.

> As has been true with many of the world's great port cities, Boston's growth demanded additional land space in the vicinity of the harbor and commercial districts. The logical direction for expansion was into surrounding marshes, where the land could be built up with fill. Thus the hills were either leveled or reduced in height to procure fill, Mill Pond was first filled, followed later by the salt marshes on both sides of the peninsula. The former shallow-water zone on the west is known today as Back Bay. Not all the filled areas were constructed at the expense of the former hills and glacial drift, however. Some of the fill consisted of solid wastes from early urbanization and commerce—the brick, stone, and mortar derived from buildings as they were replaced and the ballast from ships that arrived to carry off goods produced and sold in the city (Eschman and Marcus, 1972, p. 41).

It cannot be emphasized too strongly that man's arrogance and self-serving assumption that nature was invented for his benefit, and that intuitively he knows best how to adapt or disrupt natural systems for utilitarian purposes can have unfortunate implications for his own survival. Man has the ability to greatly modify his habit, but this is often done at a price that becomes economically unjustifiable, aesthetically detrimental, and physically disastrous.

18

Reprinted from *The Lower Swansea Valley Project,* K. J. Hilton, ed., Longman Group Ltd., Essex, England, 1967, pp. 38–46

A case history of derelict land in Swansea 1900 to 1966

K. J. HILTON

At the turn of the century, then, the Lower Valley was prosperous but ugly, prosperous because steel, tinplate and spelter with ancillary industry had taken over from copper, ugly because the meadows on the valley floor were submerged beneath man-made mountains of ash and slag and its flanks swept by fume and covered with sooty fall-out from the furnaces.

There is little evidence that the ugliness of this landscape troubled the consciences of those who were concerned with the business of creating it. The ground landlords and most of the entrepreneurs lived out of the sight and smell of the works, the employees and the townspeople accepted conditions into which most of them had been born and to which they were accustomed. It is the visitors to whom we are principally indebted for critical descriptions of the area.*

It was an age of *laissez faire*; the same kind of situation existed in Staffordshire and the Black Country, in Lancashire, Derbyshire and Shropshire, wherever coal was mined and metal smelted and forged. It was an attitude of mind that persisted until the conscience of society at large stirred, and slowly, but oh so slowly, public controls attempted to check the private spoliation of earth and river and sky.

In Swansea, as early as 1764, the burgesses resolved to keep the smoke of industry out of the town, but once the Lower Valley was given over to smelting its subsequent inclusion within the Borough did not alter the situation. Long usage had established a valuable prescriptive right to create noise, dirt and smell, which legal action failed to destroy.† In other parts of Great Britain, especially in the mining districts, leases sometimes laid down in detail conditions for the eventual restoration of sites on the termination of working, including the removal and retention of soil for this purpose.‡ Generally speaking, little was attempted in Swansea or elsewhere, either by the landlords or their lessees, to modify in any way the harsh effects of industrial occupation on the landscape, and by implication on the lives of the people who inhabited it. Even when legislation was introduced which was intended to help reclaim derelict industrial land, little was achieved. Attempts by local authorities and Government Departments were frustrated. Some idea of the extent of the national problem and of the pace of reclamation is given in Chapter 13 but it will perhaps be

* 'Landore, a spot rich in the renown of its metal and chemical works, but to the casual visitor, ugly with all the ugliness of grime and dust, and mud and smoke and indescribable tastes and odours. S. C. Gamwell, Swansea and District Guide', Swansea, 1880.

† (*a*) See a lawyer's brief for the defence in an action taken against Messrs Pascoe, Grenfell and Sons, c. 1830. Original in the Royal Institution of South Wales, Swansea.

(*b*) 'Swansea smelters enjoy the privilege of pouring dense volumes of thick sulphurous and arsenical smoke from comparatively low chimneys into the atmosphere. . . . This privilege has now in lapse of time become an established right which would not readily be conceded in many other parts of the Kingdom.' John Percy, *Metallurgy* 1861.

‡ Lease dated 1 June 1843 to Richard Blundell by the Trustees of Francis Duke of Bridgewater, quoted in 'Rehabilitation of Derelict Land in the Wigan District', J. K. Molyneux, University of Birmingham, M.A. thesis, May 1961.

helpful here, using the Swansea experience, to consider the more important reasons which explain why so little has been achieved in the Lower Swansea Valley and elsewhere up to the present.

The first serious effort to tackle the waste land of the Lower Swansea Valley was made by a public officer, George Bell, the Borough Surveyor, who in 1912 presented a report* to the Council in which he proposed that there should be a comprehensive scheme to utilize the tip waste, to create new industrial sites, that the tinplate works in the north of the valley be linked with the docks by a new road and tramway and that industrial housing on 'garden suburb lines' should be developed on the side of the valley at Cefn Hengoed. It will be apparent from the fact that nothing followed this imaginative proposal that Mr Bell was ahead of his time.

Shortly afterwards Britain was involved in the First World War, much of the heavy industry in the valley turned over to war production and all thoughts of its redevelopment were necessarily put aside. After the war there was, as we saw in Chapter 2, a steady revival in the tinplate industry, but coal mining in the valley closed down finally and spelter production contracted into a single works. Between 1920 and 1930 most of the older copper and spelter works closed leaving groups of brick and stone buildings to deteriorate in wind, weather and at the hands of vandals (Plate 6). Around them lay huge piles of furnace debris, no longer actively increasing but static, silent and barren. By the twenties the Swansea canal was semi-derelict, and the last barge was seen in the thirties. This was a time when the process of industrial closure began, a process which gradually overtook the whole area including, by 1960, all the steel and tinplate works.

In spite of the fact that the acreage of industrial waste land in this area increased steadily after the First World War, no further attempt seems to have been made either to improve its services and surroundings or to stimulate the fresh use of old sites. This reflects the inadequacy of the national policy for such areas at this time, and if local feeling was strong, it was not strong enough to persuade the local authority to 'go it alone'. The forging of Government policy for the reclamation of derelict land developed slowly in the fierce heat of unemployment which struck the older industrial regions in the thirties on a scale which had never been experienced before.

In 1932, 36·5 per cent of the working population of Wales was unemployed, in South Wales and Monmouthshire the figure was 41 per cent in July, topped only by West Cumberland with 46 per cent. In the Swansea area the peak was reached earlier, in September 1931, with 24·2 per cent unemployed. Swansea was comparatively well off. It was situated in the western anthracite part of the coalfield. Demand for anthracite was maintained, and serious unemployment due to cyclical movements was avoided.

To meet this situation, the Government first investigated the conditions of the depressed areas and followed this in 1934 with the Special Areas (Development and Improvement) Act 1934, under which two Commissioners were appointed, one for Scotland and one for England and Wales. The Commissioners were given wide powers and a special fund of two million pounds to enable them to take immediate action to relieve the social and economic conditions of these areas.

Unfortunately Swansea's *relative* prosperity excluded it along with Cardiff and Newport

---

* See Appendix, p. 44.

from the provisions of this legislation. From the beginning, therefore, the derelict land of the Lower Swansea Valley was placed outside the powers that were available to deal with it. The anomaly of the situation was referred to by the Commissioner for England and Wales in his first report, in these terms:

'In Wales, however, the exclusion of important cities and towns such as Cardiff, Newport and Swansea, has created an artificial boundary within an established region.'

In his second report, the Commissioner drew attention to the fact that in Wales the largest acreage of derelict land lay outside the special area and so could not be touched.

Grants for clearing derelict sites were approved by the Commissioner on condition that there were reasonable prospects of industrial development following the clearance.* This condition should be noted since it has influenced the interpretation of subsequent legislation and has limited in consequence the action which it has been possible to take to deal with derelict land. In order to qualify for grant-aid, derelict land not only had to be within the aid area but its reclamation had to be justified in these strict terms. Because Swansea, as we have seen, was outside the South Wales Special Area in the thirties, nothing was done in the valley between the Wars. With the outbreak of the Second World War in 1939, new legislation was postponed.

In spite of these setbacks, the experience gained in the administration of the Special Areas Acts was valuable. It had shown that more rather than less Government intervention was required. This was confirmed in 1940 by the Royal Commission on the Distribution of Industrial Population (the Barlow Report) which recommended a considerable extension of Government investment in providing the infrastructure for industrial growth in the Special Areas, as well as action to limit the industrial growth of the conurbations especially in the London region. This report influenced Government policy which was presented in a White Paper on Employment in May 1944, and to which effect was given in the Distribution of Industry Act, 1945.

The Act marked an important step forward. The old Special Areas were grouped into larger regions in which Swansea, Newport and Cardiff were finally included, so removing the earlier anomaly. The Board of Trade was given wide powers over industrial location and for the first time the reclamation of derelict land was made a special object of grant-aid. On the face of it, the Act seemed to provide a sufficiently satisfactory combination of powers and grants to enable a start to be made to strengthen the economies of the older industrial regions, to broaden their industrial base and to clear up the mess of the Industrial Revolution.

While the Government was working out a national policy, Swansea Borough Council, as the end of the war approached, also began to think of the employment needs of its demobilized population; memories of the thirties were still poignant. Thoughts were therefore turned towards the development of a light industrial estate on the lines of those developed before the war at Slough and Treforest. A report by the Borough Engineer presented in 1943 recommended, first, that the derelict sites in the Lower Swansea Valley should be acquired and cleared with *Government help* so as to improve the amenities of the

* Cmd 4957, 1935, paragraphs 34 and 55.

area and to provide sites for new industry, and secondly, that the Council should consider the development of a light industrial estate. The Council proceeded to act on the second proposal first. A site of 230 acres at Fforestfach, north-west of the town centre, was acquired (Figure 3.1) and the first turf cut by His Majesty King George VI on 15 November 1945.

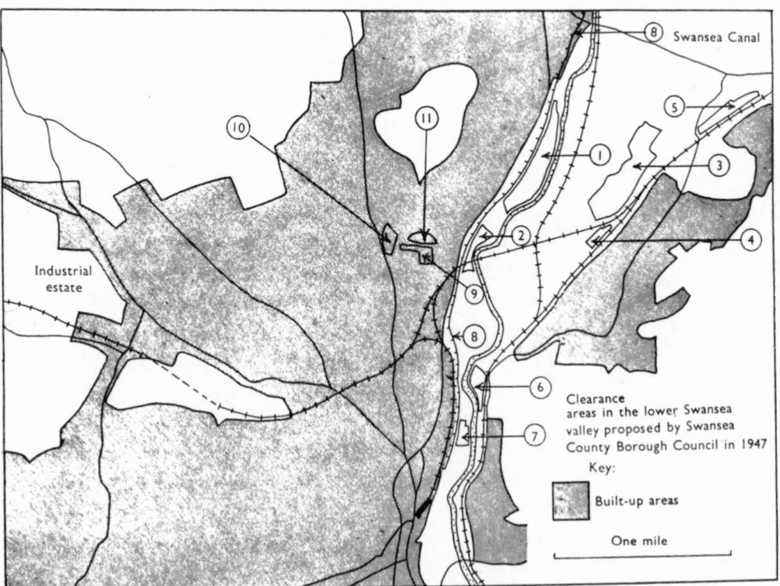

Figure 3.1 The relative location of the Valley and the Fforestfach Trading Estate and the areas of redevelopment proposed by the Swansea Borough Council between 1945 and 1960

Meanwhile, in June 1945, the Distribution of Industry Act had given the Board of Trade all the powers necessary for the development and management of industrial estates, so that it was appropriate that the Board should take over responsibility for the Fforestfach estate, and this was eventually done.

The acquisition and clearance of derelict sites in the Lower Swansea Valley was to prove more difficult. Section 5 of the Distribution of Industry Act empowered the Board to acquire *derelict* land in Development Areas, and to carry out such work as appeared expedient to enable the land to be brought into use or for improving the amenities of the neighbourhood. The Board was also able, with Treasury consent, to make grants towards carrying out such work (Section 5.3).

Swansea County Borough was a scheduled Development Area, and it seemed to the Council in 1945 that there was at last a reasonable prospect of obtaining some Exchequer help with the site clearance in the valley. These hopes came to nothing, mainly for two reasons. First, like the Special Areas Acts, one of the conditions which had to be met in the administration of the 1945 Act was that the measures taken were necessary for the relief of unemployment in the Area. In the light of employment opportunities which would be created by the decision to develop an industrial estate at Fforestfach, and of the already relatively low level of unemployment in the County Borough, additional expenditure on the preparation of industrial sites in the Swansea Valley was not considered to be justified. The fact that Swansea was a *scheduled* Development Area was of little consequence.

But there was a second and more cogent reason which had an important bearing on the way in which the Distribution of Industry Act was administered, and accounted in no small measure for the parsimony with which the Board of Trade and the other Government Departments concerned were obliged to act. Between 1950 and 1959 the country experienced an acute economic crisis which obliged the Government to reduce capital expenditure. Grants for the reclamation of derelict land were severely limited, so that during this period the legislation which promised to achieve so much could not be applied effectively.

In 1959 restrictions on capital expenditure were eased and local authorities invited to submit reclamation schemes for completion by the end of March 1960.* Difficulty was now experienced from the fact that the legal interpretation of the term 'derelict' used in Section 5 of the Act meant that the land was of no value to the owner. Since all the derelict sites in the Lower Swansea Valley were in private hands it proved impossible for the Corporation to induce the owners to make this declaration. Eventually, in order to enable some advantage to be gained from the legislation before it was repealed, the Council was able to satisfy the legal niceties in respect of a coal tip which it owned outside the Swansea Valley and this was eventually levelled.

This was the only clearance which it was possible to carry out under the Act in Swansea between 1945 and 1960. Although schemes for eleven sites in the valley area were prepared at various times by the Corporation, at the invitation of the Board of Trade in 1947 and of a Government Committee under the Chairmanship of Lord Lloyd in 1953 (Figure 3.1), nothing was achieved there.

The Distribution of Industry Act was replaced by the Local Employment Act, 1960. Although in some respects an improvement on its predecessor—the definition of derelict land for example was widened to include land that was also neglected and unsightly—the Act marked a reversal of regional location policy. Instead of Development Areas, there were to be smaller Development Districts based on employment exchange areas which in the words of the Act included 'any locality in Great Britain in which in the opinion of the Board of Trade a high rate of unemployment exists or is to be expected . . . and is likely to persist whether seasonally or generally'.

Swansea with its relatively low rate of unemployment could not qualify as a Development District although there was a net outflow of labour from the County Borough which resulted from a lack of employment opportunity in manufacturing industry within it. There were other criticisms of the policy; it was too flexible and resulted in areas listed one year being removed in the next. By 1963, however, a regional policy developed again from studies of the economies of Central Scotland and North-East England. After the change of government in 1964, this trend was strengthened, and in October 1965 Swansea qualified once more for grant-aid under the Act. In January 1966 the Government presented its policy for industrial growth and location† which returned to the Development Area policy of the 1945 Act.

* Ministry of Housing and Local Government Circular No. 22/59.
† Cmd 2874, *Investment Incentives*, January 1966.

So far as the reclamation of derelict land is concerned, the situation remains unchanged. Grants are only available if the land is in a Development Area, although these areas now include nearly all such land in Great Britain, and then only if its reclamation provides employment. The reclamation of derelict land is still not an end in itself although it is the Government's intention to introduce legislation to accomplish this.* It is hoped that the level of the new reclamation grant will be sufficiently high, and its administration sufficiently uncomplicated, to induce local authorities to act quickly so that the Lower Swansea Valley may finally be dealt with.

Besides the legislative deficiencies which have been discussed, there have been special local reasons which have contributed to inaction in the valley. From what has been said, it might appear that the Corporation has lacked initiative in dealing with what is, after all, a local problem. Let us therefore consider the valley in the light of the local situation.

First there is no shortage of land in the County Borough. With 7·8 persons to the acre, the local authority did not need to use derelict land for housing even if the Swansea Valley site was suitable in other respects, which it was not.

Although industrial sites could have been prepared in the valley there was little prospect of their being taken up: there were sites at Fforestfach with all services available which could not be let. It would be unrealistic to expect the Council to prepare industrial sites with little hope of a financial return on the rate expenditure involved. Besides, when the Fforestfach estate was acquired there was less than sixty acres of waste land in the Lower Swansea Valley that could have been used and not all of this was on one site. Industry which has since closed was actively tipping in 1943.

Admittedly something could have been done to improve the appearance of the area: derelict buildings could have been removed and trees planted, but this would have made it necessary for the Council to have acquired the land, or else to have spent the rates on im-improving land in private hands. This is to ignore the fact that there has persisted in Swansea a measure of resentment against those who blighted the land and then withdrew with their fortunes to other parts of the country. The result has been a reluctance to spend rates largely from working-class pockets to put right the depredation created for private profit.

Finally, the size of the area, the vast quantities of its debris, its physical fragmentation, its multiple ownership, all contributed to a feeling that the cost of the physical redevelopment of the area was, in the circumstances, beyond the resources of the County Borough. Government help was looked for and, as we have seen, was not forthcoming.

And so the situation has stagnated and in 1961, when the Project was set up, it seemed likely that it would continue like this indefinitely. A study of the area was an attempt to break through to a new phase of action that would be based on a full understanding of the area's problems, physical, social and economic. The study therefore is seen as simply the first stage in which information is gathered and interpreted, leading, we hope, eventually to the renewal of this devastated land. The following chapters summarize the results of this study.

* Cmd 2923, *Local Government Finance, England and Wales*, February 1966, para. 18.

Authorship

This chapter was written by K. J. Hilton. The author is indebted to L. N. Hopper for his comments on the text and to the Town Clerk of Swansea for permission to read the Corporation's files on the Landore area.

Appendix

'FLOREAT SWANSEA'

18th January 1912

To the Parliamentary and General Purposes Committee

Mr. Chairman and Gentlemen—

(1).—It is a singular fact that, in the valley of the river Tawe, surrounded by very important works and almost in the heart of industrial Swansea, a tract of land of about 200 acres in extent should still retain its primitive condition. There are no public roads across the land except one very unsatisfactory footway along which thousands of workers pass daily to and from their labours—and this very often is rendered impassable by flood water—and it seems to have been no one's business to see to it that proper intercommunication is afforded and that its development should be conducted on right lines. The land referred to lies between Landore, Morriston, Llansamlet and the Great Western Railway, and is mainly at a level of 20ft. above the sea. On this account the land is subject to flooding from tidal waters from the River Tawe and the flood water from the river and its tributaries above. The sub-soil is alluvial deposit overlying glacial drift below which is strong clay and the coal measures, and it has been proved to demonstration that the whole would form a stable foundation for anything that could be put upon it. The ownership of the soil is vested in His Grace the Duke of Beaufort and the Earl of Jersey, and except for grazing purposes the land is lying idle and practically derelict.

(2).—Signs, however, are now apparent that some of the land is being dealt with for the extension of works, but without any comprehensive scheme for its systematic and proper development, and it is in view of this that I beg to submit for the consideration of the landowners and the Corporation a sketch scheme which, if carried out in a broad-minded and energetic manner, would be to the advantage of all concerned.

(3).—The plans and sections accompanying this report* indicate intercommunication roads across the land which would effectually open it out for development, and provide means of through traffic and communication between important places and the various existing works, and for the many thousands of workers now engaged at the works and those to be hereafter established.

(4).—The level of the land would be raised by at least 15ft., and this could readily be done by the use of the waste products from the works, which at the present time are disposed of in unsightly heaps, to the detriment and inconvenience of the works owners and their neighbours. This level would be above the influence of the tidal waters, and, by the construction of a large culvert, the water of the Ffrendrod Brook and the flood waters from the river would be safely carried away. The water of the Ffrendrod could, however, be made use of as required for works purposes in cooling ponds, etc., and would be of great value in

44 * Not reproduced.

this respect. The existing main road from Morriston to Llansamlet and Neath should be raised above the flood level, and the development of the land in the valley northwards of this main road could be continued as far as Glais, so as to form one comprehensive scheme.

(5).—A trunk roadway could be obtained from a point on the proposed road between Landore to Llansamlet, passing over the Great Western Railway main line, and the Midland Railway, to Upper Bank, and from thence along existing roads, which should, however, be widened, through Foxhole, Pentreguinea and St. Thomas to the Docks. Two immensely valuable benefits of this trunk road would be easy access to the Docks for the vehicles conveying tinplates and other products, and the freeing of the chief business streets of the town of a large part of the heavy haulage traffic.

(6).—The saving in distance from Llansamlet to the Docks by the construction of this road would be about one and one-third miles, and the saving in distance from Llansamlet to Landore by the construction of the roadway shown on the plan instead of along the Morriston route would be one-third of a mile, and the gradients over each would be most favourable. Along the new roadway from Landore to Llansamlet, which should have a width of 120ft. to be in proportion with its length and importance, trunk water and gas mains should be laid for supplies to the works and the suburban districts eastwards, also pipes for electricity, telegraph and telephone cables. A double line of tramway should be laid the whole way for communication with the works and beyond. By this means the workers living in Landore and Llansamlet, etc., would be conveyed to and from their work cheaply, safely and comfortably, and members of their families would be able to convey their food also by this means.

(7).—For the hive of additional workers drawn to the valley by the anticipated establishment of the new works, dwellings could be provided on the hill side at Cefn Hengoed, which is an admirable site for the purpose, and it should be laid out on Garden Suburb lines with all the institutions which are necessary for the well-being of man.

In these scientific days it need not be feared that this site would be prejudiced by the smoke arising from the manufacturing processes in the valley adjoining, as all deleterious constituents of the fumes are now extracted for profitable purposes before discharge into the atmosphere. The ultimate smoke emitted, composed principally of carbon, we are fortunately well used to, and is only regarded as good evidence of the prosperity of the district. This place is most conveniently situated for the dwellings required, and although at present beyond the boundary of the Borough, it must soon—to meet the necessities of expansion—be added to the area under the control of the Council. Swansea is rapidly outgrowing its present boundaries. With the communication roads laid out as suggested, and with tramways, Cefn Hengoed would be in close touch not only with the existing and future works, but also with Llansamlet, Morriston, Landore, St. Thomas, and Swansea, and its inhabitants would be able to reap for themselves and their families full benefit of all the institutions of Swansea for business, education, and the recreations and pleasures of life.

(8).—I now beg to suggest that after this scheme has received the careful consideration of your Committee and the Corporation, and, if approved in principle, it should be formally submitted to the landowners and their agents, and the proprietors of the works, with a view to arrangements being made for carrying it into effect. Whether the Corporation would, in the event of the scheme being approved, pursue a pushful policy in the attraction of works
45 to the sites is a matter worthy of favourable consideration. Industries occupy a high position

among the prime causes of the growth of towns and cities. They have inherently a high rateable value, but they also produce a contingent rateable value in so far as extra dwellings, shops and other premises are required by those engaged at the factories. I understand that in America the advantage of securing the establishment of works within the areas of cities is so appreciated that land is often given for the purpose, both rent and rates free, for a period. There should be no dearth of works for the occupation of our sites, for not only are there new works constantly being started in the country, but there are the works which find it necessary to move to the ports, so as to relieve themselves of the more or less heavy railway freightage appertaining to inland sites. I believe there is a growing tendency to remove, and therefore towns like Swansea stand to gain thereby, whilst, of necessity, the inland towns from which the works depart must correspondingly suffer. Apparently a city in the North has already acutely felt the loss, due to the closing of a number of its works on account of remoteness from docks.

(9).—Swansea, with its splendid juxtaposition of perfect sites and magnificent docks, its copious water supply and proximity to the coalfields, has all the facilities necessary to successful manufacturing, and, surely, it but requires that its advantages be better known throughout the country and abroad also for its call to be strongly felt. The only objection of which I am aware that industrial site prospectors detect in regard to the Borough is that of rates, but, without erring on the side of optimism, I venture to suggest that the future will see conditions operating to lower rather than raise the local rates.

Possibly your Committee may deem it justifiable, if not necessary, civic advertising, for the Council to circulate attractively prepared hand maps displaying the features and advantages of Swansea for industrial and commercial purposes.

Your obedient servant,
GEORGE BELL,
Borough Surveyor.

References

W. H. Beveridge, *Full Employment in a Free Society*, London, 1944.
A. E. C. Hare, *The Anthracite Coal Industry of the Swansea District*, University of Wales Press Board, 1940.
The Second Industrial Survey of Wales, Cardiff, 1937.

Government publications

An industrial survey of South Wales made for the Board of Trade by the University College of South Wales and Monmouthshire, H.M.S.O., London, 1932.

Reports of Investigations into the Industrial Conditions in Certain Depressed Areas, Cmd 4728, 1934.
The First Report of the Commissioner for the Special Areas (England and Wales), Cmd 4957, 1935.
The Second Report of the Commissioner for the Special Areas (England and Wales), Cmd 5090, 1936.
Report of the Commissioner for the Special Areas in England and Wales for the year ended 30th September 1937, Cmd 5595, 1937.
Report of the Commissioner for the Special Areas in England and Wales for the year ended 30th September 1938, Cmd 5896, 1938.
The Report of the Royal Commission on the Distribution of the Industrial Population, Cmd 6153, 1940.
Employment Policy, Cmd 6527, 1944.
Distribution of Industry, Cmd 7540, 1948.

19

Reprinted from *Derelict Land,* Civic Trust, London, 1964, pp. 7–14

Derelict Land

THE EFFECTS OF INERTIA

BRITAIN'S WEALTH AND POWER were built, and to a large extent still rest, on the exploitation and industrial use of her mineral resources. This is a process which inevitably makes a mess of the land. Our forebears, for the most part, left the mess as it was: either they did not mind it, or they found the task of cleaning it up too difficult or too costly. The legacy of their neglect is that today, in England and Wales alone, more than 150,000 acres lie derelict.

We in our generation have more regard for the beauty of our countryside, more control over what is done to it and a much greater technical capacity to repair the ravages it suffers. We try to confine its despoilment by mineral extraction and industrial development within the bounds of need, and we oblige the extractive industries to make good most of the damage they cannot avoid doing. Yet each succeeding year sees a larger addition to the total acreage of land that has been worked out and left unproductive. The spread of dereliction has now reached at least 3,500 acres a year.

The area blighted by this creeping canker is, of course, much more extensive still.

The creeping canker: dramatic but desolate. In England and Wales over thirty square miles have been sterilised by the twin le

Our derelict acreage is made up of tens of thousands of separate patches. In some parts of the country these patches are sparsely scattered, but in the older industrial regions (where most of them lie) they are often close together. Where one acre in ten is laid waste, the whole landscape is disfigured; and such areas between them cover something like two thousand square miles. Throughout much of South Lancashire and South Wales, Tyneside and Coalbrookdale, South-West Yorkshire and the Black Country, the face of the earth is riddled with abandoned mineral workings, pocked with subsidence, gashed with quarries, littered with disused plant and piled high with stark and sterile banks of dross and debris, spoil and slag.

These deformities of nature do more than mar the view. Their grim desolation dulls the spirit – as their dust and fumes defile the fabric – of the human settlements that straggle among them. Smouldering pit heaps foul the air, poisonous chemicals pollute the waterways and treacherous pits endanger the lives of adventurous children. Neglected wastes breed vermin and disease. Their very existence fosters slovenliness and vandalism, invites the squatters' shack, and engenders a 'derelict land mentality' that can never be eradicated until the mess itself has been cleared up. Dereliction, indeed, breeds a brutish insensibility, bordering on positive antagonism, to the life and loveliness of the natural landscape it has supplanted. It debases as well as disgraces our civilisation.

'Where there's muck there's money' was the glib cliche that comforted our forebears' consciences. Today we are beginning to see that dirt, dereliction and decay

eep-mined coal—the shale tip and the subsidence 'flash'—and every ten months another square mile is buried and left derelict.

are major obstacles to the future prosperity of our older industrial centres. We have undertaken to abate the pollution of the atmosphere in these 'black areas'. We have made up our minds progressively to purify their streams and rivers. But as yet we have made no systematic effort to tackle the mess that sullies the earth. If clean air and (eventually) clean waters, why not clean land too? Is the job too big for us? Would it cost too much? Is is not technically feasible? Or is a comprehensive programme of land renewal prevented by nothing more than 'administrative difficulties'?

THE NATURE OF THE PROBLEM

Some of the land laid waste by industry, now as always, is continually being restored or reclaimed for development because it pays to restore or reclaim it. Such land presents no problem. Our concern is only with those derelict areas which are likely to remain offensive for a long time unless we are prepared to go to some trouble and expense to deal with them now simply because they *are* offensive. These unwanted sites can be divided into three broad categories.

A: about 36,000 acres in urban areas where undeveloped land is getting scarce and expensive. Though not immediately in demand. all sites in this category are likely to be wanted for some form of development at some time in the next half-century. But it will not be financially profitable to reclaim them for development until there is no more undeveloped farmland to be had in their vicinity at a price which is lower than the cost of reclaiming them. Land in this category may be sub-divided as follows:

(i) about 24,000 acres of spoil-heaps, abandoned buildings and miscellaneous dereliction. We should reclaim these for urban development as fast as the demand for it allows, instead of prematurely urbanising what is left of the open country in their neighbourhood. In the meanwhile we should make them inoffensive to the eye (and attractive to developers) by restoring them as far as possible to agricultural use.

(ii) about 12,000 acres of holes in the ground which are likely to be needed in due course for the tipping of town wastes, and which could thereafter be economically developed as sites for housing or playing fields. We should hold these in reserve for refuse disposal, which would otherwise spread over virgin farmland. In the meanwhile they need 'cosmetic' treatment.

B: something like 114,000 acres of industrial dereliction in less populous areas where there is no foreseeable prospect of large-scale development. These should be visually redeemed by such regrading and grassing or tree-planting as is needed to make them merge into the surrounding countryside.

C: the annual net addition to our derelict acreage. Out of some 12,000 acres a year now being taken for the working of minerals and the tipping of spoil and waste, about 8,500 are afterwards restored to farming use by the operators in compliance with the conditions attached to their planning consents. The remaining 3,500 are not restored. These should likewise be visually redeemed by landscaping of a kind that goes beyond mere 'cosmetic' titivation, if possible while the process of extraction is going on.*

* The acreage figures given above for Categories A(i) and A(ii) are based on estimates compiled in 1957 by the Ministry of Housing and Local Government. As mineral working and urban development spread, particular sites are, of course, continually being transferred from farming use into Category C, from C to B, from B to A, and from A to the 'dead-ripe' land market. Such transfers, however, are unlikely to have materially changed the acreage in any category over a period of less than a decade.

It is true, of course, that if we divert current development from farmland to land in Category A(i) and level and grass the remaining land in this category as an interim measure, we shall incur public expenditure that we could have avoided by leaving such land derelict until the cost of its reclamation was exceeded by the rising market value of alternative, undeveloped sites. If we do leave it derelict, however, we shall not only have to go on living with its ugliness, and with the social ills its ugliness engenders; we shall also be using more farmland for development than we need.

THE COST OF LAND RENEWAL

Reclamation schemes vary widely in cost, but such experience as we have suggests that if we undertook to bring all the land in Category A(i) back into some kind of use as soon as possible, instead of waiting till it was economically ripe for urban development, we should incur an average *gross* outlay of about £700 an acre. Assuming that the market value of the reclaimed land continued, as heretofore, to average about £220 an acre, the *net* cost would come to about £480 an acre, or £11½ millions in sum. Temporary 'cosmetic' treatment for the holes in Category A(ii) might add another quarter of a million. If we went on to rehabilitate visually, by afforestation or by establishing permanent grass, all the derelict land in Category B (which is unlikely ever to be wanted for urban development), the *net* cost would probably work out, on the basis of past experience, at an average of about £55 an acre, or £6¼ millions in sum. A comprehensive twenty-year programme for the renewal, by one means or another, of all the land left derelict by *past* industrial activities would therefore require a net outlay of nearly £900,000 a year. This figure would, of course, diminish if the cost of

In Lancashire alone, industry has laid waste 11,000 acres, and as many more are devastated every ten years.

In the Black Country, homes and workplaces are scattered among the refuse of abandoned mineral workings.

alternative sites on undeveloped land continued to rise – as it is more than likely to do – and takes no account of the value to the national economy of the farmland that would be saved from premature development.

If our programme also included the thorough-going visual redemption of all the land left derelict by *current* mineral working (Category C), its total cost would still be only about £1 million a year – or fivepence a head of the population. This can hardly be considered an excessive or burdensome price to pay for the aesthetic and social benefits that would accrue from the renewal of all derelict land.

THE LIMITS OF CONTROL

The rate of current dereliction might be reduced somewhat if more were known about the distribution and industrial usefulness of workable deposits, and if more care were taken to co-ordinate the activities of the various agencies responsible for the digging of holes and the disposal of wastes. There is only limited scope, however, for further abatement of the spread of dereliction by the exercise of planning control over individual mineral undertakings.

Minerals make a great and growing contribution to our national wealth; they must be worked where they are found; and they must be worked efficiently and economically.

In Durham, a partially levelled colliery tip remains a barren background for a row of miners cottages.

Except where the deposit to be worked is close to an adequate source of waste material, or where the process of extraction itself produces a sufficient quantity of spoil, full restoration of the land to its original farming use cannot be enforced as a condition of planning consent; and unless the worked-out site happens to be suitably located, its reclamation for any other use is impracticable. A comprehensive land-renewal programme must therefore reckon with the indefinitely continuing creation of new eyesores. And for these, as for the bulk of the dereliction we have inherited, landscaping will be the only remedy.

THE TECHNIQUE OF LANDSCAPING

Only fifteen years ago this would have been a confession of defeat. So many of our unsightly heaps and holes seemed then to be hopelessly expensive to reshape and quite incapable of sustaining plant life. But in those fifteen years the outlook has been transformed by the conjunction of two technical revolutions – in the mechanics of muck-shifting and tree-moving and in the science of soil-making. We can now bring to bear a battery of machines whose power, versatility and sheer numbers were inconceivable before the war; we can establish grass and trees in raw, unweathered rock, devoid of vegetable soil, and we can transplant mature trees cheaply. The forms of industrial dereliction that still cannot easily and cheaply be rendered indistinguishable from the woods and fields around them are few and far between – and even these can for the most part be effectively screened. We are no longer under any necessity, technical or economic, to leave our surroundings in a shameful and offensive condition.

This booklet does not attempt to indicate the legislative and financial provisions that would be required to make possible a really comprehensive programme of land renewal; nor does it deal with the administrative difficulties in the way of a wider and fuller use of existing powers and resources. Its scope is confined to the technical aspects of the problem confronting local authorities when they resolve to try – as a handful of them are already trying – to do the best they can in present circumstances. But whether the action in view be national and radical or local and ameliorative, the achievement of worthwhile results will depend on the recognition of two basic facts.

THE PRICE OF UGLINESS

The first is that beauty has an economic value, and ugliness an economic cost. We can estimate the enormous loss a depressing region suffers through its failure to attract new industries and through the emigration of the young people it has trained. Since we cannot tell how much of that loss should be ascribed to the ugliness of its derelict areas, we cannot *measure* the cost of leaving them derelict against the known cost of reclaiming or rehabilitating them. But that is hardly a valid reason for regarding their visual redemption as 'uneconomic'. It just does not make sense to assume that the economic cost of ugliness is nil merely because it is literally immeasurable. The seaside resort whose popularity is dimmed by conspicuous eyesores knows better. So does

In the West Country, trees planted twenty years ago have transformed the appearance of such man-made mounds.

the depressed area that can offer an industrialist the perfect site for his factory but cannot persuade him that his wife would consent to live among slag-heaps.

This study is based on the contrary assumption – that ordinary people do value the visual decencies, and that they are ready to pay a reasonable price to get derelict land restored to sightliness, whether or not it has an immediate market value for some utilitarian purpose, just as they are ready to pay for the cleansing of their streets.

THE UTILITY OF REDEMPTION

The second basic fact that must be grasped is that nobody can tell what the *potential* value of a derelict site may be for utilitarian purposes while it remains derelict. It would not be unreasonable to suppose that prospective developers took a purely objective view of a site's advantages and drawbacks – that if, for example, a derelict site offered an industrialist economies in transport that would outweigh the cost of reclaiming it, he would take it (other things being equal) in preference to a tract of farmland that was less favourably located. Paradoxical as it may seem, however, this is far from being the case. Time and again a local authority, after vainly trying for years to interest industrialists in a derelict area, has eventually graded, drained and grassed it without any hope of recovering the cost of doing so from its use as farmland – only to find that as soon as it begins to look green and pleasant it is snapped up, at a price that more than covers the cost of its redemption, by an industrialist who would not look at it in its previous condition.

Developers are, of course, ready enough to tackle derelict sites in those regions – like the Black Country – where demand is active and the only land available for development is derelict land. But where the developer has a choice between land that needs reclaiming and land that does not, and can as profitably go elsewhere if he is not allowed to exercise that choice, the planning authority will often find that the visual redemption of derelict land is the only effective way of bringing it back into active use. Indeed, the authorities which have been most active in landscaping such areas now regard this as no more than an intermediate, though indispensable, stage in the process of reclamation for urban uses. They plant and sow in the confident expectation that their trees will be chopped down and their turf stripped in a matter of months, so that the land may be used for some utilitarian purpose they cannot foresee – but they know it would remain derelict for years if they did not plant or sow. They have learnt that in such regions derelict land is for all practical purposes dead land. It is overlooked, spurned, disregarded – except as a factor depreciating the value of all land in its vicinity. It might as well not exist: better, indeed, since its existence casts a blight on the whole neighbourhood.

A local authority which sets out to rid its area of dereliction, whether or not the land is in demand for development, will often find that it has laboured to better purpose than it knew – that in seeking only to redeem the ugliness of its derelict sites it has in fact brought them back into economic circulation: back, in a real sense, to life.

20

Reprinted with special permission from *Fortune*, **57**, 103–104, 109, 194 (Jan. 1958)

Urban Sprawl

by William H. Whyte Jr.

In the next three or four years Americans will have a chance to decide how decent a place this country will be to live in, and for generations to come. Already huge patches of once green countryside have been turned into vast, smog-filled deserts that are neither city, suburb, nor country, and each day—at a rate of some 3,000 acres a day—more countryside is being bulldozed under. You can't stop progress, they say, yet much more of this kind of progress and we shall have the paradox of prosperity lowering our real standard of living.

With characteristic optimism, most Americans still assume that there will be plenty of green space on the other side of the fence. But this time there won't be. It is not merely that the countryside is ever receding; in the great expansion of the metropolitan areas the subdivisions of one city are beginning to meet up with the subdivisions of another. Flying from Los Angeles to San Bernardino—an unnerving lesson in man's infinite capacity to mess up his environment—the traveler can see a legion of bulldozers gnawing into the last remaining tract of green between the two cities, and from San Bernardino another legion of bulldozers gnawing westward. High over New Jersey, midway between New York and Philadelphia, the air traveler has a fleeting illusion of green space, but most of it has already been bought up, and outlying supermarkets and drive-in theatres are omens of what is to come. On the outer edge of the present Philadelphia metropolitan area, where there will be one million new people in the ten years ending 1960, some of the loveliest countryside in the world is being irretrievably fouled, and the main body of suburbanites has yet to arrive.

The problem, of course, is not an absolute shortage of land. Even with the 60-million increase in population expected in the next two decades, America's 1.9 billion acres of land will be quite enough to house people, and very comfortably. It will not be enough, however, if land is squandered. It is in the metropolitan area that most people are going to be living, and the fact that there will remain thousands of acres of, say, empty land in Wyoming is not going to help the man living in Teaneck, New Jersey.

The problem is the pattern of growth—or, rather, the lack of one. Because of the leapfrog nature of urban growth, even within the limits of most big cities there is to this day a surprising amount of empty land. But it is scattered; a vacant lot here, a dump there—no one parcel big enough to be of much use. And it is with this same kind of sprawl that we are ruining the whole metropolitan area of the future. In the townships just beyond today's suburbia there is little planning, and development is being left almost entirely in the hands of the speculative builder. Understandably, he follows the line of least resistance and in his wake is left a hit-or-miss pattern of development.

Aesthetically, the result is a mess. It takes remarkably little blight to color a whole area; let the reader travel along a stretch of road he is fond of, and he will notice how a small portion of open land has given amenity to the area. But it takes only a few badly designed developments or billboards or hot-dog stands to ruin it, and though only a little bit of the land is used, the place will *look* filled up.

Sprawl is bad aesthetics; it is bad economics. Five acres are being made to do the work of one, and do it very poorly. This is bad for the farmers, it is bad for communities, it is bad for industry, it is bad for utilities, it is bad for the railroads, it is bad for the recreation groups, it is bad even for the developers.

And it is unnecessary. In many suburbs the opportunity has vanished, but it is not too late to lay down sensible guidelines for the communities of the future. Most important of all, it is not too late to reserve open space while there is still some left—land for parks, for landscaped industrial districts, and for just plain scenery and breathing space.

The obstacles? There are many local efforts by private and public groups to control sprawl and save open space. But each group is going at the problem from its special point of view, indeed without even finding out what the other groups are up to. Watershed groups, for example, have not made common cause with the recreation people or utilities; farmers and urban planners have a joint interest in open space, but act more as antagonists than as allies —and all go down to piecemeal defeat.

It is going to take a political fight to bring these groups to focus on the problem, and the sooner begun the better. Many planners feel they should work first for a master government to deal with all the problems of the metropolitan area—or, at the very least, a master plan—educate the people into supporting it, then apply it to such particulars as land use. This is very orderly and logical; the trouble is the land may be gone before it works.

The proposal this article will present is based on a more pragmatic approach. It is to look at each of the different self-interests involved—such as those of the farmers, the utilities, the communities—and see what kind of plan would best unify them. Such a program will involve compromises, but it can produce action—and action that may well galvanize the whole regional planning movement.

* * * * * * *

What should the program be? Ironically, for the fundamentals of a workable plan, the best guide is not what is being done now but what was done. For there have been open-space programs in the past—brilliant ones—and unique as each may have been, together they provide several valuable lessons.

• ***New York's Central Park*. In 1844, William Cullen Bryant took a walk over the hilly countryside north of the city. It struck him that a large tract should be bought for a "central reservation" while land was still cheap, for eventually it would be surrounded by the growing city. He started to agitate for it. Ridiculous, said the *Journal of Commerce*: there is plenty of countryside for people to go out and see, so why pay for it? But the populace liked the idea; the politicians declared for it, and in 1856 it became a reality.**

▶ *Cook County Forest Preserve.* In the early 1900's a group of Chicago citizens conceived the idea of buying up large tracts of land in the country around Chicago for the enjoyment of present and future generations. In short order they lined up public support, and after several rebuffs in the courts, the Forest Preserve was finally established. Promptly it started buying land. Today there are 44,000 acres in the preserve, valued at $150 million, and Superintendent Charles Sauers is still buying land—at a rate of 1,000 acres a year.

▶ *Cleveland Park System.* William Stinchcomb, father of Cleveland's superb park system (which embraces some 14,000 acres of natural woodland), delighted in horrifying visiting planners by telling them how he planned the system. He got the idea one weekend, sketched it out on a piece of paper—then spent the next thirty years filling in the purchases.

▶ *Westchester County Park System.* Back about 1900 a private citizen named V. Everett Macy took a horseback ride along the Bronx River Valley and was appalled by the maze of shanties he saw. A group of millionaires had just built a private road on Long Island, and it occurred to Macy that it would be a good idea if a scenic road bordered by trees and meadows were built along the Bronx River. After some badgering, the state legislature set up a commission to acquire the land (New York City was to foot 75 per cent of the bill, Westchester County the rest). The parkway was put through, and though a few towns along the route chiseled some of the parkway's land, it remains a delight.

A little later, political boss William Ward, who seems to have run Westchester County on lines drawn up by the Pharaohs, was sitting on a park bench—one of Stinchcomb's parks in Cleveland, it so happened. He spied a "Keep Off the Grass" sign. This annoyed him. He began to ponder how little grass there would be for Westchester County people to enjoy if a lot of land wasn't bought up quickly. On his return, he set up the Westchester County Park Commission, and instructed it to buy up waste land. As to how it would be used, he said, they could worry about that later. Eighteen thousand acres were picked up this way, and today they constitute, save for golf courses, about the only open space in the most populated section of the county.

▶ *Ohio Conservancy District.* After the great flood of 1913, businessmen of Dayton, Ohio, decided something ought to be done. With their own money, they brought in consultant Arthur Morgan. Morgan concluded that the flooding problem couldn't be solved by local reservoirs or channels; instead, he proposed that a district be set up covering the whole watershed area. Its powers would include taxation, eminent domain, and the right to issue bonds. The businessmen got the enabling legislation passed by the legislature in 1914. With no funds from the state, the group built five dams and started acquiring land for flood control and recreation purposes. Before long, similar districts were set up throughout the state. The district form still has some legal bugs in it, but there are a score of lakes that never existed before, and thanks to the land-acquisition program, plenty of recreation land around them for people to enjoy.

▶ *The Boston Metropolitan Park System.* Under the leadership of Charles Eliot, landscape architect, the cities and towns around Boston got together in 1893 to establish "reservations" on the outskirts of the built-up area—the Blue Hills Reservation and Middlesex Fells Reservation were acquired, but urban sprawl has now extended around and beyond them. A year ago the Massachusetts General Court approved a new project for "The Bay Circuit"—a belt of open spaces some twenty miles from the State House, with proposed reservations, forests, and parks separating metropolitan Boston from Lawrence, Lowell, Worcester, and Providence. The state has been authorized to proceed.

There seem to be four clear lessons. (1) Getting something done is primarily a matter of leadership, rather than research. (2) Bold vision, tied to some concrete benefit, can get popular support fairly quickly. (3) The most effective policy is to get the land first and rationalize the acquisition later. (4) Action itself is the best of all research tools to find what works and what doesn't.

21

Reprinted from *Audubon*, **75**(4), 26–31 (1973)

Subdividing and Conquering the Desert

GARY SOUCIE

BARNUM WAS A PRETTY FAIR JUDGE of human nature. How else could you explain the success of so-called land developers in unloading each year, at premium prices, thousands upon thousands of lots in desert subdivisions in Arizona? Surely it is a congenital gullibility that brings people by the droves to plunk down their hard-earned savings to purchase little pieces of played-out rangeland and uninhabitable desert at prices several times more than the land is worth, from people and companies they know nothing about, in developments that will never be. Pity the poor suckers, yes, but pity even more the land that is the ultimate victim, and pity the future generations of Arizonans and Americans who will have to live with the messy aftermath of a dirty business Congressman Morris K. Udall aptly calls "a felonious assault on Arizona's environment."

Well over a million acres of private land in Arizona has been subdivided for sale on the installment plan like so many refrigerators and washing machines. Arizona is being sold all over the country by direct mail, by telephone solicitation, and door to door. Startled tourists have been greeted, while deplaning in Tokyo or Rome, by salesmen offering lots in Arizona's Rio Rico subdivision. And everywhere you turn within the state you are assaulted by billboards, newspaper advertisements, and radio and television commercials peddling Arizona like an underarm deodorant. It used to be that a cloud of dust on the Arizona horizon was a sign of cattle on the drive to market. Nowadays it is more likely dust raised by a herd of bulldozers gouging out subdivision road networks. Eventually, some of these roads will be paved and lined by ranch houses built cheek by jowl on one-third- and one-quarter-acre lots in a perversion of Western living. More of them will never serve traffic heavier than the parade of lot salesmen taking the suckers on their rounds, the Mom-and-Pop speculators looking for "investment" property.

Beneath the growing outrage over the wholesale swindle of a credulous consumer public through deceptive and fraudulent installment lot sales, lie the larger and more ominous environmental consequences of speculative land development. In a recently released draft of a survey of large-scale remote subdivisions in the state, the Arizona Department of Economic Planning and Development noted: "There is little documentation available concerning the statewide impact of remote subdivisions. It is not known to what extent the large amount of remote subdivision activity will alter Arizona's expected urban and rural growth patterns. The potential effect of these remote subdivisions on Arizona's natural environment and economic growth needs to be studied . . . The extent of environmental damage that may result from subdividing has not been measured objectively, although the preliminary survey did find evidence of environmental damage." In a strong editorial reaction to the study, the *Arizona Daily Star* in Tucson called for regulated and staged development of the state: "The Arizona Legislature must move quickly to counteract the butchering of the state's rural lands."

Actually, the environmental consequences of remote subdivisions cannot be separated from Arizona's general development patterns and the well-known (but apparently not yet well-*enough*-known) consumer scandal of the installment land sales business.

During the 1950s a developmental orgy of unprecedented magnitude violently transformed Arizona from a rural to an urbanized state. Between 1950 and 1960 Arizona's population jumped by 74 percent, from 750,000 to 1.3 million. Phoenix and Tucson bore the brunt of the invasion, growing by 311 and 368 percent, respectively. In 1950 the two cities contained one-fifth of the state's total population; by 1960 they contained one-half. During the 1960s the state's growth rate slowed to 36 percent, Phoenix's to 32 percent, and Tucson's to 24 percent. But the state's population continued to concentrate in the two metropolitan areas, as fast-growing suburbs like Tempe and Scottsdale absorbed the influx. Today, 55 percent of all the people in the state of Arizona live within the Phoenix metropolitan area, and another 20 percent within the Tucson metropolitan area.

The direct physical impact on Arizona's environment from the massive immigration of the past two decades was geographically limited because of the concentration of people in the two metropolitan areas. The indirect impact of highways, dams, mines, power transmission lines, and other facilities built to service and employ the new population was not so restricted. Remember the epic battle during the mid-1960s over dams in the Grand Canyon?

While the urban-suburban sprawl of Arizona's development continues apace in the metropolitan areas, a more recent trend—the phantom development of land speculation in remote subdivisions—has carried the impact into the hinterlands. According to the Arizona Real Estate Department, between 6,500 and 6,700 subdivision applications have been approved since 1941. Many of these subdivisions, particularly the earlier ones, were located to serve the influx of people into the urban areas; a great many of the more recent ones are out in the sticks, designed primarily to serve the bank accounts of the subdividers. Riding on the notoriety of Arizona's explosive development over the past two decades, the new subdividers are hustling lots on the remotest, wretchedest real estate imaginable to naive, often greedy people who think they are making a smart, safe investment in a booming area. Mostly, they are making the mistake of their lives.

By promoting a myth of scarcity ("Did you know, Mr. Soucie, that less than fifteen percent of Arizona's land is privately owned and that the state's future development will have to take place on that limited land base?") and concentrating on middle- and working-class people who know nothing about investment, land development, or Arizona, the installment subdividers are able to unload small parcels of marginal or worthless land located far from the paths of logical development at outrageously inflated prices. The subdividers and their cadres of salesmen find easy pickings among people whose only previous investment experience was in a bank savings account. Bedazzled by unfamiliar financial terms like "leverage" and enticed by the promise of doubling or tripling their money in a few short years, the suckers can't resist the easy terms of a small down payment and a few dollars a month. Most of them will be exceptionally lucky if they manage to recoup their "investment" during their lifetimes, let alone make a profit.

The astonishing thing is that it never seems to occur to these people to wonder why, if land investment in these subdivisions is such a sure bet, the banks, mutual funds, and other professional investors haven't got there first and bought it all up. As the *Christian Science Monitor* has editorialized, "The old American chimera of limitless land, open to all comers to exploit for personal profit, continues to delude public thought."

A few, but only a very few, of these remote subdivisions will become fully developed in the foreseeable future. Many more will never see development of any kind. The majority will undergo a partial development that promises to become an immense burden on the state and county governments and a major problem for economic and land-use planning. New roads, utility lines, water supply and flood control projects, facilities and amenities of all kinds, will have to be flung around the state to serve, at least partially, the needs of nonviable little communities.

The remote subdivisions that are most likely to succeed will be new towns—planned communities large enough to encompass a wide range of housing and the industrial, commercial, and public facilities necessary to provide the employment, cultural, and social opportunities that will enable them to be relatively self-contained and independent. According to the State Department of Economic Planning and Development, there are only eight such remote new-town subdivisions under development in Arizona. The best known of these is Lake Havasu City, a development of McCulloch Properties, a subsidiary of McCulloch Oil Corporation. Lake Havasu City's apparent success has been a boon to other subdividers, and even the most specious ones are likely to cite the example of Lake Havasu City in their sales pitches. The key to Lake Havasu City's viability, according to planners and state officials I talked to, was the relocation of McCulloch's boatbuilding business to provide the immediate employment base.

Another successful new-town development is Del Webb's Sun City, a retirement community located northwest of Phoenix that, like Topsy, just "grow'd" to become a town of 25,000 people. South of Tucson, Green Valley is another retirement community that developed into a full-fledged new town, although the open-pit copper mines that provide the jobs for the nonretired population have rather depressingly fouled up the town's setting.

Thirty miles east of Phoenix, McCulloch is busy developing Fountain Hills. It is a 12,000-acre subdivision nicely isolated from the city's future eastward sprawl by the Salt River Indian Reservation, the McDowell Mountains, and McDowell Mountain Regional Park, and it overlooks the reservoir site of the proposed Orme Dam on the Verde River. At full development, according to the "master area utilization plan," Fountain Hills will have an ultimate population of 70,000, sixteen schools, three eighteen-hole golf courses, shopping centers, commercial developments, light industries, hotels and motels, and, as a salesman assured me, "the richest avenue in the world." Because of its reasonably well articulated plan, its setting, its proximity to Phoenix, and McCulloch's financial resources, Fountain Hills is a pretty sure bet for success, despite its prices. Medium-density residential lots (varying in size from one-eighth to one-quarter acre) start at $8,500, and the somewhat more speculative acre-plus "residential estates" up against the mountains start at $13,000.

But even a legitimate development like Fountain Hills is not without its environmental problems. For all its planning, McCulloch Properties got off to a bad start. Its massive bulldozing during site preparation was so heavy-handed that one Maricopa County supervisor complained, "They don't need a subdivision permit; they need a mining permit." Lately McCulloch's landscaping at Fountain Hills has been brought more nearly into line with environmental sensitivity.

Typically, a subdivision's first development, after the building of an on-site sales office and the grading of a rudimentary road network, is the construction of the golf course. But the first of Fountain Hills' three links was just getting under way when I visited in March of this year. Instead, Fountain Hills began with its fountain. Not just any fountain, but *the* fountain. McCulloch goes in for gaudy excess (the firm moved London Bridge to Lake Havasu City), for they spent $1.5 million to build, right out there in arid Arizona, the world's highest fountain.

At full blast, the Fountain Hills fountain's three 600-horsepower pumps send a plume of water 560 feet into the air—that's 125 feet higher than Le Jet d'Eau in Switzerland's Lake of Geneva and five feet higher than the Washington Monument. At 7,000 gallons per minute, the fountain's flow can keep more than eight tons of water suspended in the air. Despite the fountain's use of recirculated water from the little artificial lake that doubles as an irrigation reservoir, Arizona conservationists are incensed by this conspicuous symbol of water waste and extravagance in a state that has precious little water to spare. The state's chief hydrologist told me that, on a dry day, as much as one-fourth of the water sent up into the air will not return. A Fountain Hills brochure assures that "water loss through evaporation will be less in one year than required to irrigate two acres of cotton."

And regional planners are concerned about the problems posed by a development on Fountain Hills' scale. Experience elsewhere (at Reston, Virginia, and Columbia, Maryland) has shown that, despite a new town's planned self-sufficiency, highway traffic in the area tends to increase a great deal, especially if the new town is within an easy commute of a major city where employment opportunities are more varied. Moreover, because of its proximity to public lands, Fountain Hills has not budgeted much community open space or parks in its master plan, a situation that presages increased use of public recreational facilities.

At the extreme from the new towns are the remote subdivisions that haven't a ghost of a chance of developing. Heading the list of these are the speculative lot-sales subdivisions in areas that have no water. Philip Briggs, chief hydrologist for the State Water Commission, points out that thousands of lots have been sold or are being promoted in large subdivisions in the northern part of the state where "there isn't any ground water at all. In some places there isn't a source of water within a hundred miles." Briggs explained that the few small towns in that part of the state depend on water brought in from Lake Mead in tank trucks. Arizona law does not require that there be water on or near a subdivision. And the counties are willing to approve any subdivision application on the off chance that maybe, just maybe, the developers will find water somewhere and the county's tax ratables will increase.

There are two schools of thought about the environmental impact of these shadow subdivisions. One holds that there may be a hidden environmental blessing beneath the massive consumer bilking. Once these big blocks of land have been sold to thousands of nonresident owners who will never be able to develop the land, and who will never be able to find buyers at the prices they paid for undevelopable land, the land will be locked up—preserved forever. The other school feels that this is an unalloyed calamity, foreclosing any future opportunities to use the land for nonresidential purposes like farming, ranching, grazing, recreation, or public works.

Squandering water in the desert—the preposterous 560-foot-high

fountain at Fountain Hills, highest spout in the world.

The heaviest environmental tolls will be levied by large-scale subdivisions that, for one reason or another, will become only partially developed. Desert land broken for roads and streets does not heal quickly. Fragile desert plant communities will be uprooted forever. Dust storms will blight neighboring areas. Desert winds and flash floods will erode the primitive streets into permanent gullies. Sometimes partial development occurs because a well-intentioned but underfinanced entrepreneur can't deliver the promised goods, and the failure of such marginal subdividers of raw land is likely to increase. For the persistence of fraudulent and deceptive practices, the certain coming of stricter government regulation, and the realities of oversupply have combined to turn Wall Street sour on land development. In 1970 and 1971, General Acceptance Corporation (the parent company of the biggest and most aggressive installment subdivider operating in Arizona or perhaps in the world), made two bond offerings of $50 million each and had to offer interest rates of twelve and eleven percent; the last time I checked the bond market, GAC was in a pretty rarefied minority at those interest rates.

IRONICALLY, CONSUMER PROTECTION pressure seems to be the main force propelling the phenomenon of the partially developed subdivision. To "prove" the legitimacy of their developments, subdividers have taken to bulldozing roads, sometimes even paving them, far in advance of need. Typically, today's subdivision presents two faces to the world: a small section of developed homesites for immediate construction and the rest being sold as investment property, as raw land. And to make the investment look more attractive, roads are graded throughout the speculative real estate.

When I visited Diamond Bell Ranch west of Tucson, I found a 35,000-acre cattle ranch in rather attractive cholla desert country beneath the Sierrita Mountains. Most of the ranch is public grazing land under lease, but the 8,800 acres of private land have been subdivided. A 200-acre piece in the middle of the property is being sold in one-acre developed homesites that require construction within a year. Another 30 acres has been zoned for commercial development, and the rest of the land is being sold on speculation with residential construction not permitted until some unspecified time when utilities are put in by the developer, Southwest Properties. Some houses were in place, although a few of them were model homes built on speculation. The salesman told me there were 40 houses, of which 35 were occupied. No schools, no shops or restaurants, no facilities of any kind except for a swimming pool and "hospitality ranch house." When he took me around the salesman proudly pointed out that Southwest Properties recently had spent a million dollars putting in the grid of roads bulldozed into the desert soil. Exploring on my own I found many of the roads already virtually impassable from water erosion.

At Arizona City the situation is somewhat different. Arizona City is one of half a dozen big subdivisions near Casa Grande, a copper-mining and cotton-ginning town in the flat, residentially unattractive desert country midway between Phoenix and Tucson. Arizona City is about ten years old and has a tiny shopping center, a couple of small factories, a golf course, and about 850 residents living in tiny houses on 60- by 100-foot lots. All of this development occupies less than one-third of the subdivided property, and the salesman I talked to told me that "85 percent of our business is in investment property sold in the field," meaning to people in Kansas, Nebraska, and the Dakotas who haven't the foggiest notion of what they are buying into sight unseen. Nevertheless, the development company, a subsidiary of Fuqua Industries, is spending nearly $4 million this year and next to pave the streets in four sections of land comprising 2,560 acres, or about two-thirds of the total property. It looks so much more real that way.

To hear the lot salesmen and subdividers tell it, every subdivision being sold in Arizona is a sure bet for full development. But it will be the rare subdivision indeed that will reach full development, for a number of reasons. Examine just four of the factors working against the development of most Arizona subdivisions:

Price. With a majority of subdivisions doing a majority of their business in "investment" sales, there will have to materialize a second wave of buyers who actually plan to live on the subdivisions and who will be willing to pay more than the current prices being offered and taken. And the current prices aren't to be believed. In my own visits to a number of subdivisions between Phoenix and the Mexican border I was offered property ranging from $3,295 (for an acre-plus undeveloped lot at Diamond Bell Ranch) to $19,500 (for an 80- by 110-foot developed lot at Arizona City).

These inflated prices are utterly artificial and are not related to intrinsic value, supply and demand, or comparative prices for land outside the subdivisions. Explaining the price structure to *The New York Times* editors, GAC's president and chairman, S. H. Wills, said: "The price at the time of purchase is based on future value, say ten years out, after the homesite, the neighborhood, and basic amenities of the new town are completely developed. The assessed value of the land at the time our customer purchases it may be less than five percent of the selling price." It is hard to figure out just what is supposed to trigger development of these subdivisions if a majority of customers are buying for investment on ten-year installment contracts, and the land won't be worth what they paid for it until the development becomes a full-scale reality.

Supply and demand. The Arizona Department of Economic Planning and Development surveyed all subdivisions that are at least 640 acres in size, at least three miles outside incorporated areas, and beyond the logical extensions of urban areas. According to the report, there are 182 such subdivisions in Arizona containing more than one million acres of land and with a population capacity calculated to be more than 3.5 million people. "This is 997,700 more people than are expected to be added to Arizona's current population by the year 2000." The study stresses that the capacity of the unknown number of smaller subdivisions in the state further aggravates the situation. (The Office of Interstate Land Sales Registration in the U.S. Department of Housing and Urban Development, with which all subdividers selling land across state lines are supposed to register, has files on some 460 Arizona subdivisions.)

Location. In the real estate business there is an adage that says, "The three most important things in real estate are location, location, and location." But most of the installment lot-sales subdivisions in Arizona are located outside those areas reasonably expected to develop in the foreseeable future. As the study by the Department of Economic Planning and Development pointed out, Arizona's population is expected to increase by about 2.5 million people by the end of this century, with the Phoenix and Tucson metropolitan areas alone "expected to increase by a combined total of two million people by the year 2000."

Yet Mohave County, in the northwest corner of the state, is a favorite of the subdividers, despite its shortage of water and its distance from the fast-growing metropolitan areas. Of Arizona's 14 counties, Mohave is the second largest (13,217 square miles) but the fourth least populated (31,100 people, a quarter of whom live in the town of Kingman). By the end of the century, according to the state study, Mohave County is expected to increase its population by only 23,881. Yet it has 46 subdivisions with 226,742 acres and a population capacity of 544,800, or 22 times the expected population increase. Kingman's newspaper, the *Mohave County Miner*, recently listed some 14,000 tax forfeitures of land, most of them in the large subdivisions.

Water. In an arid state like Arizona, even where there is water there may not be enough water to support large-scale residential development. When GAC was planning to subdivide the 35,000-acre Empire Ranch southeast of Tucson into enough lots to house 180,000 people, two resourceful Tucson conservationists swung into action and did what Pima County and the State of Arizona should have done in the first place. Robert Coshland, a retired businessman who is now a National Parks and Conservation Association volunteer, and Charles Costin, former president of Tucson Audubon Society, formed a committee of hydrologists from consulting firms, the University of Arizona, the City of Tucson Department of Water and Sewers, and the U.S. Geological Survey. The committee's findings, which checked out to within 10 percent of figures obtained from GAC's own hydrologic consultants, showed that there was water enough to support only 38,000 people. These findings were substantially confirmed by the State Water Commission. So the Pima County Planning and Zoning Commission approved the development only at a reduced scale consistent with the water supply. GAC defended its original plans on the grounds that it would take 60 years to reach a population of 38,000 and a century to reach the one-third capacity mark of 60,000. Some investment opportunity!

The installment lot-sales subdivisions aren't the only ones carving up the Arizona countryside. Arizona's increasingly urbanizing population has taken to weekend ruralization in vacation-home subdivisions all over the state. Last December the U.S. Forest Service published a land-use planning study of the Mogollon Rim area northeast of Phoenix. The study showed that, on private lands within the boundaries of Tonto, Sitgreaves, and Coconino national forests, there are 150 small second-home or recreational subdivisions containing 8,175 acres and 16,555 lots, 68 percent of which had already been sold and on which there were 2,902 dwelling structures and 415 mobile homes. Already the three national forests have experienced serious problems from trespass, illegal cutting of timber and firewood, unauthorized grazing of horses, litter and illegal dumps, water pollution through inadequate sewage facilities, the crowding of public recreation areas "to the exclusion of transient recreationists," depletion of wildlife resources through increased hunting and fishing, a major increase in applications for special-use permits (for access roads, powerlines, and waste disposal areas), and the increased threat of wildfires and outbreaks of destructive insects and diseases. The report concluded: "At some undetermined density, the subdivision development will begin to directly or indirectly interfere with the various product and service outputs from the national forests."

If Arizona were alone in suffering the blight of raw-land and second-home subdivisions, the problem might be a more manageable one. But land development is a big, nationwide business. No one really knows just how big it is, but a frequently cited figure is that land developers gross over $6 billion a year in sales. The federal Office of Interstate Land Sales Registration lists 2,800 developers engaged in interstate sales of lots in nearly 5,000 subdivisions in 49 states, North Dakota being the only exception. According to *Business Week*, "More than 10,000 entrepreneurs are selling land on an installment basis." *U.S. News & World Report* says that, according to the American Land Development Association, "there are now 9,000 vacation-land-development firms" in the United States.

THE ENVIRONMENTAL IMPLICATIONS of this kind of rural development are almost beyond reckoning. A Georgetown University law professor, William H. Rodgers Jr., has written in *The Washington Monthly* that "The state of New Mexico . . . has subdivision roads that, strung together, would go all the way to Mongolia." Peter Borrelli, the Sierra Club's Eastern representative, reports that New Hampshire has a second-home population of 287,000, one-third of its total permanent population. *Business Week* claims that "by the end of this century . . . an estimated 18 million acres of rural land will be urbanized."

Until now virtually nothing has been done to curb this blitzkrieg of the American landscape. Few states have even rudimentary systems for handling, let alone regulating, subdivision applications. County governments, which typically have zoning control, appear to have neither the will nor the skill to deal effectively with the problem. The federal government's only significant involvement is through the Office of Interstate Land Sales Registration, which is a full-disclosure rather than a regulatory agency. Most of the land-use bills being considered by the Congress do not come to grips with the problem in an effective way. So far, most attention and concern has been focused on consumer protection rather than environmental protection.

In his seminal essay, "The Land Ethic," Aldo Leopold wrote: "Conservation is a state of harmony between men and land. Despite nearly a century of propaganda, conservation still proceeds at a snail's pace; progress still consists largely of letterhead pieties and convention oratory. On the back forty we still slip two steps backward for each forward stride."

For all our society's new-found concern for conservation, ecology, the environment, planning, and the rest, we are still wide of the mark, and Aldo Leopold's words are as true today as when he wrote them more than a quarter of a century ago. Permit systems, emission standards, environmental messages, councils, and agencies abound, but the primal abundance of the good Earth continues to dwindle as we encourage the developers and the highwaymen to despoil and pave over 650,000 acres each year.

Conservation battles are still being lost and won, not on the main issue of man's stewardship of his planetary home, but on legal technicalities, economic arguments, and naked political pressure. There is still no real evidence that we have achieved the intellectual humility, the philosophical awareness, and the simple decency we need to live in harmony with the land. We have not achieved the land ethic that, in Leopold's words, "changes the role of *Homo sapiens* from conqueror of the land-community to plain member and citizen of it." ■

22

Reprinted from *Water Resources Res.*, **3**(2), 451–464 (1967)

Effects of Construction on Fluvial Sediment, Urban and Suburban Areas of Maryland

M. GORDON WOLMAN AND ASHER P. SCHICK[1]

The Johns Hopkins University

Baltimore, Maryland

Abstract. The equivalent of many decades of natural or even agricultural erosion may take place during a single year from areas cleared for construction. Areas undergoing rapid development near Baltimore, Maryland, and Washington, D. C., lie on the Coastal Plain and Piedmont, with slopes generally of 1–10% but sometimes of 20% and more. Soil is deep, and the annual precipitation of 42 inches (1100 mm) is evenly distributed, with high summer intensities. Average sediment yield is 200–500 t/mi²/yr (80–200 t/km²/yr), with predominantly wooded watersheds supplying sometimes even less. Intensive farming 50–80 years ago caused yields up to 1000 t/mi²/yr (400 t/km²/yr), but such high yields are no longer present owing to the continuous decline of farm acreage in the metropolitan periphery. Sediment concentrations from areas undergoing construction ranged from 3000 to over 150,000 ppm, whereas in natural or agricultural catchments the highest comparative concentration was 2000 ppm. In terms of annual values, yields from construction areas range from several thousand to a maximum of 140,000 t/mi²/yr (i.e., up to 55,000 t/km²/yr) from a small area. Total yield declines with increasing drainage area as a result of dilution from waters draining urban and other land not actually under construction. Observations demonstrate that sediment storage occurs on construction sites as well as in valley bottomlands. Actual yields from a given unit surface may be even larger than those derived from measurements in streams. Data on erosion from roadcuts in Georgia, when converted to soil loss per area, result in sediment yields similar to those from building sites: 50,000–150,000 t/mi²/yr (20,000–50,000 t/km²/yr), and local measurements indicate depths of erosion on roadcuts of 0.1–0.2 ft (3–6 cm) over time intervals of generally less than one year. Imposition of large quantities of sediment on streams previously carrying relatively small quantities of primarily suspended material produced deposition of channel bars, erosion of channel banks as a result of deposition within the channel, obstruction of flow and increased flooding, shifting configuration of the channel bottom, blanketing of bottom-dwelling flora and fauna, alteration of the flora and fauna due to changes in light transmission and abrasive effects of sediment, and alteration of species of fish due to changes produced in the flora and fauna upon which fish depend. Analysis of building permit records showed that: (1) 50% of construction sites were open for eight months, 60% for nine, and 25% for more than one year; (2) contrary to expectations, construction activity is practically constant throughout the year, with about 84% of all sites being open in any one month; (3) the average size of a construction site for one permit-bearing building is 14,400 ft² (1340 m²), a value that remained constant during the last decade. These findings, combined with statistics on highway construction, indicate that in four Maryland counties covering expanding metropolitan regions adjacent to Baltimore and Washington, at a minimum 7.2 mi² (19 km²) of land are cleared at any one time for construction purposes. Housing and other buildings account for 5.7 mi² (15 km²) and highways for 1.5 mi² (4 km²). Sediment yield is roughly 700–1800 tons per 1000 increase in population. Progressive urbanization effects an initial rise in the total sediment, soon followed by a steady decline. The proportion of sediment from the construction source, however, will increase steadily and may overtake the total agricultural yield at a not very advanced stage of urbanization. Most economic evaluations of problems posed by urban sediment are subject to much uncertainty. The problem, however, is common to all conurbations, particularly where heavy earthmoving machinery is in use. Techniques for lessening sediment yield and delivery are available. Their widespread adoption presents complex issues of a local, legal, and social nature. (Key words: Sediment; urbanization)

[1] Now at The Hebrew University of Jerusalem, Israel.

SEDIMENT YIELD, TRANSPORT, AND DEPOSITION

The Type Area

The principal area of study included metropolitan Baltimore and an area considered part of metropolitan Washington in the State of Maryland. Both cities are rapidly expanding urban centers of about 2,000,000 inhabitants each in their metropolitan areas (Figure 1). Physiographically the areas under construction are Coastal Plain or Piedmont, with slopes generally 1 to 10%, but sometimes 20% or more. Soil is very deep nearly everywhere, and bedrock is encountered in the construction process in only a few localities.

Mean annual precipitation in the type area is about 42 inches (1100 mm). This amount is nearly evenly distributed throughout the twelve months of the year. Intensities are, however, much higher in the summer. A rainfall of 2 inches per hour recurs once in about ten years. Some of the winter precipitation is snow, but snow cover rarely persists for more than a fortnight.

Sediment Production and Yield from Areas under Construction

Nearly always there is a variable 'background' quantity of sediment provided to all or to virtually all streams. Therefore, in attacking the problem of sediment pollution, one must first establish the level of this background at any given time and place if the possible problems posed by sedimentation and their amelioration are to be considered in a realistic framework.

A representative selection of large and small drainage basins in Maryland or in comparable areas which are either rural or wooded (Table 1) indicates that the average sediment yield is on the order of 200 to 500 t/mi²/yr. The data in Table 1 are derived from sampling at stream gaging stations along the rivers and are not estimates of sediment yield based on the distribution of land use in the watershed. Figures as low as 15 t/mi²/yr were recorded for a small stream in the Appalachians in Kentucky, in a heavily wooded area comparable to Western Maryland. Piedmont areas that are being farmed produce sediment yields on the order of 500 t/mi²/yr, as illustrated by Watts Branch at Rockville, Maryland.

Although all figures in Table 1 are for rural or wooded watersheds, the figures by periods for Gunpowder Falls at Loch Raven Dam and at Prettyboy Reservoir are particularly significant. For the period 1914–1943, the sediment yield to Loch Raven was 800 t/mi²/yr. A later survey, however, indicated that from 1943 to 1961 the yield had dropped to one quarter of

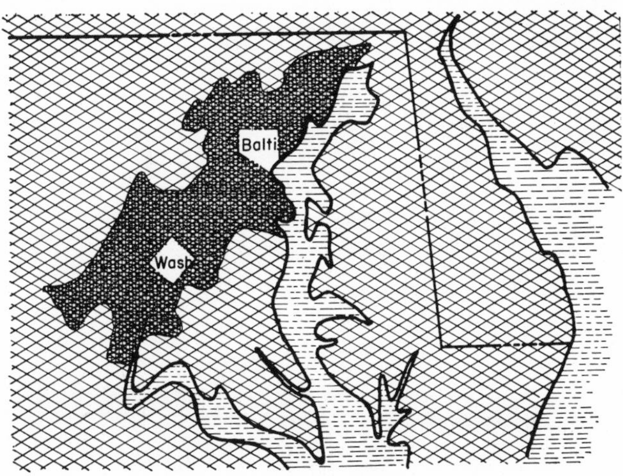

BALTIMORE AND WASHINGTON
City vs. Suburban Area

Fig. 1. The Metropolitan areas of Baltimore and Washington.

TABLE 1. Sediment Yield From Rural Drainage Areas

Stream and Location	Drainage Area, sq mi	Sediment Yield, tons/mi²/yr	Condition
Helton Branch nr. Somerset, Ky.	0.85	15	wooded [*Collier et al.*, 1962]
Watts Branch, Rockville, Md.	3.7	516	rural [*Wark and Keller*, 1963]
Northwest Branch Anacostia River nr Colesville, Md.	21.3	470	rural [*Wark and Keller*, 1963]
Georges Creek at Franklin, Md.	72.4	207	rural, wooded
Gunpowder Falls, Prettyboy Reservoir, Hereford, Md.	80	913	rural; 1933–1943 [*Holeman*, 1965]
Gunpowder Falls, Prettyboy Reservoir, Hereford, Md.	80	500	rural; 1943–1961 [*Holeman*, 1965]
Seneca Creek, Dawsonville, Md.	101	320	rural [*Wark and Keller*, 1963]
Gunpowder Falls, Loch Raven Dam, Towson, Md.	300	808	rural; 1914–1943 [*Holeman*, 1965]
Same	300	233	rural; 1943–1961 [*Holeman*, 1965]
Monocacy River, Frederick, Md.	817	327	rural [*Wark and Keller*, 1963]

its previous value, to 233 t/mi²/yr. Similarly, during 1933–1943 the rate of sedimentation in Prettyboy Reservoir was 913 t/mi²/yr, whereas between 1943 and 1961 the rate had decreased to 500 t/mi²/yr.

The earlier sedimentation rates, particularly in Loch Raven from 1914 to 1943, appear to reflect the intensive farming activity in the state, particularly in the Piedmont area, during the period 1880 to approximately 1910. Between 1880 and 1900, the acreage in farms in Maryland reached its maximum. Since then there has been a steady decline in the total area in farms in the state. The decline in cultivated area on farms is particularly rapid in a representative area peripheral to a metropolitan center such as Baltimore County where, after 1920, the area of cultivated land declined continuously at a rate of about 1200 acres per year.

From the sediment yield data and from the analysis of land area in farms, it is clear that throughout much of the state sediment yield from agricultural and wooded lands is relatively low. In addition, the difference between the present conditions and those in 1900 is perhaps most striking in areas adjacent to metropolitan regions. Here a good deal of land is no longer farmed and is instead growing up in brush and woodland until it is bought for subdivision and housing development. Hence, the sediment yield from such areas is perhaps at its lowest point during recent historic time.

Against this background of sediment yields ranging from 200 to 500 tons per square mile per annum, we may compare yields from drainage basins undergoing development through subdivision and highway construction. The figures in Table 2 are based upon measurements in stream channels and, like those for the rural area in Table 1, are not estimates of yield based on rainfall, soil, and topographic characteristics. Data are quite limited, and, as of the date of compilation, Table 2 provided the largest summary of available information known to the authors.

Data for locations 1, 2, and 5 in Table 2 are derived from the present study. Locations 1 and 5 represent periodic samplings at particular construction sites. The data for the tributary of Minebank Run are based upon a survey of deposition in a large alluvial fan downstream from a construction site.

For the small streams sampled in this study it was necessary to develop flow frequency curves by correlation with nearby gaging stations or from rainfall records and, from a relation between flow and measured sediment concentrations, to compute the annual sediment yield. This was done at Oregon Branch and at The Johns Hopkins University construction site.

TABLE 2. Sediment Yield from Selected Drainage Basins: Maryland and Other Areas

Reference Number	Stream and Location	Drainage Area, sq mi	Sediment Yield, tons/mi²/yr	Condition
1	Johns Hopkins University Baltimore, Md.	0.0025	140,000	construction site
2	Tributary, Minebank Run Towson, Md.	0.031	80,000	commercial
3	Tributary, Kensington, Md.	0.091	24,000	housing subdivision [*Guy*, 1963]
4	Tributary, Gwynns Falls, Md.	0.094	11,300	housing (yield computed from small stilling basin, probably low trap efficiency)
5	Oregon Branch, Cockeysville, Md.	0.236	72,000	industrial park
6	Cane Branch, near Somerset, Ky.	0.67	1,147	strip mine [*Collier et al.*, 1962]
7	Greenbelt Reservoir, Greenbelt, Md.	0.83	5,600	housing [*Guy and Ferguson*, 1962]
8	Little Falls Branch, Bethesda, Md.	4.1	2,320	urban & development (includes urban area as well as area undergoing development. *Wark and Keller* [1963]
9	Lake Barcroft, near Fairfax, Va.	9.5	32,500	housing subdivision (for maximum year, *Holeman and Geiger* [1959]
10	Northwest Branch Anacostia River near Hyattsville, Md.	49.4	1,850	urban & development (includes urban area as well as area undergoing development. [*Wark and Keller*, 1963; *Keller*, 1962]
11	Rock Creek, Sherrill Drive Washington, D. C.	62.2	1,600	urban & development (includes urban area as well as area undergoing development). [*Wark and Keller*, 1963; *Keller*, 1962]
12	Northeast Branch Anacostia near Riverdale, Md.	72.8	1,060	urban & development (includes urban area as well as area undergoing development). [*Wark and Keller*, 1963; *Keller*, 1962]

A glance at Table 2 shows that sediment yields from areas undergoing construction range from one thousand to roughly 100,000 t/mi²/yr. The highest figures are derived from the smallest unit areas, and in some cases the actual area under construction is exceedingly small. Thus, the yields extrapolated to a unit square mile may appear unusually large. In examples 1 and 2 (Table 2) the contributing area is the total drainage area given. In all of the others, the area under construction is considerably less than the drainage area sampled. At Kensington (item 3, Table 2), for example, *Guy and Ferguson* [1962] note that 'the disturbed area at any one time was roughly 2 to 10 acres of the total drainage area of 58 acres (0.091 mi²). The figures in Table 2 suggest that the sediment yield expressed in weight per unit area per year declines with increasing drainage area. It is important to note, however, that for the larger drainage area the entire area is not at any one time undergoing construction, whereas for the smaller areas most of the land is in fact under construction. Thus the declining unit yield is a dilution factor in the case of the larger drainage areas in Table 2.

The relationship between sediment yield, drainage area, and construction activity is expressed in Figure 2, which incorporates the data of tables 1 and 2. The stratification according to 'dilution' is a rough separation based on the percentage of the area under construction. Figure 2 suggests that the ratio of sediment yielded by watersheds undergoing construction to that contributed by 'natural' agricultural watersheds may increase with a decrease in drainage area.

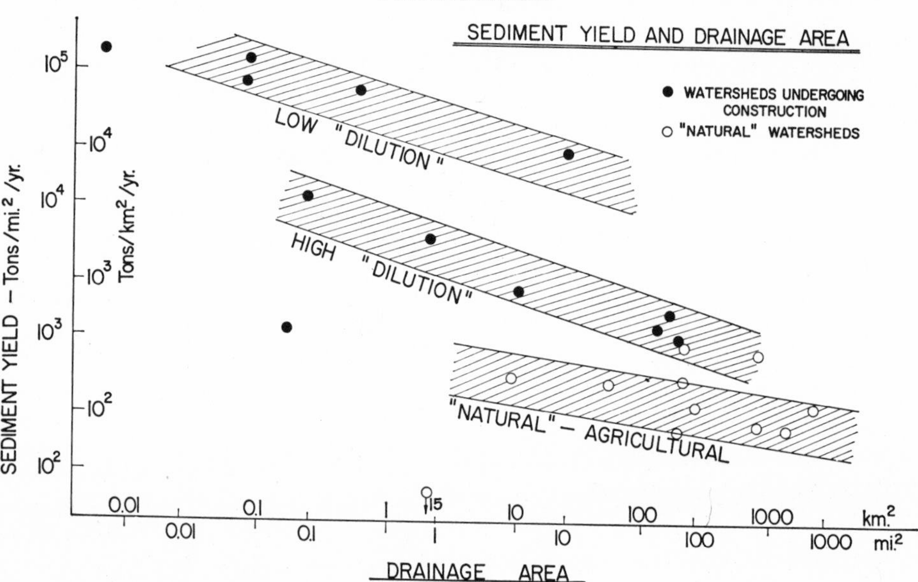

Fig. 2. Sediment yield, drainage area, and construction activity.

In contrast to runoff from rural areas, individual measurements of sediment concentration in streams often show concentrations as high as 60,000 ppm, whereas those for rural areas rarely, even in extreme events, have concentrations greater than one thousand ppm. Comparison of concentrations measured at tributary junctions where streams draining source areas under construction join streams from undisturbed watersheds confirms both the source and an expected 10- to 20-fold difference in concentration, as illustrated by Towson Run north of Baltimore, where concentration in the main channel upstream from the junction was 1500 ppm, whereas downstream concentration was 16,000 ppm as a consequence of tributary inflow with a concentration of 20,000 ppm. In Oregon Branch near Cockeysville, Maryland (Table 2, reported in detail in *Wolman* [1964]), concentrations below a 150-acre industrial park reached 30,000 ppm, whereas those upstream did not exceed 1500 ppm. Curves relating sediment concentration and discharge indicate that on the average at high flows concentrations downstream are about five times those measured above the construction site. *Keller* [1962, p. C130] reports for the Anacostia River in the vicinity of Hyattsville, Maryland, roughly a 6-fold increase in sediment yield for the drainage areas undergoing construction on the Northwest Branch of the Anacostia River between Colesville and Hyattsville, Maryland.

The data on annual yields for small areas are subject to sampling errors and to errors resulting from the shortness of the record. It is important to recognize, however, that, because of the very high sediment yields measured, even a large percentage reduction in the reported values in no way reduces either the significance of the results or the conclusions one draws from them. Thus it is clear from a comparison of tables 1 and 2 that the quantity of sediment derived from areas undergoing construction is from 2 to 200 times as large as that derived from comparable areas in a rural or wooded condition.

Although the sediment yields given in Table 2 are for areas subject to both subdivision and highway construction, some data are available on the yields from highway slopes or roadcuts alone. *Diseker and Richardson* [1962] found that soil loss, expressed in tons per acre per year, was a function of inclination of the slope, rainfall, and direction of exposure. During the winter months, in one instance at least, south-facing slopes subject to more frequent freeze and thaw provided nearly three times as much sediment as the north-facing slopes. Soil loss per square mile from the roadside cuts in the Piedmont of Georgia, i.e., for roughly the same rock type as in Maryland but for slightly higher rainfall, is of the same order of magnitude as the soil loss reported in Table 2 for the small catchments under construction. The quantity of sediment derived from roadside areas was on the order of 50,000 to 150,000 t/mi^2/yr.

Comparable figures for sediment yield are suggested by an analysis of the volume of material eroded from road cuts in the form of rills and sheet erosion. Measurements were made of the frequency of rills and the dimensions of rills and alluvial fans at the break in slope at the base of 35 road cuts in the Baltimore area. The volume of sediment in the rills represents a rough estimate of the volume of sediment removed, assuming that the divides adjacent to the rills have not been eroded. The volume applies to a strip 15 feet wide along the face of the slope. In every case the volume represented by the rills is less than the volume of material deposited in the fan at the base of the slope, indicating that sheet or surficial erosion on the divide areas also contributes to the volume of material in the fan. This result was confirmed by detailed study at several sites. The depth of erosion as shown by fans and rills was on the order of 0.1 to 0.2 feet over time intervals of generally less than one year. These rates are comparable to those observed in the road cuts in the Piedmont of Georgia and are of the same order of magnitude as those observed in several other studies of erosion on steep slopes (Table 3).

Soil loss from roadside slopes may also be expressed in terms of sediment yield per linear mile of highway construction. The exposed area per one linear mile of a divided highway ranges from 13 acres per mile on the Eastern Shore to 26 acres per mile in Central Maryland. For two-lane highways, the range is from 9 on the Eastern Shore to 16 acres per mile in Western Maryland (Table 4). The lower unit areas are applicable to the low relief of the Coastal Plain of the Eastern Shore, whereas the higher figures apply to the rolling topography of the Piedmont and the high relief of the Appalachian Valley and Ridge region. *Richardson and Diseker* [1961] imply a somewhat larger area, about 30 acres per linear mile for major interstate highways. Where the right-of-way on major highways has been designed to accommodate additional lanes in each direction, the cleared area per mile for a dual-lane highway in the Piedmont of Maryland would be increased by 12 to 15% to a value of about 30 acres per mile. For the major highway, these figures may be somewhat low, inasmuch as they do not include adjacent areas used for maneuvering equipment and for stockpiling of soil.

A computed estimate of the total sediment yield that might be expected from a mile of dual-lane highway construction in the Piedmont of Maryland based on measured sediment yields from roadcuts in the Piedmont of Georgia [*Diseker and Richardson,* 1962], considering separately the areas exposed in the flatter

TABLE 3. Bank and Slope Erosion in Diverse Areas

Location	Site	Region and Soil Type	Years of Observation	Rate of Erosion, in./yr	Angle of Slope, degrees	Source of Data
Cartersville, Ga.	Roadcut	Piedmont, Cecil clay	3	0.96	32	*Diseker and Richardson,* 1962
				0.88	37	
				0 to 1.15	17	
Oxford, Miss.	Gully headcuts	Coastal Plain silts, sands	5	7.3	90	*Miller et al.,* 1962
Perth Amboy, N. J.	Clay & sand fill	Coastal Plain	1*	0.92	43	*Schumm,* 1956
Bethany, Mo.	Fallow plot	Great Plains Shelby Loam	10	0.48	5	*Smith et al.,* 1945
Urim, Israel	Badlands	Loess-like sand and silt	1	5.0	8	*Aghassy,* 1957
				5.7	20	
				6.3	34	
				5.5	48	

* Actual period 5 weeks; estimated total erosion might be as much as 5 inches.

TABLE 4. Examples of Areas Exposed during Highway Construction
(Data provided by Maryland State Roads Commission)

Central Maryland: Frederick County	
4-Lane Divided or Dual Highway	
Area occupied by surfacing and shoulders	9.47 acres/mile
Area occupied by median, slopes and ditches	15.70 acres/mile
Area occupied by concrete gutters	0.33 acres/mile
Area exposed during construction—	25.50 acres/mile
23% of exposed area in cut	
77% of exposed area in fill	
2-Lane Highway	
Area occupied by surfacing and shoulders	5.66 acres/mile
Area occupied by slopes and ditches	7.33 acres/mile
Area exposed during construction—	12.99 acres/mile
47% of exposed area in cut	
53% of exposed area in fill	
Eastern Shore: Worcester County	
4-Lane Divided or Dual Highway	
Area occupied by surfacing and shoulders	7.63 acres/mile
Area occupied by median, slopes and ditches	5.60 acres/mile
Area exposed during construction—	13.23 acres/mile
10% of exposed area in cut	
90% of exposed area in fill	
2-Lane Highway	
Area occupied by surfacing and shoulders	4.90 acres/mile
Area occupied by slopes and ditches	3.92 acres/mile
Area exposed during construction—	8.82 acres/mile
20% of exposed area in cut	
80% exposed area in fill	
Western Maryland: Washington County	
4-Lane Divided or Dual Highway	
Area occupied by surfacing and shoulders	6.66 acres/mile
Area occupied by median, slopes and ditches	14.00 acres/mile
Area exposed during construction—	20.66 acres/mile
55% of exposed area in cut	
45% of exposed area in fill	
2-Lane Highway	
Area occupied by surfacing and shoulders	6.18 acres/mile
Area occupied by slopes and ditches	9.68 acres/mile
Area exposed during construction—	15.86 acres/mile
36% of exposed area in cut	
64% of exposed area in fill	

slopes in the median, surface, and shoulder of the road, and in the steeper cut and fill areas, suggests a yield of about 3000 tons per linear mile.

Expressed on an areal basis, it appears that the sediment contributed to drainage channels from areas undergoing construction either in subdivisions or in highways is on the order of from 2 times to several hundred times as great per unit area as it is from rural lands or woodland.

Sediment Delivery

Not all sediment eroded from exposed surfaces actually makes its way to river courses. *Roehl* [1962], for example, has shown that for the southeastern United States the sediment delivery ratio ranges from 0.45 at a drainage area of 1/10 square mile to 0.1 at a drainage area of 100 square miles. At some stages in the development of subdivisions, the topography is greatly modified both by earth moving equipment and by the initial construction of cellars, sidewalks, driveways, and streets. Sediment derived from the irregular and hummocky topography associated with areas under construction may be carried short distances to the nearest depressions. These depressions may be provided behind curbs, associated with cellar walls, or adjacent to unfinished terrace surfaces. Observations on one construction site revealed that the noncontributing area, that is, basins or essentially flat surfaces, constituted approximately 40% of the exposed area. Elsewhere deposition takes place in alluvial fans where the gradient flattens abruptly; often, of course, it is aided by vegetation. In our observations, the distance from the apex of the fan to the apron or limit of deposition will be approximately equal to the height of the exposed surface.

Although there are some moderating influences on the delivery of sediment from areas exposed during construction, some of which can be useful in ameliorating sediment supplied to streams, it must be emphasized that the data provided in Table 2 and on Figure 3 describe conditions prevailing within streams in integrated drainage systems. Lag either in the arrival time of such sediments at downstream points in the drainage basin, or in storage within the stream channels, constitutes a change in the regimen of transport and deposition in some reaches of the channel. There will be instances in which the exposed area will not contribute directly to the network of stream channels. On the other hand, if the drainage network is integrated from the construction site to the downstream reaches, it appears that at present the unit yield figures will apply to the area as a whole. Like the estimation of the effect of sediment delivery, reduction of total yields due to limited time of exposure and to estimated coincidence of rainfall periods and construction also continues to require an educated guess.

PHYSICAL AND BIOLOGICAL EFFECTS OF SEDIMENT ON STREAMS

Imposition of large quantities of sediment on streams previously carrying relatively small quantities of primarily suspended materials produces a variety of changes in the physical and biological characteristics of a stream channel. These changes include deposition of channel bars, coarsening of suspended sediments in the channel, erosion of channel banks as a result of deposition within the channel, obstruction of flow and increased flooding, shifting configurations of the channel bottom, blanketing of bottom dwelling flora and fauna, alteration of the flora and fauna as a result of changes of light transmission and abrasive effects of sediment, and alteration of the species of fish as a result of changes produced in the flora and fauna upon which the fish depend. Many of these effects were observed in the Maryland area. Oregon Branch provides an illustration.

A map of the distribution of sediment derived from construction of an industrial park on Oregon Branch shows the location of five kinds of sediments in the stream channel (Figure 3). Covering a distance of one mile downstream from the industrial park, including for comparative purposes a tributary reach of Beaverdam Run that has been free of construction activity in the recent past, the map shows both the persistent influence of the sediment to the mouth of Oregon Branch at Loch Raven Reservoir near Cockeysville, and the marked contrast between the sediment-laden Oregon Branch and the upstream portion of Beaverdam Run unaffected by construction. This upper reach of Beaverdam Run consists of a series of cobble riffles and pools. Such fine sediments as there are constitute a fine humic zone on the inside or convex portions of the normal river bends. In contrast, virtually no sections of the reach of Oregon Branch and Beaverdam Run below the industrial park are without traces of sand and silt deposits. In addition, a considerable stretch of the stream contains deposits of sand up to depths of two feet in some places (mapped as sand dune bed). In these reaches the character of the stream has been completely altered. In contrast to the pool and riffle sequence, the sand reaches resemble more the typical sand-bed channels of many rivers in the western United States. The sand moves along the bottom in dunes and completely blankets the fauna and flora previously associated with the cobble bottom.

A rough estimate of the volume of sediment

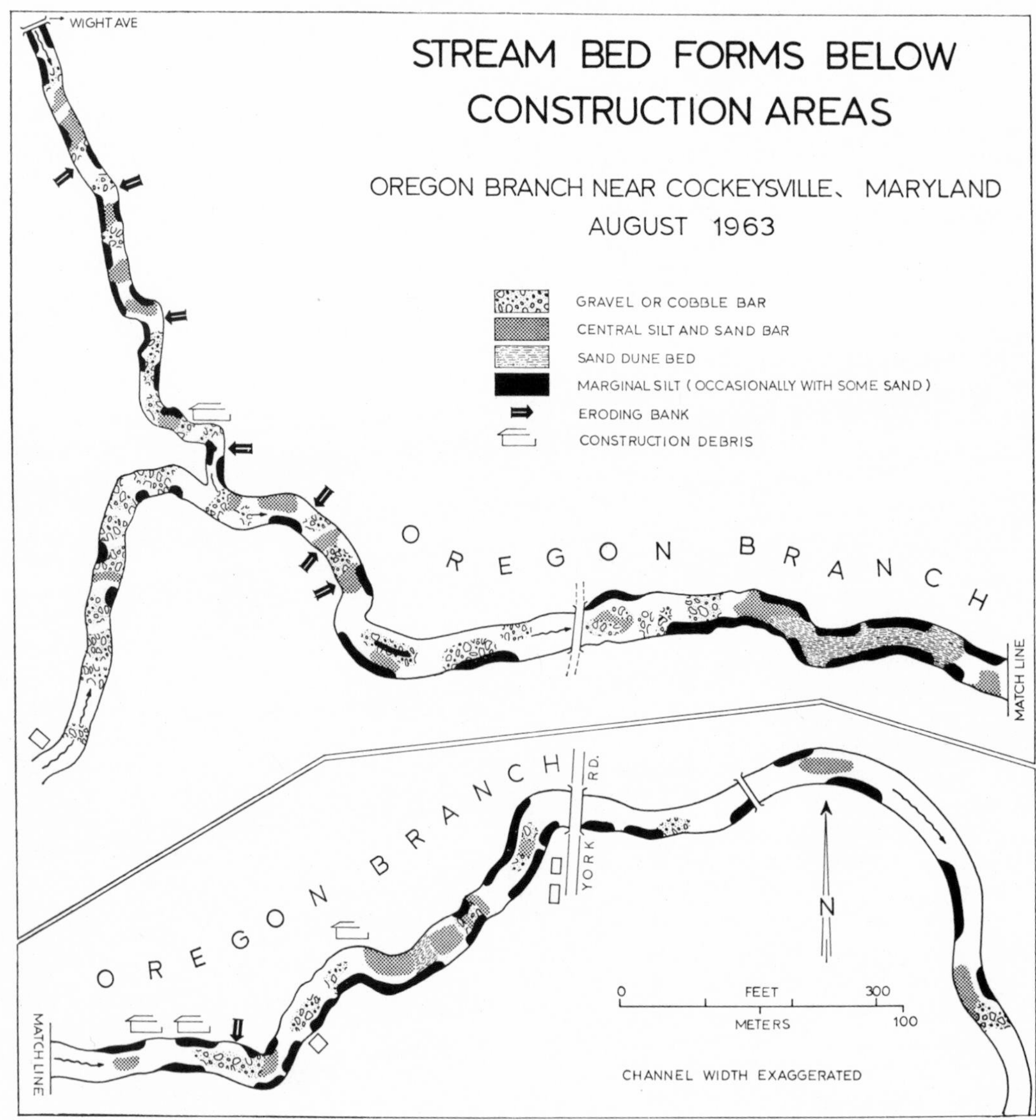

Fig. 3. Map of sediment deposition in Oregon Branch downstream from construction area.

in the channel from the industrial park to the backwater section of Loch Raven indicates that approximately ⅓ of the material removed from the industrial park is at present in the stream channel. The fact that the upper portion of Beaverdam Run, traversed by construction of a major interstate highway seven years ago, is now nearly free of sediment derived from construction, suggests that a channel of this slope and flow may be cleared of sediment in a period of seven years or less.

Construction derived sediment was recognized in Oregon Branch from its source to its confluence with Loch Raven Reservoir. Observations on a number of other streams in the area demonstrate, as one would expect, that 'the distance of influence' of the construction site varies with the nature, quantity, and caliber of sediment load derived from the exposed area as well as with the flow and topographic characteristics of the drainage basin. No simple correlations could be derived, nor has a 'limiting' distance been observed in this study, as sediment reached tidewater or reservoirs in every case in distances of less than 2 miles.

It has been recognized that large amounts of sediment can alter the reproductive and growth rates of fish, severely reducing the population and, in many instances, the number and composition of fish species [*Cordone and Kelley*, 1961; *Tarzwell and Gaufin*, 1953; *Allanson*, 1961]. Although it is likely that the transformation of a stream bed from pools and riffles to dune sand might be accompanied by a change in fish species from game fish to scavengers, as suggested by analogy with *Van Deusen*'s [1954] stream classification for Maryland, satisfactory data are not available with which to verify such alterations in Maryland streams. Older residents report such changes, however, and observations elsewhere [*U. S. Senate*, 1963, p. 827] indicate that highway and railroad construction have virtually eliminated trout from 78 miles of stream channel in central Montana, owing to sedimentation associated with channel straightening, land clearing, and construction. Fifty-four miles, 45% of the total length of the original stream channel of the Little Big Horn River, is considered lost to trout fishing as a result of construction and channel alteration. On a tributary of Clark Fork of the Columbia River, successive studies of the trout population in a reach of river altered by highway construction show a 94% reduction in both numbers and weight of large size game fish in a period of two years.

Erosion of sediment from construction sites produces high sediment concentrations as well as channel and reservoir deposits. Although deposits may alter the conveyance of stream channels as well as the flora and fauna of both channels and bodies of standing water, neither the extent nor the storage time of sedimentary deposits is predictable at present.

MAGNITUDE OF THE PROBLEM POSED BY SEDIMENT DERIVED FROM CONSTRUCTION ACTIVITIES

Duration and Amount of Land Exposed during Construction

To determine exposure time during construction, as well as a measure of the rate at which subdivision development takes place, an analysis was made of a random sample of one hundred building permits issued in Baltimore County in the 10-year period 1952–1961. The following data were obtained from the record: date of granting of the permit, date of completion of the structure, lot size, type of permit (house, commercial, etc.), and value. Field checks indicated that construction usually began shortly after issuance of permits.

Approximately 50% of the sites were open for eight months, and 60% were open for nine. Read in reverse, the sample indicated that 40% of the sites were open for more than nine months, and 25% were open for more than one year. Reports from builders on 49 units constructed in the past five years, comprising about 1000 acres, showed a median completion time of ten months, 75% completed in less than twelve months, and two units of less than seven acres each completed in four months. However, field observations also demonstrated that many commercial, school, and industrial sites are open for periods of one, two, or more years.

In addition, data from the random sample of building permits showed that the total land area exposed to construction varied little throughout the year, a condition due primarily to the initiation of new construction in the late fall and even winter months. Although land is continuously exposed, intense summer rainfall appears to be the primary cause of rapid erosion.

From records of highway, subdivision, and utility construction, it was estimated that in any given year the total area cleared for construction in each of the four metropolitan counties in Maryland bordering Baltimore and Washington was from 1 to 2.5 square miles [*Wolman*, 1964]. More recent studies of the U. S. Geological Survey (J. Wark, personal communication) indicate that land exposed in the Washington area may exceed these estimates by 1.5 to 2 times.

Metropolitan Baltimore County is growing at the rate of about 13,000 people per year. Assuming a sediment yield of 10,000 tons per square mile exposed to construction per year, a low estimate in terms of data in Table 2, sediment production is on the order of 1800 tons per 1000 increase in population. For Prince Georges County near Washington, with a somewhat larger population increase and less exposed land, the yield would be 700 tons per 1000 increase in population.

Social Evaluation of Problems Posed by Sediment

Because sediment derived from construction activities has been shown to have significant physical and biological effects on streams, reservoirs, and estuaries, an attempt was made to evaluate the social and economic significance attached to these effects. Evaluations were based upon three approaches: (1) responses to questionnaires sent to builders and public officials; (2) reports of the Water Pollution Control Commission; and (3) estimates of costs associated with sediment removal, accumulation, or damage. The questionnaires were designed not only to determine whether or not public officials and builders deemed a problem to exist but to elicit as well some evaluation of the need for legal regulation to abate the yield of sediment from construction activities.

Among the 18 public engineers responding from a total of 23 counties, 7 indicated that a problem existed and agreed in general terms that some kind of regulation might be warranted. Others suggested that, without regulation, considerable control could be effected if information on control measures and manuals designed to fit local conditions were made available. Responses to a letter of inquiry clearly indicated that the problem was severe in the major metropolitan regions but not ubiquitous.

Of 75 builders to whom questionnaires were sent, only 14 responded, and only one indicated that erosion or sedimentation posed a severe problem for a downstream property owner. Most indicated that the problems derived from sediment were slight either to adjacent property owners, to the community, or to themselves. For the builders, problems were confined to gullying of graded land and sedimentation in drains or foundations. It is interesting to note, however, that a number of engineering firms that provide designs and supervise construction for large developments indicated an awareness of the problems posed by sediment, and that some firms regularly recommended that sediment control measures be instituted on specific projects. As a rule, these measures have been recommended to forestall complaints, perhaps suits, from downstream property owners.

Among 17 reports collected by the staff of the Maryland Water Pollution Control Commission in the period from February to December 1963, six kinds of damages were reported to result from erosion and deposition of sediment: (1) stream deposition and consequent overflow; (2) turbid water unsuited for municipal use; (3) turbid water unsuited for industrial use; (4) failure of pumping equipment; (5) clogging of drains; (6) despoiling of recreation areas. Damage to municipal and industrial water supplies was reported in several areas. Where water is used for such industrial operations as vegetable processing or cloth manufacture, even small amounts of sediment may pose considerable problems. In municipal use, where storage facilities are lacking and water is pumped directly from a river, slugs of sediment associated with periods of rainfall may pose severe problems, inasmuch as the intake of water cannot be discontinued for more than very short periods of time. Highway officials have recognized this damage, and in some cases municipalities have been compensated for the construction of additional storage facilities and for changing the location of water intakes.

The public, regulatory agencies, engineers, and the courts have recognized problems posed by sediment derived from construction. However, in choosing alternative courses of action and in evaluating the magnitude of the problem, economic measures of the damages and costs associated with sediment would be exceedingly useful. Because we have been unable to locate or to construct a valid relationship between incremental concentrations of sediment in streams or of sediment accumulations in reservoirs and economic measures such as the loss in income from recreation facilities or the incremental costs of water treatment, we have compiled in Table 5 a number of estimates of the economic damages associated with erosion and deposition of sediment. It is perhaps a reflection of the state of the art that most of the figures in Table 5 are commonly recognized costs and are not necessarily an appropriate measure of value. For these reasons only a few are commented upon here.

Although there is a good deal of disagreement as to the most appropriate economic measures to be used in evaluating damages, a present cost or an assumed annual cost for the value of storage, or a cost per unit weight for dredging, appear to represent the simplest and most

TABLE 5. Alternative Estimates of Economics of Sediment Damage

Location of Sediment	Unit Cost or Value	Method of Estimation
Reservoir	\$100/acre-ft	Cost of storage of water: range \$60 to \$145 per acre-ft
	\$0.03/yr/acre-ft	Annual cost assuming rate of depletion of storage, Liberty Reservoir, Patapsco R., 0.03%/yr sedimentation at prevailing rates.
	\$1/yr/acre-ft	Annual cost assuming rate of depletion of storage, Liberty Reservoir, 1%/yr, urbanization: extremely high sediment yield 80,000 t/sq mi²
Reservoir	\$4000/acre-ft	Present value of storage per acre-ft (Liberty Reservoir)
Reservoir	\$22,000 to \$78,000/yr	Loss of reservoir use: alternative sources and emergency pumping, Worcester, Mass.
Reservoir	\$2/yd³	Dredging of small lake (Lake Barcroft, Va.)
	\$1.25/yd³	Dredging of small reservoir (Tollgate, Md.)
Reservoir	Estimated	Recreation: dependent upon % loss capacity, turbidity, etc., at \$1.00/visitor/day
Estuary	\$0.60 to \$1.25/yd³	Dredging: Baltimore Harbor — much dependent on disposal
	\$0.19	Dredging: Anacostia Area — much dependent on disposal
Channel	\$0.80/yd³	Removal of sediment: spoil placed adjacent to channel
	\$1.20/yd³	Removal of sediment: spoil removed
Channel	Value unknown	Increase in flood damage due to channel obstruction
Channel	Value unknown	Deposition of sediment during floods
Channel	Value unknown	Fish kill, substitution of less desirable species, or recreation time lost due to poor fishing
Channel	Variable	Increased costs of water treatment, \$23,400/yr in treatment of 180 mgd (Washington, D. C.)
Riparian Lands	Damage equivalent	Legal award for damages equal to cost of restoration (if less than diminution in value) plus value of loss of use

easily recognized dollar amounts (costs not values) attributable to damage from sediment deposition. Assuming various rates of loss of storage due to sediment accumulation, annual costs can be computed based either on the cost of providing equivalent storage, the cost of a particular reservoir, or the present value of an existing reservoir and its appurtenances. Several of these alternatives are given in Table 5. In addition, customary dredging costs appropriate to specific localities are listed for comparison.

Where reservoirs are located adjacent to areas undergoing rapid urban development, however, dollar values of sediment damages due to loss of storage capacity, to increased costs of water treatment, and on occasion to temporary loss of the use of the reservoir itself may be large. Thus, at Worcester, Massachusetts, loss of the use of a reservoir because of sediment from nearby airport construction resulted in expenditures of \$22,000 and \$78,000 in two successive years for supply and pumping from alternative sources (Table 5, personal communication, C. B. Hardy, March 20, 1964).

Data are also available (Table 5) that show that the cost of water treatment for both municipal and industrial uses can increase when the source becomes highly turbid. Jackson (personal communication, 1963, see *Guy et al.* [1963]) has calculated that for the water supply of Washington, D. C., reducing turbidities in the Potomac River could produce annual savings of approximately \$25,000. With increasing populations served, annual savings might increase. Simple extrapolation of the figures is difficult, however, inasmuch as the unit treatment costs may vary with scale. For the same reason, and because the turbidities of natural streams are highly variable, treatment costs and savings cannot be safely transposed from one area to another [*Garin and Forster*, 1940, pp. 13–14].

Lastly, lost recreational opportunities may represent another measure of the economic significance of sediment. In all the environments of deposition listed in Table 5, sediment poses problems to the recreational use of the resource. Not only may high concentrations of sediment produce poor fishing conditions, but deposition of sediment changes the ecology of channels and of standing water bodies. *Brown* [1942, p. 79] estimated, for example, that 49,090 person-days were lost to recreation in the Meramac River watershed near Saint Louis, Missouri, in 1940 as a result of above normal but below flood-stage flows of high turbidity. At the much disputed figure of $1.00 per recreation-day, this would represent an annual loss of $49,090. The computation, however, involves many assumptions, including the reduction in recreation due to floods and to 'above normal' flow, the value of the fishing-day, and the allocation of losses specifically attributable to sediment.

Because economic data and sophisticated analyses are limited, it is relatively easy to minimize their significance. In evaluating the problems posed by sediment, then, it is unwise to measure the degree of public interest and therefore the values associated with such problems solely on the basis of the apparent economic data. Public officials, householders, fishermen, engineers, contractors, and courts have all recognized that sediment derived from construction does create problems. Recent legal controls adopted in Montgomery County, Maryland, as well as regulations of the Maryland State Department of Water Resources, suggest that citizens not only recognize the problem but place significant value on amelioration.

Conclusion

The physical and biological effects of sediment erosion and deposition are clearly apparent even to the casual observer in the field. No one who has seen the streams, ponds, and reservoirs that have been affected by large concentrations and large quantities of sediment can have any doubt as to either the source of such material or as to its possible effects. The damages have been made most apparent where plaintiffs in court have successfully recovered costs and reimbursement for damages sustained. Less likely to be able to seek a legal remedy is the public, who will ultimately bear the cost of the destruction of fishing, of removal of material from channels and estuaries, and of loss of esthetic values in its environment.

The areas most affected by sediment derived from construction are obviously those undergoing most rapid development. It is also true that it is in these same areas that people will live most closely together, and the activities of one group of society will most closely affect the interests of all the others. It is in these regions of high population density that the maximum use and value can be derived from the adjacent water resources. The fact that these values cannot always be expressed in simple economic terms does not lessen their significance. The physical effects on the environment of large quantities of sediment have been demonstrated. Relatively simple measures can be instituted that will reduce or moderate the quantities of sediment contributed to the natural environment in metropolitan regions. These include reduction of the time of exposure, vegetative traps, and diverse types of detention structures well documented in the agricultural conservation literature [*Guy et al.*, 1963]. Should public policy call for some action to ameliorate the quantity of sediment derived from construction activities, as we believe it should, it should also be recognized that we must deal in the realm of the reasonable and possible and not with extremes. It is unrealistic to expect that all of the sediment derived from construction can at reasonable costs be prevented from reaching the stream channels. It is equally unreasonable to demand that an effort be made to achieve such an objective. It is not unreasonable, however, to suggest that modest controls can be effective in moderating the quantities of sediment now being contributed to water bodies in areas undergoing major urban development.

Acknowledgments. The authors are indebted to the Maryland Water Pollution Control Commission, Annapolis, Maryland, to whom an original report [*Wolman,* 1964] upon which this paper is based was presented. G. B. Anderson of the Soil Conservation Service, Fairfax County, Virginia, and Henry Silbermann of the Water Pollution Control Commission provided continuing help and information during the study. Essential data were compiled and made available by the Maryland State Roads Commission. Both the Homebuilders Association of Maryland and the Associated Builders and Contractors provided valuable assistance. Our debt is particularly great to the 14 builders who took time to reply to an elaborate questionnaire. The U. S. Geological Survey provided basic data on sediment quantities in streams. E. R. Keil, State Conservationist, Soil Conservation Service, and his staff provided a review of problem areas in Maryland. Professor R. L. Green of the University of Maryland visited the field with the senior author. Thanks are due to the firm of Matz, Childs and Associates for providing data and technical assistance. R. C. Zimmerman, at the time graduate student at The Isaiah Bowman Department of Geography, The Johns Hopkins University, Baltimore, Maryland, served as field assistant in summer 1963. Lastly, it is a pleasure to thank Mrs. Roger Stenerson for collecting invaluable field data.

REFERENCES

Aghassy, Y., The morphology of badlands in Palestine, M.S. thesis, Dept. of Geography, The Hebrew University of Jerusalem, 1957.

Allanson, B. R., Investigations into the ecology of polluted inland waters in the Transvaal, *Hydrobiologia, 18*, 94 pp., 1961.

Brown, C. B., Floods and fishing, *Land Quarterly*, 78–79, 1942.

Collier, C. R., et al., Influence of strip mining on the hydrologic environment of parts of Beaver Creek basin, Kentucky, 1955–1959, *U. S. Geol. Surv.*, open-file report, 276 pp., 1962.

Cordone, A. J., and D. W. Kelley, The influence of inorganic sediment on the aquatic life of streams, *Calif. Fish and Game, 47*, 189–228, 1961.

Diseker, E. G., and E. C. Richardson, Roadside sediment production and control, *Am. Soc. Agr. Engrs., 4*, 62–68, 1961.

Diseker, E. G., and E. C. Richardson, Erosion rates and control measures on highway cuts, *Am. Soc. Agr. Engrs., 5*, 153–155, 1962.

Garin, A. N., and G. W. Forster, Effect of soil erosion on the costs of public water supply in the North Carolina Piedmont, *U. S. Dept. Agr., SCS-EC-1*, 106 pp., 1940.

Guy, H. P., Residential construction and sedimentation at Kensington, Maryland, paper presented at Federal Inter-Agency Sedimentation Conference, Jackson, Miss., Jan., 1963, 16 pp., 1963.

Guy, H. P., and G. E. Ferguson, Sediment in small reservoirs due to urbanization, *Am. Soc. Civ. Engrs., Proc., J. Hydraul. Div., 88*, 27–37, 1962.

Guy, H. P., N. E. Jackson, K. Jarvis, C. J. Johnson, C. R. Miller, and W. W. Steiner, A program for sediment control in the Washington Metropolitan region, *Interstate Comm. Potomac River Basin, Tech. Bull. 1963–1*, 48 pp., 1963.

Holeman, J. N., and A. F. Geiger, Sedimentation of Lake Barcroft, Fairfax County, Va., *U. S. Dept. Agr. SCS-TP-136*, 12 pp., 1959.

Holeman, J. N., and A. F. Geiger, Sedimentation of Loch Raven and Prettyboy Reservoirs, Baltimore County, Md., *U. S. Dept. Agr. SCS-TP-145*, 17 pp., 1965.

Keller, F. J., Effect of urban growth on sediment discharge, Northwest Branch Anacostia River basin, Maryland, *U. S. Geol. Surv. Prof. Paper 450-C*, pp. C129–131, 1962.

Miller, C. R., R. Woodburn, and H. R. Turner, Upland gully sediment production, *Int. Assoc. Scient. Hydrol. Publ. 59*, Symposium of Bari, pp. 83–104, 1962.

Richardson, E. C., and E. G. Diseker, Roadside mulches, *Crops and Soils, 13*(5), 1 pp., 1961.

Roehl, J. W., Sediment source areas, delivery ratios, and influencing morphological factors, *Int. Assoc. Scient. Hydrol., Publ. 59*, Symposium of Bari, pp. 202–213, 1962.

Schumm, S. A., Evolution of drainage systems and slopes in badlands at Perth Amboy, N. J., *Geol. Soc. Am. Bull., 3*, 600–615, 1956.

Smith, D. D., D. M. Whitt, A. W. Zingg, A. G. McCall, and F. G. Bell, Investigations in erosion control and reclamation of eroded Shelby and related soils at the conservation experiment station, Bethany, Mo., 1930–1942, *U. S. Dept. Agr. Tech. Bull. 883*, 175 pp., 1945.

State of Maryland, State Roads Commission, Specifications for materials, highways, bridges, and incidental structures, 507 pp., 1962.

Tarzwell, C. M., and A. R. Gaufin, Some important biological effects of pollution often disregarded in stream surveys, *Purdue Univ. Eng. Bull., Proc. 8th Industrial Waste Conf.*, 33 pp., 1953.

U. S. Senate, 88th Congress, *Congressional Record*, statement by E. B. Welch, Destruction of natural fish habitat is ruining Montana's fishing streams, entered in record by Sen. Metcalf (Mont.), pp. 826–841, 1963.

Van Deusen, R. D., Maryland freshwater stream classification by watershed, *Chesapeake Biol. Lab. Contr. 106*, 30 pp., 1954.

Wark, J. W., and F. J. Keller, Preliminary study of sediment sources and transport in the Potomac River basin, *Interstate Comm., Potomac River Basin, Tech. Bull. 1963–11*, 28 pp., 1963.

Wilson, J. N., Effects of turbidity and silt on aquatic life, *U. S. Public Health Serv. Seminar*, 235–239, 1962.

Wolman, M. G., Problems posed by sediment derived from construction activities in Maryland, Rept. to Md. Water Pollution Control Comm. (now Dept. of Water Resources), 125 pp., 1964.

SUPPLEMENTARY REFERENCES

Diseker, E. G., and E. C. Richardson, Roadside sediment production and control, *Am. Soc. Agr. Engrs., 4*, 62–68, 1961.

State of Maryland, State Roads Commission, *Specifications for Materials, Highways, Bridges, and Incidental Structures*, 507 pp., 1962.

Wilson, J. N., Effects of turbidity and silt on aquatic life, *U. S. Public Health Serv. Seminar*, 235–239, 1962.

(Manuscript received December 22, 1965;
revised November 7, 1966.)

23

Reprinted from *Sediment Problems in Urban Areas* (U.S. Geol. Surv. Circ. 601-E), Government Printing Office, Washington, D.C., 1970, pp. 1–8

Water in the Urban Environment

Sediment Problems in Urban Areas

By Harold P. Guy

INTRODUCTION

A recognition of and solution to sediment problems in urban areas is necessary if society is to have an acceptable living environment. Soil erosion and sediment deposition in urban areas are as much an environmental blight as badly paved and littered streets, dilapidated buildings, billboard clutter, inept land use, and air, water, and noise pollution. In addition, sediment has many direct and indirect effects on streams that may be either part of or very remote from the urban environment. Sediment, for example, is widely recognized as a pollutant of streams and other water bodies.

One obstacle to a scientific recognition and an engineering solution to sediment-related environmental problems is that such problems are bound in conflicting and generally undefinable political and institutional restraints. Also, some of the difficulty may involve the fact that the scientist or engineer, because of his relatively narrow field of investigation, cannot always completely envision the less desirable effects of his work and communicate alternative solutions to the public. For example, the highway and motor-vehicle engineers have learned how to provide the means by which one can transport himself from one point to another with such great efficiency that a person's employment in this country is now commonly more than 5 miles from his residence. However, providing such efficient personal transport has created numerous serious environmental problems. Obstacles to recognition of and action to control sediment problems in and around urban areas are akin to other environmental problems with respect to the many scientific, engineering, economic, and social aspects.

PROBLEM EXTENT

In a study of sediment problems in urban areas, it is necessary to remember that sediment movement and deposition was a part of the natural environment before the intervention of civilization. Like flooding, the sediment problems become important only when man is affected. Sometimes the problems result from natural conditions, but usually they result when the natural circumstances are altered to effect such a different kind of environment that previous small unnoticed problems are greatly magnified. Severe sediment problems occur, for example, when covering vegetation is removed in construction areas, when the flow regime in channels is altered by realinement or by increased or decreased flow, or when fill, buildings, or bridges obstruct the natural flowway.

The average sediment yield from the landscape and the condition of the stream channels tend to change with the advancing forms of man's land-use activity, as indicated by table 1. As in many other situations involving intensive use of resources and rapid growth, one can expect that sediment problems will be most serious during the urban construction period (E). This is not to say that problems are not likely to occur during the stable period (G) because physical and esthetic values or quality standards with respect to both water and property are expected to increase with time. For example, a stream carrying an average suspended-sediment concentration of 200 mg/l (milligrams per liter) after 2 years into the stable period may be more acceptable than 100 mg/l after 20 years into the stable period.

It is impossible to isolate sediment problems completely from the many interrelated problems

E1

Table 1.—*Effect of land-use sequence on relative sediment yield and channel stability*

[Modified from Wolman (1967)]

Land use	Sediment yield	Channel stability
A. Natural forest or grassland.	Low	Relatively stable with some bank erosion.
B. Heavily grazed areas.	Low to moderate	Somewhat less stable than A.
C. Cropping	Moderate to heavy	Some aggradation and increased bank erosion.
D. Retirement of land from cropping.	Low to moderate	Increasing stability.
E. Urban construction.	Very heavy	Rapid aggradation and some bank erosion.
F. Stabilization	Moderate	Degradation and severe bank erosion.
G. Stable urban	Low to moderate	Relatively stable.

associated with urban development, especially with respect to water (Anderson, 1968; Leopold, 1968). However, the sediment problems can usually be classed into groups related to land and channel erosion, stream transport, and deposition processes (Guy, 1967), regardless of the land-use phases mentioned in table 1. Land erosion, including the sheet, rill, and gully forms, is likely to be most severe during the urban construction period (E), though it may be present to some degree regardless of land use. Channel erosion is most severe during the stabilization period (F), especially when channels have been realined, waterways have been constricted, and (or) the amount and intensity of runoff have been increased because of imperviousness and "improved" drainage. Sediment transport problems are usually associated with the pollution of water by sediment from either or both the esthetic or physical utilization viewpoints. Transport problems also occur in regard to coarse sediment when the transport capacity in a stream section does not match the input supply of the coarse sediment—hence, aggradation or degradation. The sorting and differential transport of sediment result in deposition problems ranging from the fan deposits at the base of graded banks to deposits in reservoirs and estuaries.

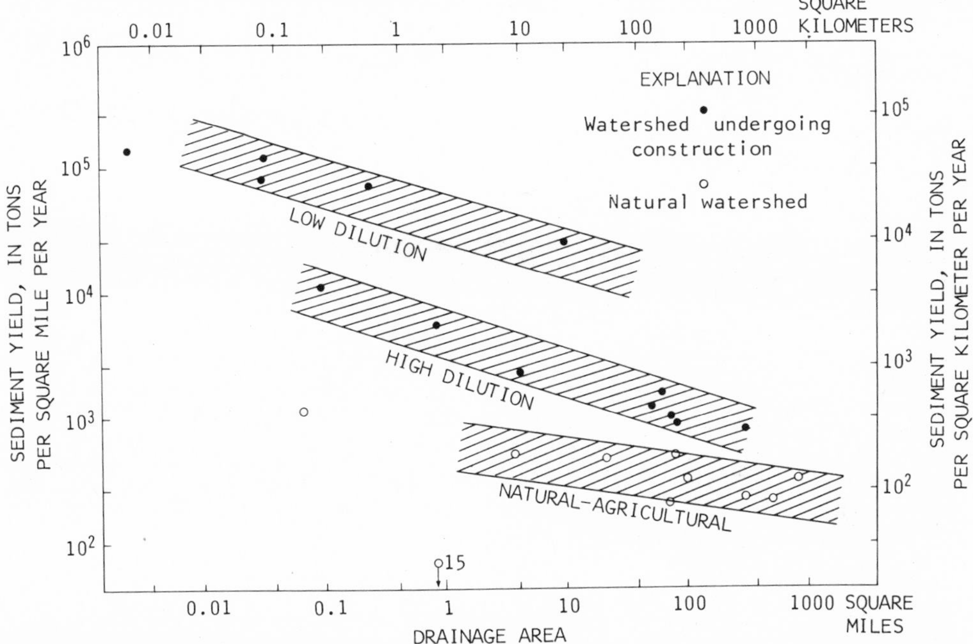

Figure 1.—Effect of construction intensity and drainage area on sediment yield (from Wolman and Schick, 1967, p. 455). Most of the data are from the Baltimore and Washington, D.C., metropolitan areas. The term "dilution" refers to drainage from relatively stable nonconstruction areas.

The following is a list of some of the urban sediment erosion, transport, and deposition problems:

1. Public health may be affected in a number of ways. Efforts to control mosquito breeding have been ineffective because sediment has filled drainage channels. Also harmful bacteria, toxic chemicals, and radionuclides tend to be absorbed onto sediment particles. The absorbed substances may not be harmful in their original residence but become hazardous when transported into a water supply or deposited and perhaps concentrated at a new location.
2. Sheet, rill, and gully erosion and associated deposition may cause undesirable changes in graded areas typical of urban construction sites. Figure 1, from Wolman and Schick (1967, p. 455), shows the effect of the intensity of construction and drainage-basin size on sediment yield. In figure 2 it will be rather expensive to remove the deposit in the yard, to repair the erosion damage on the graded bank, and to repair the drainage channel on the terrace. Erosion and subsequent deposition in cut-and-fill areas can easily exceed 1 cubic yard for each 100 square feet.
3. Dispersion of soil particles by raindrop impact seals the land surface and thereby reduces infiltration, increases stream runoff, and decreases groundwater recharge.
4. Deposition of coarse sediments may reduce the flow capacity or completely plug natural and manmade channels (fig. 3) as well as close drains.
5. Floodwater damage is increased manyfold in homes, stores, and factories because of sediment. Evaporation can erase many of the effects of a "pure water" flood, but it cannot do so when the flow contains suspended sediment.
6. Streams and other bodies of water are damaged esthetically by unsightly deposits as well as by fine sediment in suspension. Though stream esthetics are

Figure 2.—Severe rill and gully erosion from the January 1969 storms in a new residential area near San Bernardino, Calif.

A

B

Figure 3.—Effect of coarse-sediment deposition on flow capacity in urban channels. *A*, Flow of sediment in floodwater from the January 1969 storms plugged a Glendora, Calif., concrete-lined channel and caused overflow and deposition on nearby property. The channel had been partly cleaned after the flood and before the picture was taken. *B*, Three feet of deposition in the lower part of this boulevard channel in Boulder, Colo., caused flooding by a flow of less than one-fifth the design capacity of the channel.

considered much more inclusive than recreation alone, Brown (1948, p. 79) has estimated that recreation losses in the Meramec River basin near St. Louis, Mo., in 1940 amounted to 49,090 person-days as a result of above-normal flows (but less than floodflows) of high turbidity.

7. Water-treatment costs for domestic and industrial uses are increased. Reduction of Potomac River sediment turbidity to optimum could produce an annual savings of $25,000 per year (1963 values) for Washington, D.C. (Wolman, 1964, p. 68).
8. Erosion and (or) deposition in channels (fig. 4), estuaries, and other water bodies may cause bridge or culvert failure as well as serious ecological changes by alteration of species composition and population density (Peters, 1967).

A

B

Figure 4.—Examples of channel erosion and deposition resulting from urbanization. *A*, Bank erosion and degradation from increased runoff from impervious areas, tributary to Montclair Creek, Mobile, Ala. *B*, Deposition and plugging of drain from intensive sediment movement during residential construction, tributary to Rock Creek near Washington, D.C.

9. Impoundments for municipal water storage are often built upstream from cities. The release of clear water from such impoundments can create serious degradation and bank erosion in downstream areas where picnic and other recreational facilities are planned.
10. Reservoir storage and channel conveyance for water supply are lost. Wolman (1964, p. 63) indicated that the alternative cost per acre-foot of storage lost to sediment in water storage and recreation reservoirs in Maryland ranges from less than $100 to over $78,000.
11. Maintenance costs are increased for streets, highways, and other public-use areas. (See fig. 5.)
12. As implied in the introduction, perhaps the most serious urban sediment problem is the general deterioration of the total environment—a condition usually not recognized by the public.

As with many hydrologic problems, most urban sediment problems have visual impact for relatively short periods of time because they are rainstorm related (Guy, 1964). Also, because these problems are usually rooted within the urban or urbanizing area, they are limited to relatively small areas of the country. However, because of the intense capital investment in and human use of urban areas, the recognition of and solution to sediment problems become socially and economically very important.

Sediment damage is apparent when a storm-drain inlet becomes clogged, rill erosion cuts a graded area, a traffic accident occurs because of a wet fine-sediment deposit on a street, a swimming area must be closed because of

Figure 5.—More than 1,000 cubic yards of debris deposited on a short section of Ledora Avenue, Glendora, Calif., during the January 1969 storms by sediment flow and floodflow from nearby recently burned foothill area.

turbid water, a water-treatment plant cannot clarify water, or a recreation lake is filled with sediment (Guy and Ferguson, 1962). Because sediment is often part of a complex environmental problem (Ferguson and Guy, 1970), many other sediment problems go unnoticed even though they may be economically significant. A study of air pollution in Chicago showed that dustfall amounts ranged from 21 to 61 tons per square mile per month at 20 stations during 1966 (American Public Works Association, 1969, p. 25). The Chicago study also showed that street-litter sweepings consisted of more than 70 percent dirt and rock by weight—the remainder was classified as metal, paper, vegetation, wood, and glass. Higher percentages of dirt occurred in the litter after rainstorms, even in a business area that was 100 percent built up.

A sound sediment-measurement program in and adjacent to urban areas will help people to recognize what the problems are, where they occur, and when to expect them. Such a sediment-measurement program should document erosion sources and amounts, concentration in runoff, stream-channel changes, and the location and amounts of deposition. The measurement program, though mostly a documentation of the nature of conditions, will provide the basis upon which research needs (Guy, 1967) can be evaluated.

There are many laws concerning problems of sedimentation (Busby, 1962, 1967). In general the cases make it eminently clear that downstream owners can recover damages if changes and costs are well documented. In States where the civil law rule applies, a higher land is entitled to have flow discharge across the property of a lower landowner as it does in nature. Sometimes, however, a "reasonableness of use" rule is applied *(Sainato* v. *Potter,* 159 A. 2d 632, 222, Md. 263) where strict application of the civil law rule would result in hardship to either party. In considering aspects of sedimentation law, the following quotation from the decision in *Neubauer* v. *Overlea Reality Co.* (142 Md. 87, 98, 120 A. 69, 73) is of additional interest,

> It is no answer to a complaint of nuisance that a great many others are committing similar acts of nuisance upon a stream. Each and every one is liable to a separate action, and to be restrained.

Roalman (1969) described "a bounty on water polluters" based on the Harbor Act of June 29, 1888 (25 Stat. 209), as amended on June 7, 1924 (S. 1942), whereby any private citizen can bring action against almost any water polluter. Though it has been little used for the past 80 years, it provides for a stiff fine and a jail sentence for the polluter, and it specifically directs that a bounty be paid to the citizen who proves his case—literally a bounty law on water polluters.

SOME ASPECTS OF PROBLEM SOLUTION

Of the many facets of sediment problems in urban areas, the foremost are recognition and evaluation. Recognition would be easier if specific data on the cost of the many kinds of sediment problems in urban areas were available. The costs of sediment problems are rarely computed, and then they are generally estimated, even under the relatively less dynamic and more familiar rural conditions. Moore and Smith (1968) showed that "rural erosion and sediment" problems in the United States cause more than a $1-billion loss each year, $800 million of which occurs from erosion of cropland. Brown (1948) reported that annual damage from sediment deposition alone in rural areas amounts to $175 million. This in itself is 1.7 times the average annual flood damages for the 20-year period 1925–44. In the accounting of flood damages, sediment deposition was apparently not considered a flood cost.

The economic aspects of sedimentation in all its forms from erosion to deposition have been discussed recently by Maddock (1969). His section with regard to municipalities consists of only two paragraphs, as follows:

> The economic problems associated with the control of turbidity in municipal and industrial water supplies are well known. Equally or perhaps more important, however, every community has its water courses. As the community grows, it seems inevitable that there will be a decision of some kind that will modify the behavior of these streams. Discharges are diminished or increased, stream channels are straightened or confined, and sediment loads are modified. These modifications generally result in problems that are solved at relatively high expense. The expense for one modification is not very great, but there are so many modifications that the aggregate costs are large.
>
> The writer has discussed this phase of the erosion and sediment problem with engineers whose practice is largely in the municipal engineering field. Almost without exception, they all say that the control of natural drainage is one of the most irritating and aggravating problems they have to deal with. Many high-cost drainage projects result from an inability to cope with what appear to be relatively simple problems. Thus an alluvial channel must be transformed into a pipe or a lined channel because its slope is too steep for the amount of water it is expected to carry. Straightening alluvial channels seems to be a minor adjustment but it inevitably leads to more serious problems. A realization that most natural channels respond to the movement of both water and sediment would do much to prevent obvious mistakes.

Evaluation of the sediment problem is also complicated because sediment measurements are rather expensive and because sediment erosion, movement, and deposition are occurring in a highly dynamic and complicated environment. For example, in a drainage basin undergoing residential development (Guy, 1965), the area denuded of vegetative cover and subject to intensive erosion is continually changing. The process is complicated by the fact that storms occur as somewhat random events. The environment, too, is complicated by the fact that subsoils of varied erodibility are exposed to varying degrees with time and that manmade drainage may concentrate the magnitude and location of channel flow. During stabilization after urban construction (table 1, F), channel instability is marked by serious degradation and severe bank erosion as a result of increased flows of relatively low sediment concentration from impervious areas.

As already mentioned, heavy loads of sediment are moved into channels below construction areas; the fine particles move through rapidly and the coarser particles tend to fill the channel system. In regard to the period of returning stability after development, Dawdy (1967, p. 242) stated,

> the slug of coarse sediment produced during construction may well travel through a channel system as a discrete mass or wave, causing geomorphic changes. These, in turn, change the hydraulics of the channel, cause bank erosion, and may alter the ecology of the stream. No data nor studies of the impact of urban sediment on downstream ecology are available, however. If a channel system is steep enough and discharge is sufficiently great to transport the contributed sediment, the geomorphic and hydraulic effects may be short lived, and the impact of the sediment and of its associated problems is transferred downstream to a major river, a lake or reservior, an estuary, or the ocean.

With our advanced state of technology, solutions to the physical urban sediment problem are usually available even though the problem may occur under a dynamic and complicated environment. Such solutions may seem economically and socially expensive, but in the light of our high standard of living the expense will prove to be relatively low. Because of the importance of sediment control, it is to be hoped that implementation will not be fraught with institutional difficulty.

In many situations, a program to obtain sediment knowledge is justified in order to wisely choose a suitable solution among many alternatives. A complete sediment-evaluation program may, in reality, be a complete systems study of input-storage-output components. For example, where the problem involves a stream channel, it is essential to know the sources of the inflowing sediment, the degree and extent of transport in the stream, and the nature of the deposit, in terms of time and space, at the estuary or other body of water.

Several steps needed to achieve control of urban sediment have been outlined by Guy and others (1963). These are:

1. Public-program adjustments, including a specific policy toward potential problems, planning and zoning, local ordinances, and assistance to insure proper judicial interpretation.
2. Erosion-control measures, including the proper use of vegetation for both temporary and permanent control, diversions and bench terraces, stabilization structures, storm drainage systems, storage of excess rainfall on lots, floodwater retarding structures, and the provision of "blue-green areas," usually parks, along streams and in headwater areas having critical runoff.
3. Adequate education of both the general public and urban officials is essential. Such education in turn requires adequate sediment information, without which neither 1 nor 2 can be effectively accomplished.

Attempts to control some of the sediment problems in the Los Angeles area have involved the construction of numerous "debris" basins on small streams draining steep foothill areas. Figure 6 shows debris accumulation in Santa Anita basin after the storms of January 1969. Sediment yields of as much as 124,000 cubic yards per square mile per year have been noted to occur as long as 5 years after the accidental burning of the vegetal cover (Tatum, 1965, p. 891). The primary purpose of these debris basins is to prevent heavy sediment loads from clogging drains and streams in developed urban areas. Bank erosion and other sediment problems are reduced in the Los Angeles area by stabilization of banks and sometimes streambeds in an attempt to increase the flow capacity through urban areas.

A good example of an institution attempting to control sediment in urban development, and thus to

Figure 6.—Sediment accumulated in Santa Anita debris basin near Sierra Madre (Los Angeles area), Calif., as a result of the storms occurring during January 1969. Inspection of the delta at the spillway and channel downstream indicated that much sediment of the larger sizes had overflowed the system at the end of the storm period.

eliminate or reduce many sediment problems, is Montgomery County, Md. It was the first county (July 1965) to adopt a "Sediment Control Program" that requires approval of subdivision development plans by the Department of Public Works, which in turn is in consultation with the Soil Conservation Service. If the developers' plan for erosion and sediment control seems inadequate, then the Soil Conservation Service is asked to recommend suitable measures. Sometimes the measures may include only revision in timing and location of construction activity. In October 1966, the Fairfax (Va.) Board of Supervisors adopted a set of subdivision land-erosion-control measures similar to those of Montgomery County.

Sedimant control is also being effected as a result of Executive Order 11258 issued in 1966 through the authority of the Water Quality Act of 1965. This order requires a review of all Federal and federally aided operations where there is a significant potential for reduction of water pollution by sediment. The reviewers may prescribe suitable remedial practices as necessary. This should prove particularly significant in view of sediment problems in connection with urban and suburban highway construction (Vice, Guy, and Ferguson, 1969).

CONCLUSIONS

Much of the disturbed soil in urban construction areas erodes and becomes sediment in streams; the sediment damages water-control works and aquatic habitat, degrades water quality, increases flood damages, and lowers the environmental attractiveness. During the process of stabilization of an area after construction, streams tend to erode their beds and banks as a result of increased runoff. All such sediment, whether from construction erosion or from channel erosion, is transported by streams and often deposited somewhere downstream at a location previously assigned to the movement or storage of water.

Documentation of erosion sources and amounts, of sediment concentration in runoff, of stream-channel changes, and of the location and amounts of deposition together with an economic analysis of sediment damages and a pertinent research program will provide the knowledge needed to find the best solutions to a wide variety of existing and future urban sediment problems. Aside from the knowledge needed for better design of systems, documentation of sediment conditions will provide baseline information from which damages, both on site and downstream, can be evaluated. Defense against damage claims often rests upon attempts to demonstrate that the claimant had no knowledge of preexisting conditions, that the source of damages was not discernable, or that conditions had always been so.

Increasing numbers of communities will likely attempt to alleviate their many sediment problems because of the adverse effects of such problems on the local environment. The public sentiment needed to support such programs to control sediment is built from a series of events that restrict, offend, or otherwise concern people.

REFERENCES CITED

American Public Works Association, 1969, Water pollution aspects of urban runoff: Federal Water Pollution Control Adm., Pub. WP–20–15, 272 p.

Anderson, D.G., 1968, Effects of urban development on floods in northern Virginia: U.S. Geol. Survey open-file report, 26 p.

Brown, C.B., 1948, Perspective on sedimentation—purpose of conference: Federal Inter-Agency Sedimentation Conf., Denver, Colo., 1947, Proc., U.S. Bur. Reclamation, p. 307.

Busby, C.E., 1962, Some legal aspects of sedimentation: Am. Soc. Civil Engineers Trans., v. 127, pt. I, p. 1007–1044.

——— 1967, Aspects of American sedimentation law: Jour. Soil and Water Conserv., v. 22, no. 3, p. 107–109.

Dawdy, D.R., 1967, Knowledge of sedimentation in urban environments: Am. Soc. Civil Engineers Proc., v. 93, no. HY6, p. 235–245.

Ferguson, G.E., and Guy, H.P., 1970, Sedimentation as an environmental problem: Jour. Soil and Water Conserv. (In press.)

Guy, H.P., 1964, An analysis of some storm-period variables affecting stream sediment transport: U.S. Geol. Survey Prof. Paper 462–E, 46 p.

——— 1965, Residential construction and sedimentation at Kensington, Md.: Federal Inter-Agency Sedimentation Conf., Jackson, Miss., 1963, Proc., U.S. Dept. Agriculture Misc. Pub. 970, p. 30–37.

——— 1967, Research needs regarding sediment and urbanization: Am. Soc. Civil Engineers Proc, v. 93, no. HY6, p. 247–254.

Guy, H.P., and Ferguson, G.E., 1962, Sediment in small reservoirs due to urbanization: Am. Soc. Civil Engineers, Proc., v. 88, no. HY2, p. 27–37.

Guy, H.P., and others, 1963, A program for sediment control in the Washington Metropolitan Region: Washington, D.C., Interstate Comm. Potomac River Basin, May, 48 p.

Leopold, L.B., 1968, Hydrology for urban land planning—a guidebook on the hydrologic effects of urban land use: U.S. Geol. Survey Circ. 554, 18 p.

Maddock, Thomas, Jr., 1969, Economic aspects of sedimentation: Am. Soc. Civil Engineers Proc., v. 95, no. HY1, p. 191–207.

Moore, W.R., and Smith, C.E., 1968, Erosion control in relation to watershed management: Am. Soc. Civil Engineers Proc., v. 94, no. IR3, p. 321–331.

Peters, J.C., 1967, Effects on a trout stream of sediment from agricultural practices: Jour. Wildlife Management, v. 31, no. 4, p. 805–812.

Roalman, A.R., 1969, A bounty on water polluters: Urbana, Ill., Am. Water Resources Assoc., Water Resources Bull., v. 5, no. 2, p. 62–65.

Tatum, F.E., 1965, A new method of estimating debris-storage requirements for debris basins: U.S. Dept. Agriculture Misc. Pub. 970, Paper 89, p. 886–897.

Vice. R.B., Guy, H.P., and Ferguson, G.E., 1969, Sediment movement in an area of suburban highway construction, Scott Run Basin, Fairfax County, 1961–64: U.S. Geol. Survey Water-Supply Paper 1591–E, 41 p.

Wolman, M.G., 1964, Problems posed by sediment derived from construction activities in Maryland: Annapolis, Md., Report to the Maryland Water Pollution Control Commission, p. 1–125.

———1967, A cycle of sedimentation and erosion in urban river channels: Geografiska Annaler, v. 49, ser. A, p. 385–395.

Wolman, M.G., and Schick, A.P., 1967, Effects of construction on fluvial sediment, urban and suburban areas of Maryland: Water Resources Research, v. 3, no. 2, p. 451–464.

U. S. GOVERNMENT PRINTING OFFICE : 1970 O - 397-595

24

Reprinted from *Water Resources Res.*, **8**(6), 1530–1540 (1972)

Stream Channel Enlargement Due to Urbanization

THOMAS R. HAMMER

Regional Science Research Institute
Philadelphia, Pennsylvania 19101

Abstract. Stream channel enlargement occurs in response to the change in streamflow regimen accompanying urbanization. This empirical study relates the imputed increase in channel cross-sectional area to detailed land use data and other information for 78 small watersheds near Philadelphia. Important differences between the effects of various types of impervious land use are observed: large channel enlargement effects are found for sewered streets and area of major impervious parcels such as parking lots, and much smaller effects are observed for unsewered streets and impervious area involving detached houses. Relatively low channel enlargement effects are attributed to all types of impervious development less than 4 years old and also to street and house area more than 30 years old. The influence of impervious development on channel size is found to be significantly related to topographic characteristics of the watershed, to the location of impervious development within the watershed, and to man-made drainage alterations. Although the relative importance of these interactive factors proves difficult to establish, the most critical determinant of the amount of channel enlargement resulting from a given level of urbanization appears to be basin slope.

It has been widely recognized that urban development in a watershed causes change in streamflow regimen [*Anderson*, 1968; *Leopold*, 1968]. The process of urbanization tends to increase the peak flow magnitudes through the spread of impervious area, which increases the volume of runoff, and through drainage alterations (such as storm sewerage), which facilitate the movement of runoff through the basin. The study reported here has focused on a phenomenon that accompanies the increase in peak flows, namely, the enlargement of stream channels due to urbanization.

Observers in the past have suggested that stream channels tend to maintain a state of quasiequilibrium with the flow regimen of the stream such that there is a constant frequency of overbank flow. This frequency has been estimated at approximately 1.5 years [*Leopold*, 1964]. For watersheds affected by urbanization, *Leopold* [1968] has hypothesized that stream channels tend to enlarge by an amount sufficient to maintain a similar quasiequilibrium state under the altered flow regimen; thus the amount of channel enlargement would be roughly proportional to the increase in the 1.5-year flood. Although recent findings have caused the common bank-full frequency hypothesis to be seriously questioned [*Kilpatrick and Barnes*, 1964], the notion that stream channels respond to urbanization by enlarging in roughly the same proportion as the increase in peak flows does appear intuitively plausible.

Channel enlargement resulting from urbanization has been considered an important subject of investigation for two reasons. First, the process of channel enlargement itself involves a serious reduction in the aesthetic and recreational value of the stream and incurs monetary costs in many instances. For small streams this effect must be considered one of the major negative impacts of urbanization on stream quality. Second, a more detailed treatment of urbanization is possible when studying channel enlargement than when studying peak flow increase, since in the former case it is not necessary to rely on stream gage data and hence a larger sample of streams can be employed. This circumstance has allowed the present study to consider empirically a wide variety of factors relevant to the hydrologic impact of urbanization.

CHANNEL MEASUREMENT PROGRAM

The study has involved 78 watersheds 1–6 mi^2 in area in the Pennsylvania portion of the

Philadelphia metropolitan region (consisting of Philadelphia, Bucks, Montgomery, Delaware, and Chester counties). All watersheds were located in the Piedmont physiographic area. Fifty of the sample watersheds contained some degree of urbanization in the form of large-scale residential, commercial, or industrial development; 28 watersheds contained only rural land uses.

The channel measurement process consisted of stretching a tape across the stream so that it was level and perpendicular to the channel and measuring the vertical distance between the tape and the earth surface at 2-foot intervals. The depth of the channel at each point was computed by subtracting from each measurement the vertical distance between the tape and the point chosen as the bank top. These data were then used to compute the overall channel width, depth, and cross-sectional area for each cross section. (The computation of width and depth was based on the use of a computer program to find the best fitting rectangular approximation to the channel cross section.)

It was found early in the study that the channels of many small streams are quite irregular and show considerable variation in cross-sectional area; this irregularity is particularly true for streams that drained urbanizing areas. For such streams it was obvious that only at a limited number of channel points could the channel be in quasiequilibrium with the flow regimen of the stream. Because of this finding no attempt was made to obtain measurements that would provide a complete characterization of the channel within a chosen reach. Rather, measurements were made only at points of apparent quasiequilibrium with streamflow.

Elaborate criteria for identifying quasiequilibrium channel points were developed as part of the study. These criteria are described in detail elsewhere [*Hammer,* 1971*a*]. The most important feature of these points is that the lower bank, the elevation of which defines the bank 'top' when computing channel dimensions, consists of a berm or bank segment that has been recently constructed by the stream, i.e., by deposition of sediment. The most commonly recognized situation in which such bank segments are found is that described in the familiar meander model of channel behavior, which specifies that a meandering stream will erode its bank at the outside of a bend and will build a succession of new bank segments at the inside and thus a 'floodplain' will be constructed within the bend. An equally common situation found in the present study, however, was the existence of recently built bank segments at points where the channel had apparently become overwidened through scouring.

Four or more cross-sectional measurements were executed for most of the streams. The two variables of interest computed from these data were the channel cross-sectional area and the ratio of channel width to depth. The latter variable was formulated to test the possibility that channel enlargement due to urbanization typically involves a greater proportionate increase in channel width than in channel depth or vice versa. In preliminary studies the width to depth ratio was found to be correlated with channel slope and watershed area but showed no significant relationship to the degree of urbanization or to the apparent increase in cross-sectional area caused by urbanization. Thus the remainder of the analysis was concerned only with channel cross-sectional area, expressed as an average for each stream.

LAND USE AND OTHER WATERSHED DATA

The collection of watershed data involved the use of a grid system for each watershed, the grid squares being 40 acres in size. Thirty variables pertaining to land uses and topographic characteristics were measured and recorded for each grid square. Each topographic variable (e.g., land slope) was measured as an average for land in the square. The grid square size of 40 acres was recognized to be inappropriately large for the consideration of factors such as land slope, since a great deal of variation can occur within such an area. A smaller size would have resulted in an infeasible number of grid squares to be considered however.

The set of land use measurements consisted of an exhaustive partitioning of the land area in each grid square into 17 categories. These measurements were executed by using aerial photographs (1 inch = 400 feet) and an intensive field survey of the sample watersheds.

The major focus of attention was land in impervious uses. Three basic categories of impervious area were considered: streets and sidewalks, houses and related impervious area, and all other impervious area. The first of these categories included the area of all paved streets, highways, rural roads, and expressways plus the area of paved sidewalks. The second included all impervious area associated with single-family (or two-family) houses, namely, the houses themselves; paved driveways, walks, and patios; and outbuildings, such as garages, sheds, and small barns. (These two categories will henceforth simply be referred to as 'area of streets' and 'area of houses.') The category of 'other' impervious area included a wide variety of land uses: commercial buildings, apartment houses, factories, airport runways, shopping centers, row houses, and especially parking lots. Approximately two thirds of the land in this category consisted of paved area instead of structures.

Within the 78 sample watersheds these three categories of impervious surface accounted for approximately equal portions of the total impervious area. Measurement of these variables was greatly facilitated by the fact that most of the impervious development in the sample watersheds was suburban and fairly recently constructed. Thus there was great uniformity in street widths and in house types, and also most of the other impervious area occurred in large parcels, e.g., shopping centers.

The length of time that impervious development had been in existence was expected to be important to channel enlargement. Therefore the impervious area in each of the three groups was subdivided into three age categories: area less than 4 years old, area 4–15 years old, and area greater than 15 years old. (This division was made possible by the fact that the aerial photographs were 4 years out of date and the topographic maps were approximately 15 years out of date at the time of the study.) Later in the study a fourth age category was created, applying only to street and house area; this category was the development constructed prior to 1940, as was estimated by using aerial photographs and the U.S. Census of Housing.

Another aspect of impervious development considered important was the existence of street storm sewerage. Although an exact determination of which street segments were underlain by storm sewers was not feasible, it was observed that the existence of curbing (usually associated with sidewalks) usually implied the existence of storm sewers and vice versa. Thus the procedure adopted was to consider any street segment with continuous curbing to be sewered. By using this definition, estimates were prepared for each grid square of the area of sewered streets and the area of houses fronting on sewered streets in each of the various age categories.

The major nonimpervious land uses considered were nonimpervious developed land, wooded land, land in cultivation, and 'open land.' The nonimpervious developed land category consisted primarily of lawn area; it was obtained for each grid square by subtracting the area rendered impervious from the overall area of land in intensive nonagricultural use. Open land was obtained as an overall residual by subtracting from total land area the amount of wooded land, land in cultivation, and land in intensive nonagricultural use. Land in this category consisted largely of pasture and unused grassland.

The topographic and drainage system factors measured for each grid square were the average land slope, the length and average slope of the flow path from the grid square to the point at which the flow reached the stream channel, the length and slope profile of the stream channel from the point just mentioned to the watershed mouth, and the extent of man-made alterations to these drainage path components. With regard to drainage alterations, any portion of the drainage path from the grid square to the watershed mouth would be considered altered if that portion consisted of a smooth artificial channel (e.g., a pipe) the cross-sectional area of which was at least as large as the probable area of the natural channel that it replaced. A number of variables in addition to those given above were considered, including several minor land uses; some of these are mentioned below.

FORM OF THE REGRESSION ANALYSIS

The dependent variable in the regression analysis was a quantity involving channel cross-sectional area; this quantity was termed the 'channel enlargement ratio.' This variable incorporated an empirical relationship between channel cross-sectional area and watershed size for unurbanized basins. The relationship, estimated by using the 28 rural watersheds in the sample, was the following (with a correlation coefficient equal to 0.87):

$$\log C = 1.3945 + 0.6573 \log A \qquad (1)$$
$$C = 24.8A^{0.657}$$

where C is the channel cross-sectional area in square feet and A is the watershed area in square miles.

The channel enlargement ratio R was computed as follows for each of the 78 sample watersheds:

$$R = C/24.8A^{0.657} \qquad (2)$$

The channel enlargement ratio consisted of the channel cross-sectional area of each stream as a proportion of the expected channel area in the absence of urbanization; thus the ratio expressed the amount by which channel size was imputed to have increased because of urbanization. (Whereas the subject streams were observed only once instead of over a period of time, the use of the term channel enlargement ratio is justified only by the fact that the ratio was indeed found to be strongly related to urbanization. This finding indicates that the channels of the urbanized streams had in fact enlarged relative to their preurbanization size.) Values of the enlargement ratio in the sample ranged from 0.7 to 3.8, the majority lying between 1.0 and 2.0.

The basic set of independent variables used to explain the channel enlargement ratio consisted of the proportions of the watershed area devoted to various land uses. In addition, a large number of interaction variables were formulated to investigate the possible influence of topographic and other factors on the effects produced by impervious land uses. An interaction variable was prepared by multiplying, for each individual grid square, a land use measurement times some other characteristic of the square, e.g., average land slope; the resulting figure was summed over all the grid squares and was divided by the watershed area.

Many of the grid square characteristics incorporated in the interaction variables were factors that would not be relevant to the amount of runoff yielded by the grid square itself but that might affect the contribution of this runoff to peak flows at the watershed mouth. An example of such a factor is the distance of flow from the grid square to the stream channel. In dealing with factors of this nature the following assumption was made: the relative importance of the various impervious land uses to channel enlargement when they are weighted by such a factor should be the same as their relative importance in unweighted form. This assumption led to the use of a single interaction variable for each factor, in which the factor was multiplied by a linear combination of impervious land uses for each grid square instead of by an individual land use. The coefficients in this linear combination were intended to equal the respective regression coefficients of the impervious land uses in unweighted form. This equality of coefficients was achieved by iterating the regression.

Two independent variables not involving land uses were included in the final regressions. One of these was a watershed shape index measuring the deviance of the watershed from circularity. This variable was the moment of the watershed about its center of mass (as a two-dimensional figure) divided by the moment of a circle having the same area. The other variable was a soil drainage index based on the USDA Soil Survey classification of soils as being 'well-drained,' 'moderately well-drained,' 'somewhat poorly drained,' or 'poorly drained.' Arbitrary scores of 4, 3, 2, and 1 were assigned to these soil descriptions, respectively, and the average score for soils in each watershed was computed. These two variables were both consistently strong in explaining the channel enlargement ratio.

REGRESSION RESULTS

Four different sets of regression results were obtained as the final outcome of the data analysis. These regressions differed with regard to the grouping of impervious land uses, the treatment of age categories of impervious area, and the formulation of interaction variables. Only one set of regression results is reported here in full; this regression involved the least complex group of independent variables. The other regression results are described somewhat less formally in the following interpretive sections.

The regression reported here contains only one interaction variable, which deals with the average slope of the flow path from a given grid square to the watershed mouth. This average slope, expressed as a percent, was multiplied by the following linear combination of impervious land uses for each grid square: $0.83\ X_1 + 3.25X_2 + 3.79X_3$, where X_1, X_2, and X_3 denote the area of houses, the area of streets, and the other impervious area, respectively. The results of this regression are presented in Table 1.

The two variables not involving land uses were entered in the form of deviations around their means. Thus note that the constant term in the regression represents an estimate of the effect on channel enlargement of land not included in any of the independent variables dealing with land uses. (A watershed containing none of these land uses and having average values of the soil drainage index and the watershed shape index would have a channel enlargement ratio equal to the constant term 0.90.) The land category not included among the independent variables was open land, which accounted for approximately 30% of the land area in the sample watersheds.

TABLE 1. Multiple Regression Results with Channel Enlargement Ratio as Dependent Variable

Independent Variable	Regression Coefficient	Standard Error of Coefficient
Land in cultivation	0.3896	0.1291
Wooded land	−0.1518	0.1151
Land in golf courses	1.6416	0.5538
Area of houses >4 years old fronting on sewered streets	0.8291	0.7462
Area of sewered streets >4 years old	3.2499	0.8998
Other impervious area >4 years old	3.7855	0.4486
Nonimpervious developed land plus impervious area <4 years old and unsewered streets and houses	0.1870	0.0890
Interaction variable: average slope of flow path to watershed mouth	0.2966	0.0350
Watershed shape index	−0.1990	0.0776
Soil drainage index	−0.1072	0.0247
Constant term	0.9025	

Multiple $R^2 = 0.9813$.

Each of the regression coefficients for independent variables dealing with land uses represents the difference between the channel enlargement effect of the given use and the effect of open land. Thus the effect of land in cultivation, for example, would be 0.90 + 0.39 = 1.29. For the major impervious land uses the channel enlargement effects include interaction with slope of flow. To calculate typical values of these quantities, the following relationship was estimated for watersheds in our sample: $S = 1.87A^{-0.4}$, where A is watershed area and S is the average slope of flow to the watershed mouth from all points in the watershed as a percent. Thus the typical channel enlargement effect associated with the sewered street area, for example, could be calculated as the constant term plus $3.25(1 + 0.297S)$, or $0.90 + 3.25[1 + 0.297(1.87A^{-0.4})]$. The estimated channel enlargement effects of the various land uses for a typical 1-mi^2 watershed are presented in Table 2.

The values listed in Table 2 would be multiplied by the proportions of watershed area devoted to various uses to yield an estimate of the channel enlargement ratio in any particular situation. For example, an urbanized 1-mi^2 basin might have 70% of its area in nonimpervious 'developed' land and 10% in sewered streets, 10% in houses fronting on sewered streets, and 10% in other impervious area; the expected channel enlargement ratio in this case would be $0.7(1.08) + 0.1(2.19) + 0.1(5.95) + 0.1(6.79) = 2.25$. The predicted channel cross-sectional area in square feet would be $2.25 \cdot 24.8 = 55.8$.

General evaluation of results. In considering the overall levels of effect predicted by these results, it is useful to compare them with the findings of earlier studies investigating the effect of urbanization on peak flows. *Leopold* [1968] has summarized the results of a number of these studies. He focused on the ratio of average annual flood after urbanization to average annual flood before urbanization for a 1-mi^2 watershed. This ratio is related in tabular and graphic form to two urbanization variables, the percent of watershed area rendered impervious and the percent of sewered watershed area.

The values described by Leopold for the average annual flood ratio are quite similar to the values indicated by this study for the channel enlargement ratio. For example, the estimated average annual flood ratio of a 100% impervious, 100% sewered watershed would be just under 7. This value corresponds closely to the channel enlargement effect found in the present study for other impervious area, which would have to be the predominant land use in a totally impervious watershed. As another example the hypothetical watershed mentioned earlier, 10% of its area being in each of the three major impervious uses, would have an average annual flood ratio of approximately 2.5 (corresponding to 30% impervious area and 60% sewered area). This value is similar to the estimate of 2.25 obtained here for the channel enlargement ratio. (A more complete comparison of the results of this study and the data summarized by Leopold is presented in *Hammer* [1971*b*]. A number of assumptions regarding typical characteristics of urbanization were required to convert the variables used in this study to the form considered by Leopold; these assumptions are too involved to describe here.) The general agreement between the results for channel enlargement and the data pertaining to average annual flood is consistent with the common bank-full frequency hypothesis and tends to lend support to the procedures employed in this study.

Although the equation reported above should yield accurate predictions of channel enlargement in most situations, it is likely that the effects attributed specifically to sewered street area and other impervious area are biased upward. Intercorrelation between the various aspects of urbanization has allowed these variables to 'borrow' causal influences that properly should have been attributed to other factors. The factors whose influences have been borrowed would include the following in order of probable importance: alterations to the natural drainage system, impervious area of unsewered streets and houses, and impervious area less than 4 years old. It was possible to establish the separate influences of some of these factors in other forms of the regression involving complex variables (see equation 3 below). But the possibility of bias due to intercorrelation was present throughout the analysis.

Land uses other than impervious area. The results obtained for nonimpervious land uses were generally reasonable. Land in cultivation was found to have a positive influence relative to open land, and land in forest was found to

TABLE 2. Channel Enlargement Effects of Land Uses in a 1-Square-Mile Basin—Version 1

Land in cultivation	1.29
Wooded land	0.75
Land in golf courses	2.54
Area of houses >4 years old fronting on sewered streets	2.19
Area of sewered streets >4 years old	5.95
Other impervious area >4 years old	6.79
Nonimpervious developed land plus impervious area <4 years old and unsewered streets and houses	1.08
Open land (residual category)	0.90

have a negative influence. This pattern was observed in all regression results, including regressions that involved only the 28 rural streams. The coefficient for land in forest was not significantly different from 0 at the 5% level in the regression reported above; but this variable was retained because of its statistical significance in other regressions and because of the stability of its estimated effect throughout the analysis. (A similar situation prevailed for area of houses fronting on sewered streets.)

Quite a large regression coefficient was obtained for land in golf courses. This land use was expected to have a greater impact on channel size than most nonimpervious land uses, owing to its drainage characteristics and to the watering of fairways during summer months.

Nonimpervious developed land was an important land use in the sample watersheds, accounting for more than 20% of the total land area surveyed. A small but significant positive coefficient was obtained for this land use both when it was combined with impervious area categories (unsewered streets and houses and impervious area less than 4 years old) and when it was entered singly. The positive coefficient was not unexpected, since the developed land category contained a variety of land uses besides residential lawn area. This category included some land in intense use (such as unpaved parking areas) and much land immediately bordering sewered impervious surfaces (such as highway medians and land between streets and sidewalks). The estimated effect for this use must be viewed only as an overall average for developed land not actually rendered impervious; the possibility remains that the effect of established lawn area per se might be less than that of open land.

Types of impervious area. The largest effect on channel enlargement was estimated for other impervious area. Area of sewered streets was next and was followed by area of houses fronting on sewered streets. This pattern was maintained in all regressions, although the relative sizes of estimated effects did vary considerably (see Table 2 versus Table 3).

It was hypothesized that the great influence attributed to other impervious area and the relatively small importance attributed to houses had to do with the size of impervious parcels involved. Parking lots and large buildings might yield storm runoff in such quantities that the proportion lost to infiltration or depression storage during flow to the stream would be minimal, whereas this proportion might be large for runoff from houses, driveways, patios, and so on. A partial test of this hypothesis was conducted by giving separate consideration to other impervious area found in parcels greater than 5 acres in size (which accounted for approximately half the total); but the regression coefficient for this subcategory did not differ significantly from the coefficient for the remaining other impervious area.

The large effect estimated for other impervious area is striking in view of the fact that this effect holds without regard to drainage facilities present. (Drainage facilities specifically serving these areas were not surveyed in the study.) To test for the possible importance of proximity to sewered streets, a variable was formed in which other impervious area was weighted by the density of sewered streets for each grid square. No importance was attributed to this variable in the regression however.

Low effects were obtained throughout the analysis for area of unsewered streets and houses fronting on unsewered streets. As was indicated earlier, it is believed that the importance of street sewerage to the effects produced by street and house area was somewhat exaggerated. One suspected reason for this exaggeration is the existence of a negative correlation among urbanized watersheds between the proportion of streets that are unsewered and the efficiency of the drainage facilities for streets that are sewered. This correlation would lead to a downward bias in the regression coefficient for unsewered streets and an upward bias, relative to average conditions, in the coefficient for sewered streets (and similarly for houses). A second reason is the probable existence of correlations between the proportion of unsewered streets and various characteristics of the surrounding nonimpervious land. (See the discussion of age of impervious area below.)

In one version of the regression the area of streets in residential districts with detached houses was added to the area of houses to form a single 'residential impervious area' category. Two variables relating to this category were entered in the regression, i.e., sewered residential impervious area and all residential impervious area weighted by average land slope, as a percent, for each grid square. The coefficients obtained for these variables were, respectively, 2.02 and 0.18 (see equation 3). Although the importance attributed to land slope may be questionable, the channel enlargement effects thus yielded for sewered versus unsewered area are probably more reasonable than those obtained in other formulations. For residential impervious area located in a 1-mi^2 basin on land with a slope of 5%, the estimated channel enlargement effects would be approximately 4.2 for sewered area and 2.0 for unsewered area; if land slope were 10%, the effects would be 5.2 and 3.0.

A special category of houses, not heretofore mentioned, was given separate treatment in the study. This category included houses having direct, underground connections between gutter downspouts and the storm sewerage system. This sort of construction was found only in the city of Philadelphia, where these connections are required by building codes. The estimated channel enlargement effect of houses possessing this feature was consistently very high and similar to the effect of other impervious area. Thus in the final runs of the regression this land use was included with other impervious area.

Age of impervious area. The length of time that impervious development had been in existence was important in the study in two different ways. First, since stream channel enlargement must require some length of time to be accomplished, one would expect that the observable effect of a parcel of impervious area on the stream channel at a given time would be positively related to the age of the parcel at that time. Second, the results of the study have suggested that relatively old impervious area, in existence more than 30 years, may have less effect on the stream channel than development constructed somewhat more recently.

With regard to the first of these considerations, an assumption was made that the relative importance of age of development should be the same for all types of impervious area. For example, if the influence of street area 4–15 years old is only 75% as great as the influence of street area more than 15 years old, owing to the time element in channel enlargement, then the same percentage should apply to house area and to other impervious area in these two age categories. The incorporation of this assumption in the analysis reduced the number of parameters to be estimated but made it necessary to iterate the regression, i.e., to estimate the influences associated with type of impervious area and age of impervious area in successive rounds.

In the initial phase of analysis (before separate consideration was given to impervious development more than 30 years old) the following results were obtained for the various age categories. Impervious area less than 4 years old was found to have no positive influence relative to open land, but impervious area 4–15 years old was attributed an influence fully as large as that of development more than 15 years old. In response to these results, area 4–15 years old and area more than 15 years old were simply added together for each impervious area type, and impervious area less than 4 years old was deleted from the regression as a separate factor. This action yielded results such as those shown earlier.

It was observed in the analysis that watersheds with relatively old development tended to have relatively low values of the channel enlargement ratio. Thus separate consideration was given to area of sewered streets and area of houses fronting on sewered streets that had been in existence for more than 30 years at the time of the study, i.e., were built before 1940. The result was that notably lower effects were estimated for area more than 30 years old than for area 15–30 years old, especially in the case of house area. (The level of statistical significance that can be attached to the addition of a separate >30-year category is indicated by the fact that in regressions for which this step simply involved adding one independent variable the variable would be found significant at the 5% level but not at the 1% level.)

A likely explanation for this finding is that the drainage facilities serving older residential areas might tend to be relatively poor, either because they were underdesigned to begin with cr because they have deteriorated over time. It is probable that an equally important cause, however, was the association between age of development and characteristics of the land not rendered impervious. Older residential developments tend to have more trees, shrubbery, and other dense vegetation than newer developments; also the soil structure itself has had more time to recover from being disturbed (if indeed it was ever disturbed). The negative influence of these factors on runoff and stream channel enlargement would, in the absence of other relevant variables, be attributed to the age of impervious area.

Regardless of which explanation is more important, it is difficult to say whether the relatively low effects estimated for older impervious area should be interpreted to mean that the impact of any residential development should be expected to decrease eventually or whether the low effects pertain only to development of a certain type that was built primarily before 1940.

When streets and houses more than 30 years old were given separate consideration in the regression, the estimated influence of impervious area 4–15 years old and area 15–30 years old differed appreciably. Also positive regression coefficients were obtained for impervious area less than 4 years old, although these were never statistically significant. The channel enlargement effects estimated in this case are shown in Table 3.

Influences of natural watershed features. One of the principal aims of the study was to state the importance of watershed features and the location of development within a watershed in such a fashion that the channel enlargement effects of development in different watersheds or at different points in a given watershed might be compared. The desire to obtain results that would be usable for intrawatershed comparisons made it necessary to consider topographic factors pertaining to individual grid squares instead of overall basin indices. Also the inter-

TABLE 3. Channel Enlargement Effects of Impervious Land Uses in a 1-Square-Mile Basin—Version 2

Impervious area <4 years old and unsewered street and house area	1.08
Area of houses fronting on sewered streets	
Houses 4–15 years old	3.36
Houses 15–30 years old*	4.15
Houses >30 years old†	1.08
Area of sewered streets	
Streets 4–15 years old	4.20
Streets 15–30 years old*	5.16
Streets >30 years old†	3.76
Other impervious area	
Area 4–15 years old	6.26
Area >15 years old	7.99

* Built after 1940.
† Built before 1940.

action variables incorporating these factors had to be rather complex in form to avoid certain anomalous situations. (See the discussion at the end of this section.) This enterprise was successful in that statistically significant results were obtained for a set of variables having the desired properties. However, serious questions of interpretation remain.

The major factors to be considered were the watershed size, the distance and slope of flow to the stream channel (i.e., from a given grid square), the distance and slope of flow in the stream channel to the watershed mouth, and the existence of portions of the drainage network that had been altered by man. An additional factor, average land slope in the grid square itself, was used to weight individual types of impervious area (instead of weighting the linear combination of all impervious uses).

As a basis for the formulation of variables it was hypothesized that the impact of impervious development on channel enlargement at the watershed mouth is reduced, relative to potential impact, by an amount that is positively related to the intervening distance of flow (in unaltered portions of the flow path) and negatively related to the slope of the flow path. Slope would be relevant because of its influence on flow velocity and also because it would serve as a surrogate for the amount of flood detention (e.g., overbank storage) that would be likely to take place during peak flow periods. With regard to drainage alterations it was hypothesized that flow in fully altered watercourses (as defined earlier) would not involve any reduction in impact. These assumptions are of course naive in view of the complexities of basin hydrology.

Flow to channel and flow in channel were treated in two separate variables, each of which involved distance divided by a function of slope (for individual grid squares). The quantity used to weight impervious development in the final form of the flow to channel variable consisted of the flow distance to the stream channel divided by the square of the average slope of this flow path. The flow in channel variable was based on measurements of the length, slope, and drainage area of a series of separate channel intervals. The quantity used to weight impervious development in this variable consisted of a summation, over all channel intervals relevant to a given grid square, of the interval length divided by a slope index pertaining to the interval (see equation 3 below).

The influence of watershed size was intended to be expressed by way of a third variable involving only watershed area A raised to some exponent. Therefore steps were taken to remove the association with watershed size from the flow to channel and flow in channel variables. Both these variables were divided by the quantity $0.985A^{0.524}$, which represented an estimate (based on the current sample) of the average flow distance in miles from all points in a watershed to the watershed mouth. In addition, the slope index used in the flow in channel variable incorporated an adjustment for the association between channel slope and drainage area. Thus the influence of watershed size was effectively isolated in the watershed size variable. The form of this variable that worked best was $A^{-0.5}$ with a positive coefficient.

The equation estimated in this phase of the analysis (the variables not relating to impervious development being omitted) is presented in (3). In this equation the impervious development in each grid square is multiplied by a term that could vary from 1.3 (for development located at the mouth of a 1-mi^2 watershed) down to very small or even negative values. Within the sample watersheds studied, however, the variation in this term was generally moderate.

The influence attributed to watershed size per se is somewhat smaller than that expected.

According to the estimated equation the average effect of impervious development in a typical 5-mi² watershed (net of the effect of open land) would be approximately 13% less than the average net effect of the same type of development in a 1-mi² watershed.

$$R = 1.0 + \frac{1}{A} \sum_i (2.02M_i + 0.180N_iP_i + 4.71Q_i)\left\{1.0 + 0.302A^{-0.5} - \left[\left(1.98 \frac{S_i}{T_i^2} + 0.126 \sum_{k\in\Omega_i} \frac{U_k}{V_k}\right) \Big/ 0.985A^{0.524}\right]\right\} \quad (3)$$

where

- R, estimated channel cross-sectional area for a given watershed, square feet;
- A, watershed area, square miles;
- i, subscript denoting individual grid square in the watershed;
- M_i, sewered residential impervious area more than 4 years old (consists of sewered street and house area in single-family residential districts), square miles;
- N_i, total residential impervious area more than 4 years old, square miles;
- P_i, average land slope in grid square i, percent;
- Q_i, other impervious area more than 4 years old, square miles;
- S_i, length of unaltered portion of the flow path from grid square i to the stream channel, miles;
- T_i, average slope of flow to channel, percent;
- k, subscript denoting individual channel interval in the watershed;
- Ω_i, set of channel intervals across which runoff from grid square i drains during flow in channel;
- U_k, length of unaltered portion of channel interval k, miles;
- V_k, slope index for channel interval k.

(The channel slope index for interval k equals the average slope for the interval, as a percent, divided by the quantity $1.00W_k^{-0.53}$, where W_k is the average drainage area of the stream in square miles in interval k. This quantity represents expected channel slope for the given drainage area, as estimated by using a large sample of channel intervals from the 78 sample watersheds.)

The influence attributed to both flow to channel and flow in channel was heavily dependent on slope. For a watershed with a typical channel configuration and typical slope values the reduction in net effect of impervious development due to flow to channel would range from 0% to approximately 20%; the range would depend on where the development was located and whether the flow path had been altered. In the sample watersheds with the lowest slope values, however, the imputed reduction ranged up to 50%. Very similar percentages were estimated for reduction due to flow in channel (although the typical influence per unit distance in this case was only one third as great as that for flow to channel).

Thus for an 'average' location in a typical watershed the reduction in net effect of impervious development associated with both flow components would be on the order of 20%, relative to the net effect if the development were located at the watershed mouth or if the entire flow path had been altered by man. Conversely, the typical result of altering (e.g., piping) all watercourses in a basin would be to increase the net effect of impervious development by 25%. If the channel enlargement ratio had been 2.2 before alteration, the new value would be 2.5.

The importance attributed to drainage alteration in the above equation is considerably smaller than that expected on the basis of other studies involving peak discharge [*Anderson*, 1968]. Furthermore, other regression equations containing no mention of drainage alteration were able to explain channel enlargement equally well (see below). Throughout the analysis, variables expressing the extent of drainage alteration as a separate factor were tested but were found to lack statistical significance. This result can be partially explained by the high correlation between drainage alteration and the amount of impervious development, which would allow the effects of the former to be attributed to the latter. (A particularly high correlation exists with area of sewered streets, since street sewerage almost always implies alteration of a significant portion of flow to channel.) However, the result does indicate that drainage alteration is less important than land use characteristics for basins such as those studied here.

As described earlier, a form of the regression was also employed in which only one interacaction variable, involving the overall slope of flow, was used. Surprisingly, the level of statistical explanation in this form of the regression was fully as great as that in the form just discussed. The ability of the overall slope of flow variable to substitute for variables expressing watershed size, flow to channel, flow in channel, and land slope was due to the high levels of intercorrelation between these variables. The fact that the substitution was possible reflects negatively on the probable accuracy of the coefficients shown in (3).

Use of the equation involving the overall slope of flow variable to compare the influence of impervious development at different locations in a watershed could lead to erroneous conclusions. For example, because of the typical upward concavity of watercourses, the average slope of flow to the watershed mouth is likely to increase with distance of flow; but the influence of impervious development presumably decreases with distance of flow. Thus the overall slope of flow factor must be considered in the nature of an overall basin index, which is suitable only for comparing the average effects of development in different watersheds.

SUMMARY AND CONCLUSIONS

The study has indicated that important differences exist between the channel enlargement effects of different impervious land uses. The effect of impervious area associated with detached houses is small unless the gutter downspouts connect directly with storm sewers. The effect of street and sidewalk area is large if the streets are sewered but is small otherwise. Other impervious area, which consists primarily of contiguous impervious surfaces exceeding 1 acre in size, has a very large channel enlargement effect. Influence on channel size increases with the length of time that impervious development has been in existence, as is expected, but relatively low effects are observed for street and house area more than 30 years old. The latter fact may or may not indicate that the impact of residential development tends to decrease eventually.

The impact of impervious development appears to be positively related to channel slope, slope of flow to channel, and slope of the developed land itself (in the case of residential area). It is negatively related to the distance of flow to channel and flow in channel, excepting portions of the flow path that have been altered by man. The channel enlargement ratio associated with a given intensity of development also bears a mild negative relationship to watershed size. Although the relative importance of the various topographic and drainage system characteristics is difficult to establish, the slope factors appear to be more influential than distance factors (which involve location of development within the watershed). Man-made alterations to the drainage system other than sewerage of the impervious area itself are attributed a milder influence than that expected.

Acknowledgments. The author wishes to express appreciation to Dr. Luna B. Leopold for guidance throughout the study and to Dr. Robert E. Coughlin for editorial and other valuable assistance. This research has been supported partially by Federal Water Quality Administration grant no. 16090 DYX and partially by contract no. 14-31-0001-3406 with the Office of Water Resources Research.

REFERENCES

Anderson, D. G., Effects of urban development on floods in northern Virginia, open file report, U.S. Geol. Surv., Washington, D. C., 1968.

Brown, D. A., Stream channels and flow relations, *Water Resour. Res., 7*(2), 304–310, 1971.

Hammer, T. R., Criteria for measurement of stream channels as an indicator of peak flow history, *Discuss. Pap Ser. 36,* 56 pp., Reg. Sci. Res. Inst., Philadelphia, Pa., 1971*a*.

Hammer, T. R., The effect of urbanization on stream channel enlargement, Ph.D. thesis, 330 pp., Univ. of Pa., Philadelphia, 1971*b*.

Kilpatrick, F. A., and H. H. Barnes, Jr., Channel geometry of piedmont streams as related to frequency of floods, *U.S. Geol. Surv. Prof. Pap. 422-E,* 10 pp., 1964.

Leopold, L. B., M. G. Wolman, and J. P. Miller, *Fluvial Processes in Geomorphology,* 522 pp., W. H. Freeman, San Francisco, Calif., 1964.

Leopold, L. B., Hydrology for urban land planning—A guidebook on the hydrologic effects of urban land use, *U.S. Geol. Surv. Circ. 554,* 18 pp., 1968.

(Manuscript received May 11, 1972;
revised June 27, 1972.)

25

Reprinted from *Coastal Geomorphology*, Donald R. Coates, ed., State University of New York, Binghamton, 1973, pp. 263–278

BARRIER ISLANDS: NATURAL AND CONTROLLED

Robert Dolan

ABSTRACT

The Outer Banks of North Carolina extend from the Virginia-North Carolina border south to Cape Lookout, a distance of 240 km. These islands were originally one continuous biophysical system, but the upper section has experienced three decades of dune and beach stabilization, coupled with extensive public and private development. In 1957 the stabilized islands became the Cape Hatteras National Seashore. The southern segment, which includes Core Banks, remains in a natural state and is authorized to become the new Cape Lookout National Seashore. The responses of these two different systems to the inshore processes are of special interest for both preservation and management reasons.

Natural barrier islands are much better adapted to steady-state processes and extreme events than are the man-manipulated islands. Since there is little resistance to the storm surge movement across the natural barriers, wave energy is dissipated across the wide berm, among the low dunes, and finally in the grasslands and marshes behind. These islands actually gain material from the beach as the surge moves across the islands, and such deposits serve as sources of supply for new dune growth.

Within the stabilized segment of the Outer Banks, the massive and unbroken man-made dunes act as an impenetrable obstruction to a storm surge, so the energy dissipation and sediment transfer processes are significantly different. The most important differences are associated with the restrictions of the run-up profile and the elimination of oceanic overwash. Overwash is the major means by which low barrier islands retreat before the rising sea. It is the only way massive quantities of coarse sediment can be moved inland from the beach.

INTRODUCTION

Man's role as an agent of landscape change was a topic of interest of geomorphologists long before the 'environmental crisis' became a national issue in the United States. The lists of geologists who have made reference to the effects of man is long and distinguished, but I find R. F. Peel's statments (1952, p. 264), in a rather obscure book for Americans, is one of the most articulate:

> "The earth is not an inert and haphazard collection of materials that can be altered piecemeal without danger. Land, water, and air are all active, and all interact on one another through a host of connected processes. The physical environment of any region is somewhat like a highly complex machine, and a machine which is often rather delicately balanced. Unthinking alteration of one part of it will inevitably affect others, and may set in motion a sequence of changes having unforeseen consequences which may spread far beyond the immediate locality. Man has been producing such changes on the face of the earth for thousands of years through his practices of agriculture and animal husbandry, and the effects, until recently little heeded or even suspected, have in many areas been wholly disastrous. In considering the contribution a knowledge of physical geography can make to human welfare we may thus usefully glance at the effects, often quite unintentional, of man's interference with nature in the past."

Problems within the coastal zone offer excellent opportunities to investigate the impact of man's manipulations of the natural environment. This is a case study of an investigation conducted along the Outer Banks of North Carolina.

BACKGROUND

For many years the policy of the Army Engineers, and some of the other land management agencies, has been to control or prevent certain natural events that were considered to be harmful or destructive. In fact, this effort to control the beach-energy system has been described in terms of actual "combat" with nature. For example, in the Coastal Engineering Research Center the U.S. Army Corps of Engineers concludes its technical report (1964), *Land Against the Sea,* with this sentence (p.43): "Our campaign against the encroachment of the sea must be waged with the same care that we would take against any other enemy threatening our boundaries." I believe this strategy led to unbalanced conditions which eventually culminated in undesirable shoreline responses.

Through experience with sea walls, groins, land fills, and much trial and error engineering, we are now beginning to realize that natural change is often essential to the maintenance of geologic and ecologic systems; however, it is also clear that an uncontrolled natural system, undergoing periodic perturbation, creates serious land management problems. This means that extensive areas must somehow be maintained safely for those who wish to use them for recreational purposes, and yet these same systems must be allowed to remain in a dynamic state.

This management contradiction is a serious problem in areas subject to the greatest physical stresses – the Barrier Islands of North Carolina provide an excellent example of the dilemma land managers face today along the mid-Atlantic coast (Fig. 1). The low profile of these islands, their narrowness, sand compostion, exposure to high wave energy, coupled with a gradually rising sealevel, have created a state of almost continual physical and ecological change (see also Godfrey, this volume).

OUTER BANKS

The Outer Banks extend from the Virginia-North Carolina border south to Cape Lookout, a distance of 240 km (Fig. 1). Originally, these islands were one continuous biophysical system, but the upper section has been altered by more than 40 yr of dune and beach stabilization, coupled with extensive shoreline development. In 1957 the stabilized islands became the Cape Hatteras National Seashore. The southern segment of the Outer Banks, which includes Portsmouth Island and Core Banks, remains in essentially a natural state and is authorized to become part of the new Cape Lookout National Seashore. The responses of these two systems to waves and storm surge are of special interest to the National Park Service for both preservation and management reasons. They can also be compared to determine some of the geologic implications of man-made modifications, as well as the economics associated with maintaining altered environments.

THE NATURAL SYSTEM

The earliest known descriptions of the Outer Banks date from the late 18th century; however, by this time the islands had been settled, and cattle, sheep, horses, and hogs had been introduced for at least 100 yr (Dunbar 1958). Therefore, some uncertainty exists concerning the extent to which the islands were originally more extensively vegetated, and that grazing and woodcutting by the early settlers combined to reduce the island cover or grasses and trees, creating a somewhat desolate, unnatural condition.

The presence of man and domesticated animals have surely had some effect on the vegetation of the Outer Banks; however, the observations of Price (1926), Welch (1885), Pinxhor and Ashe (1897), Kearney (1900), and Engels (1942), all indicate that the islands have always been sparsely vegetated. For example, the regular occurrence of storm surges, oceanic overwash, and extreme tides from Pamlico Sound preclude the development of permanent forests except at a few broader areas.

The unaltered barrier island system adjusts to periodic storms since there are no natural obstructions in the path of the waves and surges. Most of the initial storm stress is sustained by the broad beaches. Because no resistance is created by impenetrable landforms, water flows between the dunes and across the islands with the result that energy is rapidly dissipated. On the sound side the fringes of marsh act as a buffer to reduce erosion from waves and surges

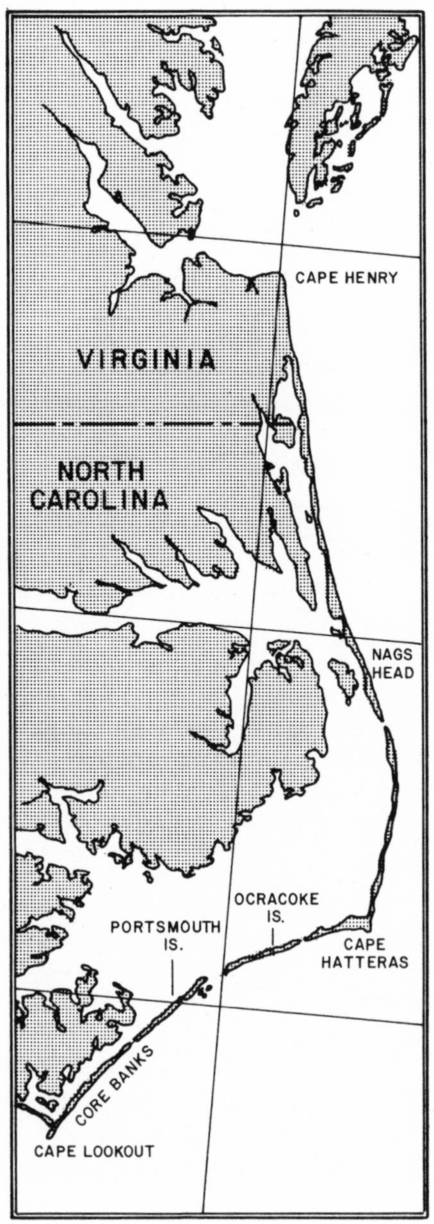

Figure 1. The North Carolina barrier island system. Cape Lookout is the southern segment and Cape Hatteras the northern reach.

Figure 2. Sand fencing with natural materials in the 1930's. Photo by the National Park Service.

generated on Core and Pamlico Sounds.

The combination of extreme high tides and large waves occasionally succeeds in eroding the low-lying beach foredunes, carrying sediment completely across the island and into the marshes. This process of "oceanic overwash" has been well documented by Godfrey (1970). Godfrey has also documented the important role overwash plays in marsh formation by replenishing sediments and creating new land on the sound side of barrier islands. Because of steadily rising sea level (Hicks, 1972), the beaches along the Core Banks have in most places receded, resulting in increased wave attack on the dunes and subsequent overwash and build-up of the marshes. The net effect has been a gradual westward movement of the islands. During severe storms inlets may be closed.

THE STABILIZED SYSTEM

The frequency of destructive storms along coastal North Carolina, with ocean overwash, precluded the establishment of a permanent road network on the Outer Banks until the 1930's. It was determined at that time to construct a protective dune system between the proposed road and the beach. In the period between 1936 and 1940, the CCC and WPA, under the direction of the National Park Service, erected almost 1,000,000 m of sand fencing to create a continuous barrier dune along the Outer Banks (Fig. 2) – including Hatteras, Pea, and Bodie Islands (Stratton, 1940). Most of this construction took place in the zone comprising the original low beach dunes and a strip 30-100 m wide behind the foredune. The sand which collected around the fencing was further stabilized with some 2,500,000 trees and shrubs, and enough grass to protect 3,254 acres of dunes and sand flats. This was augmented in the late 1950's by the National Park Service, so that at present almost a continuous mass of vegetation blankets the barrier island from south Nags Head to the southern tip of Ocracoke Island (Fig. 3).

COMPARISON: CONTROLLED VERSUS NATURAL SYSTEMS

Thirty years of artificial dune stabilization has greatly altered the geological features of the Cape Hatteras sector of the Outer Banks. A comparison of cross sections of Hatteras Island (Fig. 4), indicating the altered condition, with the profile of Core Bank representing what many interpret as the natural condition, demonstrates the extent to which stabilization has brought changes in the beach and dune morphology. Analysis of aerial photographs shows there is a most striking difference between the natural and the controlled barrier islands. In addition the artificial barrier dune system is associated with a change in beach width. The unaltered parts have beaches ranging from 125 to 200 m wide, averaging about 150 m. Along many of the Hatteras and Bodie Islands beaches which were altered 30 yr ago, the shoreline has receded to widths of 30 m or less. Ocracoke Island, which was extensively altered 10 to 15 yr ago, has intermediate width beaches with barrier dunes, ranging from 50 to 100 m, and averaging 75 m. This beach narrowing process, combined with the presence of permanent barrier dunes, has created a situation in which high wave energy is concentrated in an increasingly restricted run-up area, resulting in a steeper beach profile, increased turbulence and accelerated sediment attrition. The net effect is increased erosion and further narrowing of the beach. Ultimately, the beach face becomes so narrow that wave up-rush is applied directly to the stabilized dune (Fig. 3). This is occurring at several places within Cape Hatteras National Seashore, and has resulted in a gradual undercutting of the dune front, with eventual destruction of the dune system and endangering man-made structures behind the dunes (Fig. 5).

Coarser beaches are steeper, and if they become steep enough to initiate wave reflection, a new set of interactions is started which may result in a

Figure 3. Stabilized barrier dunes of the Outer Banks. This photo was taken in the early 1940's—note that already the shoreline is moving in on the barrier dune system and that overwash is all but eliminated.

concentration of the energy dissipation process in narrower zones. The increased stress and turbulence across the narrower beach results in higher attrition and winnowing rates and leads to accelerated losses of fine sand (1.25 mm).

There are few plants that can tolerate the extreme conditions in the vicinity of a beach subject to high wave and surge action. Figure 4, the representative transect across the Core Banks, illustrates two important points: (1) a wide zone of no vegetation between the shoreline and the extreme backshore and (2) low dune and overwash deposits in the central part of the island. In contrast, along the transect across the stabilized and fertilized dunes on Hatteras Island, grasses may be as close as 10 to 20 m of the high tide line, because of increased protection from storm surge. The great height of the stabilized dunes, up to 10 m, provides a region of protection from salt spray and flooding, allowing extensive growth of shrubs within 30 m of the high water mark.

The high stabilized dunes not only divert salt spray from the zone immediately behind the dune, but they also prevent flooding and overwash. Because of this protection the shrub community normally found near the back of the island has spread seaward, and in many places forms an impenetrable thicket 3-4 m high (Fig. 6). The most successful shrubs in this invasion have been wax myrtle, silverling, yaupon holly, and salt marsh elder. Attempts are now underway to check the spread of shrubs by several methods including controlled fires.

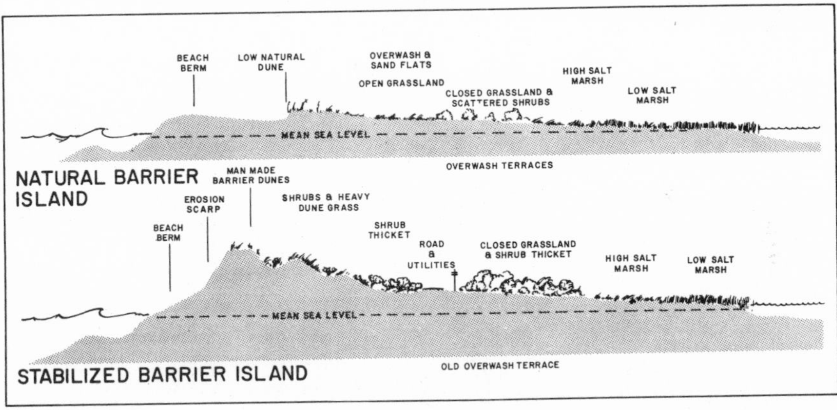

Figure 4. Cross sections of the barrier islands. The upper diagram is typical of the natural systems and the lower typical of the stabilized barriers of North Carolina.

Figure 5. The motel area near Buxton (Cape Hatteras) on Hatteras Island. All that remains of the one-time barrier dune is the sand fencing. The sands have been stripped away by wave action.

Figure 6. A dense scrub growth has completley replaced open sand flats and marsh grasses on Bodie Island. In the 1920's this area was open grasslands and shifting sands.

DISCUSSION

From a geomorphic point of view, the Outer Banks of North Carolina are one of the most dynamic systems in nature. Because oceanic overwash plays an essential role in this process, an unbalanced situation develops wherever artificial barrier dunes have been built. Further compounding the seriousness of the situation has been the false impression of safety and stability offered by the barrier dune. Numerous structures, including motels, restaurants, beach cottages, park facilities, and a U.S. Naval Base at Cape Hatteras have been built immediately behind the barrier dune in the belief that the dunes provide permanent protection from encroachment by the sea. Instead the beach has steadily narrowed. Subsequently, the barrier dune has eroded away leaving these structures with little protection from extreme events.

When Hurricane Ginger moved inland near Cape Lookout, N.C. on September 30, 1971 it provided an excellent opportunity to compare the impact of a severe storm on the two adjacent barrier island systems. Simultaneous field investigations were underway at both Cape Hatteras and Cape Lookout, and NASA (Wallops Island) provided before-and-after Ginger color I.R. aerial photography.

The patterns of change along most of the Core Banks, as determined from the Wallops Island aerial photography and site visits were similar – flattening of beach face, retreat of berm crest, burial and deposition on the backshore, entrapment of sand by grasslands, and general flooding.

Wihin the stabilized segment of the Outer Banks, the massive and unbroken man-made dunes acted as an impenetrable obstruction to the surge, so the energy dissipation and sediment transfer processes were significantly different. Photographs taken three days after the seas of Ginger had subsided (Figs. 7 and 8), and the before-and-after profiles (Fig. 9), illustrate the important implications of these differences. The man-made dunes absorb the full impact of the surge and storm waves and erode rapidly. The run-up profile is restricted to the narrow beach face. Sands are not transferred inland, but rather offshore or alongshore. In the case of Ginger, recession of the seaward face of the barrier dunes near Cape Hatteras averaged between 3 and 5 m.

The storm drove sea water completely across the islands from Cape Lookout north to Portsmouth Island (Fig. 1). Drift lines in the vicinity of the Cape Lookout Lighthouse were up to 0.7 m above that level 43 km to the northeast on Portsmouth Island. The surge was slightly lower near Cape Hatteras.

Profiles surveyed at 2 m intervals across Core Banks and Hatteras Island during the summer of 1971 were resurveyed shortly after the hurricane and again during the summer of 1972. Elevation changes of the berm surface relative to bench marks on the Core Banks profile were also measured. Figure 9 allows comparison of before-and-after profiles along two typical transects, illustrating an increase of land elevation on Core Banks and severe erosion on Hatteras Island. On Core Banks, the storm flattened the beach face by moving sand

Figure 7. Post-Hurricane Ginger on Core Banks three days after the storm. Note the wide beach berm and stringers of overwash sand.

Figure 8. Post-Hurricane Ginger on Hatteras Island. The abrupt scarp of the man-made dune is clearly evident.

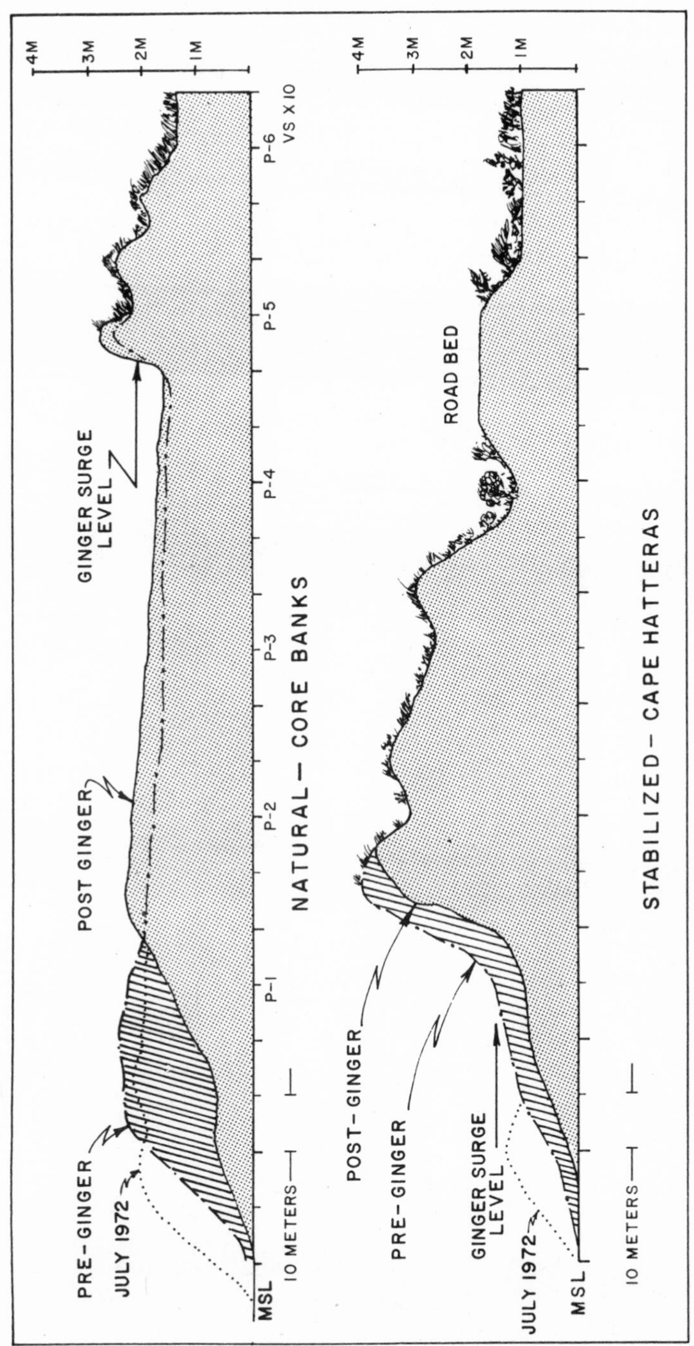

Figure 9. Profiles of Core Banks and Hatteras Island before and after Hurricane Ginger.

offshore as well as over the berm, with the beach crest moved back about 40 m. However, the mean sea level intersect retreated very little. At the time of the first resurvey, nine days after the storm, a new berm was forming. A substantial part of the berm material moved onto the backshore and was transported up to 100 m inland.

Oceanic overwash, and the opening and closing of inlets, creates serious problems in maintaining a permanent highway down the center of the Outer Banks. In the past it has been necessary to clear the highways when covered with sand deposited by overwash, and the roads have been rerouted several times when erosion destroyed the dunes and threatened the fixed routes (Fig. 10). Bridges have been abandoned and roads built where inlets have closed. In other cases it has been necessary to fill in recently formed inlets and replace the destroyed highway. The Ash Wednesday storm of 1962, for example, opened a

Figure 10. The receding shoreline has forced the relocation of several sections of the main road along the barrier islands.

new inlet between Buxton and Avon which required $1.4 million to rebuild the dune system and replace the roadway. This same storm destroyed segments of over 15 mi of the artificial dune system which also had to be rebuilt.

Although the present system is undependable, endangered, and expensive to maintain, alternatives are even more expensive and somewhat questionable in terms of application and economics. One approach has been to attempt to maintain the beaches by constructing groins at right angles to the beach, or by dredging sediments and pumping them into the beach (Fig. 11). The cost of extensive groin fields runs into millions of dollars, and has not been very effective on the Outer Banks at Hatteras Lighthouse. Dredging and beach nourishment may cost $1 million per mi, and in most cases this too is only a temporary measure.

Another suggestion has been to build a reinforced dune system at critical sites

Figure 11. The groin field installed near Cape Hatteras had design problems even before it was completed. Note the structural failure in the foreground.

by forming sea walls of sand bags. A structure such as this has been estimated to cost about $4 million per mi and ignores the basic fact that once the beach is gone, nothing will stop surge and surf action.

Survival of the development on the natural beach environment along coastal North Carolina requires a strategy of submission and rapid rebuilding. This is the key to success. Unfortunately, man has attempted to draw a line and prevent the sea from passing. The results have been unexpected and negative. Because the Cape Hatteras portion of the Outer Banks has already developed to the point where it is impossible to remove the highway, it must be maintained; however, as the system continues to narrow, new instances of overwash, erosion of the artificial barrier dunes, and inlet formation can be predicted. Many of the structures which have been built in the proximity of the shoreline will be lost, and the highway will require relocation within a few years (Fig. 12).

The Cape Lookout section of the Outer Banks, on the other hand, presents an entirely different situation. The islands from Portsmouth Island south to Cape Lookout and then west along Shackleford Bay are undeveloped. There are no highways, utilities, or permanent settlements to protect. Placement of a permanent roadway down the island would require a continuous artificial dune system for protection and stabilization. The National Park Service plan is, however, to leave Portsmouth Island, Core Banks, and Shackleford Banks in a

Figure 12. The final chapter of man's confrontation with nature.

natural state.

CONCLUSIONS

With the rapid deterioration of the barrier dune systems along the Outer Banks of North Carolina in recent years, and the large expenditures of resources necessary to reestablish or maintain them, or both, my research suggests that now is the time to review the basic concept of dune construction in light of the geological and economic implications. If sea level continues to rise, as all evidence seems to suggest (Hicks, 1972), the resources required to maintain extensive areas of barrier dunes may exceed the economic and psychologic value attached to their existence. The barrier islands, in their natural condition, can survive severe perturbations of tropical and extratropical storms by the low resistance they present to storm surges. These natural islands are not being washed away, but rather they are moving back by processes that were fundamental in their origin, processes that continue to be important if they are to be preserved in a natural state.

ACKNOWLEDGEMENTS

My colleagues in this effort are Paul Godfrey and William Odum. This research is supported by the Office of Natural Science, National Park Service, Washington, and the Chesapeake Bay Ecological Studies Program, National Aeronautics and Space Administration, Wallops Island, Virginia.

REFERENCES

Brown, R.H. 1948. *Historical geography of the United States:* Harcourt, Brace and Co., N.Y. 596 p.

Dolan, R. 1972. Barrier dune system along the Outer Banks of North Carolina: a reappraisal: Science, v. 176, n. 4032, p. 286-288.

Dunbar, G.S. 1958. *Historical geography of the North Carolina Outer Banks:* Louisiana State University, Coastal Series No. 3, Baton Rouge, 234 p.

Engels, W.L. 1942. Vertebrate fauna of the North Carolina coastal islands, a study in the dynamics of animal distribution. I:Ocracoke Island: American Midland Naturalist, v. 28, n. 2, p. 273-304.

Engels, W.L. 1952. Vertebrate fauna of the North Carolina coastal islands. II:Shackleford Banks: American Midland Naturalist, v. 47, n. 3, p. 702-742.

Godfrey, P.J. 1970. Oceanic overwash and its ecological implications on the Outer Banks of North Carolina: National Park Service, Office of Natural Science Studies, Washington, 32 p.

Hicks, S.D. 1972. As the Oceans rise: NOAA, v. 2, n. 2, p. 22-24.

Kearney, T.H. 1900. The plant covering Ocracoke Island:a study in the ecology of the North Carolina strand vegetation: Contributions, U.S. National

Kearney, T.H. 1900. The plant covering of Ocracoke Island: a study in the ecology of North Carolina strand vegetation: Contributions, U.S. National Herbarium, v. 5, p. 261-319.

Peel, R.F. 1952. *Physical Geography:* The English University Press, London, 290 p.

Price, J. 1926. A description of Ocracoke Inlet: N.C.H.R., v. 3, n. 4, p. 624-633.

Stratton, A.C. 1943. Reclaiming the North Carolina 'Banks': Shore and Beach, v. 11, n. 1, p. 25-27.

V
Landscape Management

Editor's Comments on Papers 26 Through 32

Effective management of the urban-area landscape involves the implementation of careful planning and cooperation by the general public. The people and the courts must uphold enlightened laws and environmental principles both in letter and in spirit. The electorate must be properly informed in order to enact appropriate laws that are consistent with the ecological environmental framework of the region. Thus landscape management becomes a concern for the greatest possible number of people who must be responsive to the maintenance of the best possible conservation and utilization balance. Landscape management of cities and the urbanization process is so complex that it can only be accomplished by interdisciplinary teams that possess a great variety of skills and expertise. The focus of these volumes, however, concerns geomorphology, and the thesis expounded is that the involvement of this discipline is particularly vital, because it is the geomorphologist who is especially schooled in understanding the land–water ecosystem. It is his knowledge that is essential for planning appropriate managing procedures that will minimize human deformation of nature's equilibrium system.

Previous parts of this volume have dealt with some of the physical problems in urban areas and how sudden damage or gradual, but more insidious, environmental decay can occur when planning has been inadequate or neglected—floods, landslides, erosion, sedimentation, urban sprawl, wetland destruction, channel modifications, and surface water – groundwater distribution. Remedial practices have also been mentioned, which, if followed, would serve to inhibit some of these excesses or at least counter their trends. In Part V we shall explore a fuller range of these ideas, both on a particular local scale and on a comprehensive regional scale. Seven articles are used as aids in providing the following insights: importance of trees (Legget and Crawford); significance of open space and methods to achieve it (Kent, Whyte); topographic and hillside planning (Dash and Efrat, Swain); greenbelt satellite cities (Mishchenko); and philosophical rationale for landscape amenities (Smith).

Although the three volumes in this series deal with the geomorphic aspects of the physical environment, it would be shortsighted not to mention the very important role played in city planning by consideration of the human dimensions, since they often dominate the decision-making process. For example, at various times in various cities such elements as mass transit, slum clearance, central-city renovation, and the attraction of industry are given first (and perhaps even the only) priority. Perception is another social drive that can be important in the planning process. Lynch (1960) states, ". . . a systematic consideration of the interrelations between urban forms and human objectives would seem to lie at the theoretical heart of city planning." And Welsh (1966) concludes:

> . . . perception of the urban environment comes to us through all of our senses, and it involves much more than the mere visual appearance of buildings and streets . . . smells and sounds are important in perception and . . . the environment includes animals, vehicles, and people, as well as structures (p. 30).

The perceived attitude toward the overcrowded city by the inhabitants, as shown in several Gallup polls (such as the one of May 5, 1968), is not favorable; more than 80 percent say that they would prefer to live in less congested environments. Dispersal of former urban populations in Britain and the Netherlands has not always been successful, however, and some families prefer to return. Nevertheless, the people that plan and manage urban areas must consider not only the physical needs of the populace but the natural amenities of landscape that are environmentally sympathetic to the human spirit. Planning must consist of identifying the goals and establishing the priorities of many sectors of society and must be responsive to the community desire for a good place to live, work, and enjoy leisure. Planning must include, and articulate to the people, such diverse elements as transportation, living, shopping, and working facilities; natural areas for open space, scenic aesthetics, hazard prevention, and recreation; and maintenance and conservation of land and water resources.

There is a voluminous literature on the evolution and planning of cities, a general topic that is far beyond the scope of this volume. For perspective, however, it must be pointed out that the Renaissance (about 1300–1700 A.D.) saw a quantum jump in city design; medieval communities were restructured around themes that accentuated beautification, symmetry, spaciousness, and relief from overcrowding. The Industrial Revolution (1700–1900 A.D.) witnessed a dramatic reversal; overcrowding again occurred in cities, lack of design was prevalent, and pollution abounded.

The redesign of the city of Paris in the mid-1850s became the forerunner of what was to become a largely twentieth-century revolution in planning. Arango (1970) points out how Paris under the genius of Georges Eugene Haussmann, when the government was dominated by Louis Napoleon, was completely renovated and had "all the qualities of a Renaissance product. . . ." Three principal objectives were build into the new city management program: (1) straight-line communications between important points and the central nucleus were established by through boulevards with strip parks designed to bring nature to the heart of the city; (2) open parks were developed with small and large green spaces for the enjoyment of everyone; (3) the incorporation into all buildings and spaces of a type of beauty aimed at dispelling the earlier "ugliness, darkness and irrationality of the overgrown medieval town."

In the United States the 1893 Chicago World's Fair had a profound influence on later city planning, because exhibits and models demonstrated the "city beautiful plan." Hartford, Connecticut, (1907) organized the first official city planning commission, and New York City (1916) developed the first U.S. city planning ordinance. Cincinnati, Ohio, (1925) instituted the first master plan to be adopted by a major city, and Levittowns in the New York metropolitan area and at Park Forest, Illinois, (1947) ushered in the mass building of housing and the new-community phase of urbanized areas. In 1927 the federal government became interested in aiding municipalities to control land use in their incorporated zones. In 1933 the Federal Housing Authority and the National Planning Board helped inaugurate slum clearance and city planning, and the 1941 FHA handbook, *Urban Development for Cities,* provided guidelines for city expansion. With a few exceptions, however, cities did not enlarge their planning base until the 1960s. Until then the primary city concern with areas not under their own jurisdiction was to secure water supplies (see the article in Part II by Van Burkalow) and to control flooding (see the article in Part III by Bigger). The 1960s saw the advent of planning for metropolitan areas on a countrywide or regional basis. The universal realization that the city should not isolate itself from contiguous lands and that problems must be examined in coordinated attempts seems to have happened in only the last decade. This is especially apparent if one considers the paucity of municipal publications dealing with land use, terrain evaluation, resource analysis, and open-space natural areas. The Introduction to this volume contains bibliographic citations of some early reports that evaluate the landscape as a resource to be managed in urban areas.

The following sections illustrate various components that must be considered to institute effective plans so that the physical environment of cities can be properly managed. A management strategy should be economical of time and energy whenever possible. For example, much wasted motion can be saved by the realization that many cities have the same types of physical problems, whereas other problems may be different and need a different range of priorities for their solution. With common problems, such as urban sprawl and flooding, useful methods for solution can be shared; each city does not have to "reinvent the wheel" and can draw on experiences elsewhere, thus avoiding duplication of effort. Priorities for problem solution will differ from city to city, and it is possible that the ranges of alternatives and the preferred solutions will differ.

All good planning programs incorporate such ideas as the determination of appropriate goals, establishment of priorities, suggestions for alternatives, design for continuing evaluation, and procedures for implementation and management. In addition, the axioms of proper landscape planning for urban areas are the following:

1. A regional approach. Problems do not suddenly start at municipal borders; instead they are fluid and transcend artificial boundaries.

2. A comprehensive and integrated systems approach. Many problems are related and cannot be handled by a piecemeal or cosmetic technique.

3. A methodology that optimizes natural land–water ecosystems. If this principle is ignored, large distortions will produce harmful feedback into the system.

4. Conservation – preservation of some natural open spaces. These must be planned and not a mere residual after other matters have been satisfied.

5. Multidisciplinary approach. No single discipline has a monopoly on solutions and many must be involved in the decision-making process.

All planning is useless if positive action does not occur. In the words of the Greek poet Homer, "It is not meet to stand here wasting our time or idly loitering, for there is still a great work to be done."

The authors of the articles in Part V are all renowned and respected experts in their fields and many have received international acclaim. For example, Robert F. Legget was Director of Building Research of the National Research Council of Canada, a post that he held from 1947 to 1969. He formerly taught for 11 years at Queens and Toronto Universities and has served as president of the Geological Society of America. He is the author of *Geology and Engineering* and *Cities and Geology,* as well as many other publications. He is recognized as being the dean of geological engineering. T. J. Kent, Jr., is Professor of City Planning at the University of California at Berkeley. In 1948 he established the Department of City and Regional Planning at Berkeley and served as chairman for 12 years. Formerly he was Director of City Planning for the City and County of San Francisco. He is the author of many publications, including the book *The Urban General Plan,* and was principal author of the Berkeley Master Plan. Jacob Dash is Deputy Director for General Planning and Head of the Planning Department for the Ministry of Interior, Israel. William G. Swain is a partner in the landscape architect firm of Griswold, Winters, Swain & Mullin in Pittsburgh, Pennsylvania. He has designed a variety of landscape architectural projects, ranging from school-site development to recreational and park design. His park projects include neighborhood sites, county regional parks, and state parks. He has been involved with four commissions from the U.S. Corps of Engineers in eastern Ohio and western Kentucky. Anthony Wayne Smith has written numerous articles on environment and ecology and is President and General Counsel for the National Parks & Conservation Association.

Natural Areas—Parks, Open Space, Greenbelts

The federal definition of open-space land is contained in the open-space provisions of the Housing Act of 1961 (75 Stat. 149), Title VII, Section 706:

> (1) The term "open-space land" means any undeveloped or predominantly undeveloped land in an urban area which has value for (a) park and recreational purposes, (b) conservation of land and other natural resources, or (c) historic or scenic purposes.

Likewise, the definition of urban area is given as follows:

> The term "urban area" means any area which is urban in character, including those surrounding areas which, in the judgement of the administration,

> form an economic and socially related region, taking into consideration such factors as present and future population trends, patterns of urban growth, location of transportation facilities and systems, and distribution of industrial, commercial, residential, governmental, institutional, and other activities.

President Kennedy summarized ideas in proposing a federal open-space program in his Housing Message to Congress on March 9, 1961:

> Land is the most precious resource of the metropolitan area. The present patterns of haphazard suburban development are contributing to a tragic waste in the use of a vital resource now being consumed at an alarming rate.
>
> Open space must be reserved to provide parks and recreation, conserve water and other natural resources, prevent building in undesirable locations, prevent erosion and floods, and avoid the wasteful extension of public services. Open land is also needed to provide resources for future residential development, to protect against speculation, and to make it possible for state and regional bodies to control the rate and character of community development.

President Johnson also emphasized the need for preservation of open space in a speech at the University of Michigan in May, 1964:

> Open space is vanishing and old landmarks are violated. Worst of all, expansion is eroding the precious and time-honored values of community with neighbors and communion with nature.

A 17-month study for open space of the major urban–metropolitan areas of California was conducted by Eckbo, Dean, Austin, and Williams. The report is summarized in Williams (1969). The study analyzed 49,209 of California's total of 156, 573 square miles. The purpose was to

> . . . provide a clear guide to both state and local governments for the planning and acquisition of major open land reservations in and near the various metropolitan areas. In so specifying . . . the Planning Agency seeks to identify those open land acquisition opportunities whose scale and desirability will not only command public endorsement but, if accomplished, also function effectively as major determinants of the course and character of metropolitan expansion (p. 11).

The preservation of natural areas can result either from the nondevelopment of land parcels or by careful planning for the retention of green spaces and open corridors. The principle of greenbelts dates back at least to the thirteenth century B.C.; the Bible describes the Levitical cities as being surrounded by pasture lands for use by the city dwellers. Archeological data from the excavation of the city of Gezer suggest that this pattern of land use endured at least until the fourth century B.C. The city had an area of 22 acres with a greenbelt 15 times larger. The greenbelt idea occurs again in the writings of Sir Thomas More about the imagined land of Utopia (1515–1516). The cities of Utopia were surrounded by agricultural lands; when cities filled, instead of overrunning the adjacent land, the exceess population built new towns beyond the agricultural belt. A different type of open space was designed by Frederick Law Olmsted in 1857 and became known as New York City's Central Park. It was largely built from 700 acres of reclaimed swamps that had been used by squatters. It took 4,000 men working 16 years to complete, and contains 843 acres, 62 miles of foot and bridal paths, and 114 miles of drainage channels. This single action is generally cited as the turning point that influenced other American communities to set aside natural lands for public use and recreation. Olmsted often remarked that the park was a place for city folk who could not afford trips to the White Mountains or the Adirondacks.

> The main object and justification of [Central Park] is simply to produce a certain influence in the minds of people. . . . The character of this influence is a poetic one and it is to be produced by means and scenes, through observation of which the mind may be more or less lifted out of moods and habits into which it is, under the ordinary conditions of city life, likely to fall.
>
> . . . the enjoyment of scenery employs the mind without fatigue,and yet exercises it; tranquilizes it and yet enlivens it; and thus, through the influence of the mind over the body, gives the effect of refreshing rest and reinvigoration to the whole system.

His total impact in the design of beauty and on the field of landscape architecture has been enormous through the heritage he left in 40 public parks, as well as private estates, college campuses, and entire suburbs. For example, he orchestrated the Buffalo and Boston park systems so that they would have connected landscaped corridors weaving through the urban gridwork. He predicted the migration to the suburbs and designed such commuter villages as Riverside near Chicago, which still is regarded as a model of suburban planning.

Charles Eliot was Olmsted's most apt pupil. Eliot's energy and foresight were instrumental in starting the Metropolitan Park Commission of Boston in the 1890s, and he wrote:

> It is everywhere agreed that a great and growing population such as now inhabits Boston and her wide-spread suburbs should, for its own best health, provide itself with all possible open spaces in the form of public squares and playgrounds. Meanwhile the available open ground is being rapidly occupied, and Boston, like New York, may yet be compelled to tear down whole blocks of buildings to provide herself with the needed oases of light and air. . . .
>
> As I conceive it, the scientific Park System for a district such as ours would include (1) Spaces on the ocean front. (2) As much as possible of the shores

> and islands of the Bay. (3) The courses of the larger tidal estuaries . . . . (4) Two or three large areas of large forest on the outer rim of the inhabited area. (5) Numerous small squares, playgrounds, and parks in the midst of dense populations (Eliot, 1902, pp. 316–319).

By 1925, the Metropolitan Commission that he helped to found had expended $21,000,000 and owned 7,400 acres of woodland, 13 miles of seashore, 57 miles of riverfront property, and 59 miles of parkway.

Although the importance of open space has been recognized down through the ages, new vitality and rationales for its preservation have had a rebirth in the last decade. As the general manager for state parks in the New York City metropolitan area remarked, "Open space is like virignity . . . once lost, it can never be regained" (*New York Times,* March 4, 1968, p. 49). In talking about natural areas, Thomas Jefferson said that communities should be planned with an eye to the effect made upon the human spirit when able to surround itself with a maximum of beauty. Open space is valuable because it can serve at least four diverse functions: the productive, protective, recreational, and aesthetic. The article by Legget and Crawford shows the importance of trees in the urban environment, and the material reproduced from Kent's monograph documents the need for open space in the San Francisco area.

> One healthy acre of mature white pine trees spaced 14 feet apart (approximately 200 trees) will produce enough oxygen in a single growing season to keep 200 mature persons alive for a whole year. Thus a village or town of 2,000 persons should have at least 10 acres of forest land in its midst to achieve a normal oxygen–carbon dioxide balance (Shomon, 1971–1972, pp. 15–16).

In addition to reducing carbon dioxide content, vegetation filters dust, pollen, ash, and other air-borne particles. Green spaces in Leipzig, Germany, were found to reduce dust from 210 to 50 particles per cubic centimeter. The air in areas surrounding Central Park has 100 percent more sulphur dioxide than air in the park. Vegetation also produces benefits in the microclimate of cities. Trees help to compensate for the "heat island" effect by cooling air through evapotranspiration. Ancient Babylon used trees to block the dry, hot desert winds, and trees are used in Moscow to aid in the regulation of summer heat.

The importance of trees, vegetation, and green areas led to the concept of greenbelts, which has been heralded by some as the most important concept in open-space planning for urban areas since Ebenezer Howard's Garden City, which he introduced in 1898. In England the Green Belt Act of 1938 was passed, which zoned the greater London area with concentric rings, with the third ring (15 to 18 miles from London's center) being a mixture of agricultural and recreational areas. In 1947 Parliament passed additional legislation, the Town and Country Act, which gave government the power to freeze development in the greenbelt. The original purpose of the greenbelt idea was to form a distinct boundary between the city and the country, thereby preventing urban sprawl. When city population exceeded a critical threshold and threatened greenbelt maintenance, new towns were to be constructed beyond the greenbelt. Thus greenbelts can serve a variety of purposes — to regulate the size of cities, provide agricultural and recreational land, and retain an unspoiled landscape that can moderate air and water pollution. By 1959 the London Green Belt included 840 square miles. The greater Moscow greenbelt constitutes 30 percent of the city's total area and contains 200,000 acres of green space and forests. The greenbelt of Warsaw effectively limits expansion of the inner city. Ottawa, Canada, is the major North American city with a greenbelt. Here the 37,000-acre, 2.5-mile-wide greenbelt was designed not only for farming, forestry, and recreation, but also as protection for the water supply through reforestation and construction of water-storage facilites. All land is government owned, and farming and timber-right leases help defray the land costs.

There is a variety of other schemes for the planning and management of open spaces. One approach calls for a type of "planned sprawl" with development occurring around permanently secured open areas. Another plan is the "radial-corridor" concept, which calls for open spaces between the spokes of a wheel-like system of communities. A variation of this was suggested in the 1920s for London by Sir Raymond Unwin. His plan called for open space in circular ovate patterns that would be interlaced with built-up or vacant areas of London. A virtue of this type of plan is that it can take advantage of the natural topography and be designed along drainage lines. The clearest and most succinct apostle for this type of "natural process planning" is seen in the publications and works of Ian McHarg.

McHarg's ideas have been expressed in his own articles (see Part I), in books such as the very influential *Design With Nature* (1969), and in other publications (e.g., Wallace, ed., 1970) that champion his thesis. Advocates of planning along natural topographic lines instead of artificial lines, such as greenbelts, which arbitrarily cut across natural terrain divisions, point out several advantages:

> A major weakness of the greenbelt idea . . . lies in the fact that it is compositional and intended to contain growth. It cannot allow for the flexibility of the organism it serves. Its conceptual basis is unrelated to any factor of regional natural process (Roberts, 1970, p. 158).

Thus Roberts argues for a type of planning in which there is the identification of

> . . . physiographic characteristics of an area and understanding the role they play in natural process . . . as the basis for an open space pattern or system. This system will help maintain the balance of nature, provide regional recreation as one of its major uses, and go far toward enhancing the urban fabric with an interfusion of amenity (p. 167).

Hackett (1971) also builds on this theme by showing the importance of careful mapping surveys that will economize the planning so that minimum area is developed and all is not lost from the existing landscape:

> This latter aim can be achieved first by preserving certain elements of the

> existing landscape which will retain at least the threads of continuity. Such features as streams, hedgerows, small woodlands, and some of the old buildings can be incorporated in the new layout. . .
>
> The second proposal for landscape continuity is to site roads and buildings so that they emphasize the structure of the landscape. Roads can be aligned to emphasize valleys, and the topography can be followed and even emphasized in the heights of the buildings.
>
> In order to bring about development closely related to the landscape, a landscape planning survey and analysis of the kind previously described for new towns should be undertaken before any other site planning decisions are made—it is, after all, a matter of evaluating one's assets before embarking on a new enterprise. In the matter of landscape appearance, if the change from the urban to the rural landscape can be accomplished by a peripheral zone of development which respects the structure of the landscape instead of by the customary suburban housing estate, the result will not only be an effective transition, but will also contribute to a residential environment which belongs to and is not applied upon the site (pp. 84–85).

Geomorphic Mapping and Resource Planning

The theme of the importance of geomorphic (and geologic) mapping and its use in decisions on urban siting and resource development is developed in this section. Such work is vital to minimize predicted damages, such as those published in a recent report for California (California Division of Mines and Geology, 1971). In this report Woodward-Lundgren & Associates estimated the following dollar value losses that would occur in California due to urbanization up to the year 2000. The figures are ". . . based on the projected growth, the severity of geologic problems in the potentially urban areas, and the G.P. values." The total foreseeable losses amount to a staggering *$174 billion* and have been calculated under the following categories (in billions of dollars): earthquake shaking, $18.6; flooding, $75.9; landslides, $42.1; expansive soil, $11.9; tsunamis, $1.2; fault displacement, $1.2; erosion activity, $0.752; subsidence, $0.05; loss of mineral resources covered by urban areas, $22.4; groundwater depletion and degradation, $0.05; and volcanic eruption $0.008. The majority of these losses fall in the realm of geomorphology, the exceptions being earthquake, fault displacement, and volcanic eruptions. Thus it is dramatically obvious that the geomorphologist must play a vital role in the planning and management of urban areas, not only in California, but everywhere. Such planning must also be compatible with the conclusion reached in a meeting of the Smithsonian Institution on Land Use and Urban Growth in 1973 in which Laurence S. Rockefeller (1973) stated:

> The massive urban growth forseeable by the end of the century must be managed without destroying what we most value in the distinctiveness of our

> neighborhoods and communities, the beauty of our countryside, coastal lands and mountains, and the delicate rhythms of nature.

The reproduced articles that are especially relevant for this topic are by Dash and Efrat and by Swain. They illustrate the importance of planning when fitted into the topography of the urban area.

Many aspects of the land–water ecosystem have been mentioned in previous parts of this volume. Additional information on how to achieve terrain stabilization is given in Volume III of this series, and it is pertinent to urban areas as well. The areas in which the geomorphologist can be helpful in the design and management of the urban landscape must include the following:

1. *Soils.* The strength and bearing capacity of soils will determine the type of structure. Their erodibility will influence costs of construction and erosion-control devices. Infertile soils should be reserved for industrial development and more arable soils for garden-type development. Poorly drained soils and areas should be restricted to development where public sewerage is available.

2. *Hillslopes.* Since building on steep slopes may endanger public safety and welfare, construction on slopes greater than 12 degrees should be discouraged whenever possible. Surface and subsurface geologic materials, structures, and water conditions must be thoroughly evaluated to determine whether the area is "hazard-prone topography" that can be easily triggered into landsliding.

3. *Stream channels.* Natural characteristics should be maintained whenever possible, but when altered the man-made channels should be designed with hydraulic geometry properties consistent with the hydrologic regime. A balance should be achieved so that channel bottoms and sides are minimally eroded while still preventing siltation, which reduces flood-carrying capacity.

4. *Resources.* The tangible resources of soil, sand and gravel, and water supply must be carefully mapped, evaluated, and placed in priority systems of maximum beneficial use consistent with conservation of the natural features and processes.

5. *Landscape aspect.* The aesthetic and recreational resources which provide some of life's important amenities are vital qualities in management. Involved is the identification of natural areas of unusual geomorphic–ecologic interest, areas where vegetation prospers, sites that command the best vistas, and comfortable microclimates. For example, housing for the elderly should be located in areas that are sheltered from winds and still have the maximum possible warmth and sunshine.

It is important that geomorphic mapping and planning precede development whenever possible. It is equally necessary that reports should be written in a clear and understandable manner.

> . . . the geologist commonly presents his findings in a style and language unintelligible to those outside his discipline. However technically competent a geologic inventory of the environment may be, it must be meaningfully related to the planner, engineer, architect, and developer, in such a manner

> that they can synthesize it into a workable design for managing the environment (Hilpman, 1969, p. 19).

For the first time in Connecticut, for example, the U.S. Geological Survey is now producing a series of maps with nontechnical format for easy comprehension and direct use by a wide range of planners and decision makers involved in land use and resource management. The first of the series focused on the Hartford area and showed flood-prone areas, landforms, depth to water, and drainage areas by a multicolor environmental mapping technique. During the past two decades the Geological Survey has had a special interest in the San Francisco Bay area. In the 1950s maps and tables were produced that showed the geology and engineering properties of earth materials: permeability, slope stability, and foundation characteristics. On January 1, 1970, the Geological Survey combined forces with the Agency for Housing and Urban Development on a multiyear project to map earthquake shocks, identify flood-prone areas, assess the impact of solid-waste disposal and subsurface fluid-waste storage on water resources, and prepare inventories of water and mineral resources. In a news release on October 28, 1970, W. T. Pecora, then U.S. Geological Survey director, characterized the project as

> . . . yielding a harvest of regional knowledge that will help the area improve its long range urban planning and decision-making.
>
> . . . we are trying to establish a frontier for the application of earth science knowledge to an unprecedented number of complex problems resulting from rapid urban growth.
>
> Inevitably this will impose great demands on the water and land resources of the regions involved—the land surface; the soils and vegetation; waters and minerals; and the opportunities and hazards which the land presents.

It is important to prepare appropriate plans and management techniques prior to large-scale development of an area to utilize the land and water resources to their optimum beneficial extent. Many top-grade sand, gravel, and surface-stone deposits necessary in construction are being wastefully covered up in many areas. For example, Chicago is currently expanding at a rate of 15.6 square miles per year and is paving over important resources.

> At the present time, one of the most serious challenges to the mineral producers in urban areas is the growing amount of regulation by local government through zoning ordinances. The courts have upheld the right of zoning boards to prohibit the opening of a new quarry or pit and to close down an existing mineral operation if it is ruled to be a nuisance.
>
> Advance planning for multiple or sequential land use, with land rehabilitation and optimum final land use in mind, can be of great assistance in

> helping stone, sand, and gravel producers to retain their present operating rights or to gain new rights in the face of threats from more stringent zoning ordinances (Risser and Major, 1967).

An example of planning that preceded anticipated growth is the study by McComas (1968).

> The Hennepin region of north-central Illinois is expected to undergo accelerated industrial growth as a result of a new major steel plant located there. Accompanying the industrial growth will be an expansion of facilities for serving an increased population. This report describes the geology and natural resources and their relation to development and land use of the region (p. 2).

The Denver area is a study in contrasts illustrating elements of both good and bad landscape management. It is usually agreed that the multiple use of a given resource or of a locality generally leads to maximum human benefits. Triple use has been made of a site in Denver that originally was a sand and gravel pit; when the resource was mined out, the locality was used for landfill purposes until the late 1950s. It is now the site of the Denver Coliseum, which was constructed in 1962. Conversely, Wright (1969) points out that the city of Denver requires $150 million to correct past mistakes made in the lack of design of urban drainageways and that a total of several hundred millions will be necessary for the entire metropolitan area. The money that must be spent on the urban drainage will equal or exceed that spent for pollution control and sanitary sewer system development in the next 10 years. Wright also emphasizes the cost benefits that accrue when proper planning and management have occurred:

> 1. Disposal of appropriate industrial wastes. 2. Lowered groundwater table. 3. Controlled rising groundwater table after urbanization. 4. Reduced stream maintenance costs. 5. Reduced street construction costs. 6. Improved movement of traffic. 7. Improved public health environment. 8. Lower cost open space. 9. Lower cost park areas and more recreational opportunities. 10. Improved quality of classified streams. 11. Opportunities for close-in solid waste disposal sites. 12. Development of otherwise undevelopable land. 13. Opportunities for lower building construction cost (p. 51).

The importance of mapping surficial materials and the planning for site development that acknowledges vistas have been emphasized in many countries where landscape amenities have influenced future development.

> The importance of the careful mapping of drift deposits, which has characterized the current programme of resurvey in the north-east, has been demonstrated at the proposed new town site of Washington, south-east of Newcastle [England]. During the course of collecting information, a Survey officer called at the office of the engineers concerned with the planning of

> the already determined site, only to find that they were assuming that the entire area was underlain by a virtually uniform spread of boulder clay. It was demonstrated that the area was, in fact, a complex of intermixed glacial and post-glacial deposits, including boulder clay, laminated clay, sand and gravel, all of which were extensively smeared by solifluxion and downwash deposits. As a result of the ensuing discussions the planners were supplied with a revised geological map, accompanied by explanitory sections and a geotechnical interpretation showing the site divided into areas classified in terms which attempt to define the foundation problems that might be encountered . . . parts of the town area have now been replanned (Woodland, 1968, p. 551).

> . . . [the mapping] included the analysis made in 1944 of view-points and views for the city of Jerusalem, with special emphasis on the ridge lines of the topography. A more comprehensive study was the landscape survey made for the new town of Harlow in England which, besides the viewpoint/topographic approach, identified features worthy of retention. A step forward was made with the brief given for the thorough study of the landscape for the site of Cumbernauld New Town in Scotland—carried out and carefully used in full co-operation with the planners and architects. Another example was the landscape study made for the new town of Cramlington . . . (Hackett, 1971, p. 41).

A vital and paramount concern for all landscape management is the thorough mapping, analysis, and understanding of water resources and hydrologic systems. Thus water planning must be an integral component of any type of comprehensive management. Topics related to water are so encompassing that they have been threaded throughout this volume, and also occur in other volumes of the trilogy. At this time, one last aspect of water management will be mentioned — the importance of establishing a strong educational base that can lead to "grass-roots" support and community-wide involvement in helping to solve some of the many interrelated problems associated with water management. The League of Women Voters (1966) describe the type of planning they feel necessary in an chapter titled "On the Edge of a Big City —the Interface of the Urban and Rural Environment ('rurban')," sometimes referred to as "exurbia."

> The Sudbury, Assabet, Concord (SuAsCo) River Basin, in eastern Massachusetts, is a small one—charming but full of problems. It lies just west of State Route 128, the circumferential highway around Boston, on the edge of crowded suburbs. Many of the towns in the basin have doubled in population during the last 10 years, and continue to mushroom at the same rate. Major highways and industrial growth have added to the pressures of these communities. Their problems are typical of those that occur on the frontal edge of any expanding metropolitan region.

> The area has great natural beauty, due in large measure to its three small

> rivers, its ponds, and related wetlands. In a few of the 36 communities in the Basin, strong leadership has developed for preserving these natural assets.
>
> A significant conservation program is now under way in the SuAsCo Basin. It is a particularly interesting example of coordinated efforts in a rapidly growing suburban and rural area to preserve sections of natural beauty and conservation significance (p. 126).

The League shows how through group action "Many victories have been won in the conservation battle . . . [and] the tide has definitely turned in favor of the long-range view of preserving our natural resources for the future." For example, the League was instrumental in organizing conservation commissions in all but four communities. These commissions spent nearly $500,000 on 47 projects for land acquisition, which was two thirds of everything spent in the entire state at the local level for such purposes.

The job of the geomorphologist, or other disciplines involved in urban planning and management, lies not only within the urban area, but extends to the surrounding region as well. As pointed out earlier, the city is a metabolic system with a two-way flow of elements, both in and out of the city. For example, Van Burkalow's article in Part II showed the importance of obtaining areas outside the city for purposes of water supply. We now show that contiguous lands must be obtained for the export products and by-products of city living, and three examples will be provided—wastes, recreation, and transportation.

Part IV introduced the topic of waste disposal and how such materials could bring about landscape abuse. Of course, the corollary is that proper management can lead to minimum environmental degradation by these materials. Such management must be based on proper geomorphic planning, such as the guidelines provided under the Pennsylvania Solid Waste Management Act of 1969 with various amendments. Publications of the federal government and from the Illinois State Geological Survey provide important information for the planning of solid-waste sites (see, e.g., Hughes, 1967; Cartright and Sherman, 1969; Sorg and Hickman, 1970; Toftner and Clark, 1971; Hughes, Landon, and Farvolden, 1971).

The multiple use of strip mines for the disposal of solid wastes is now planned for southeastern Tennessee. The method is claimed to solve two problems, the ugly strip mined areas and the disposal of wastes. The same area will be used for three different purposes: mineral resources, waste burial, and, when appropriately filled, recreational purposes.

The nutrient value of waste waters, when properly managed, can become still another type of resource. Some early quantitative studies for the use of waste effluent in spray irrigation have been done in Pennsylvania under the leadership of Richard Parizek. Effluent from Pennsylvania State University is used for crops on their experimental farmlands. The waste-water system returns about 500,000 gallons per day of effluent to nearly 60 acres of disposal area.

> The application of treated effluent to croplands and forested areas was

> initiated in 1962 to develop a means of spraying effluent on land throughout the year, to determine the degree of renovation of effluent, to explore the possibility of conservation of water and to measure the effect on soils, crops, trees and wildlife.
>
> The yields of various crops were compared for areas receiving zero, one, or two inches per week of effluent. The effluent in 1964 increased hay yields 300 per cent, corn grain 50 per cent, corn stover 103–36 per cent and oats 30 – 40 per cent (Parizek et al., 1967, p. 63).

A variety of other changes were also noted, including significant height increase in conifer trees and significant increase in herbaceous vegetation. Eighty percent of the water applied from April to December was recharged into groundwater reservoirs, and the quality of water in sandpoint and deep wells showed no significant changes.

> . . . regional irrigation districts could be set up to pipe effluent along trunk lines to surrounding agricultural lands in areas where water may be beneficial. The city and farmers could share expenses. Water enriched with nutrients may in fact prove to be a resource with market value under the right economy. By this scheme, water would be disposed of from the cities' point of view, and render benefits to the agriculturalist during the growing season when streams are in low flow and pollution is most serious. During high flows, a combination of irrigation and stream dilution may prove feasible in some area (Parizek and Myers, 1968, p. 439).

The most auspicious management of waste waters as a beneficial water resource occurs in the urban area of Muskegon, Michigan.

> The impact of Muskegon County's urban growth and heavy industry on its environment has been disastrous. The shorelines had always been its most striking feature. But decades of industrial sprawl, pollution, and landfill had left the lakes in a degraded condition. The mining of sand and unregulated growth patterns had destroyed large areas of the shoreline dunes. Air pollution grew offensive near the cities, and the fringe areas became characterized by leapfrogging urban sprawl. Thus, the history of Muskegon County reflects the continual exploitation of its natural resources for the short term benefits of a few.
>
> The citizenry grew aware that piecemeal solutions to the County's problems would not be sufficient to reverse the downward economic spiral. Rehabilitation of their environment was also demanded. The County needed a vision and embarked upon an aggressive metropolitan program through the creation of the Muskegon County Metropolitan Planning Commission (Muskegon County, Mich., 1973).

The report then goes on to describe the system of waste-water treatment. This is not a conventional system, but in part is patterned after the Penn State experience in attempting multiuse of water as a resource. The irrigation land consists of 6,000 acres surrounding the treatment plant with cells and storage basins. The design calls for 55 irrigation machines with a radii from 750 to 1,300 feet, and water application of 2.5 million gallons per acre over a 7-month period. The living filter of the soil will provide a tertiary treatment base. After percolation the remaining water is collected in a drainage system that contains 35 wells, 70 miles of perforated pipe and 19 miles of main drain pipe, 10 miles of drainage ditches, and two pumping stations. The underdrainage assures that soils and subsoils do not become waterlogged, and allows water to leave the area only after careful monitoring. The waters will eventually be discharged into the watercourses. The nutrient-laden waste water will be used to irrigate animal feed crops, and $70 to $100 per acre grass and grain crops per year are anticipated. When the cost of harvesting the crops is included, the net income for the project will total about $300,000 per year.

> Although irrigation with wastewater has been practiced at more than 400 locations in the United States, and extensively in Europe and Australia, Muskegon County is the first large metropolitan area in the United States to develop a total wastewater management system that recycles nutrient and reclaims water of drinking water quality (Muskegon County, Mich., 1973, p. 15).

Urban dwellers increasingly feel the need, and have the affluence, to seek recreational facilities not only in adjacent lands, but in regions that may be far distant from their home. The aspect of parks within city limits was previously discussed, but a few words are in order for these other parameters of land use. Years ago New York State realized the necessity for the establishment of recreational sites near metropolitan centers. Thus there was established the very extensive Long Island State Park System with more than 10 major parks and several smaller parks within the commuting area of New York City. Jones Beach State Park is typical and comprises 2,400 acres on 6 miles of the western part of a barrier island. The total cost was more than $100 million (Shapiro, 1967), including approach causeways, a 17-mile Ocean Parkway, and the dredging of 40 million cubic yards of fill used to raise the elevation of the park and parkway to a 15-foot height above sea level. By 1966 the park had 14 million visitors per year and had reached recreational saturation; so a second nearby park was developed on the western 5 miles of another barrier island (Fire Island) and was named Robert Moses State Park, after the man who was influential in the development of the park system. An interesting variation on the park and recreation theme is the policy of the Southern California Edison Company, which has been developing parks out of lands used for their right of ways. These parks range from 2 to 25 acres in size and have been given for use to 18 different cities.

Another permutation on the park-planning theme concerns recent plans, laws, and controversy that now engulfs management practices within the Adirondacks region of New York. Whereas discussing parks within cities is one problem, an unusual twist involes the analysis of cities within parks.

In the Adirondack Mountains the Horizon Corporation, one of the major land developers of the Southwest, bought 24,345 acres of land from the Northern Lumber Company and wants to put up a community of thousands of recreation homes and second homes. Horizon bought the land in April, 1971, for $2.3 million, almost $100 an acre. Engineers for Horizon outlined development plans to Richard Grover, director of the office of the St. Lawrence County Planning Board. The plans call for a "biseasonal community"—summer and winter—of 6,000 to 9,000 lots with an eventual population of 21,000 to 36,000. The lot sizes sould vary from 1 to 10 acres, with the majority in the 1½- to 2-acre range, and would sell for about $5,000 each. To attract buyers to the development, Horizon would build at least one championship 18-hole golf course, a ski center, an Olympic-sized swimming pool, a resort motel, and a shopping center. The company would also create three lakes out of what are now the naturally wild Deerskin Creek and Grass River.

Horizon's action stirred a major battle between conservationists, who saw the proposed development as setting a pattern for the destruction of the nation's remaining natural areas, and those who contended that the project would boost the area's sparse and sagging economy. Stewart L. Udall said that, if the large-scale land speculators are allowed to invade the Adirondack Park with their lot sales schemes, this could mean the gradual dismemberment and degradation of one of the nation's finest conservation reserves. R. P. Van Gytenbeek, chairman of the Colorado Spring Planning commission declared, "My experience with Horizon Corporation is that they are high-use developers and that they have very little concern for the environment (*New York Times,* May 9, 1972)."

As an answer to extensive real estate development and land speculators in the Adirondacks, the New York Legislature in May 1973 passed the Adirondack Park Agency Act, a comprehensive plan governing use of land. Within the area are private lands of 3.7 million acres with magnificent lakes, valleys, and mountains. Together with the 2.3 million acres already owned and protected by the state, it forms the largest park in the coterminous United States, twice as big as Yellowstone National Park. All private lands were classified in the park area into six categories and density limits fixed in the case of four. Future growth is permitted mainly in existing towns. Designations are based on an inventory of environmental factors, such as soil, slopes, water resources, wildlife, and potential for sewage disposal. The plan transcends simple zoning and is one of the most ambitious attempts to make development compatible with nature. The act proclaims:

> The basic purpose of this article is to insure optimum overall conservation, protection, preservation, development and use of the unique, scenic, historic, ecological and natural resources of the Adirondack park (Adirondack Park Agency, 1973, p. 1).

Court challenges concerning the constitutionality of the Act and decisions rendered under the Act were made by Ton-da-Lay, Ltd. They petitioned the state supreme court to override Commissioner Henry L. Diamond's decision denying their planned development of a vacation and second-home community. They had planned a community of 20,000 persons on an 18,386-acre tract in Franklin County. In his denial Diamond stated:

> . . . it is clear that the majority of the people of the state have mandated a high degree of concern for both public and private land in enacting the recent added protection for the Adirondacks. To grant permits which would dilute this protection runs counter to the intent of the Legislature and the policy of the people of the state (New York State Environment, v. 3, n. 5, p. 9).

Other aspects of planning and management are contained in many publications. Fabos (1973) presents a highly informative model for the assessment of landscape resources, and uses the Boston metropolitan region as an example. In 1968, New York State started a program entitled Land Use and Natural Resource Inventory of New York State (LUNR). The entire state is being systematically mapped on air photographs because "A detailed inventory of land use and natural resources is generally recognized as a prime requisite for effective planning" (Hardy, 1970). LUNR classifies lands into a series of sets and subsets, such as agriculture active and inactive, forest land, water resources including lakes and ponds, streams and rivers, wetlands, marine lakes, rivers and seas, residential land use, commercial and industrial land use, outdoor recreation land use, extractive industry land use, public and semipublic land use, transportation land use, and nonproductive land. On a regional and interstate basis the New England River Basins Commission (1973) has undertaken an inventory and studies that will lead to the planning and management of the Long Island Sound region.

> The New England River Basins Commission is preparing a comprehensive, coordinated, joint plan for the conservation and development of the water and related land of Long Island Sound in Connecticut and New York from Throgs Neck to the Race. The purpose of the Long Island Sound Regional Study which will lead to the plan is to recomend ways through which water and related land management can provide an environment of clean water, open space and beauty that enriches human dignity and enjoyment while maintaining solid economic opportunity for the some 11 million people within the region. This is consistent with the requirements of the Water Resources Planning Act of 1965, which provides basic authority for the study (iii, preface).

A final note on the geomorphic planning of facilities used by inhabitants and travelers to urban areas concerns the development of such massive installations as the new jetport in Texas.

> The Dallas–Fort Worth Regional Airport, covering 18,000 acres of land, will be the largest in the world. And from the beginning, it was designed to fit harmoniously into the environment.

> The airport is three times larger in land area than New York's Kennedy International, twice as large as Chicago's O'Hare, and six times as large as Los Angeles International. The airport, in fact, is larger than Manhattan Island.
>
> 12,000 acres of the property will be conservation treated as soon as possible. Streams that pass through the airport area will be protected. The master plan insures that wastes will not contaminate these waterways. The airport is designed so that grading and paving make minimum changes in the natural drainage patterns.
>
> Runoff is more rapid because of paved surfaces, which is a planned advantage in that the airport runoff gets into the streams before the crest from the total watershed and therefore does not increase flood levels (McLendon, 1973, pp. 12, 14).

New Towns, Laws and Governmental Action

The term "new town" has been used to describe those emerging communities where environmental concerns play an important role in their design and management. They were first developed on an important scale in Britain. In this section we discuss new towns and also analyze the laws and various governmental actions taken in the interest of the environment and the conservation of nature. The two reproduced articles that are especially relevant to this section are by Mischenko, who describes the new cities in the Moscow region, and Whyte, who discusses how the legal easement principle can be used as a tool for the prevention of urban sprawl.

The United States has examples of most types of "new towns," but they exhibit a wide range of environmental awareness and success in maintaining natural areas.

1. Company towns. Growth of this type town peaked before 1900 but would include such towns as Gary, Indiana, Kohler, Wisconsin, Pullman, Illinois, Kingsport, Tennessee, and Lowell, Massachusetts.

2. Real estate communities. Typical of some of the early ones were Roland Park, a suburban section of Chicago developed in 1891, and Forest Hills Gardens, Long Island, in 1911.

3. Garden cities. One of the best examples is Radburn, New Jersey, founded in 1928, a major experiment in the history of American urban development.

4. Greenbelt community development. The 1935 Executive Order created the Resettlement Administration, which included a provision for greenbelt towns. Three areas were selected for development: Greenbelt, Maryland, on the outskirts of Washington, D.C., Greenhills, Cincinnati, Ohio, and Greendale, Milwaukee, Wisconsin. Greenbelt, Maryland, was especially unsuccessful, but helped provide some guidelines for the planning of future communities.

5. Power and reclamation projects. Boulder City, Nevada, was established in 1930 by the Bureau of Reclamation and in 1937 emerged as a permanent town with a master

plan conceived with reference to the site of the dam. Norris, Tennessee, was built between 1933 and 1935 by the Tennessee Valley Authority to house workers employed on the Norris Dam project.

6. Atomic energy towns. Examples include the Atomic Energy Commission communities of Oak Ridge, Tennessee, Hanford, Washington, and Los Alamos, New Mexico. Only since 1947 has permanent construction been substituted for temporary war materials. The planning and policies instituted by the AEC illustrate the value of adequate financing and the importance of local participation in planning for the future.

Just as there has been a variety of stimuli for new-town developments, there are also diverse approaches to accomplishing urban renewal and with it concomitant beautification in the satellite communities. Many planners have largely built around the automobile, and their designs are dominated by freeway construction, parking facilities, and auto – urban oriented centers for shopping and business. Other recent approaches indicate that the car is inimical to healthy cities and seek high-speed public transportation combined with pedestrian-oriented centers of living and commerce. Retention and rejuvenation of historic locales is also receiving much attention, as in Georgetown, Greenwich Village, and the French Quarter. The demolition of unsightly slums followed by redevelopment has occurred in old congested areas in Philadelphia, Pittsburgh, Washington, and New York, often creating sad displacement problems for former inhabitants. In some cities, such as Wilmington, Delaware, a reverse type of homesteading is being tried wherein people are given an old building free if they renovate it to meet building codes within a certain time period. The new towns of Reston, Virginia, and Columbia, Maryland, have emphasized clustered development of buildings around recreation lakes surrounded by green areas of open space; such towns are essentially an urban village within an urban area within a metropolitan region. The purpose of the smaller, unified communities is to provide the individual with greater opportunity and scope for activities in the affairs of society and a greater feeling of personal identity in governmental structures and attitudes. Much of the early thrust for such feelings originated in England with the "garden-city" concept.

According to Lewis Mumford, Ebenezer Howard's classic book *Garden Cities of Tomorrow* (1902) (first published in 1898 as *Tomorrow: A Peaceful Path to Reform*) has "done more than any other single book to guide the modern town planning movement and to alter its objectives." Howard synthesized the earlier work of utopians like Kropotkin and Charles Fourier and sought to relieve the congestion of London by long-range planning and balanced growth. He hoped to capture and utilize the facilities of modern technology without sacrificing the social advantages of a city. Thus decentralization would eliminate the physical and social dichotomy between the city and its rural countryside. In 1899 Howard helped found the Garden City Association (later named the Town and Country Planning Association) with the basic purpose of demonstrating the feasibility of his ideas. The Garden City was to contain a rather compact developmental community with 1,000 acres at the center surrounded by a 5,000-acre agricultural greenbelt. Promoters of the idea, such as Mumford, wanted the communities built outside large urban centers to take the population overspill. Garden cities would have their own industries and achieve an internal financial balance, would reduce commuting and be protected from chaotic sprawl, and would be the answer to the dying "megalopolis," a favorite word used by Oswald Spengler in his *The Decline of the West.* H. G. Wells gave the concept his prediction treatment in his 1902 book *Anticipations* when he wrote:

> Enough has been said to demonstrate that "town" and "city" will be, in truth, terms as obsolute as "mail coach". For these new areas that will grow but of them we want a term, and . . . we may for our present purposes call these coming town provinces "urban regions".
>
> Through the varied country the new wide roads will run, here cutting through a crest and there running like some colossal aqueduct across a valley, swarming always with a multitudinous traffic of bright, swift (and not necessarily ugly) mechanisms; and everywhere amid the fields and trees linking wires will stretch from pole to pole. . . . All that is pleasant fair of our present countryside may conceivably still be there among the other things. There is no reason why the essential charm of the country should disappear; the new roads will not supersede the present high roads, which will still be necessary for horses and subsidiary traffic: and the lands and hedges, the field paths and wild flowers, will still have their ample justification. A certain lack of solitude there may be perhaps . . .

The first Garden City Ltd. was the new city of Letchworth, England, started in 1903 37 miles north of London. A later one also designed by Howard working with another group in 1919 became known as Welwyn Garden City. By the late 1930s both towns were rather prosperous. The World War interrupted further planning until the enactment by the British Parliament of the New Towns Act of 1946. This legislation gave the government authority to designate land areas as sites for new towns and to appoint development corporations to be charged with planning and implementation. Thus the new towns have now become government projects and are carried out in accordance with public objectives. Additional legislation, The New Towns Act of 1959, defined and regulated future ownership of the new towns. Since 1947, 21 new towns have been designated in Great Britain with approximately 650,000 people. The garden-city concept when combined with the greenbelt idea has guided much of urban-area planning in Britain and the interfusing of growth with open space and residual agricultural lands.

> This concept has been adopted as a basic element of British planning, and applied with considerable concern for the natural characteristics of the sites. Frederick Gibberd and Peter Shepheard, in designing Harlow and Stevenage, new towns outside London, took great care that soils should be tested to ascertain those that were best for farming, recreation, forests, etc. They advocated that in so far as possible the belt of agricultural land should penetrate the town. Anyone who has visited Harlow, however, sees that the open space dissects the town, is overscaled and breaks down all possibility of collective urban identity (Roberts, 1970, p. 155).

A variation of the more self-contained towns, as conceived by Howard, were such communities in England as the Hampstead Garden Suburb designed by Barry Parker and Raymond Unwin in 1907, in which all emphasis was on social amenities without local industry.

Other countries have carefully watched such planning innovations and have provided their own modifications as in Germany, Finland, Sweden, France, the Netherlands, Israel, and the United States. In Germany the Krupp industries built special housing with open-space design for about 16,000 workers. Nòrdweststadt, near Frankfurt, is designed for 50,000 people and contains ample green space, a blend of low and high buildings and artfully planned pedestrian traffic within the city. In Sweden the new towns of Vallingby, Arsta, and Forsta near Stockholm are tastefully laid out, but lack industry and serve largely as dormitories for the city of Stockholm. Tapiola, Finland, is 6 miles west of Helsinki on a beautiful archipelago with charming housing, a sound industrial base, and a population almost evenly divided between white- and blue-collar classes (Frederick Gutheim, in Eldridge, 1967b, p. 836; see also Strong, 1971, for additional examples of foreign new-town developments).

New community planning in the United States has taken a wide variety of forms. At New Seabury on Cape Cod the town was designed as a second-home development around special-interest clustering for golfers, sailers, horse riders, and the like. The suburban community of Radburn, New Jersey, is more self-contained, with residences that face gardens not streets, and the streets serve mainly as service roads. The 1972 spring issue of *Environmental Affairs* carries articles on a debate concerning the plans for Palm City, Florida, a city with an anticipated population of 750,000. The controversy centers on the degree of effectiveness of the planning procedure regarding such matters as waste-water treatment and disposal, canal design, solid-waste disposal, preservation of tidal wetlands, preservation of intracoastal waterways, maintenance of general environmental quality, beach and sand-dune preservation, tree preservation, preservation of natural area, and air pollution control (Young and Dea, 1972; Bird, 1972). Two of the best-known and widely acclaimed model new towns are Reston, Virginia, and Columbia, Maryland. The U.S. Geological Survey liked the general theme of Reston so much that they built a $45 million facility on a 105-acre site there. In similar manner the town of Columbia, which lies between Baltimore and Washington, D.C., will be a complete new city on lands that before constituted 165 farms, 15,600 acres, and cost the developer $23 million to purchase. The town is designed for a population over 100,000, with 30,000 people in its plants, offices, stores, and institutions. There will be nine smaller towns within the complex, each with its own schools, churches, and services centered around a village green. Towns will be separated by 3,500 acres of permanent open space. There will be five lakes, stream valleys, forests, 26 miles of riding trails, parks, and recreation areas, which will interlace the entire city. In addition to businesses (center downtown), there will be an 80-acre lake as a front yard and a 50-acre forest at its side. The three major stream valleys were preserved, including more than 3,000 acres of forest (Rouse, 1967).

Although much of the earlier new-town planning was done by private groups, and even the magnificently planned communities of Reston and Columbia were done by private enterprise, governmental action is becoming increasingly important. The wide range of codes, zoning, ordinances, laws, and legislative acts are being used for enrivonmental preservation, conservation, and protection. Of course, another role of government is to take over the complete organizational pattern of population movements and location. For example, 900 new towns were built in the Soviet Union between 1917 and 1965, during a time that urban population was growing from 26.3 million to 124.8 million. Moreover, decentralization has been accomplished on a nationwide scale by inhibiting the growth of large cities such as Moscow and promoting the growth of smaller cities. In Brazil the government has planned and built an entire new city at Brasilia with a man-made lake that arcs around the city on three sides. In England the Town and Country Planning Act of 1968 gave direction to local planning authorities to carry out surveys of their areas, including the principal physical characteristics.

> The provisions in the Industrial Development Act, 1966 and the Local Authorities Act, 1966 for acquiring such land and making grants towards the cost of the reclamation works are enabling local authorities to make an increasing contribution to the restoration of the nation's landscape resource . . . (Hackett, 1971, p. 108).

Little (1968) provides examples of local ordinances and state laws in the United States that especially apply to the preservation of lands in urban areas and adjacent lands. These include the New York General Municipal Law, Section 247; Hillsborough, New Jersey, Clustering Ordinance, Article VIII; New York General Municipal Law, Section 281, Cluster Enabling Act; New Jersey Farmland Assessment Act, and Connecticut Assessment Act, Public Act No. 490, which declares, for example:

> (a) it is in the public interest to encourage the preservation of farm land, forest land and open space land in order to maintain a readily available source of food and farm products close to the metropolitan areas of the state, to conserve the state's natural resources and to provide for the welfare and happiness of the inhabitants of the state (b) that it is in the public interest to prevent the forced conversion of farm land, forest land, and open space land to more intensive uses as the result of economic pressures caused by the assessment thereof for purposes of property taxation at values incompatible with their preservation as such farm land, forest land and open space land . . . (p. 143).

The Town of Ramapo Drainage Commission Legislation has proved especially effective. In 1965 when John F. McAlevey first ran for town supervisor of the rapidly expanding New York suburb of Ramapo, he campaigned on a platform of controlling growth. He won the election and each one since. His first step was to develop a mster plan for the entire area and then to have authorized zoning ordinances based on that plan, which became law in 1969. Before any project can be approved in Ramapo, the developer must prove that it conforms to the master plan and will not overload municipal services, including sewer, roads, parks, and playgrounds. If these services do not exist, the developer has either to wait until the township builds them on schedule or else provide them at his own cost.

> Last year, ruling on a suit by landowners and developers who wanted to overthrow McAlevey's program, the New York State Court of Appeals upheld—and praised—Ramapo's scheme. Says McAlevey: "What we fought for was the right of a community through its elected officials to chart its own destiny" (*Time*, Oct. 1, 1973, p. 96).

A variety of procedures are thus being used to restrict or limit growth, and to prohibit development except for specially approved locations. The forerunner for laws on a statewide basis was 1961 legislation passed in Hawaii. In 1960 the Hawaii legislature started debates on solutions to the problems the islands were experiencing. A combination of newly granted statehood, introduction of jet travel, and tourist-population expansion was causing Honolulu and other urban areas to experience sprawl and land-resource exploitation. The legislature responded with the passage of a zoning law, the Hawaiian Land Use Law, whereby land was to be treated as a natural resource to be protected, instead of a commodity to be bought and sold.

> Hawaii in 1961 passed a novel law that created a Land Use Commission. This body then divided the state into three classes of land—urban, agricultural, and conservation. Urban areas were for concentrations of people, agricultural for farm and garden production along with homes on lots of at least five acres, and conservation land was to be protected for natural resource or watershed purposes or managed for park recreation and scenic beauty. The Land Use Commission gathered its data for zoning by holding regular hearings in regions conveniently designated as conservation districts (Saltonstall, 1972, p. 160).

In 1970, Vermont, in response to an alarming second-home developmental boom, authorized a land-use plan governing the entire state. The law affects all developments that plan 10 or more housing units. It also imposed a capital-gains tax on land sold for development, if the land is held less than 6 years. When Governor Thomas P. Salmon took office in January 1973, he said, "Let us tell the developers and let us tell the rest of the country right here and now that Vermont is not for sale." The new legal stipulations control land development and speculation. One unprecedented feature links real estate taxes, previously determined by assessed value of land, directly to landowner's incomes. This will allow those with low income to remain on land even when the value of surrounding lands skyrocket; it means their property does not go up for tax purposes. Another law requires developers to meet a long list of environmental requirements, including control of erosion, water supply, and so on, before they can turn their first shovelful of earth. For example, a subdivider who wants to build on a floodplain must now prove that his development will not imperil the health, safety, and welfare of the public during a flood. Also in 1970, Maine passed the Site Location and Development Law that gave the state government power to

> . . . control the location of . . . developments substantially affecting the local environment in order to insure that such developments will be located in a manner which will have a minimal adverse impact on the natural environment of their surroundings.

It also provided state veto powers over new commercial and industrial development, including residential developments of 20 acres or more, that (1) do not have the financial ability to carry out antipollution measures required by state and federal law, (2) have an adverse effect on the natural environment including scenic character and property values, (3) might be built on soil of a type unsuited to the nature of the undertaking. Other laws passed in 1970 and 1971 give the state the authority to protect wetlands and to require local communities to zone all land within 250 feet of navigable water by July 1973 or suffer state intervention. The result is a major extention of state authority over land-use controls, which places Maine among the leading states in environmental protection.

There is a variety of other state laws with prohibitions concerning the prevention of environmental degradation for certain specific actions. A recent Connecticut law imposes a $1,000 a day fine on violators who dredge or fill wetlands without a permit and makes them pay the bill for restoration of the lands to their former natural state. In June 1971, New Jersey passed a bill that sewage sludge and industrial wastes must be dumped at least 100 miles off shore. Obviously, neither of these measures is perfect, but they are much preferable to former practices, which created even greater ecologic havoc.

Shore-protection objectives can often be satisfied by directly controlling the use of both public and private lands through such regulatory devices as zoning, ordinances, subdivision regulation, building codes, and permits. In Massachusetts, such orders have proved effective in the regulation of wetlands. In Oregon, courts have upheld the right of government to prevent backshore property owners from fencing private property between mean high water and the line of vegetation. Similar rulings have been made in Texas. Although Michigan has no zoning power related to its shoreland, other than in high-risk areas, the state does have the authority to review all subdivisions along Great Lakes shores and to impose restrictions for buyer protection against inundation. Excellent building codes are in effect at Pompano Beach, Florida, and Wrightsville Beach, North Carolina. In Wisconsin, communities are authorized to zone floodplains, including the Great Lakes shore, and if they fail to do so the state will.

Since 1970 a number of states and the federal government have passed specific legislation that deals with the management of coasts. The Delaware Coastal Zone Act of 1971, the first of its kind, bars heavy industry for a 2-mile zone along the state's 115-mile coastline:

> The coastal areas of Delaware are the most critical areas for the future of the state in terms of the quality of life.It is, therefore, the declared public policy of the state of Delaware to control the location, extent, and type of industrial development in Delaware's coastal areas. In so doing, the state can better

protect the natural environment of its bay and coastal areas and safeguard their use primarily for recreation and tourism.

In the election of November 7, 1972, California voted for the protection of the 1,072-mile shoreline from uncontrolled commercial development. The California coastal law sets up a state coastal-zone conservation commission along with six regional commissions to guide future coastal development; when combined with the Environmental Quality Act of 1970, the coastal law controls all development within 1,000 feet of the shore. It requires both state agencies and private developers to publish detailed reports of the environmental impact of their projects. The state of Washington voted to place the management of shorelines in the hands of state officials. Also, in 1972 the federal government passed the Coastal Zone Management Act:

> The Coastal Zone Management Act is the first piece of land control legislation passed by Congress; it includes water control as well. It carries with it encouragement that state government begin to exert control over federal activities along the coastlines. This represents a considerable challenge to the traditional concepts of local autonomy in these matters (Gardner, 1973, p. 21).

The management of coastal areas involves matters on a regional scale, and consideration must be made of the total environment, which includes such diverse entities as coastal physical processes, recreation and aesthetic appreciation, living resource extraction, nonliving resource appraisal, waste disposal, transportation, residential – commercial – industrial considerations, and ecological use. For example, on Long Island, New York, the Nassau – Suffolk Regional Planning Board has instituted a Regional Marine Resources Council that is evaluating six major coastline problem areas, including wetland management, shore erosion and stabilization, water use, and resource development. Even in Italy, after 27 months of heated debate, the parliament passed a law that states, in part, "The safeguarding of Venice and of its lagoon is declared to be a problem of pre-eminent national interest." As a result, $510 million has been appropriated over the next 5 years to bring fresh water from inland rivers, preserve the lagoon and its surrounding wetlands, build Venice's first sewage system, stop air pollution, and restore city housing and monuments.

Coastal management involves setting priorities and, if we want to save our physical environment, Inman and Brush (1973) point out:

> Coastal communities are presently in the curious position of rapidly acquiring and improving beach frontage while at the same time they lack criteria for evaluating that the beach will still be in existence in 10 or 20 years. Certainly the future of any coastal man-made structure placed in the path of the longshore movement in a littoral cell is questionable, and great reservations should accompany any commitment to build such a structure.
>
> It is imperative that we develop the means to preserve the beaches and

> harbors that we now have and that we develop practical techniques for creating new beaches and nearshore structures that are less damaging to the environment. From an environmental standpoint, there are three fundamental steps necessary for the good design of coastal structures: (1) identification of the important processes operative in an environment, (2) understanding of their relative importance and their mutual interactions, and (3) the correct analysis of their interaction with the contemplated design (p. 30).

Money is another formidable tool that is often necessary for landscape management; there must be both the *will* and the *way*. Twenty-six states have laws that provide lower taxes for farmlands and 16 of these states institute penalties if the land is sold and subdivided. In November 1972, New York voters overwhelmingly passed the $1.15 billion Environmental Quality Bond Act. These monies will provide $600 million to continue the $1 billion Pure Waters Bond Act of 1965 to purify the state's waters. $150 million was designated to help meet air pollution problems, and the remaining $400 million ($157 million for parks and open-space acquisition) was budgeted to preserve and enhance land resources, combat solid wastes, and provide additional fishing and recreational opportunities. Florida also passed by a three to one vote in November 1972 a $240 million bond issue for the purchase of environmentally critical or jeopardized areas. Such areas include Big Cypress Swamp (whose purchase is being aided with federal funds) and other sites important for water supply and other environmental amenities and necessities. Assisting such ventures has been a federal open-space land program that since 1961 has given grants of $44 million for 360 state and local land-acquisition projects in 36 states, totaling more than 136,000 acres in urban areas. These sites are used for park, recreation, conservation, scenic, and historic preservation purposes.

On top of state and federal policies regarding laws and the management of landscape systems, counties and local communities are also enacting a series of rules and regulations to aid in the prevention of mismanaged and abused landscapes. Specific local laws are being passed that add other guidelines for development (or prohibitions of), including building codes, zoning stipulations, and ordinances. For example, in the urban areas that are permitting additional expansion on a controlled basis, one form for new development is the designation that it must be accomplished by "cluster planning." This type of development saves construction of long roads, sewer lines, and other services while preserving a maximum of land resources. Tax relief is also being given to important agricultural lands when owners pledge not to sell to developers for a specified period of time. Thus when taxes are rising on lands being developed, the taxes on contiguous lands that are preserved in original status are not being raised, and may even be lowered. Other means for land conservation include the requirements by local governments that developers must either contribute open space or provide the money to acquire open space before construction of new projects can commence. Prohibition of future growth is becoming a policy practiced by more and more communities. Boca Raton, Florida, a city of 41,000, voted in 1972 to establish a ceiling on growth. The new statute places a limit for the urban area of 40,000 dwelling units, or about 100,000 population. After this figure is reached, the city will deny further housing-construction permits. In New Mexico there is a citizen's group called the New Mexico Undevelopment Commission that propagandizes against newcomers entering the State. Governor Tom McCall of Oregon began a visitor policy of encouraging visitors to come to Oregon but not to stay; however, in 1972 he suggested they not come at all, and was instrumental in having the state's travel advertising budget slashed 30 percent. Future landscape development can benefit from other recent ideas. Boulder, Colorado, in 1967, adopted the first sales tax to help support open-space purchase and has already bought or optioned more than 2,700 acres in the urban area. In 1965, Marin County, California, placed two thirds of its 300,000 acres in an agricultural preserve, and later 100,000 acres were further placed under a preservation contract whereby local governments were authorized to reduce property-tax assessments.

Summary

This volume is concluded with the very thought-provoking and beautifully positive statement "Countryside" by Anthony Wayne Smith. The future environmental course of the United States, with equal accountability and application throughout the world, could be best served by following the guidelines that occur in two recent environmental publications. One is the 384-page monograph by the task force on land use and urban growth, headed by Laurence S. Rockefeller (1973). This report was made for the President's Citizen Committee on Environmental Quality. One major recommendation calls for a federally assisted green-space program, which would give permanent protection to greenbelts around cities and buffer zones between and within urban areas. A "national lands trust" with federal funding is advocated to assist state and local land-use agencies in the designation, planning, and conservation of green open spaces that are becoming urbanized and in jeopardy of submitting to urban sprawl. Another positive step in planning is the 1973 Environmental Plan for New York State, a preliminary edition for a proposed master plan that seeks to be a "guide for public and private decision-making. Its goal is to maintain, restore and enhance the environment which we all share and are dependent upon for the basic requirements of life." The plan was prepared by the Department of Environmental Conservation, which has publicized the plan and held public hearings throughout the state to determine public interest and support and obtain feedback for the final version, which will be voted in a referendum at a later date. The plan speaks to the total environment, but a large share applies to urban areas and the problems of land use, growth, pollution, and terrain degradation in and near cities. Dasmann (1968) stated many of the principles that are embodied in the plan, and the following quotation forms a fitting finale to the landscape environmental approach to urban areas:

> An environmental approach to conservation implies that each broad natural region be regarded as an organic whole and developed to provide an optimum habitat for man. Looking at the spectrum of land and land-use patterns, ranging between highly industrialized cities at one extreme and

empty wilderness at the other, we must seek to develop each area to express its fullest potentialities. Cities should no longer be ugly work centers, in which the economically unfortunate are forced to live a closed and barren life and from which the more fortunate flee at every opportunity. Cities can be developed not only to provide the qualities of urban living which are implied in the word "civilization" but also to combine the lost values of rural beauty and natural scene. By proper planning, cities can become places of charm and appeal to the human spirit in which the dweller will consider himself fortunate. This may mean, ultimately, for most cities a complete reshaping, a tearing down and rebuilding to combine scenic beauty, recreational space, and other aesthetic values, with the more functional necessities of working, marketing, eating, and sleeping.

The cities and towns of the future can be developed in close relationship with the surrounding rural areas. Farm and city have long been separated by the devastated land of the "urban fringe." Farm lands have been cut off from city dwellers by fences and "no trespassing" signs in a somewhat vain attempt to defend them against the inconsiderate and the vandal. In a pattern of environmental conservation, farm land and town land may flow together. Good agricultural soils would continue to grow better crops, but building sites, homes, gardens, parks, and recreational areas could flow from the city outward into the hilly ground, the stream side, the now weedy and barren waste areas that are a part of most farming regions (p. 89).

26

Reprinted from *Canadian Building Digest,* **62**, 1–4 (Feb. 1965)

Trees and Buildings

by R. F. Legget and C. B. Crawford

UDC 624.131.46:624.131.52

Trees are most desirable features of the environment of buildings, adding their own special beauty to any urban scene. The welcome shade they provide in high summer has long been a recurring theme of writers. It is always regrettable when they have to be cut down to make way for new buildings, even though this is frequently unavoidable. The planting of new trees, on the other hand, is one of the most welcome subsidiary aspects of urban development and redevelopment; and the old saying that one of the happiest sights in the world is an old man planting a new tree is no mere figure of speech but a timely reminder of the living character of trees, on a time scale comparable with that of human life.

The growing of trees is, therefore, a necessary complement of building, chiefly for aesthetic reasons, but with at least some utilitarian value. The extent to which modern buildings still depend upon the materials derived from trees is widely recognized, but the further aesthetic association of trees and buildings is all too often taken for granted. To some it may be surprising to find a Digest devoted to the subject, so little attention does it normally receive. Others, however, will appreciate why *Trees and Buildings* are to be discussed, and can anticipate what is to be said if they have had the misfortune to encounter the problems that can sometimes arise when trees are planted too close to building foundations.

The Problem

It is the purpose of this Digest to explain the problem, to suggest how it can be avoided, and to outline remedial methods to correct damage that trees may have caused. For serious damage can result from the encroachment of roots into the immediate environment of foundations if the local soil is one that is susceptible to swelling or, more particularly, to shrinking with change in moisture content. Since trees are living organisms, they need water for their continued existence and to support their natural growth. If they cannot get their necessary supply from rainfall, their root systems will try to draw water from the soil in which they grow. If this water is abstracted from a soil that is volumetrically susceptible to moisture change, soil shrinkage may result, with serious structural complications leading at the least to the unsightly cracking of a building superstructure if not, indeed, to more serious damage.

Trees and their Roots

About 10 per cent of the wood mass of a tree is to be found under the ground surface in the form of roots, which extend quite surprising distances. The total length of all the roots of a large oak tree, for example, will be several hundreds of miles. The functions of the roots are not only to provide anchorage in the ground for the tree, but, more importantly, to obtain and provide the minerals and water necessary for its well-being. If normal sources of water adjacent to the tree dry up, the root system will spread in a remarkable effort to discover alternative supplies. As an extreme example, it is on record that tamarisk roots were found 100 feet below ground surface when the Suez Canal was excavated. In more recent studies, there are many cases in which roots of common deciduous trees have been traced through horizontal distances of over 100 feet from the trees of which they were a part.

These immense root systems are necessary because of the vast quantities of water used during the (summer) growing season. Water is contained in all the tissues, both dead and alive. Young leaves may contain up to 90 per cent of water; and even tree trunks contain as much as 50 per cent. But although the formation of 100 grams of cellulose requires 55 grams of water, a tree will lose correspondingly by transpiration almost 100,000 grams of water, or one thousand times as much as its gain in weight.

It is this dramatic process of transpiration, activated by solar energy, that is responsible for drawing water from the root system to the topmost leaf of the tallest tree, as high as 350 feet above the ground in the case of California redwoods. The process is automatically controlled by nature. For each type of tree a certain amount of water is regularly required for transpiration and, to a minor degree, for tree building. It is this insistent demand that causes the spread of root systems when normal water supply is reduced.

It is from rainfall that trees get their vital water supply, rainfall after it has soaked into the surface of the ground and so become available to the root system near the ground surface and immediately around the tree. In all districts, however, variations in annual rainfall always occur. In occasional years, the variation may be so great that there is common talk of "a dry year." In Ottawa, for example, the total rainfall during June and July 1955 was less than 2½ inches, as compared with the long-time annual average of 7 inches. And when dry years do occur the root systems of trees will spread in a search for the water so essential to the life of the tree. If this happens in a sandy soil, no effects may be noticed at the ground surface. If, however, the local soil is a clay that is influenced by changes in moisture content, then the abstraction of water from the voids in the soil will lead to a shrinkage in its volume, with consequent settlement of the ground surface.

Critical Soil Types

Important areas of southern Canada are underlain by clays that are affected in this way, so that the problem created by the presence of trees adjacent to buildings is a very real one for Canadian architects, engineers and builders. The soil underlying much of the Prairies is a clay that has the dual distinction of shrinking with decrease of moisture content below its natural value and of expanding if the moisture content is increased above this value.

The great industrial area of the St. Lawrence and Ottawa Valleys has as its subsoil an unusual type of clay (commonly called *Leda Clay*) that derives some of its properties from the fact that it was deposited by settlement in sea water when the area was submerged, in glacial time, beneath what is known as the Champlain Sea. Its natural moisture content is often quite high. Because of the way in which the minute soil particles are arranged as a result of its formation, it has a quite remarkable – and unfortunate – shrinkage potential.

The process is not fully reversible and rewetting the soil after shrinkage will not usually restore it to its original volume. This compounds the practical problem since, if serious surface settlements do occur due to the shrinkage of Leda Clay, restoration of the original moisture content of the soil may not bring the ground back to its original level.

Fortunately, these critical soil types can be readily detected by simple soil tests carried out upon samples obtained from test borings put down in advance of construction. It is, therefore, always possible to predict the possibility of trouble with these soils and to prepare the design of foundations and landscaping in such a way as to obviate trouble after the building has been erected.

Some Examples

To those readers who have not experienced trouble with foundations on clay soils caused by trees, the foregoing discussion may appear to be somewhat theoretical. Before presenting any further general comments, therefore, some practical, possibly mundane, examples will be briefly recorded.

In order to have available actual figures for just such a purpose as this (and for other research reasons) DBR/NRC carried out a few years ago some detailed observations of ground movements near a row of medium sized elm trees immediately adjacent to the Building Research Centre in Ottawa. The single row of trees averaged 55 feet in height; they are growing in Leda Clay, the depth to bedrock being beyond all possible influence from the surface.

Groundwater level was close to the surface at the start of the summer but receded as the year progressed. It was a "dry summer" with considerably less rain than usual, so that the observations made may be regarded as typical of what does happen in the vicinity of elm trees growing in the Leda Clay in the St. Lawrence and Ottawa Valleys when rainfall does not satisfy the water demand.

By levelling well-secured observation points against a fixed deep benchmark, soil movements around the trees to depths of 14 feet and to distances up to 50 feet were observed throughout the summer. It was found that even at a depth below the surface of 13 feet, and at a distance of 20 feet from the row of trees, a vertical settlement of ½ inch took place. Surface settlements ranged from over 3 inches at the trees to ½ inch almost 50 feet away. At a depth of 5 feet, a common depth for house foundations in the Ottawa district, the settlements varied from a maximum of 2¼ inches 5 feet away from the trees to ¾ inch 30 feet away.

The older part of Ottawa is known to many as a "city of trees." It is not surprising to find that, beautiful as are the rows of large trees to be found (for example) along O'Connor and Metcalfe Streets, and particularly on the shorter cross streets in this part of central Ottawa, they have made their presence all too evident by cracks in the older residential buildings in this area.

A survey of 574 buildings showed differential settlements, in the same building, varying up to 14 inches. The consequent cracking and tilting of windows and doorways can well be imagined. In every case of serious settlement large trees were growing nearby in the open garden areas that (fortunately) are still to be found here. The correlations obtained throughout the survey between the presence of trees and the settlement and associated cracking of buildings left no possibility of doubt that the trees were responsible. Any visitor to Ottawa who walks along one of the streets mentioned can see vivid evidence of the effect of trees by merely looking at the undulations in the sidewalks and noticing the "culprit trees" nearby.

[Would the reader kindly turn back and read the opening paragraph so that he will realize with what regret the presence of trees has thus to be indicted. If he will read on, he will see what can be done to combine the beauty of trees and the stability of foundations.]

Ottawa is not peculiar in this respect. Similar settlements adjacent to trees are to be seen in Montreal and in many other urban areas in the St. Lawrence and Ottawa Valleys where Leda Clay is the underlying subsoil. In the cities of western Canada the same phenomenon is to be observed where the local soil is a variety of the peculiar clays of the Prairies. To single out any location for special mention would be to make invidious comparisons, but it can at least be recorded, with all due anonimity, that there is a small town in Saskatchewan in which the ground settlements will probably one day be internationally famous in the annals of soil mechanics.

The problem is not confined to Canada. There are well authenticated records from Africa, Australia, Belgium, Burma, China, India, Palestine, the Sudan and from Texas. Some of the most valuable have come from soil mechanics workers in Great Britain. Typical of British examples are houses so badly cracked due to soil shrinkage that their corners had to be shored up, the troubles being caused by Lombardy poplar trees within 20 feet of one house, and a combination of oak trees and young poplars 35 feet away from another. A completely uncracked wing of a four-storey block of flats was found to have separated from the adjoining block by as much as 2 inches due to the effect of elm trees.

Remedial Measures

The record could be continued but enough has probably been said to show that in areas where the local soil is a clay that shrinks (or swells) with change in its moisture content some cracking of masonry buildings, and especially of smaller masonry structures, may be due to the presence of trees growing too close to the buildings. If cracks develop or increase at the end of a very dry period, the probability can be regarded almost as a certainty.

In all but minor cases a soil expert should be consulted, if only to confirm that the trouble is indeed due to the presence of trees. If the trouble has developed at the end of an exceptionally dry period, extensive watering of the ground around the trees may effect a restoration of the soil to something like its original condition and the cracks may close. Future watering in dry periods can then give a reasonably permanent solution. [When this advice was first given by DBR/NRC, the sanity of the staff was questioned; leaving a garden hose turned on over a long weekend led to the substantial closing of a 1¼ inch crack in a new brick building.]

When cracking in a building can be definitely linked with the presence of adjacent trees, especially poplars, other than during real drought, and especially if they have been planted very close to a building, then the only solution is to cut down the offending trees and to remove as much as possible of the main root system.

Preventive Measures

Such destruction of living trees is always regrettable, even though occasionally essential, especially since trouble might have been avoided by more care in the original planning. Local experience can here be helpful, but only when gained from sound practitioners who are themselves fully conversant with the effect of trees upon clay soils. The following may be regarded as essential requirements in all such preliminary work.

(1) Accurate knowledge of soil conditions at the building site *must* be procured, and by a proper soil survey for all larger buildings. If the soils that will support the foundation are not influenced volumetrically by change in moisture content, problems with trees need not be anticipated; but if they are, then foundation and landscaping design must be adjusted accordingly.

(2) Shrinkable clays bring into foundation design problems other than those caused by trees, since soil moisture content can be influenced by many other factors. Precautions as to the depth of the foundation below ground level and the necessary rigidity of the foundation itself, as incorporated in the design of an experienced foundation engineer, will therefore usually serve this dual purpose.

(3) If trees are already growing on the building site, every effort should be made so to locate the structure that it conforms with the suggestions in the next paragraph. If this cannot be done then, with natural reluctance, trees that are going to be too close to the building must be cut down and their root systems removed. It is far better that this should be done and new trees planted appropriately than that aesthetic claims should over-rule sound judgement, with the possibility of damage to the building and the eventual inevitable removal of the trees in any case. Care should be taken that the removed trees have not already desiccated the clay, which may then swell under the changed environment.

(4) If trees are to be planted as a part of the landscaping around the building, a good working rule has been found to be that *trees should preferably be planted no nearer a building on shrinkable clay than the eventual height to which the tree may be expected to grow*. This rule may require modification if the topography around the building varies. Even in its application, attention must be given to the differing transpiration characteristics of trees.

This Digest may therefore well conclude with a list (from a paper by Ward[1]) of the more common trees in order of *decreasing* water demand, and so of *decreasing* trouble-potential:

Poplar	Broad leaved deciduous
Alder	
Aspen	
Willow	
Elm	
Maple	
Birch	
Ash	
Beech	
Oak	
Larch	Deciduous conifer
Spruce	Evergreen conifers
Fir	
Pine	

[1] Ward, W. H., "The Effects of Fast Growing Trees and Shrubs on Shallow Foundations," Jour. Inst. Landscape Architects, p. 3-12, April 1947.

27

Reprinted from *Open Space for the San Francisco Bay Area: Organizing to Guide Metropolitan Growth*, Institute of Governmental Studies, University of California, Berkeley, 1970, pp. 5–15

Open Space for the San Francisco Bay Area: Organizing to Guide Metropolitan Growth

T. J. KENT, JR.

Existing Bay Area Open Space: A Gift of Geography

Individuals from every walk of life—rich and poor, longshoremen and bankers, visitors and residents—have strongly favorable impressions of San Francisco and the Bay Area. Among the great metropolitan cities of the world, the metropolis formed by the urban and suburban communities in the nine-county Bay region has a very high ranking as a place to work, to live in and to visit.

Why is this so? The social and economic forces that shaped this cosmopolitan community over the past 100 years are well documented. They are basically no different from those that have created every large metropolis since the beginning of the Industrial Revolution.

What distinguishes the San Francisco Bay Area from its metropolitan peers is the remarkable way a dramatic geographic setting has been used to accommodate the man-made system of cities. The existing open spaces in the Bay Area's metropolitan environmental structure are of critical importance: the great central open space and "blue belt" of the Bay; the headlands, cliffs, beaches and Pacific Ocean on the west; and the vast, marvelous complex of valleys, foothills, ridges, and mountains of the region's middle and outer rings, have had a decisive influence in shaping a Bay Area "way of life."

In the past, Bay Area leaders set aside tens of thousands of acres of land for watersheds on the Peninsula, in the Eastbay, and in Marin County; they succeeded in retaining, as open space, the Golden Gate headlands, Angel Island, the Eastbay regional parks, the Point Reyes peninsula and seashore, Mt. Tamalpais, and Mt. Diablo; they placed a moratorium on Bay filling, and established a permanent Bay conservation agency. If these things had not been done, we would now have a less livable, less workable, and far less distinctive metropolis.

The existing system of regional open space, however, which we tend to take for granted, also includes many privately owned areas and geographic features that have had great influence in determining the relationships between the primary and secondary cities within the region. These include San Bruno Mountain; the western slopes of Marin County; the Napa Valley vineyards; the foothills, forests, rivers, and ridges of Sonoma and Napa counties; the great broad fields of Solano County; the Livermore Valley; the slopes of Mount Hamilton; and the green foothills and mountain ranges of San Mateo, Santa Clara, and Santa Cruz counties.

Pressures for Urbanization

Most forecasters anticipate that the Bay Area's population will have doubled between 1960 and 1990, rising from approximately 3½ million to more than 7 million. If we do not greatly enlarge the permanent elements of our existing open space system in advance of this anticipated further urbanization, the area's distinctive individuality as a world metropolis will be lost. Moreover, our existing metropolitan physical structure will be weakened. If we fail to maintain the Bay Area's characteristic quality of concentrated, intensive development on a large framework, sprawl at the edges will cause loss of accessibility to the regional centers. Destructive development trends will emerge that are not consciously wanted by anyone, but that may prove to be irreversible if they are not stemmed during the 1970's.

Unfortunately, we already have large urbanized stretches that are indistinguishable from Los Angeles sprawl or the postwar suburban tracts on the outskirts of New York and Chicago. But the main elements of our metropolitan structure have been compactly developed along transportation routes, and are still well articulated. Thus far this has resulted primarily from the area's topography, rather than from any publicly established regional development policy. High-density San Francisco, the identifiable cities of southern Marin County, the string of well-established municipalities of the San Mateo Peninsula, and the communities in the valleys east of the Berkeley and Oakland hills delineate the pattern. Even the four-mile-wide, 40-mile-long stretch of urbanized territory from Richmond to Fremont, situated on the plain between the Bay shoreline and the Eastbay hills, has a combination of specialized industrial and commercial districts, regional shopping centers, and suburban communities that still function primarily as elements of an integrated metropolis.

The Bay Area's geographically spread out clusters of cities have functioned well because most of the urban elements are individually compact, or because they have maintained their original central districts and thus can be served, as mentioned above, by a coordinated commuter transportation system. The Bay Area's principal transit services have always been designed to strengthen the region's relatively few major employment centers, making them accessible to residents throughout the region's five county core. Consequently, Bay Area central district workers have continued to have a wider effective choice of housing than has been available in many other metropolitan communities in the United States, especially in recent years.

Shaping the Next Surge of Growth

Despite its fortunate history of city building, the Bay Area must face the possibility that acceleration of postwar sprawl during the next two decades could precipitate a major city planning disaster. The next great surge of development will in part be contained, as was most of our postwar growth, by the region's topographic barriers, but the major units of the new growth of the 1970's and 1980's should not be permitted to leapfrog and spread to more remote locations or to develop on the edge of existing communities at densities too low to enable the new areas to be integrated into the central commuter-core of the region.

To implement such metropolitan development policies, early action will have to be taken to conserve, in some fair way, major privately owned elements of the regional open space system in the outer ring. If such measures are not taken, and suburban sprawl and the automobile win the next and perhaps final round in the development battle now taking place in the outer ring of the Bay Area, these forces will weaken and then destroy the region's newly reestablished rapid transit system, cancel out the massive capital investments that have revitalized the central districts of the metropolis, and dismantle the city-system that has taken more than 100 years to build.

Ample land is available within and adjacent to existing growing communities to accommodate the estimated population growth for the next 20 years at densities lower than Berkeley's, i.e., in a compact and workable pattern, with single family dwellings available for most families. If we enlarge our permanent regional open space system, future urban growth can be shaped into such human and realistic dimensions.

The elemental importance and interrelationships of the Bay Area's open spaces, and of the region's great natural beauty, were discussed in an unusual way by the late Dr. James G. Whitney, Berkeley psychiatrist, at the Bay Area's first conference on regional open space, held in 1959. Responding to a statement that the elimination of open space would contribute to mental illness, Dr. Whitney said,

> I know of no scientific proof of this proposition. Intuitively I believe it to be true, but not quite in the way it has been put. Open space is not a specific necessity for mental or any other kind of health. The failure of "the long ocean voyage" and beautifully landscaped sanitaria are demonstrations of this fact. *But a society which does not care for beauty in all its aspects and which is without a reverence for nature is spiritually undernourished. An undernourished society is weaker, sicker, and less wise. Such a society certainly will be less able to deal with all of its afflictions and challenges, one of which is mental illness.*[1] [Emphasis supplied.]

[1] Frances W. Herring ed., *Regional Parks and Open Spaces: Selected Conference Papers* (Berkeley: Bureau of Public Administration, University of California, 1961), p. 86.

Objectives of a Metropolitan Open Space System

After Congress adopted the first financial aid program for open space projects in 1961, broad support for the establishment of regional open space systems in hundreds of growing urban areas, and in every large metropolitan region, became evident throughout the country. The national goals of the program were based on pioneering work during the postwar decades by volunteer conservation groups, particularly in New York, Hawaii, Philadelphia, Washington, and the San Francisco Bay Area. These goals were restated in 1968 in the regulations of the United States Department of Housing and Urban Development. They specified that open space project applications were to be judged in terms of their potential effectiveness (1) in helping to curb urban sprawl; (2) in preventing the spread of urban blight; (3) in encouraging more economic and desirable urban development; and (4) in providing needed recreational, conservation, scenic, and historic areas.

The open space policy objectives adopted by the local governments of the Washington, D. C. metropolitan area indicate how the national goals relate to a specific region. In a 1966 report, the National Capital Regional Planning Council defined their objectives as follows:

> Open space should be preserved (1) to provide ample outdoor recreation opportunities to the ever-increasing numbers of residents and visitors in the National Capital Region; (2) to conserve natural resources, scenic beauty, and rural units of economic production; and (3) to guide urban growth into efficient corridors of development and compact communities as outlined in the Year 2000 Policies Plan [for Metropolitan Development].

During the past three years, conservation leaders in several of the nation's largest metropolitan areas have begun to articulate an additional major objective for regional open space programs: the use of open space systems to slow down, and if necessary, to stop the growth of population in the larger metropolitan regions. This objective is the result of an uneasy, growing awareness of the far-reaching ecological and social damage that apparently can be caused by sustained, rapid, uncontrolled urbanization. In contemporary terms, therefore, regional open space objectives for the Bay Area should be concerned primarily with:

1. protection and enhancement of life;
2. prevention of urban sprawl; and
3. limitation of the size of the metropolis.

Protecting and Enhancing Life

The first objective covers a broad range of programs requiring the preservation of large open areas adjacent to or near the built-up metropolis and its outlying cities. These open areas should be safeguarded now because they will be needed in the foreseeable future for watershed protection, flood control, regional parks, wildlife protection, specialized agricultural production, fire protection, protection against earthquake and landslide hazards, and for similar basic purposes. The very large amounts of land required are indicated by the 1966 Bay Area Preliminary Regional Plan prepared by the Association of Bay Area Governments. Envisioning an estimated 1990 population of 7,200,000, the ABAG report recommended the permanent reservation of 1,209,000 acres of open space land for these purposes.

The programs outlined above are now recognized as essential to the protection of life and property in the metropolitan region, and to the future welfare of its economy. Not yet fully appreciated, however, is the *interdependence* of the system's separate elements; this becomes evident only when the system is viewed in its entirety, and in relation to basic ecological needs. Only after a regional open space plan has been outlined for a large, rapidly growing metropolitan area does it become apparent that one of the clearly articulated, conscious aims of the comprehensive program should be insurance against serious ecological disturbances. An example is the damaging effect of covering too large an area with a "suffocating" blanket of urban development. Unfortunately, until recently this aim has usually been difficult to justify until after ecological imbalance has occurred.

The potential drainage and sewage disposal problems of an interior valley, such as Nicasio Valley in Marin County, and the potential air pollution problems in such "air-pockets" as Livermore Valley in Alameda County, illustrate the need for regional ecological studies before decisions are made committing areas such as these to intensive urbanization. In such cases, ecological considerations probably would be the major factor in deciding to keep certain large areas in agricultural use, rather than permitting them to be used as sites for urban communities. In view of our uncertainty concerning ecological relationships, and the obvious examples of thoughtless—and subsequently self-damaging—urban aggression against nature that we have permitted, the objective of enhancing life in growing metropolitan areas suggests a policy of caution and conservatism in planning for urban expansion. This developmental conservatism should be evident in the large scale and the comprehensive, integrated design of our metropolitan greenbelt and open space systems.

There are, of course, other good reasons justifying permanent retention of extensive land areas in agricultural use. In metropolitan regions such as the Bay Area many economic activities located in cities are directly related to the nearby production and to the marketing of agricultural products. Close-in agriculture activities will be protected when the second open space objective is achieved and the greenbelt element of the comprehensive land development system no longer permits urban growth by sprawl. Once urban growth is controlled, the values of existing agricultural land as real estate will be readjusted, making it normal and economically sound for dairying, sheep and cattle raising, fruit growing, truck farming, and other agricultural activities to be conducted in large open land areas within and adjacent to metropolitan regions.

The objective of *enhancing* life in metropolitan areas sooner or later will become as important as the current objective of *protecting* life in our great cities. When this happens, we will realize that large-scale metropolitan open space systems will once again make possible the production of fresh vegetables, fresh fruits, fresh eggs and milk, and other basic foods that can only be produced by the region's local resources of man and nature. Few Bay Area residents need to be reminded of the life-enhancing difference between fresh blackberries, artichokes, and apples, and their usual supermarket counterparts; between fresh crab and frozen crab; between fresh and frozen salmon and sole; between fresh tomatoes and supermarket tomatoes.

Thus, a regional open space system of the scale now considered necessary, initially for other reasons, will not only insure retention of unique and highly valued agricultural lands such as the Napa Valley vineyards. It will also lead to an increase of our production, use, and appreciation of local agricultural commodities, since very large areas will be available for extensive as well as intensive agriculture. Appreciation of the cycle and balance of nature in the region's surrounding and supporting landscape will be enhanced, as a natural consequence.

It may be a happy coincidence that a revival of our once-strong regional agricultural tradition will develop at the very time when so many young people are actively seeking and finding ways to live and work on the land. The too-typical reaction against this urge toward nature—which views it as a rejection of our affluent, highly specialized urban society—may miss the main objective and desire being expressed. In any case, the present combination of circumstances appears most propitious: as a consequence of the necessity to establish large scale open space systems for a combination of other requirements, we may be able to respond in understandable and constructive ways to the deeply felt but subtle needs of people of all age groups and all conditions. These seem to demand a close, practical, and harmonious relationship with nature and the land—a relationship that trends of the last half century will destroy, if they are allowed to continue.

Preventing Urban Sprawl

The second primary objective of the Bay Area open space program is the prevention of urban sprawl. This has been an accepted goal of a small but steadily increasing number of city planners, political leaders, and conservation-minded civic leaders throughout the United States since the automobile facilitated the suburban tract explosion during the 1920's. Both common sense and painstakingly detailed cost-benefit studies have established the fact that disorganized, scattered, sprawling urbanization is both economically and socially a costly, wasteful way of enlarging the metropolis.

Despite the reasonableness of the objective, the United States has not thus far been able to formulate an alternative capable of achieving acceptance and of being implemented. The recent study sponsored by the Bay Area conservation group, People for Open Space, and supported by a Ford Foundation grant, is probably the first American anti-sprawl program for a major metropolitan region that has been spelled out in sufficient detail to be enacted, financed, and implemented if the civic and political leaders of the region decide to accept it. The conclusions and recommendations of the study will be considered in detail in later sections of this essay.

Two historical realities explain our failure to prevent metropolitan sprawl. The first is governmental, the second is professional, and they are closely related. When large-scale, spread-out suburban growth began in the 1920's, most of our central cities and their outlying suburban communities were organized in ways that limited their governmental jurisdictions to land that was already urbanized. Although cities that originally were geographically distinct subsequently grew together physically, they retained their separate governments. Thus there came to be many independent local governments in every large metropolitan region. No single regional government was concerned with the growth of the metropolis as a whole. Today, fifty years later, the governmental situation is basically unchanged.

Even if metropolitan regional governments had existed in the 1920's, however, the American city planning profession at that time possessed insufficient practical experience to understand the essential, economically and politically painful measures that must be taken if metropolitan sprawl is to be halted. Only in 1917 was the profession established in a formal way, as an organized group of practitioners. Since then, the only stable governmental clients in the major metropolitan regions have been individual cities and counties. During this period, city planners and their governmental superiors have made impressive improvements in the ways in which central cities have been redeveloped, and outlying individual large-tract subdivisions designed.

In the absence of a regional governmental client, however, the city planning profession has tended to think of open space measures aimed at preventing urban sprawl in terms of limited county government powers and practices. These, it will be argued, are not likely to be strong enough to prevent it on a metropolitan scale. Thus, the normal cycle of society's challenge and the profession's subsequent response now requires action by political leaders to create a regional governmental agency possessing the motivation and authority to govern metropolitan growth.

When limited regional governments have been established, the city planning profession should be able to respond with plans and programs bold enough to achieve the objective while there is still time. Efforts to establish control of metropolitan growth, and to learn how to govern it effectively in the public interest, have been late in maturing. But this has also been true of efforts dealing with health, education and human rights for the American people. Once the reasons for the delay are understood and the necessary preparations have been started, however, there still is reason to believe that a society as well intentioned as ours can succeed in doing the job.

Preventing sprawl simply means controlling the location and timing of new development in order to assure the compactness of urban patterns and the establishment of a permanent open space system. Within the context of a metropolitan region this can only be done by a metropolitan governmental agency required and empowered to govern growth in accordance with a regional development plan.

The limiting factors with which we must work in devising feasible alternatives to continued growth by sprawl include: our system of private land ownership and development; the large number of local governments which our political beliefs and traditions require; and our state and federal constitutions. Once a regional governmental agency exists, however, and once a physical development plan to govern metropolitan growth has been agreed upon, the anti-sprawl objective can be achieved as in Sweden, by public control or ownership of *all lands to be urbanized.* The other possible alternative as proposed for the Bay Area calls for public control or ownership of *all lands needed for the permanent regional open space system.* Either method can be made to work, but the latter is more suited to the traditions and conditions of the Bay Area.

Limiting the Size of the Metropolis

Once the anti-sprawl decision banning further growth by scattered tract developments has been made, some form of public debate will begin on limiting the size of the population that can reasonably be provided for in the Bay Area, so as to forestall an oppressive and unacceptable degree of overcrowding, disorganization, pollution, and congestion.

During the early 1960's such disparate commentators as the editors of *The New Yorker,* and a famous conservative, the late Lucius Beebe, both seriously questioned the continuing, ever more intensive development of New York's gigantic complex of central districts on Manhattan Island.[1] In 1968 the New York Regional Plan Association found that it had to question any population increase for the great metropolis beyond the trend estimate for the year 2000. After careful study, the National Committee on Urban Growth Policy in 1969 advocated a redirection of urban growth trends in the United States in order to facilitate the building of new large cities away from the nation's existing major metropolitan concentrations. When individuals and groups as varied as these reach such conclusions and express them publicly, it may be assumed that the time has come for a fair hearing on one of the primary objectives of a Bay Area regional open space progam: the conscious design of a system that will enable those responsible for the future of the Bay Area to regulate, and if necessary to limit, the size of the metropolis within the Bay region.

While visiting San Francisco in 1961, the British biologist Sir Julian Huxley was interviewed by a San Francisco *Chronicle* reporter. When asked about his impressions of urban growth in the Bay Area since his last visit here, in relation to worldwide urbanization trends, he responded: "We are making our cities impossible to live in because of size. A city can only become so large before it becomes an uneconomic unit. I think that New York, London, and Tokyo are already beyond that size."

The suggestion that it may prove to be in the public interest *to limit the size of the metropolitan Bay Area* will perhaps seem far-fetched to some. Others may view such a limitation as being dangerously harmful to prospects for future beneficial economic development. But it would be disingenuous not to raise the issue at this time. It is bound to come

[1] See Appendix I for Lucius Beebe's column "Don't Let It Happen Here," San Francisco *Chronicle,* September 19, 1965.

up sooner or later, because any metropolitan open space proposal that takes into account both the requirements for ecological survival and basic metropolitan physical-structure considerations is certain to precipitate debate on this question after the proposal is adopted, if not before.

The Bay Area has already pioneered in implementing some extremely controversial regional enterprises, after several years of debate. Today the area's residents can best serve their long-term interests by facing and debating the issue of optimum metropolitan size as soon as possible. The Bay Area does not need to remain a captive of trends that have produced "overgrown" metropolises, of which New York, Los Angeles, Tokyo, and London are outstanding examples. In fact, some of these "examples" are already trying to turn back and undo what they have done.

Today more than 8 million people live within the inner boundary of the greenbelt established around London between 1938 and 1955. Beyond the metropolitan greenbelt, but still within the London region, an additional 5 million people live in growing cities and new towns that are separated by their own greenbelts.

For many years, leaders at all levels of government in the London area have agreed that the central metropolis of 8 million is too big for its own good. Since 1947, costly programs have been reducing population densities in several central London boroughs. National economic development policies have also been designed to encourage the growth of other regions in Britain. Is it wise, or is it unwise for the Bay Area, whose population increased from 1½ million to 4½ million between 1940 and 1970, to ignore this English struggle with megalopolis?

The adoption of a metropolitan open space plan and implementation program for the Bay Area would be an act of major consequence. The primary objectives of the system should, therefore, be clearly understood in advance. The program will pose formidable administrative difficulties, not the least being the need to maintain a clear distinction between two different sets of objectives. First are those of the antisprawl greenbelts, i.e., the permanent, more or less continuous, more or less circular, broad bands of open spaces around both the metropolitan commuter-core area and the outlying cities. Second are the objectives of the other regional open space programs, whose open lands will provide the main spatial resources for the entire regional city-system. Some of these lands will not necessarily be kept permanently open. They will provide the sites, for some years, for extensions of existing communities and, perhaps, for a limited number of new towns.

A full exposition and explanation of the objectives of the metropolitan greenbelt and open space system should help to encourage the boldness that will be needed if appropriate open space policies are to be adopted during the early 1970's. Public understanding of the goals will also encourage the perseverance essential for implementation of a balanced program aimed at all three primary open space objectives: protecting and enhancing life, preventing urban sprawl, and limiting the size of the metropolis.

28

Reprinted from *The Israel Physical Master Plan,* Ministry of the Interior, Jerusalem, 1964, pp. 65–68

The Israel Physical Master Plan

J. DASH and E. EFRAT

With the foundation of the State of Israel, planning on a national scale was launched and town planning was incorporated into this larger framework. Apart from aesthetic and health considerations and the building use of plots, social and economic considerations, arising from national needs, were taken into account. Certain basic principles, coupled with that intensive urge for development in all spheres characteristic of a new country, determined the design and functions of the various towns and found expression in their detailed planning schemes. The following basic needs had to be borne in mind:

a) The need for decentralisation of the urban population. This has three implications on the town planning level, namely —
   1) The size of the towns;
   2) The density of the residential zones; and
   3) The size of the industrial areas.

b) The need for public and private services of a high standard;

c) The need for the preservation of agricultural land and open spaces around towns;

d) The need for the gradual reduction and eventual elimination of real estate speculation.

With regard to the outer fringes of the towns, Israel's position is far better than that of most other countries. The Shikkun form of housing, the isolation of industrial zones, the strict policy of preserving agricultural soil, the absence of building strips along railway lines and the comparatively small amount of privately owned land around the towns all help to fulfil the basic principles outlined above.

In Israel today no general plan is drawn up for any town without the preparation of a detailed programme. The first part of this programme concerns the social-economic aspect, defining the hinterland of the future town, its economic and social potentialities, its population target and the institutions of regional or national importance to be located there. The second part of the programme contains calculations concerning housing and recreation requirements, the social institutions which will serve the prospective population and their distribution throughout the various centres. The areas needed for these and similar services are also worked out.

After the design for this general plan, known as the "Town Outline Scheme", has been drawn up, it is submitted to the Local and District Commissions and to the Minister for their approval. In due course the Outline Scheme is divided into Detailed Schemes and Detailed Building Plans.

The following Schemes give the reader an idea of the problems of town planning and town building arising in the different regions of Israel. Thus special planning was required for Jerusalem, the capital of the country, on account of its unusual topography, its political situation — being divided between Israel and Jordan — and its historic and religious local and universal significance. Zefat and Tiberias are examples of towns with a rich historic past, special topographic conditions and a landscape which requires a distinctive architectural design — Zefat against the background of the high mountains of the Galilee and Tiberias against the background of the Sea of Galilee. Nazareth appears as the administrative capital of the Galilee and as a city holy to Christians. It recently received a large increase in urban population in the upper quarter of the town. Haifa and Elat are two examples of port cities. Haifa is the second largest city in Israel. On the one hand, it contains the main port, which has served the entire country since the thirties; on the other, it has developed along the slopes of the Carmel in typical neighbourhood units. Elat is the southernmost town in Israel. Its port constitutes a gateway to Africa and Asia. Founded 15 years ago, it is far removed from the rest of the country. Beër Sheva, the capital of the Negev, is contemplated as the fourth largest city in the country, with a future population of about 200,000. Ashqelon is seen as the southernmost holiday resort, and as a tourist and industrial centre on the Coastal Plain. Bet Shemesh serves to illustrate the planning and development of a new immigrant town, of which there are many more all over the country.

JERUSALEM OUTLINE SCHEME

1. BACKGROUND

The War of 1948 severed Jerusalem into two halves and completely altered the status of Jewish Jerusalem. Instead of being a central crossroad, it now lay at the end of the narrow Jerusalem Corridor, which is accessible only from the West. The armistice line runs right through the city, cutting it off from the Old City and from several quarters in the North-East. Although Mount Scopus remained Israel territory, it was disconnected from the rest of the city.

Jerusalem is not an ordinary town, but the capital of the State of Israel, the historic, spiritual and religious centre of the Jewish people throughout the world, the object of religious veneration and pilgrimages and a centre for cultural events and conventions. Accordingly the city plan must fulfil not only the ordinary requirements of any urban settlement but also make provision for the following special needs:

a) The location of the seat of government and administration;

b) The planning of suitable sites for national and government institutions;

c) The provision of local government institutions and cultural and commercial activities commensurate with the status of a capital city;

d) The appropriate display of historic and archaeological sites;

e) The siting of the university campus and other institutions of learning;

f) The preservation of unique quarters and villages;

g) The provision of green open spaces;

h) The co-ordination of all plans with the Old City and the surrounding areas in the hope that peaceful relations with the neighbouring countries will one day be resumed.

In working out a solution to all these problems, the following factors had to be borne in mind:

a) The special geographic status of the city, caused by the artificial state boundaries which cut it in two;

b) The specific topography of the city;

66 c) The needs of the existing and of the expected population particularly as regards sources of employment;

d) The role of Jerusalem as a tourist centre.

The topography of Jerusalem is of special significance and affects the entire character of the city. Jerusalem has clearly demarcated natural boundaries: the Valley of Refaim in the South, Nahal Soreq in the North and West, and the Ben Hinnom Valley in the East. There is practically no flat ground within the entire confines of the city, which is made up exclusively of valleys and hills, at a maximum height of 2,500 feet (800 m.). In accordance with the topographical structure, the mountains and mountain slopes were selected for building purposes while the valleys were left as open spaces. The built-up hills constitute compact neighbourhood units and lend Jerusalem its special character. The green spaces and parks serve as the lungs of the city while the open valleys help to expand the view.

2. The Outline Scheme

The Outline Scheme had to take into account previous developments as well as the special topography of the city. Close to 4,200 acres (17,000 dunams) were allotted for residential purposes. In the Eastern part of the city, the quarters lie close together and have a higher building density; about 75% of the inhabitants live in that part of Jerusalem. It is intended that in future the population should be more equally distributed. The Western part of the city consists of a number of hills and each is planned as a compact neighbourhood unit. The intermediate space, consisting of steep slopes and valleys, is planned as green open space for afforestation and nature reserves to serve the neighbouring quarters. Each neighbourhood unit is to have a cultural, commercial and educational centre, a special zone for artisans and craftsmen and the most essential services. Thus it may develop its own social, cultural and economic life. This ring of built-up hills with open spaces between them gives the city its special character.

Jerusalem has a number of old quarters which no longer respond to present-day demands, as regards density of population and sanitary conditions, and have therefore to be reconstructed. Such reconstruction is to be effected on the basis of detailed plans and the more solid and stable buildings or buildings of historic or architectural significance will be preserved. Holy places and archaeological sites are given special care and attention, as are certain typical old quarters e.g. Shaare Hessed, Mea Sheärim, Zikhron Moshe, parts of the Bukharian Quarter and some villages which have been incorporated into the city.

The main civic, cultural and administrative centre of Jerusalem has been located in Romema, around the National Convention Centre. Romema was chosen mainly because of its high altitude, overlooking the entire vicinity. It is near the main roads leading to the Old City in the East and the rest of the city in the West. Various municipal events can easily be held here in view of the closeness of the Convention Centre. The Romema Quarter is only partly developed and much space is still available for well laid out development, including ample parking space. This Quarter moreover, lies right at the entrance to the city, so that its special character becomes immediately apparent to the incoming visitor. The commercial centre has been extended as far as the entrance square and the seat of government. It has been proposed that only public buildings should be erected round this square thus marking its special importance.

The main stress has been placed on the seat of government and the university campus. The government centre has been located on a hill overlooking the surrounding area South of and adjacent to the main town centre. It will include all government institutions, the Knesset (the Israel Parliament), a large parade ground and office buildings, of which three have already been erected. It is surrounded by a green belt in the valleys. The detailed plan has been worked out by the Planning Department. The University has been built on Giv'at Ram, adjacent to the government hill. The University plan was worked out by a team of architects and the University buildings and the Jewish National and University Library are surrounded by ample grasslands and parks. The service roads enter the University at the back. The Neve Shaanan hill, South of the government hill, is to be the site of various museums. Adjacent to it are the green spaces of the Valley of the Cross with its Monastery.

As the capital of the country and as the possessor of many historic and archaeological treasures, it is important that Jerusalem should have sufficient open space. This requirement is also dictated by the city's topography. No buildings are to be erected on the steeper slopes and in the valleys. Apart from providing entertainment and recreation, the open spaces will form a suitable setting for the seat of government, the University, the Herzl Tomb, the Memorial to the Victims of the Nazi Holocaust (Yad Va-Shem), the Hadassah Hospital near En Kerem and other public places. All wadis, valleys and rifts lying between the hills on which the city is built are to form a network of gardens, parks and fields. Mount Herzl is to form the focal point of this green belt, which will join up with the national park in the Mountains of Judea. Although this park area contains vestiges of ancient forests, at present most of it lies bare, awaiting future afforestation and cultivation. The valleys further serve as openings for panoramic viewpoints. In several places, e.g. near the Monastery of the Cross, at San Simon, in the vicinity of En Kerem, on the Hill of Miss Carrie, and in Nicopherya near the railway lines — usually in the vicinity of historic or holy places of interest to tourists — exist interesting olive groves which are to be carefully preserved.

View of Jerusalem and Mount Zion

Around the Rose Garden and Omariyya, an area has been reserved for embassies and villas. The plan also indicates a number of areas which for some time to come will be used for farming. As the population grows, these areas will become very valuable for recreation and amusement purposes. Care will be taken to put them at the disposal of the public when their leases terminate.

The rate of industrial employment in Jerusalem is lower than in Haifa or Tel Aviv whereas the percentage of persons employed in administration and in cultural and religious institutions is higher in Jerusalem than elsewhere. Because of the non-availability of local raw materials and the transportation difficulties involved, industry is limited to the manufacture of light articles requiring a high degree of skill in their production. Industry of this sort also requires a smaller area per person. In the Outline Scheme, sites for industry and trade have been assigned to the city as a whole as well as to the different neighbourhoods. The industrial areas are to be located mostly in the North of the city, at Romema, Giv'at Shaul and Sanhedriya. An additional industrial area has recently been sited in the South of the city. The planners estimate that the existing and projected industrial zones, covering about 450 acres (1,800 dunams), will be sufficient for the needs of the future population.

Stone buildings are characteristic of Jerusalem. This form of building, in addition to its beauty, enhances stability and saves maintenance costs. The relevant bye-law, requiring all structures to be faced with natural stone, should be kept in force, especially in those areas which are already built in this fashion. However, owing to the high cost involved and in view of public housing needs, the zones to which this regulation applies have been reduced. A plan, corresponding to the present Outline Scheme, has been drawn up in which the city is divided into building zones of natural stone, artificial stone, and concrete with stucco finish.

The inter-urban roads have been marked in accordance with the Regional Plan. The Security Road, i.e. the entrance to the city via Ramat Raziël, is to pass behind Mount Herzl, with a branch road from Yefe Nof to Rehavya. Main traffic arteries between the different quarters and the main roads of the various quarters are also shown on the plan. A connection between the South-Eastern and Western quarters and additional roads from the South of the city to the North, which will by-pass the existing town centre, have been planned. Ben Zvi Avenue will link the South of the city with the North. Agrippas Road has been planned to run parallel to Yafo Road to connect with King George Avenue to improve urban communications. A second parallel route to Yafo Road will run between Ben Zvi Avenue and Princess Mary Avenue, i.e. Bezalel Road and its continuation, Hillel Road. The Plan also includes a site for a central bus station and makes provision for parking spaces in all parts of the city.

Model of the Government Building and the Hebrew University Campus in Jerusalem

Reprinted from *Landscape Architecture,* **50**(2), 76–80 (1959–1960)

MAN VS. GRAVITY

THE CONTINUED BATTLE OVER STEEP LANDSCAPES

Perched on the hillsides of the world, standing at the brink of steep landscapes, wrestling with the sheer inertia of stubborn rock and earth, man has enlisted the world's mightiest machinery in his daily compromise with gravity. The results are among the most highly visible of his accomplishments—and defeats. Here are seven case histories: the work of designers seeking new and more livable relationships between man and the steep landscapes which he seeks to re-shape for his profit and use.

MAKING UP FOR 200-YEAR LOSS IN PITTSBURGH

By WILLIAM GRANT SWAIN

Of Griswold, Winters and Swain, Landscape Architects and Site Planners, Pittsburgh, Pennsylvania

TIME and man have been unkind to the steep hillsides of Pittsburgh. Instead of aging gracefully, the city shows the deep wrinkles and scars of a two-century "binge," a masquerade whose theme has been "Progress." Those many years have brought us, now, to a sprawling metropolitan area of 35,460.70 acres that had its beginning as a small settlement at the edge of a narrow flood plain, where the Allegheny and Monongahela rivers joined to form the Ohio. It might have grown something like this.

The rich, bottom-land gardens that supplied the outpost Fort Pitt gradually gave way to the rutted streets of a settlement village, and it was not long until the open farms of Grant's Hill, to the east of the Point, became less of a frontier and more of a city. Beyond, up the comparatively gentle slopes down which wound the early roads, linking Philadelphia with our young nation's "Gateway to the West," was more buildable land. It, too, soon was dotted with houses and shops. North of the Point, across the Allegheny, was another and larger plain providing more space for early industry and for the homes of the workers who arrived at unparalleled rates. The Fort had long since disappeared along with the dangers and uncertainties that characterized the mid-eighteenth century. By 1800 the mold had been formed.

Mills had sprung up along the narrow banks of the rivers. Keelboats reigned supreme, carrying goods which began to flow downstream to new frontiers, and bringing back the Indian corn, the hides, and the tales that fed Pittsburgh's expansion. Before long, the Portage Railroad carried the canal boats across the western range of the Alleghenies, thus providing the inexpensive link with the East that assured the city's future. The valley and the rolling hills were soon saturated.

Pathways, perches, pitiful arteries

Next, in the outward push, the tributary valleys, narrow and dark with the first wisps of smoke, became as densely settled as the Point. The hilltops, no matter how remote, supported the homes of those citizens who were motivated to escape the confinement of an exploding metropolis. Movement about the city was quite difficult and circuitous, for in between the valleys and the peaks were the precipitous slopes that characterize this part of western Pennsylvania. Steep paths were started by the hardy, and they grew in proportion to the traffic. Houses were perched along these routes with little concern but for the day ground was broken. The "arteries" became pitifully inadequate.

Although there is a degree of conjecture in the foregoing account, it offers a likely view of what has happened here and of a pattern that may have been repeated elsewhere.

In 1910, observing the results of a century and a half of such growth, the Pittsburgh Civic Commission, with commendable foresight, recognized the economic liability of congestion and the perils of further uncontrolled expansion. The Commission retained Frederick Law Olmsted to make a study of the main thoroughfares and the downtown district. As predicted by a newspaper reporter of the day, the Olmsted report has become a guide for planners throughout the United States.

> Not only Pittsburgh but the other municipalities of America owe a debt of thanks to Mr. Olmsted and to the Pittsburgh Civic Commission.*

Olmsted's vision of 1910

The investigations led to many related solutions for

**The Outlook*, Feb. 25, 1911.

problems arising out of the topography. The Olmsted report stated:

> No city of equal size in America, or perhaps in the world, is compelled to adapt its growth to such a difficult complication of high ridges, deep valleys, and precipitous slopes, as Pittsburgh.*
>
> . . . .
>
> Generally speaking, the slopes are of little value for business purposes and are not well adapted to residential use, the cost of development being excessive in proportion to the location value of the improved property. . . . As a rule these "unavailable areas" are unoccupied and unproductive, and are mainly held by owners not resident in the locality, whose sole interest in them is in the hope—sometimes a forlorn hope—of an ultimate speculative profit. In far too many cases they . . . [contribute] to the slatternly conditions in the midst of which so many of Pittsburgh's working people . . . are compelled to live.†
>
> . . . .
>
> These steeper and more irregular pieces will be of greater use to the public than they could be to private occupants.‡

In the half century since 1910, despite Olmsted's recommendations, the momentum of the first one hundred and fifty years has been difficult to overcome. Today, the task of conservation is the key to Pittsburgh's renaissance.

Needed: public control of steep slopes

Many of the hillsides singled out by the report have suffered further desecration; some of the speculators' hopes must not have been so forlorn, after all. Recently, studies have been made by the office of Griswold, Winters

* *Pittsburgh, Main Thoroughfare and the Downtown District*, 1910, by F. L. Olmsted. Part III, p. 93.

† *Ibid.*, Part IV, p. 109.

‡ *Ibid.*, Part IV, p. 111.

and Swain, and, in general, our findings paralleled the earlier work. We echo the need for public control of steep slopes which comprise about thirty per cent of the city's area. We have recommended revision and reinforcement of building codes to require proper drainage, retaining walls, adequate minimum side distances, and setbacks. A large part of these slopes is unbuildable, except at great expense; and this fact, coupled with enforced codes, will deter development.

There still exists, however, a strong need for public acquisition of a large part of the slopes which now support grossly inadequate housing. When such properties become tax delinquent, they should be taken by the City and adapted to public use. The restoration of the natural forests is the best such "use" we can propose; furthermore, it is the one offering that has the best chance of being realized. Not long ago, a large section of hillside was turned over to the City by the Pennsylvania Railroad, and we are looking forward to the day when neighboring plots will be acquired, affording an unbroken backdrop of green hillside, 400 feet high, stretching a distance of eight miles, across the Monongahela River from the central part of the city.

In some locations, the steep landscape can be used for multiple housing units, wherein the individual plots would be large enough to accommodate the necessary grading. Codes should require that any such development include planting, designed to stabilize as well as beautify. Contiguous, low-gradient boulevards, serving the housing units and proceeding on to hilltop communities, would pass through park-like surroundings with magnificent, sweeping vistas over the city.

So close to downtown, yet . . .

Perhaps the greatest, yet unrealized potential inherent in the hills is their unique relation to the downtown area. In all except a relatively few isolated spots, the view is blocked by buildings on the crest. The public is denied enjoyment of a spectacular urban landscape. Upon the same basis as for the slopes, we propose the ultimate removal of private buildings and the prohibition of new construction except that of essentially public character, such as restaurants. There are two encouraging results of this recommendation. The City Council has acquired two pieces of property to augment acreage already owned at the site of an overlook that can be described only in superlatives. The first project at Rue Grande Vue is in the planning stage, and construction is scheduled for 1960. Ultimate plans call for ample parking and bus access.

Neighborhood "overlook" plan

The second encouragement has come in the form of a request from the City for our specific selection of property, in a new plan of lots, to serve as a neighborhood overlook. There are many secondary, yet equally exciting, views in directions other than toward the Golden Triangle, and we have located small platforms, to be erected as part of the program of the Department of Parks and Recreation, scattered throughout the city.

No American city claims a more spectacular view than the one from Grandview Avenue.

From Rue Grande Vue the prospect of Pittsburgh is unrivaled.

Photograph by Newman Schmidt

Generally, they are to be only one lot wide, accommodating one or two automobiles, designed for the enjoyment of people living within walking distance and not necessarily for the community as a whole. In a number of locations they occur at the top of the monumental stairs that dot the city—tiny resting places suspended over the slopes.

Connecting these panoramic drives and overlooks, we have proposed a "Scenic Belt." Pittsburgh is circled by belt routes, at intervals averaging two or three miles apart, which permit traffic to by-pass the central congestion. The route we have selected does not depend upon these or other traffic arteries in taking people from one scenic point to another. The tour offers many startling surprises which do not seem to be dimmed by repetition. We were impressed, during our extensive survey trips, by the proximity of sections of town which, by ordinary connections, seem quite remote from each other. This is, truly, a recreational benefit for Sunday drivers that our unique topography affords. For the most part, the "Scenic Belt" requires only minimum improvement of existing rights of way, a few short additions, and the erection of sign posts. Quite a large segment of the belt passes through rural areas, right in the heart of the city, often just over the hill from our most densely populated sections. Exploring is always fun—when you know you can find your way back home!

No estimate has been made of the cost of the over-all program. But, it is significant that a large number of the hillside ideas are concerned with the simple conversion of liabilities to assets, not calling for great expenditures, nor requiring reduction of revenues. Since the study might be characterized by the words *special interest* (it was combined with a study of the recreational potential

Plan and perspective of suggested neighborhood overlook platform

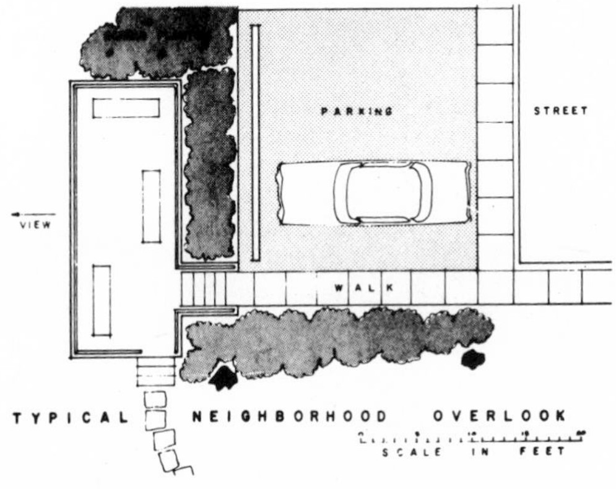

of the three rivers), it rests with planners to weigh and judge its relative merits when portions of the city are scheduled for redevelopment. The first two encouragements breed others, and we are hopeful of seeing the implementation of many of the proposals. It seems to us that similar opportunities might exist in other cities having steep landscapes, to the extent that their leaders may say, along with ours:

> We will not, again, waste time in neglect of a great natural gift—the hills that enhance our metropolitan centers, our neighborhoods, our industry, and the lives of our citizens.

30

Reprinted from *Soviet Geography*, **3**(3), 35–43 (1960)

SATELLITE CITIES AND TOWNS OF MOSCOW

G. Ye. Mishchenko

(From the volume of articles Goroda-sputniki (Satellite Cities), pp. 40-49)

(Abstract: The suburban area of Moscow consists of a green belt and an outer suburban zone, containing both satellites of Moscow and "independent" urban agglomerations without direct links to the capital. The problem of limiting the population growth of Moscow should be solved by promoting the expansion of existing satellite places and by limited construction of new satellite cities. Care should be taken not to urbanize the green belt, set aside for recreation, or to reduce the forest area in the outer suburban zone.)

Among Soviet cities Moscow has the largest suburban area with a dense network of functionally diversified populated places linked with the central city. Many of them are its satellites.

Moscow's suburban area (outside of the new city limits established in 1960 along the belt highway) can be divided into two zones (see map, p. 36):

(1) a green belt, or inner suburban zone;

(2) an outer, so-called 50-kilometer suburban zone.

Until recently a third zone was distinguished within the Moscow suburban area for purposes of the general plan of reconstruction of Moscow, approved in

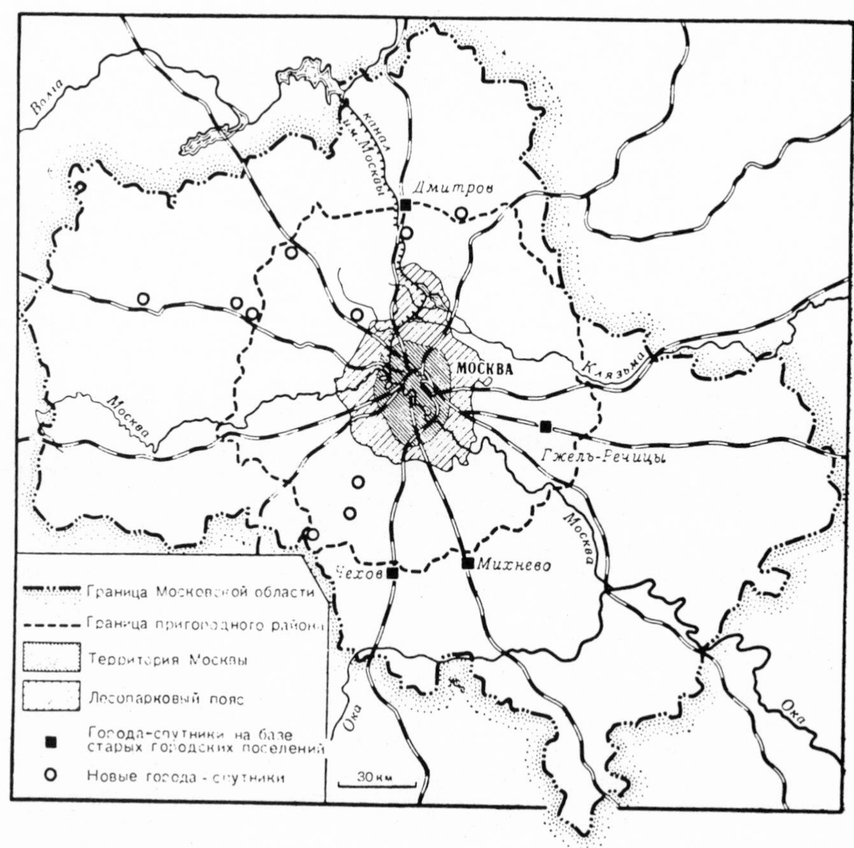

Moscow's Suburban Area and New Satellite Cities

Legend: Boundary of Moscow Oblast
Boundary of the suburban area
Territory of Moscow City (within belt highway limits)
Green belt
Satellite cities developed from former urban places
New satellite cities

1935, which envisaged enlarging the city area by about 34,000 hectares within a radius of 15 to 17 kilometers from the city center. This and other areas situated within the new Moscow belt highway (a total of 52,000 hectares) were included within the city limits by the decree of the Presidium of the Supreme Soviet RSFSR dated August 18, 1960 (see Soviet Geography, December 1960, p. 90, map, pp. 91-92). The annexed area includes five cities (Tushino, Kuntsevo, Perovo, Lyublino and Babushkin), several towns and many villages. Its total population is about 20 per cent of the population of Moscow proper within its old limits, about half being concentrated in the cities. A large part of the residents of this annexed zone work in enterprises and institutions of the capital. At the same time a small number of Muscovites work in enterprises situated within the annexed zone. Under the seven-year plan a large volume of housing construction, cultural services and other projects are to be provided for the zone.

The green belt, about 10 to 12 kilometers wide, has been established as a reservoir of fresh air for Moscow and as a place of recreation for residents of the capital. The area of the green belt is 1,800 square kilometers. Its territory includes nine cities (Mytishchi, Balashikha, Reutov, Lyubertsy, Lytkarino, Odintsovo, Krasnogorsk, Khimki and Dolgoprudnyy), many towns and summer resorts and more than 600 villages. Its population (including rural areas) is more than 20 per cent of that of Moscow (within its 1959 city limits). About 70 per cent of the green-belt population lives in cities and about half of its urban working population is employed in the capital. (Editor's note, S. G.: The green belt, initially placed under the jurisdiction of Moscow City by the August 1960 decree, was transferred to the jurisdiction of Moscow Oblast in November 1961, except for a few places that contain municipal services and utilities directly connected with Moscow City; see Soviet Geography, January 1962, pp. 72-73.)

The outer suburban zone, with an area of 12,000 square kilometers, is situated beyond the green belt and includes 25 cities (Pushkino, Zagorsk, Shchelkovo, Elektrostal', Noginsk, Zhukovskiy, Podol'sk, Zvenigorod, Dmitrov and others), 36 towns and more than 80 summer resorts. The population is more than 40 per cent of that of Moscow (within its 1959 city limits). A large part of the working population of the cities and towns of this zone is employed in Moscow.

The population density in the green belt is about 520 per square kilometer, in the outer suburbs 170 to 180, and in the rest of Moscow Oblast outside of the suburban zone 50 to 60. The population of the entire suburban area is more than 70 per cent of that of Moscow within its previous (1959) city limits. Three-fourths of the population lives in the eastern half of the suburban area, which also has a substantially higher population density.

The radial-ring pattern characteristic of the layout of Moscow has also developed historically in the capital's suburban area and is continuing to predominate there. The radial structure has been determined by old roads leading from Moscow toward Leningrad, Ryazan', Gor'kiy and other cities. Railroads also run in these directions. The ring structure has been determined by roads linking places within the suburban area. The ring connections were very faintly expressed in the past and began to develop only in recent years.

The radial-ring structure of the suburban area, with sharp predominance of the radial pattern, has led to the location of populated places chiefly along the radial routes and their concentration near Moscow. This has produced along several radii a continuous chain of populated places, extending for 50 to 70 kilometers from the center of Moscow, as far as Ramenskoye along the Ryazan' railroad, and Zagorsk along the Yaroslavl' railroad. Because of this pattern, the population density ranges from 300 to 1500 per square kilometer in the green belt and from 20 to 340 in the outer suburban zone. The higher figures apply to areas along the radial transportation routes, and the lower figures to areas between transport lines.

The cities and towns of the suburban area are generally small. There is only one city with a population of more than 100,000 -- Podol'sk. Most of the urban places range from 10,000 to 100,000.

However, large clusters of populated places occur in some parts of the area. For example, the virtual merger of the cities of Mytishchi, Kaliningrad, Pushkino and several towns along the Yaroslavl' railroad has produced a large agglomeration (with a population of more than 200,000) showing evidence of further growth. Such an agglomeration has also been formed along the Ryazan' railroad (Lyubertsy, Zhukovskiy, Ramenskoye and several towns). A large cluster of populated places exists in the eastern part of the suburban area as a result of the virtual merger of the cities and towns of Balashikha, Saltykovka, Kuchino, Reutov, Zheleznodorozhnyy and others.

Cities and towns of Moscow's suburban area have developed rapidly in Soviet times. New cities and towns have arisen, such as Elektrostal', Khimki and Krasnogorsk, and part of the population employed in Moscow has settled in the suburban area for lack of housing in the capital.

Cities and towns of the suburban area can be divided into five categories in terms of the intensity and character of their ties with Moscow:

1. Cities and towns, a large part of whose population is employed in Moscow. These include mainly places situated close to Moscow and on convenient transportation lines (Odintsovo, Balashikha, Pushkino and others). The population that works in Moscow but lives in the suburban area is about 18 per cent of that of the capital (within its 1959 limits).

2. Populated places adjoining enterprises that provide municipal services for Moscow, such as the towns of the Rublevo, Vostochnyy, Cherepkovo and Severnyy water-supply stations, towns adjoining sewage-disposal plants, building-material enterprises and so forth. These populated places though situated at some distance from Moscow, come under the jurisdiction of the Moscow City Soviet and their population is included in that of Moscow.

3. Cities and towns containing enterprises and institutions that are closely linked with Moscow by supplementing or serving industrial enterprises, research institutions and experimental stations in the capital.

4. Cities and towns whose population is employed in enterprises and institutions that have no direct ties with Moscow's city-forming functions but serve the economic needs of the entire country (Elektrostal', Noginsk and so forth). The

population of this type of city is linked with Moscow only insofar as cultural services are concerned.

5. Summer resorts in which 300,000 to 400,000 residents of Moscow spend their summer. Many of these towns have become places of permanent residence for people who are working in Moscow or in the suburbs.

Among the populated places of the suburban area, especially the large ones, there are many cities and towns that perform various functions and are "mixed" in terms of the character and intensity of their ties with Moscow.

Which of these cities and towns can be regarded as satellites of Moscow? This question, as we will see later, is not only of theoretical importance, but of great practical significance in solving the problem of settlement within the Moscow agglomeration.

The network of populated places becomes more closely knit and the density of population sharply increases as one approaches Moscow. The highest concentration of population is found along the lines of transportation within a distance of 50 to 70 kilometers from the central city. This gives rise to a radial pattern of settlement. It shows that the capital exerts considerable influence on the formation of surrounding populated places, many of which owe their origins and development to Moscow and have permanent links with it.

However, not all populated places of Moscow's suburban area are satellites. Whether a given city or town should be classed as a satellite depends both on its functional ties with Moscow and on its distance from Moscow.

By functional ties we mean organic, stable ties, i.e. ties whose interruption would render the life and activities of the given city abnormal. These ties may lie in the fields of (a) production, (b) workers' residence, (c) recreation, and (d) cultural services and municipal facilities.

Cultural-service ties are the most common between suburban cities and towns of the suburban area and Moscow. The residents of nearly all these places use the cultural institutions and the shopping facilities of Moscow to a greater or lesser extent. Moreover, the cultural influence of Moscow extends far beyond the suburban area or even the oblast. Cultural-service ties alone therefore do not justify classing a populated place as a Moscow satellite.

Among the five categories listed above, we can regard as "complete satellites" of Moscow the cities and towns of Groups 2 and 3 having a functionally integrated structure (production, housing, services, recreation) and organic production ties with Moscow. Cities and towns of Group 1 are essentially "dormitory" suburbs.

Cities and towns of Group 4 cannot be regarded as satellites of Moscow. From among Groups 1, 2 and 3 we can classify as Moscow satellites those places in which functional ties with Moscow account for at least 50 per cent of the total volume of productive functions of the given city or town.

The distance between the given populated place and Moscow is also of great importance.

Cities and towns that have merged with Moscow (Tushino, Perovo, Kuntsevo, Babushkin, Lyublino, Lenino and others) cannot be classified as satellites or "dormitory" suburbs because they are essentially part of the capital and, under the new administrative division of Moscow, are part of the city's boroughs. It would seem that populated places can be regarded as sufficiently "independent" formations only at a distance of more than 8 to 10 kilometers from the Moscow city limits.

The maximum distance of a "dormitory" city or town from Moscow whould be set at the equivalent of 50-to-55-minute commuting, corresponding to about 20 or 30 kilometers of travel. The maximum distance for satellite cities and towns should be set at the equivalent of 70-to-80-minute commuting, corresponding to about 50 to 80 kilometers, and in exceptional cases to 100 to 120 kilometers.

The problem of limiting the growth of large cities, which is of concern to city planners of the entire world, is especially acute in the Soviet Union in the case of Moscow.

Under the general plan of 1935 the future population of Moscow was estimated at 5 million compared with 3.66 million in 1935. This figure applied to the entire population employed in Moscow enterprises and institutions and living in the city. In order to limit population growth, planners prohibited the construction of new industrial enterprises in Moscow, except for those serving the population and municipal utilities. Subsequently, the prohibition was extended to the 50-kilometer suburban zone. The decision was based on the inadvisability of letting gigantic cities form and on the need for more uniform distribution of productive forces.

However, in the 25 years since 1935 the urbanizing basis of Moscow and its suburban area has continued to expand rapidly as a result of the development of industry and educational and research institutions. This has been accompanied by population growth, through both natural increase and in-migration from other regions.

According to the 1959 census, the population of Moscow was more than 5 million within its city limits (Narodnoye khozyaystvo SSSR v 1959 godu (The National Economy of the USSR in 1959), statistical yearbook, Moscow, 1960), and including populated places in the area annexed in 1960, the population was more than 6 million (not counting the green belt). Furthermore, as was noted above, many people working in Moscow live in the suburban area. The population of that area has also increased considerably. Natural increase alone is expected to raise its population 20 per cent by 1975-80.

It must be assumed that part of the population of the Moscow agglomeration will move to the eastern regions of the USSR in accordance with the long-range plan of location of productive forces. However, this will solve only part of the problem, and not even the most important part. The problem of settlement in the Moscow agglomeration will remain acute and extremely complex.

In order to make possible the further reconstruction and expansion of Moscow and assure it the world's highest level of working, living and recreation conditions, the party and government decided to extend the city limits to the belt highway under construction (thus expanding the city area to 875 square kilometers). At the same time the government ordered drafting of a general plan of reconstruction and development of Moscow with a new terminal date (1980) and of regional plans for Moscow and Moscow Oblast.

There are two ways of solving the problem of settlement in the Moscow agglomeration:

1. To settle all those working in Moscow in the city itself by further expanding the city area. On the basis of established housing density standards for residential buildings of four to five stories and the planned minimum floor space of 15 square meters per person, it would take the entire (or almost the entire) area of 875 square kilometers provided for the city's expansion to accommodate just the population of more than 5 million. To accommodate the future population of the city (envisaging the natural increase expected by 1975-80), the city area would have to be expanded by 350 to 400 square kilometers.

2. To limit the population of Moscow to about 5 million and settle the remaining population in satellite cities and in part in places of the "dormitory" type.

The second alternative impresses us as the correct one. Further concentration of population in Moscow itself and expansion of its city limits would transform Moscow into a gigantic city with all the shortcomings inherent in such cities. It would also be undesirable to extend the city's built-up area beyond the belt highway, which serves as a typical suburban superhighway.

Furthermore, it would be incorrect to build up an additional area of 350 to 400 square kilometers in the green belt because that zone was designed for recreation rather than urbanization. Therefore the green belt should be gradually freed of all unimportant structures, small enterprises and warehouses, and be used basically for wooded parks, recreation areas, boarding homes and beaches. The inclusion of the reservoirs of the Moscow Canal system in the green belt provides additional opportunities for mass recreation facilities on water. Artificial lakes are to be created in other parts of the green belt, particularly in the south and southwest sectors, which are devoid of natural water bodies.

In view of the fact that a large part of the people employed in Moscow are now living in the suburban area and since these people should not be resettled in Moscow, there is a need for rebuilding and, in some cases, expanding existing populated places in which these people reside, and to transform them in part or entirely into satellite cities of the "dormitory" type. This applies especially to populated places adjoining the Ryazan', Yaroslavl' and Kursk railroads because expansion of these places would not require the cutting of additional forest area. However, excessive growth of such places should be avoided because, in principle, they do not represent a desirable form of settlement.

With the growth of existing satellites, there arises the need for moving out of Moscow individual departments of enterprises serving the city (such as the central foundry industry, local industry, building industry) as well as pilot plants and research institutions. These enterprises and institutions should be moved not too far from Moscow because they are closely linked to enterprises and institutions in the capital, but at the same time they sould not be left in the city itself. They would serve as an urbanizing basis for new satellite cities, most of whose population would be locally employed. Moscow's new satellite city near Kryukovo is being built on the basis of such assumptions.

The specialization of agriculture in the Moscow suburban area, with its emphasis on vegetable and fruit gardening and the creation of large state farms, requires the formation of large agricultural settlements approaching the urban type. These places would also be satellites of Moscow.

There is a danger that the growth of satellite cities in the Moscow suburban zone will lead to a reduction of the forest area and open spaces and to excessive concentration of populated places. This is a serious threat and it should be borne in mind in any decisions relating to the location of satellite cities.

However, it seems to us that it is quite possible to solve the problem of satellite city growth without causing damage to the natural landscape of the suburban area. This requires:

1. The location of new satellite cities and the expansion of existing cities at a considerable distance from Moscow (at least 50 kilometers), thus saving the most precious forest areas for recreation purposes. This rule should apply especially to the western suburban area, whence the prevailing westerly winds bring fresh air to Moscow.

2. The building of new satellite cities should be limited as much as possible and greater emphasis should be given to the reconstruction, expansion and urban improvement of existing cities and towns.

In addition there must be a prohibition on further construction and expansion in the suburban area of independent urban places that are not satellites of Moscow (Group 4).

In locating satellite cities and especially cities and towns of the "dormitory" type, proper attention must be given to the provision of reliable and convenient transportation routes. It is evident that part of the population (individual family members) of even the "complete satellites" will be employed in Moscow. Residential areas for persons employed in Moscow should therefore be linked with the capital by above-ground trains and other surface lines, and satellite cities on electric suburban railroads and major automobile routes leading to Moscow.

The average population of satellite cities will range between 60,000 and 100,000. Further study of the problem of settlement in the Moscow suburban zone will provide a firmer basis for the optimal size of satellite cities. It may prove necessary to increase the estimated size of such cities.

The general plan of Moscow for the next twenty years should cover the city proper, the green belt and the outer suburban zone. All basic city-planning problems should be solved for that area: settlement patterns, architectural and planning organization, transportation, recreation and planting of greenery, engineering works, etc. The long-range boundaries of the suburban zone should also be defined.

31

Reprinted from *Landscape Architecture,* **50**(1), 8–13 (1959)

LANDSCAPE: A VANISHING RESOURCE

THE SHATTERED MYTH: "THERE'LL ALWAYS BE ENOUGH LAND"

This is a radical, if not obnoxious, idea: that America's landscape, the loadstone of the pioneer, has its limits—some of which already have been reached. Yet these papers, presented at the recent ASLA Annual Meeting in Chicago, not only measure the nature of the crisis but offer solutions for the protection and improvement of that vanishing resource, the American landscape.

OPEN SPACE, NOW OR NEVER

By WILLIAM H. WHYTE, JR.
Assistant Managing Editor, *Fortune*

I SHOULD LIKE to talk about one tool for saving open space. I do so not because I think that it alone can do the job. It can't; for it is only one of many tools. But it offers, I submit, the sharpest cutting-edge for getting action now.

Some of my planner friends tell me that this is wrong, that it is a piecemeal approach to a very complex problem; that we should think not so much of specific tools, but of an orderly, comprehensive, master-planning approach for all of our metropolitan regions. They are for action, but they say we need much more study and research.

Well, they've been saying that for over ten years, and nothing has happened. Nothing has happened because the citizen has not been shown a practical way of halting sprawl—and it is not until he sees one that he will really become involved. He doesn't have to be sold on the idea that the desecration of the countryside is terrible. The trouble is that he is afraid the means would have to be socialistic, and he is apt to have a sneaking feeling that the mess is somehow the price of progress, and that, after all, people have to live somewhere. Planners can show him that there *is* a practical way; but they are not doing so, for many of them do not themselves know, and they are displaying little initiative in trying to find out. Who is going to fill the vacuum of leadership?

Opportunity: the easement principle

I would submit that there is a great, and demanding, opportunity for the landscape architects. If I am correct, there is no group that has applied itself more to the hard task of hammering out ways and means; the report* on open-space tools that Charles Eliot and his colleagues drafted for the Society last year is, to my way of thinking, perhaps the most valuable single document on open space that has been issued in years.

Because of this report, much of what I have to say this afternoon could be redundant. But it frees me from the necessity of talking about such important tools as severance tax, subdivision control, sale and leaseback, and the like. What I want to do is to expand on one of the tools mentioned—the use of the easement principle for the public purchase of development rights. Over the last two years I've had an opportunity to talk with

The author graduated from Princeton University with the degree of B.A. *cum laude* in 1939, and became a writer on the staff of *Fortune* in 1951. He was recipient of the Benjamin Franklin magazine writing award in 1953, and the Liberty and Justice Book award of the American Library Association in 1957.

*"Preservation of Open Spaces," in LANDSCAPE ARCHITECTURE for Jan. 1958, pp. 82-89.

many groups about it in different communities over the country; to explore objections to the idea; to try to find out what kind of people most want to support it, or fight it.

What I found out has led me to submit several propositions. Before going on, let me state them briefly:

1) The first crucial efforts for open-space conservation are not going to be achieved by metropolitan agencies. Maybe they should be—but that is another matter.

2) Open space is going to be secured where open space is—out in the counties, on the edge of suburbia.

3) The counties may dislike the city, but they look on the state as an ally, and this is a great advantage in gaining the necessary legislation.

4) The key people are the people who own the land.

5) For their own self-interest, they are far more ready for action than many realize.

6) The gentry have a strong bias for the natural landscape versus "manicured" parks; and too many park officials, thinking only of conventional, outright acquisition, are missing a great opportunity to exploit this bias.

7) The biggest obstacle to a program which will work is a reliance on the police power, and serious confusion as to the distinction between it and the power of eminent domain.

This leads to the final, all-important question:

> In conserving open space, are we primarily trying to prevent something harmful from happening—or are we trying to secure a benefit?

This is no haggling over terms. Open space must be viewed as a *benefit*, for *all* tax and legal questions come back to this concept.

Chopped-up suburbia

Let's first sketch briefly a not-so-hypothetical case and how the easement principle could be applied to it. We shall assume a county on the outer part of a metropolitan area. About a third of it—the part nearest the city—has been pretty well chopped up by scattered subdivisions; actually, only a fraction of the land has been developed, but in such a scattered way that it looks filled up. The middle third of the county, however, has a few years of grace. There are several sizable towns in it, and there is a fair amount of new subdivision right around them. But in the open country there has yet to be much subdivision. It consists mostly of gentleman farms and large estates. The rest of the county beyond consists chiefly of regular farms and several large wooded areas.

We shall also assume that the citizens have had the sense to realize that the developers are beginning to eye this territory. Some of them are against any kind of development, and when they talk of "the new people" their intonation suggests that they wish like the devil they'd stay away. But most of the citizens realize that development is necessary and that the speculative builder is not necessarily a villain. What ruined the built-up part of the county was not the fact of development, but that the pattern of it had been left almost entirely up to the builder; and if the community hadn't decided what growth pattern it wanted, the builder could hardly be expected to tackle the planning job for them.

He was interested in making money. To make money, he looked for cheap land. And so he leapfrogged, leaving behind him a "scatteration" of bits and pieces of open land—and a trail of unrequited cupidities. While the total amount of land actually built on was small, it had been scattered just enough to rob the community of options which it would very much like to have five to ten years from now—for parks, for planned industrial districts, and for just plain breathing space.

Creek valleys to be saved

But there is still time to channel the growth pattern of the rest of the county. As a first priority, the community decided that a main creek valley should be saved. (For the moment let me leave the word *community* unqualified.) It is only about five miles long by a quarter of a mile wide, but it and its tributaries set the dominant character for an area of some fifty square miles. Mainly, the people want to save it because it is beautiful; but for the same reason it is beautiful, it is valuable for other reasons. It is a big enough area to farm economically, and its soil is rich and deep. It is the heart of the area's drainage system; the streams that poke up into the surrounding hills are a magnificent storm-sewer system. Its flood plains act as a huge sponge to temper the flow in rainy weather and to mete it out slowly in dry (a boon downstream communities would be quick to miss). The community wants new developments, too; but by saving this valley, it figures, the kind of developments it will attract will be all the better. So will it be better able to attract the kind of industry it wants, for it knows that plant-location experts are becoming more and more concerned with the kind of environments employees are going to have.

Hedging against the future

The community has looked at the open space, in short, not as a mere buffer, but as functional space—and functional right now. By saving the open space, it also has reserved for itself future choices. If later, for example, it wants to buy part of the valley for a park, it has guaranteed itself that the choice will be there to make. But this is incidental; quite aside from the matter of future uses, watershed benefits of most scenic spaces are quite enough to justify the question of public purpose in any court test.

The community officials go to the landowners, and say something like this: We know you'd like to keep this land open, but we also know that you've got taxes to think about, and we can't ask you to turn down the developer's bid just to make us happy. So we want to offer you something in return. We want to pay you for giving up the right to put up billboards or chop this into a subdivision. You keep title to the land. You continue to enjoy all present and all future reasonable uses of the land; the easement "runs with the land" and applies to any future owners. Subject to that, you can pass it on to your heirs, or sell it to anyone you like.

How much will it cost? Even though condemnation may rarely be used, easements fall under the law of eminent domain, and in gauging costs the usual rule-of-thumb is the difference between what the land would fetch on the market without the easement and what it would fetch with the easement. In an area where the developers are waving $2000 and $3000 bills around, the cost would be too high; in open farm land, however, the difference would be very little.

Giving can be its own reward

In such areas, indeed, it would virtually pay the landowner to *give* an easement:

1) For one thing, he gets the protection on his flank that so many landowners are concerned about; though condemnation should be infrequent, it can be used to secure an easement for a landowner who would like to exploit commercial benefits his neighbors have provided.

2) Often only a part of a man's property would fall in the easement area, and in many such cases the remainder of his property would be made all the more valuable for subsequent development.

3) The landowner is protected from rising assessments based on the subdivision potential (of the property).

But what about our tax base? This question, which occurs so inexorably when anything new is suggested, should be swatted down vigorously. An open tax plan would raise the tax base. In the first place, the owner affected still pays fair taxes. The point is that his land is not being taxed as though it required the services of subdivision land; as a matter of fact, the community will probably net more money from him than from the higher taxes of the subdivision. The existence of an amenity such as a park or an open space, it should be demonstrated to the citizens, almost always raises adjacent land values—a fact of which some of the biggest developers are very cannily aware. One of the great attractions of Park Forest, for example, is that it was backed up against the Cook County Forest Preserves—and the developers' promotion efforts, quite properly, went to some length to drive home the advantages.

While we're on this point, let me interject a note of cautious optimism: I doubt that developers are going to march on state legislatures to demand open-space legislation, but it's quite possible they won't fight it as hard as some expect. Several big developers I've talked to on this matter seem genuinely interested, for they see it would be to their self-interest. The land manual put out by the National Association of Home Builders constantly reiterates the advisability of seeing to it that surrounding land is protected by covenants, zoning, and such; and these offer much less real protection to long-term property values.

Zoning is not enough

I would now like to touch briefly on several other important questions that people raise. Some, of course, cannot satisfactorily be answered until there is more action—the question of the unearned increment, for example, gained by owners next to open spaces; the jurisdictional conflicts; and the like. But there is a considerable body of precedent to guide us. This past year I have been completing a report to try to bring together the pertinent data bearing on the main questions.*

The key question, it seems to me, lies in the distinction between the police power and the power of eminent domain. I am sure you will understand that in the remarks which follow I am not trying to underrate the great role that zoning and the official map have to play. I wish to argue that there is a point beyond which the police power cannot be used, and I think there is an unfortunate tendency among people to overlook this.

Many times I have heard this rebuttal: The easement plan sounds fine, but why go to so much trouble? Why not simply zone such selected areas against development? This doesn't cost the public anything; it doesn't involve a lot of haggling with individual landowners; and it is a tool that people pretty well accept now.

Let's go back to our stream valley a moment, and think of one particular piece of property. The meadows on the lower part of it are a flood plain. Then it begins to roll gently up, with the back part of the property hills of about 200-foot elevation. For the flood plain itself, the police power is eminently advisable. It would be clearly harmful if subdivision were permitted on it,

*This report, to be published by the Urban Land Institute, 1200 18th St., N. W., Washington 6, D. C., toward the end of this year will be available from the Institute at a price to be announced.

and there is no reason why the public should pay a landowner anything for not making people miserable.

To secure the benefits of space

But can we use the police power to tell the landowner there can't be any subdivision on the rest of his property, either? Here we come to the all-important distinction between the police power and the power of eminent domain. What does the public really want in this case—to prevent something harmful, or to secure a benefit? The distinction may seem hazy to some people, but a distinction there is; and it is one the courts are well aware of. What the public really wants in open space is a benefit, and they are too mean to pay for it. The owner is expected to provide it for them, and to pay the whole cost by giving up extra profits he would otherwise enjoy.

A beginning in California zoning

Even where the landowners themselves want open-space zoning, there are several built-in defects. The case of Santa Clara County in California is a case in point. Several years ago, appalled at the way scattered subdivisions were wrecking the rich valley floor for agriculture, the farmers and the County Planning Commission pioneered the idea of "exclusive agricultural zones." After getting enabling legislation from the state, they set up several zones forbidden to developers—and to the cities and towns which had been annexing farms so vigorously. For good measure, county planner Karl Belser got several golf clubs and a private airport under the protection of exclusive agricultural zoning, also. "The uses," he said, with only a flicker of a smile, "are not incompatible with agriculture."

The farmers are glad they've done it—there wouldn't be much farm land left if they hadn't—but they now feel that zoning is not enough. As surrounding land prices have soared—up to some $4000-$5000 an acre—the temptation to sell out can become very strong, and it's not too hard to get a farm de-zoned. Belser and the farmers have decided to pursue the easement principle, and such a program has been sketched in the new general plan for the county.

Golf clubs versus the tax bludgeon

As many farmers are aware, the most important defect in zoning is that it gives no real protection from rising assessments. For a preview of things to come, consider the sad plight of the golf clubs of San Mateo County, the great bedroom community south of San Francisco. Like most golf clubs, those of San Mateo County have been hit by rising taxes, but San Mateo's are unique in that they have banded together in common cause and have gone to the state legislature for help.

Several years ago one of the clubs sold a small portion of its land for a rather handsome price. The tax assessor promptly raised the assessment on the rest of the club's acreage; and on the general principle that the other eight clubs had been getting away with murder, too, he raised their assessments to the value of the surrounding land. "But we don't want to sell out to developers," the golf clubs complained. "That's what you say," the assessor responded, "but you *could* sell out, and I'm supposed to tax land at its fair market value." A little later, up went the taxes another notch.

Mindful of Santa Clara's agricultural zoning, the golf clubs had an idea. They would get themselves set up as "exclusive recreational zones"; and to put teeth in it, they went to the state legislature and got a bill which directed assessors to tax such land only on the basis of its present use.

That's all very well, said the San Mateo assessor, but he took his orders from the constitution, which told him to tax the land at fair market value; and since zoning could be easily changed, an assessment of fair market value had to reflect the fact. The golf clubs wanted it both ways, he suggested—to get low taxes—but keep the chance to sell out and make a killing. He has a point.

In less built-up areas, assessors are likely to be much more lenient, but as the population of areas mounts and the pressures for more tax money grow insistent, many a low-tax idyll is going to be shattered.

A severance tax plan would have advantages. So long as the land remained open, it would be taxed at the assessed value of open land; if it were subsequently developed, then the owner would have to pay, retroactively, the difference between the low assessment and a higher one, and this could have a strong deterrent effect.

Even without such a plan, however, an easement provides constitutional protection against unfair taxes. The "fair market value" of such land is its value as open land, and its worth cannot be based on the going price of subdivision land for the simple fact that it can't be subdivided. There must, of course, be a public benefit involved, and there can't be any easement unless a public agency is willing to negotiate it. In the case of golf clubs, for example, there is a clear benefit to the whole community in the continued existence of such open spaces.

A "tax dodge for the rich"?

Is there not a danger that the easement device may be tagged as a tax dodge for the rich? Again, we must come back to the crucial importance of establishing a benefit. About the time an open space is on the verge of being ruined—whether by a highway, a development, or whatever—people become suddenly aware that there is a benefit. At this very moment, undoubtedly, there are scores of protest meetings over outrages about to be committed—and if they run true to form, nine out of ten will be futile.

The trick is to demonstrate the benefit before it is threatened. One way might be to threaten it, and a little showmanship in this regard wouldn't hurt.

Semantics: "conservation easement"

While we're on the subject of public relations, let me note briefly the question of nomenclature. Charles Eliot has warned that the term "development rights" is open to misinterpretation, and the more I have talked to groups the more I think he is right. The term conveys the idea that the public agency acquires the right to subdivide the property, and some planners have the mistaken idea that the basic plan is to use the rights to stage the timing and exact location of development—somewhat as the British attempted to do. This is not the case. The idea is simply to acquire the rights to keep the land open. "Development rights," furthermore, also can convey a negative stance; it emphasizes what is not to happen rather than the positive benefit. For this reason I have been using the term "conservation easement"; perhaps another will prove better, but it does have the advantage of stressing the positive benefit aspect, and in broad terms.

Next, a question which has worried some park boards: Will not an easement program undercut the job of acquiring gifts of land in fee simple? There is good reason to believe it will greatly stimulate such gifts. Any of us who have talked to big landowners on the outer edge of suburbia know that, characteristically, many of them have a very strong feeling for the natural landscape as it is and, though they don't always say it voluntarily, a distaste for regular park development—"manicured" is a word they often use and with an unmistakable intonation. Many of these people would like to give land, but they fear it would be changed into something they would hate to see—tot lots, green benches, and such.

Is this bias to be deplored—or understood? By failing to recognize how the easement device can unlock gifts that otherwise wouldn't be made, too many park officials are leaving unexploited a great opportunity. Consider how the two tools can complement each other: by giving a landowner the guarantee of unspoiled landscape for the bulk of his land, through easements, an avenue of approach is opened up for securing a gift of land outright to a part of the property ideal for park purposes.

In this job of soliciting gifts there is another troublesome question. It is one that landowners are likely to bring up quite emphatically: "If I give an easement to my property, am I not making myself a sitting duck for condemnation later by other public agencies? Because, theoretically, the land will fetch less on the open market, might not highway officials, or park officials, cast a covetous eye?"

The question here is one of equity; certainly, if later the public feels the most important use requires acquisition of the land in fee simple, they have proper recourse to eminent domain. At the same time, however, the landowner should not be penalized for his generosity. In the easement deed, accordingly, it will be vital to include a clause saying that, in the event of later condemnation, the restrictions of the easement shall be null and void. In other words, the fair market value the public will have to pay is the fair market value for unrestricted land.

State and county seeing eye to eye

Who's to be in charge? To deal with a metropolitan problem, some planners maintain, you need a metropolitan government, or, at the very least, a metropolitan agency. Anything less, they hold, would be a piecemeal solution; worse yet, premature, for it would divert citizen interest from the task of striving for a long-range, comprehensive plan for the whole region.

This big-picture view has much to commend it, but unfortunately there is no metropolitan government now, and not much likelihood of any for some years. While awaiting the millennium, then, open spaces will have to be secured where the open spaces are—out in the counties. And while the county is an imperfect form of government, unduly antagonistic to cities and such, it is what we have to work with. There is also the institution of the state government. It tends to be prone to cities, but it does exist, and counties look on it as an ally. They very well should, considering how disproportionately represented they are in its legislature, but this is not without some advantages.

A state-county program is politically realistic. In Pennsylvania, for example, a bill has been drafted by which the state's Department of Forests and Waters would work with counties in selecting "conservation areas" and securing easements from the owners in them. Eventually the program could be turned over to regional agencies, but for getting things started the state already has the money (it has $4 million a year "oil and gas lease fund" earmarked for just about any program connected with conservation); and it has the administrative machinery.

But while state authorization is a "must," local governments can do a lot on their own. It is significant that the initiative for state legislation has been coming from them. This June, thanks to the leadership of Monterey County, the California Legislature passed—by unanimous vote—a general open-space bill for all cities and counties in the state. For the first time a state has declared that it is a public purpose to secure land or easements so as to conserve the natural landscape. For subsequent tax and legal developments this is a critical declaration.

Lower Merion Township, in Pennsylvania, introduced a similar bill in the Pennsylvania legislature in April, 1959 —as a matter of fact, it helped spur the Monterey people to their bill, which fact, in turn, is now helping the Pennsylvania people.

Equity-holders joining forces

But harnessing the support of landowners is only a start. The big job ahead is to bring together all the other groups with an equity in open space. It's surprising how many different groups want essentially the same end but have failed to see their allies; matter of fact, they are likely to assume others are the enemy. The farmers who couldn't care less about providing amenity for unborn generations of city people, see open space as a defense *against* the city. The city people, who are skeptical of the farmers' crop-land argument, want the land saved but with pure motives and metropolitan devices. Park officers, most of whom still think only of conventional land acquisition, have yet to see that the bias of the gentry is better exploited than deplored. Utilities, which suffer heavily from sprawl, remain too ideologically musclebound to lend support. Golf clubs haven't even thought of it.

"Education" isn't going to bring these groups together; it's going to take a good fight, and the best way to get it going is to start the controversial job of selecting actual open spaces. Let planners, who say we need more study, go off and study. They've been saying it for ten years, and they had their chance and did nothing. They can offer no moratorium; the assessors are not freezing taxes; the highway engineers are not laying down their transits; the developers are not stopping their bulldozers.

And what is so difficult about selecting land? Any planner who can't point now to at least one area worth saving should get himself in another line of work. Long-range planning studies are indeed necessary, but we need some *retroactive* planning, too—that is, to get the land first and then, later, at leisure rationalize with studies how right we were to have done it all along.

Let us trust our instincts. Aesthetics is the driving force for action, but it is not something separate from economics. Look at the desecration of a countryside and your instincts tell you that anything that looks this terrible *can't* be good economics—that it isn't progress, that it isn't inevitable. . . .

And that we had better get cracking.

Reprinted from *Natl. Parks Conserv. Mag.*, **47**(10), 2, 35, (1973)

COUNTRYSIDE

WITH THE FALL EQUINOX, autumn returns to the northern hemisphere. A wave of brilliant color washes the woods of Appalachia from Maine to the Carolinas. The last swallows have long since left for the south; junco and chickadee arrive. Countrymen close their barns against the cold; city men escape from the freedom of the countryside, return to the shelter of the prison cities.

Time was when the open country was home for most of mankind. Cities were for a minority, a privileged group perhaps, predatory, alien to the purposes and tempos of the vast majority. The change was as of yesterday: a century and a half since the industrial hells of England appeared; a hundred years in America; as a short breath to a lifetime, for the history of man.

The powerful flow of the human tide from country to city has borne all the aspects of inevitability. Men adapted to it, did not make it. They went to the city for jobs, and hopefully for money. They went there also, some of them, to share in the cultural intensities which the early cities did indeed provide, until choked by the mills, traffic, streets, crowds. A few found power and great wealth as the supercities preyed on the land and its people, drawing the abundance of soil, forest, and mineral riches into their grasp.

THE RURAL VALUES are spaciousness, sunlight and wind by day, darkness and silence at night. They are what a man feels when he steps from his door directly into fields that slope to a flowing stream. They are in houses open to the calls of the frogs in the spring, the birds in early summer, the cicada when summer deepens. They are in the flowers of the earth, bloodroot, adders-tongue, cowslip after the snows, aster and goldenrod before they return. They were in the old communities; not that the towns of agrarian America were invariably centers of enlightenment and brotherly affection; but within them people knew one another as persons, and from that knowledge love and wisdom could arise.

All this wealth has been lost, massively, violently, crushingly, but not yet hopelessly lost. The early cities, economic and cultural centers integrally related to the land, lost their own inner life as their centers hardened, compacted, as they ringed themselves in traffic away from their natural setting. These barriers of traffic must now be surmounted in the daily commuting of millions, consuming hours and years of lives in barren transportation; for others there is no escape from the confinement. Within the metropolis the ease of meeting and communication which was thought to be its greatest virtue has vanished. More comfortably can one journey from Washington to New York than from Wall Street to uptown Manhattan.

AS URBANIZATION, blindly fatalistic, assumed the aspects of the ideal, of a value in itself, simultaneously it lost its justification. Over most of the modern world, crowds enter the cities, forced from the land, finding mainly unemployment, poverty, disease, congestion. In the industrial countries, the human spirit perishes within walls of glass and steel, in sunless, treeless streets, amidst noise and fumes and frantic wheels. The human will freezes, paralyzed, impotent against asphyxiation by the internal combustion engine.

As economic engines the cities are absurd; food must be brought from hundreds of miles at enormous expense in preservation and packaging; vast stores of the energies of city people must be expended merely to bring the wherewithal of life to the urban table; the countryman finds this wealth readily at hand in garden, berry-bush, fruit tree.

What arrogance leads anyone to suppose that this insensate flow of urbanization can be reversed? The American people, if the polls are to be trusted, regret their dislocation from country to city; most people long to escape, to find their way back somehow to the rural setting. That change of attitude has actually occurred, and is of signal significance.

OUR EFFORTS at escape have been clumsy; suburbanization held out its lure for a generation or so, only to be frustrated by the burdens of commuting. Urban sprawl despoiled the natural world around the cities, brought centerless developments devoid even of the physical aspects of community. The country cabin and second home have multiplied the economic burden of housing, and have all too often destroyed the rural environment which they sought to find. These efforts have been haphazard, reflexes against inhumane conditions brought on by technological, industrial, and economic forces which must now be opposed deliberately if salvation is to be found.

A certain arrogance will indeed be needed, and most assuredly a release of new imaginative powers,

Continued on page 35

Continued from page 2
if the countryside is to be redeemed as the true home of man, and if the evil of urbanization, as it has recently revealed itself, is to be ended. The work of transformation will not be accomplished in a decade, nor in a generation. The catastrophe which has required a century and more to overwhelm us will not be righted in less than another century, more likely half a millenium; and so patience, endurance, and conviction will also be needed. And yet, among the beneficial results of science and technology has been our generalized sense of competence, the widening of a faith, perhaps recently shaken, that men can in fact, if they will, command their own collective destiny.

If a vision guides, perhaps the first step is to visualize the alternatives; then we can examine into what practical measures may be available for their realization. The image will not be the agricultural society of the past in all its aspects; the long days of toil in the fields, the drudgery of the household, the big family and its labor supply, the overburdened work animals, the isolation and parochialism; these are behind us. The machine, even the factory, which can be made serviceable, even automation, which can be made tractable, even technology, if it can be domesticated: these emergents can be forced into the service of mankind, can be made to yield abundance, security, leisure, foundations for a cultural efflorescence, seated within a generosity of field and forest. Granted a rapid stabilization and a gradual reduction of population, essential to any future human order, the small cities which dot the land can be revitalized without any grave impingement on the environment, and new communities can be built in reasonable number. The big cities can be opened up, and the countryside brought back to them in broadened open spaces, parks, and avenues freed from curbside parking and the uproar of traffic.

With a shift of budgetary priorities from the construction of superhighways and useless dams, and from arms to education, as expanded institutions of world order permit, new schools, with room space for small classes, and with more teachers, aided by the mechanical marvels of the age, microfilm, television, can make high quality universal education as readily available to rural communities as it was thought to be in the cities. And the art gallery, library, concert hall, theater will be seen as functions of interest, attention, leisure, and abundance, not of urban concentration.

Perhaps there will be a new sense of time within the new society; or better, we shall return to an almost forgotten, basically rural sense of time, familiar to older generations, a slow time, not the modern frenzy, an ample time, with room for reflection, for a return upon the spirit. Perhaps also a remembered sense of security; a world which is in constant flux can yield no man security of spirit; within the reborn countryside we shall build our houses again for the centuries, for the continuity of generations, and shall preserve our churches once again as symbols of eternity.

In the meantime, campaigns for the defense of the countryside and for an attack on the problem of urbanization will have to be mounted. Land-use planning based on the preservation of rural values, not the exploitation and destruction of the land, will be fundamental. The entire environmental protection arsenal must be deployed. Pollution abatement programs must not be compromised. The old soil conservation programs should be reactivated, as contrasted with lake building, fruit of speculative ambitions. Ecological forestry action will be essential, and vigorous wildlife restoration and protection.

A workable system of industrial plant location and continuity should be developed without delay, not focused on unending growth, which many communities are now resisting, but on stable employment for settled populations within the essential economic and cultural amenities. Telically valid plant location will mean small plants for a variety of human reasons, a varied product within a coherent region, a deliberate reduction of transportation, both for materials and product, and a rigorous respect for the surrounding environment.

A generalized stabilization, as contrasted with endless expansion, will be fundamental to the new order, always including stabilization and reduction of population and a differential economic stabilization, correcting for the needs of underprivileged groups and nations, but working toward a sufficiency, not a surfeit, of beneficial goods, and against harmful commodities. The frame of reference will be the metropolis no longer, but the verdant fields, the refreshing woods, the clean and sparkling streams of the resurrected and beloved countryside.

—*Anthony Wayne Smith*

References

Ackerman, W. C. 1971. The Oakley Project—a controversy in land use, Environ. Geol. Notes No. 46, Illinois State Geological Survey.

Adirondack Park Agency. 1973. Adirondack Park land use and development plan and recommendations for implementation, Adirondack Park Agency, New York State, 35 pp.

Advisory Committee on Intergovernmental Relations. 1968. *Urban and Rural America: Policies for Future Growth,* Advisory Committee on Intergovernmental Relations, Government Printing Office, Washington, D.C., 168 pp.

Alabama Geological Survey, 1971. Environmental geology and hydrology, Madison County, Alabama, Meridianville Quadrangle, Geol. Surv. Ala., Atlas Series 1, 72 pp.

Amato, P. W. 1969. Environmental quality and locational behavior in a Latin American city, Urban Affairs Quart., v. 5, n. 1, pp. 83 – 101.

Arango, J. 1970. *The Urbanization of the Earth,* Beacon Press, Boston, 175 pp.

Artim, E. R. 1973. Geology in land use planning, Washington Div. Mines Geol. Information Circ. 47, 18 pp.

Betz, F., Jr. (in press). *Environmental Geology,* Dowden, Hutchinson & Ross, Stroudsburg, Pa.

Bird, H. P. 1972. Environmental and economic impact of rapid growth on a rural area: Palm Coast, Environ. Affairs, v. 2, n. 1, pp. 154 – 171.

Blumenfeld, H. 1965. The modern metropolis, Sci. Amer., v. 213, n. 3, pp. 66 – 74.

Bogue, D. J. 1956. Metropolitan growth and the conversion of land to nonagricultural uses, Scripps Foundation Studies in Population Distribution No. 11, Miami University, Oxford, Ohio, 33 pp.

Bue, C. D. 1967. Flood information for flood-plain planning, U.S. Geol. Surv. Circ. 539, 10 pp.

Burton, I., and Kates, R. W. 1964. The floodplain and the seashore, Geograph. Rev., v. 54, n. 3, pp. 366 – 385.

Burton, I., Kates, R. W., and Snead, R. E. 1969. *The Human Ecology of Coastal Flood Hazard in Megalopolis,* Dept. Geog. Res. Paper No. 115, University of Chicago, 196 pp.

California Division of Mines and Geology, 1971. Urban geology master plan for California: a method for setting priorities, California Division of Mines and Geology, var. pages.

California Water Pollution Control Board. 1961. Effects of refuse dumps on ground water quality, Calif. Water Pollution Control Board Publ. 24, 107 pp.

Cartwright, K., and Sherman, F. B. 1969. Evaluating sanitary landfill sites in Illinois, Environ. Geol. Notes No. 27, Illinois State Geological Survey, 15 pp.

Chapman, V. J. 1949. The stabilization of sand-dunes by vegetation, in Inst. Civil Eng., Conf. Proc., London, pp. 142 – 157.

Christiansen, E. A., ed. 1970. Physical environment of Saskatoon, Canada, Natl. Research Council Can. Publ. No. 11378, 68 pp.

Christie, T. L. 1967. Is Venice sinking?, Saturday Review, March 25, pp. 40–42.

Claire, W. H., ed. 1969. *Urban Planning Guide,* Amer. Soc. Civil Eng., Manuals Rept. Eng. Practice No. 49, 299 pp.

Clawson, M. 1959. New ideas for the changing landscape, Landscape Architecture, v. 50, n. 1, pp. 20–23.

Clawson, M. 1962. Urban sprawl and speculation in suburban land, Land Econ., May, pp. 99–111.

Clawson, M. 1971. *Suburban Land Conversion in the United States* (Resources for the Future), Johns Hopkins University Press, Baltimore, 406 pp.

Cloud, P. E. 1969. Geology, cities and surface movement, in *Planning Conservation of the Physical Environment,* Highway Research Record No. 271, NRC-NAS, Washington, D.C., p. 1–9.

Coates, D. R. 1971. Legal and environmental case studies in applied geomorphology, in *Environmental Geomorphology,* D. R. Coates, ed. (Publications in Geomorphology), State University of New York, Binghamton, pp. 223–242.

Coates, D. R., ed. 1972. *Environmental Geomorphology and Landscape Conservation, Volume I: Prior to 1900*, Dowden, Hutchinson & Ross, Stroudsburg, Pa., 485 pp.

Coates, D. R., ed. 1973. *Environmental Geomorphology an Landscape Conservation, Volume III, Non-Urban Regions,* Dowden, Hutchinson & Ross, Stroudsburg, Pa., 483 pp.

Cohen, P., Franke, O. L., and Foxworthy, B. L. 1970. Water for the future of Long Island, New York. N.Y. Water Resources Bull. 62A, 36 pp.

Conservation Report, eds. 1973. Conservation Report No. 40, National Wildlife Federation, pp. 538–551.

Constandse, A. K., compiler. 1967. *Planning and Creation of an Environment: Experiences in the Ysselmeerpolders,* Royal Institute of Netherlands Architects, 89 pp.

Corps of Engineers. 1964. Land against the sea: U.S. Army Coastal Eng. Center Misc. Paper No. 4-64, 43 pp.

Corps of Engineers. 1971a. Shore protection guidelines, National Shoreline Study, Department of the Army Corps of Engineers, Government Printing Office, Washington, D.C., 59 pp.

Corps of Engineers. 1971b. Shore management guidelines, National Shoreline Study, Department of the Army Corps of Engineers, Government Printing Office, 56 pp.

Corps of Engineers. 1973. Help yourself: a discussion of the critical erosion problems on the Great Lakes and alternative methods of shore protection, Department of the Army, North Central Division, Chicago.

Craine, L. E. 1969. *Water Management Innovations in England,* Resources for the Future, Inc., 123 pp.

Darby, H. C. 1956. *The Draining of the Fens,* Cambridge University Press, New York, 314 pp.

Dasmann, R. F. 1968. *Environmental Conservation,* Wiley, New York, 375 pp.

Davis, J. H. 1957. Dune formation and stabilization by vegetation and plantings, U.S. Army Corps Eng. Beach Erosion Board Tech. Mem. No. 101, 47 pp. and appendixes.

Davis, K., compiler. 1959. *The World's Metropolitan Areas,* University of California Press, Berkeley, 115 pp.

De Bell, G., ed. 1970. *The Environmental Handbook,* Ballantine, New York, 367 pp.

Detwyler, T. R., and Marcus, M. G., eds. 1972. *Urbanization and Environment,* Duxbury Press, North Scituate, Mass., 287 pp.

Diamond, D. 1972. Water planning, Town & Country Planning, v. 40, n. 9, pp. 403–404.

Dobrovolny, E., and Schmoll H. R. 1968. Geology as applied to urban planning: an example from the Greater Anchorage Area Borough, Alaska, Proc. XXIII Int. Geol. Congr., Sec. 12, 39, Prague.

Eckel, E. B. 1970. The Alaska earthquake March 27, 1964: Lessons and conclusions, U.S. Geol. Surv. Professional Paper 546, 57 pp.

Eldridge, H. W., ed. 1967a. *Taming Megalopolis: Volume I. What is and What Could Be,* Doubleday, Garden City, N.Y., 576 pp.
Eldridge, H. W., ed. 1967b. *Taming Megalopolis: Volume II. How to Manage an Urbanized World,* Doubleday, Garden City, N.Y. 588 pp.
Eliot, C. W. 1902. *Charles Eliot: Landscape Architect,* Houghton Mifflin, Boston, 770 pp.
Eschman, D. F., and Marcus, M. G. 1972. The geologic and topographic setting of cities, in *Urbanization and Environment,* T. R. Detwyler and M. G. Marcus, eds., Duxbury Press, North Scituate, Mass., pp. 27–50.
Fabos, J. G. 1973. Model for landscape resource assessment: Part I of the Metropolitan landscape planning model, Univ. Mass. Agri. Exp. Sta. Res. Bull. No. 602, 141 pp.
Ferguson, D. E. 1972. Annual compilation and analysis of hydrologic data for urban studies in the Houston, Texas Metropolitan Area, 1970, U.S. Geol. Surv., Texas District Open-File Report, 275 pp.
Feth, J. H. 1973. Water facts and figures for planners and managers, U.S. Geol. Surv. Circ. 601-I, 30 pp.
Gardner, R. R. 1973. Policy alternatives, in Managing Our Coastal Zone, Proceedings of Conference, New York State Sea Grant Program, pp. 21–24.
Geyer, A. R., and McGlade, W. G. 1972. Environmental geology for land-use planning, Environmental Geology Report 2, Pennsylvania Topographic and Geologic Survey, 44 pp.
Gilluly, J., Waters, A. C., and Woodford, A. O. 1959. *Principles of Geology,* 2nd ed., W. H. Freeman, San Francisco, 534 pp.
Glacken, C. J. 1970. Man against nature: an outmoded concept, in *The Environmental Crises,* H. W. Helfrich, ed., Yale University Press, New Haven, Conn. pp. 127–142.
Godfrey, P. J., and Godfrey, M. M. 1973. Comparison of ecological and geomorphic interactions between altered and unaltered barrier island systems in North Carolina, in *Coastal Geomorphology,* D. R. Coates, ed. (Publications in Geomorphology), State University of New York, Binghamton, pp. 239–258.
Goodey, B. 1971. *Perception of the Environment,* Centre for Urban and Regional Studies, Univ. Birmingham Occasional Paper No. 17, 92 pp.
Gottman, J. 1961. *Megalopolis: The Urbanized Northeastern Seaboard of the United States,* Twentieth Century Fund, New York, 810 pp.
Gulick, L. 1958. The city's challenge in resource use, in *Perspectives in Conservation, H. Jarrett, ed., Johns Hopkins Press, Baltimore, Md., pp. 115*–137.
Hackett, B. 1971. *Landscape Planning,* Oriel Press, England, 124+ p.
Hackett, J. E., and McComas, M. R. 1969. Geology for planning in McHenry County, Ill. State Geol. Surv. Circ. 438, 29 pp.
Hardy, E. E. 1970. Inventorying New York's land use and natural resources, New York's Food and Life Sciences, v. 3, n. 4.
Haveman, R. H. 1965. *Water Resource Investment and the Public Interest,* Vanderbilt University Press, Nashville, Tenn. 199 pp.
Hawley, A. H. 1973. Ecology and population, Science, v. 179, pp. 1196–1200.
Hilpman, P. L., ed. 1968. A pilot study of land-use planning and environmental geology, State Geol. Surv. Kansas Report No. 15D, June.
Hilpman, P. L. 1969. Urban growth and environmental geology, in The Governor's Conf. Environ. Geol. Special Publ. No. 1, Colorado Geological Survey, pp. 16–19.
Hirshleifer, J., DeHaven, J. C., and Milliman, J. W. 1960. *Water Supply: Economics, Technology, and Policy,* University of Chicago Press, 378 pp.
Howard, E. 1902. *Garden Cities of Tomorrow,* S. Sonnenschein & Co., Ltd., London, 167 pp.
Hoyt, W. G., and Langbein, W. B. 1955. *Floods,* Princeton University Press, Princeton, N.J., 469 pp.
Hughes, G. M. 1967. Selection of refuse disposal sites in northeastern Illinois, Environ. Geol. Notes No. 17, Illinois State Geological Survey, 18 pp.
Hughes, G. M. 1972. Hydrogeologic considerations in the siting and design of landfills, Environ. Geol. Notes, No. 51, Illinois State Geological Survey, 22 pp.
Hughes, G. M., Landon, R. A., and Farvolden, R. N. 1971. Hydrogeology of solid waste disposal

sites in northeastern Illinois, U.S. Environmental Protection Agency SW-12d, Government Printing Office, Washington, D.C., 154 pp.
Inman, D. L., and Brush, B. M. 1973. The coastal challenge, Science, v. 181, pp. 20 – 32.
Jagschitz, J. A., and Bell, R. S. 1966. Restoration and retention of coastal dunes with fences and vegetation, Rhode Island Agricultural Experiment Station, Contribution No. 1149, 43 pp.
Johnson, J. H. 1970. *Urban Geography: An Introductory Analysis,* Pergamon Press, Elmsfold, N.Y., 188 pp.
Johnson, S. L., and Sayre, D. M. 1973. Effects of urbanization on floods in the Houston, Texas metropolitan area, U.S. Geol. Surv. Water-Resources Investigation 3-73, 50 pp.
Kaye, C. A. 1968. Geology and our cities, N.Y. Acad. Sci. Trans., Series II, v. 30, n. 8, pp. 1045–1051.
Kellaway, G. A., and Taylor, J. H. 1968. The influence of landslipping on the development of the city of Bath, England, Proc. 23d Intern. Geo. Congress, Prague, v. 12, pp. 65 – 76.
Kiersch, G. A. 1964. Vaiont Reservoir disaster: Civil Eng., v. 34, n. 3.
Koppelman, L. E. 1964. A plan for open-space in Suffolk County, Suffolk County Planning Committee, Hauppauge, N.Y., 121 pp.
De la Haba, Louis. 1973. Mexico, the city that founded a nation, National Geographic, v. 143, n. 5, pp. 638 – 669.
League of Women Voters. 1966. *The Big Water Fight,* The League of Women Voters Education Fund, Stephen Greene Press, Brattleboro, Vermont, 246 pp.
Legget, R. F. 1973. *Cities and Geology,* McGraw-Hill, New York, 624 pp.
Leopold, L. B., and Maddock, T., Jr. 1954. *The Flood Control Controversy,* Ronald Press, New York, 278 pp.
Lessinger, J. 1962. The case for scatterization: some reflections on the National Capitol Regional Plan for the Year 2000, J. Amer. Inst. Planners, Aug.
Linton, R. M. 1970. *Terracide,* Little, Brown, Boston, 376 pp.
Little, C. E. 1968. *Challenge of the Land,* Pergamon Press, Elmsford, N.Y., 151 pp.
Lung, R., and Proctor, R., eds. 1969. *Engineering Geology in Southern California,* Association of Engineering Geologists, Arcadia, Calif., 389 pp.
Lynch, K. 1960. *The Image of the City,* MIT Press, Cambridge, Mass., 194 pp.
McBride, G. A., and Clawson, M. 1970. Negotiation and land conversion, J. Amer. Inst. Planners, Jan., pp. 22 – 29.
McLendon, N. 1973. A giant fits into the Texas environment. Soil Conserv., v. 39, n. 2, pp. 12–14.
McComas, M. R. 1968. Geology related to land use in the Hennepin region, Ill. State Geol. Surv. Circ. 422, 24 pp.
McGill, J. T. 1964. Growing importance of urban geology, U.S. Geol. Surv. Circ. 487, 4 pp.
McHarg, I. L. 1969. *Design with Nature,* Natural History Press, Garden City, New York, 197 pp.
McKenzie, G. D., and Utgard, R. O. 1972. *Man and His Physical Environment,* Burgess Publishing, Minneapolis, 338 pp.
Martin, R. C. 1960. *Water for New York,* Syracuse University Press, Syracuse, N.Y., 264 pp.
Martin, W. T. 1953. *The Rural – Urban Fringe,* University of Oregon Press, Eugene, 109 pp.
Marx, W. 1967. *The Frail Ocean,* Ballantine, New York, 274 pp.
Mattern, H. 1966. The growth of landscape consciousness, Landscape, v. 15, Spring, pp. 14–20.
Merriam, R. 1960. Portuguese Bend landslide, Palos Verdes Hills, California, J. Geol., v. 68, pp. 140 – 153.
Metropolitan Washington Council of Governments. 1968. Natural features of the Washington metropolitan area, the Council, Washington, D.C., 49 pp.
Morgan, A. E. 1971. *Dams and Other Disasters: A Century of the Army Corps of Engineers in Civil Works,* Porter Sargent, Boston, 422 pp.
Morton, D. M., and Streitz, R. 1967. Landslides, Calif. Div. Mines Geol. Mineral Inform. Ser., v. 20, n. 11, pp. 135 – 140.
Mozola, A. J. 1969. Geology for land and ground-water development in Wayne County, Michigan, State of Michigan Department of Natural Resources Report of Investigation 3, 25 pp.

Mozola, A. J. 1970. Geology for environmental planning in Monroe County, Michigan, Mich. Geol. Surv. Div. Report Invest. 13, 34 pp.
Muskegon County. 1973. Muskegon County, Michigan, wastewater management system no. 1, Bauer Engineering, Inc., 16 pp.
National Academy of Sciences. 1972 *The Earth and Human Affairs,* National Research Council, National Academy of Sciences, Canfield Press, San Francisco, 142 pp.
National Parks & Conservation Association. 1973. A startling reply: National Parks & Conserv. Mag., v. 47, n. 11, p. 29.
Nelson, H. J. 1959. The spread of an artificial landscape over southern California: Ann. Assoc. Amer. Geographers, v. 49, n. 3, pt. 2, p. 80 – 99,
New England River Basins Commission. 1973. Long Island Sound regional study—bibliography for planning, New England River Basins Commission, 183 pp.
Nichols, R. L., and Marston, A. F. 1939. Shoreline changes in Rhode Island produced by hurricane of September 21, 1938, Geol. Soc. Amer. Bull., v. 50, pp. 1357 – 1370.
Niering, W. A. 1968. The ecology of wetlands in urban areas, Garden J., v. 18, n. 6, pp. 177–183.
Niering, W. A. 1970. The dilemma of the coastal wetlands: conflict of local, national, and world priorities, in *The Environmental Crises,* H. W. Helfrich, ed., Yale University Press, New Haven, Conn., pp. 142 – 156.
Northeastern Ilinois Planning Commission. 1968. A regional armature for the future: the comprehensive general plan for the development of the northeastern Illinois counties, Northeastern Illinois Planning Commission, Chicago, 12 pp.
Oakeshott, G. B. 1970. Controlling the geologic environment for human welfare, J. Geol. Educ., v. 18, n. 5, pp. 193.
Office of Planning Coordination. 1971. LUNR: Land use and natural resource inventory of New York State, Office of Planning Coordination, State of New York, 21 pp.
Parizek, R. R., and Myers, E. A. 1968. Recharge of ground water from renovated sewage effluent by spray irrigation: Amer. Water Resources Conf. Proc. 4th, pp. 426 – 443.
Parizek, R. R., et al. 1967. Waste water renovation and conservation, Penn. State Univ. Studies No. 23, 71 pp.
Perlmutter, N. M., and Soren, J. 1962. Effects of major water-table changes in Kings and Queens County, New York City, U.S. Geol. Surv. Professional Paper 540-E, pp. 136 – 139.
Peterson, E. T. 1954. *Big Dam Foolishness,* Devin-Adair, New York, 224 pp.
Peterson, J. T. 1973. The climate of cities: a survey of recent literature, in *Climate in Review*, G. McBoyle, ed., Houghton Mifflin, Boston, pp. 264 – 285.
Pickard, J. P. 1967. Dimensions of metropolitanism: Urban Land Institute, Research Monograph 14, Washington D.C., 93 pp.
Piper, A. M. 1965. Has the United States enough water?, U.S. Geol. Surv. Water Supply Paper 1797, 27 pp.
Poland, J. F., and Davis, G. H. 1969. Land subsidence due to withdrawal of fluids, in *Reviews in Engineering Geology,* vol. II, Geological Society of America, New York, pp. 187 – 269.
Rantz, S. E. 1970. Urban sprawl and flooding in southern California, U.S. Geol. Surv. Circ. 601-B, 11 pp.
Reis, R. I. 1965. Legal planning for ground water production, Southern Calif. Law Rev., v. 38, pp. 484 – 493.
Reis, R. I. 1967. A review and revitalization: concepts of ground water production and management —the California experience, Natural Resoruces J., v. 7, n. 1, pp. 53 – 87.
Risser, H. E., and Major, R. L. 1967. Urban expansion — an opportunity and a challenge to industrial mineral producers, Ill. State Geol. Surv. Environ. Notes No. 16, 19 pp.
Roberts, W. H. 1970. Design of metropolitan open space based on natural process, in *Metropolitan Open Space and Natural Process,* D. A. Wallace, ed., University of Pennsylvania Press, Philadelphia, pp. 148 – 189.

Robinson, F. L. 1973a. Floods in New York—1969, N.Y. State Dept. Environ. Conserv. Report Invest. RI-13, 33pp.

Robinson, F. L. 1973b. Floods in New York—1970: N.Y. State Dept. Environ. Consv. Report Invest. RI-13, 20 pp.

Robinson, F. L. 1973c. Floods in New York—1973: U.S. Geol. Surv. Open-file Report, Albany, N.Y., 33 pp.

Rockefeller, L. S. 1973. *The Use of Land: A Citizen's Policy Guide to Urban Growth.* T. Y. Crowell, New York, 384 pp.

Rouse, J. W. 1967. The city of Columbia, Maryland, in *Taming Megalopolis,* vol. II, H. W. Eldridge, ed., Doubleday, Garden City, N.Y., pp. 838–848.

Saltonstall, R., Jr. 1972. *Your Environment and What You Can Do About It,* Ace Books, New York, 285 pp.

Savage, R. P., and Woodhouse, W. W., Jr. 1969. Creation and stabilization of coastal barrier dunes: 11th Conf. Coastal Eng. Proc., pp. 671–700.

Savini, J., and Kammerer, J. C. 1961. Urban growth and the water regimen, U.S. Geol. Surv. Water-Supply Paper 1591-A, 43 pp.

Schmid, A. A. 1968. Converting land from rural to urban uses, Resources for the Future, Johns Hopkins Press, Baltimore, 103 pp.

Schneider, W. J. 1968. Water data for metropolitan areas: U.S. Geol. Surv. Water-Supply Paper 1871, 397 pp.

Schneider, W. J. 1970. Hydrologic implications of solid-waste disposal, U.S. Geol. Surv. Circ. 601-F, 10 pp.

Schneider, W. J., Rickert, D. A., and Spieker, A. M. 1973. Role of Water in urban planning and management, U.S. Geol. Surv. Circ. 601-H.

Seaburn, G. E., and Aronson, D. A. 1973. Catalog of recharge basins on Long Island, New York, in 1969, N.Y. State Dept. Environ. Conserv. Bull. 70, 80 pp.

Shapiro, S. M. 1967. Jones Beach State Park—a progress report, Shore and Beach, v. 35, n. 1, pp. 2–7.

Sheaffer, J. R., Ellis, D. W., and Spieker, A. M. 1969. Flood-hazard mapping in metropolitan Chicago, U.S. Geol. Surv. Circ. 601-C, 14 pp.

Shepard, F. P., and Wanless, H. R. 1971. *Our Changing Shorelines,* McGraw-Hill, New York, 579 pp.

Shomon, J. J. 1971–72. More greenspace for urban America, Conservationist, Dec.–Jan., pp. 14–17.

Sjoberg, G. 1965. The origin and evolution of cities, Sci. Amer., v. 213, n. 3, pp. 55–62.

Slosson, J. E. 1969. The role of engineering geology in urban planning, in The Governor's Conf. Environ. Geol. Special Publ. No. 1, Colorado Geological Survey, pp. 8–15.

Smyth, A. H., ed. 1907. *The Writings of Benjamin Franklin,* 10 vols., Macmillan, New York.

Sorg, T., and Hickman, H. L., Jr. 1970. Sanitary landfill facts, U.S. Department of Health, Education, and Welfare, Bureau of Solid Waste Management, Government Printing Office, Washington, D.C.

Spengler, O. 1932. *The Decline of the West,* 2 vols., Knopf, New York.

Spieker, A. M. 1970. Water in urban planning, Salt Creek basin, Illinois, U.S. Geol. Surv. Water Supply Paper 2002, 147 pp.

Spits, A. 1970. Holland's struggle against the water: The Delta Works, The Society for Making Holland Better Known Abroad, The Hague, 55 pp.

Stewart, D. P. 1971. Geology for environmental planning in the Barre-Montpelier Region, Vermont, Vermont Geol. Surv. Environ. Geol. No. 1, 32 pp.

Strahler, A. N., and Strahler, A. H. 1973. *Environmental Geoscience: Interaction Between Natural Systems and Man,* Hamilton Publishing, Santa Barbara, Calif., 511+ pp.

Strong, A. L. 1971. *Planned Urban Environments,* Johns Hopkins Press, Baltimore, 406 pp.

Tannehill, I. R. 1938. Hurricanes of September 16 to 22, 1938, Monthly Weather Rev., v. 66, pp. 286–288.

Temporary State Commission. 1972a. Compendium of water supply studies, Temporary State Commission on the Water Supply Needs of Southeastern New York, New York State, 149 pp.

Temporary State Commission. 1972b. Scope of public water supply needs, Temporary State Commission on the Water Supply Needs of Southeastern New York, New York State, 150+ pp.

Thomas, H. E., and Schneider, W. J. 1970. Water as an urban resource and nuisance, U.S. Geol. Surv. Circ. 601-D, 9 pp.

Time, eds. 1973. The new American land rush, Time, Oct. 1, pp. 80–99.

Toftner, R., and Clark, R. 1971. Intergovernmental approaches to solid waste management, U.S. Environmental Protection Agency, Solid Waste Management Office, Government Printing Office, Washington, D.C.

UNESCO. 1964. *Urban–Rural Differences in Southern Asia,* Allied Publishers Private Ltd., India, 147 pp.

U.S. Department of Agriculture. 1970a. *Contours of Change,* U.S. Department of Agriculture Yearbook, Government Printing Office, Washington, D.C., 366 pp.

U.S. Department of Agriculture. 1970b. Controlling erosion on construction sites, Soil Conserv. Service Agri. Inform. Bull. 347. 32 pp.

Van der Burgt, J. H., and Bendegom, L. V. 1949. The use of vegetation to stabilize sand-dunes, in Inst. Civil Eng. Conf. Proc., London, pp. 158–170.

Van Veen, J. 1962. *Dredge Drain Reclaim,* 5th ed., Martinus Nijhoff, The Hague, Netherlands, 200 pp.

Vesper, W. H. 1961. Behavior of beach fill and borrow area at Prospect Beach, West Haven, Connecticut, Corps of Eng. Beach Erosion Board Tech. Mem. No. 127, 29 pp.

Vesper, W. H. 1965. Behavior of beach fill and borrow area at Seaside Park, Bridgeport, Connecticut, U.S. Army Coastal Eng. Res. Center Tech. Mem. No. 11, 24 pp.

Vesper, W. H. 1967. Behavior of beach fill and borrow area at Sherwood Island State Park, Westport, Connecticut, U.S. Army Coastal Eng. Res. Center Tech. Mem. No. 20, 25 pp.

Vice, R. B., Guy, H. P., and Ferguson, G. E. 1969. Sediment movement in an area of suburban highway construction, Scott Run basin, Fairfax County, Virginia, 1961–64, U.S. Geol. Surv. Water-Supply Paper 1591-E, 41 pp.

Wallace, D. A., ed. 1970 *Metropolitan Open Space and Natural Process,* University of Pennsylvania Press, Philadelphia, 199 pp.

Weeks, W. F., and Campbell, W. J. 1973. Icebergs as a fresh water source: an appraisal, U.S. Army Cold Regions Res. Eng. Lab. Res. Report No. 200, 22 pp.

Wells, H. G. 1902. *Anticipations of the Reaction of Mechanical and Scientific Progress Upon Human Life and Thought,* Harper & Row, New York, 342 pp.

Welsh, G. S. 1966. The perception of our urban environment, in *Perception and Environment: Foundations of Urban Design,* R. E. Stipe, ed., Institute of Government, University of North Carolina, Chapel Hill, pp. 3–10.

Wheatley, P. 1972. The concept of urbanism, in *Man, Settlement and Urbanism,* P. J. Ucko, R. Tringham, G. W. Dimbleby, eds., Gerald Duckworth & Co., London, pp. 601–637.

White, G. F. 1965 *Human Adjustment to Floods: A Geographical Approach to the Flood Problem in the United States,* Dept. Geog. Res. Paper No. 29, University of Chicago.

White House Conference on Natural Beauty. 1965. *Beauty for America,* Proceedings of the White House Conference on Natural Beauty, Government Printing Office, Washington, D.C., 782 pp.

Whyte, W. H., Jr. 1968. *The Last Landscape,* Doubleday, Garden City, 376 pp.

Williams, E. A., directed. 1969. *Open Space: The Choices Before California,* Diablo Press, San Francisco, 187 pp.

Winkler, E. M. 1973. *Stone: Properties, Durability in Man's Environment,* Springer-Verlag, New York, 230 pp.
Woodhouse, W. W., Jr., and Hanes, R. E. 1967. Dune stabilization with vegetation on the outer banks of North Carolina: U.S. Army Coastal Eng. Res. Center Tech. Mem. No. 22, 45 pp.
Woodland, A. W. 1968. Field geology and the civil engineer, Yorkshire Geol. Surv. Proc., v. 36, pt. 4, n. 30, pp. 531–578.
Wright, K. R. 1969. Environmental design of urban storm runoff works, in The Governor's Conf. Environ. Geol. Special Publ. No. 1, Colorado Geological Survey, pp. 50–52.
Young, N., and Dea, S. 1972. An approach to a new city: Palm Coast, Environ. Affairs, v. 2, n. 1, pp. 127–153.
Zielbauer, E. J. 1966. Challenging flood control problems in southern California, in *Engineering Geology of Southern California,* R. Lung and R. Proctor, eds., Association of Engineering Geologists, pp. 228–301.

Author Citation Index

Subject Index